ESSENTIAL PURE MATHEMATICS

J. K. Backhouse M.A.
Formerly Tutor, Department of Educational Studies, University of Oxford
Formerly Head of the Mathematics Department, Hampton Grammar School

S. P. T. Houldsworth M.A.
Lately Headmaster, Sydney Grammar School
Formerly Assistant Master at Harrow School

B. E. D. Cooper M.A.
Formerly Headmaster of St Bartholomew's School, Newbury

This edition prepared by
P. J. F. Horril M.A.
Formerly Head of the Mathematics Department, Nottingham High School

J. R. Wood M.A.
Head of the Mathematics Department, Nottingham High School

LONGMAN

Addison Wesley Longman Limited
*Edinburgh Gate, Harlow, Essex CM20 2JE, England
and Associated Companies throughout the world.*

© Longman Group Limited 1991

First published 1991
Seventh impression 1997
ISBN 0 582 06658 1

The Publisher's policy is to use paper manufactured from sustainable forests.

Set in Monotype Lasercomp Times Mathematics 569

*Produced by Longman Singapore Publishers Pte Ltd
Printed and bound in Singapore*

Contents

Chapter 4   The gradient of a curve

Chapter 5   Velocity and acceleration

Chapter 6   Maxima and minima

Chapter 7 Integration

Chapter 8 Further differentiation

Revision Exercise 1

Chapter 9 Further integration

Chapter 10 Some useful topics in algebra

Chapter 11 Quadratic equations and complex numbers

Chapter 12   Matrices

Revision Exercise 2

Chapter 13   Permutations and combinations

Chapter 14   Series

Chapter 15   The binomial theorem

Chapter 16   Vectors

Chapter 17   The general angle and Pythagoras' theorem

Chapter 18   Trigonometrical identities

Chapter 19   Further topics in trigonometry

Revision Exercise 3

Chapter 20   Derivatives of trigonometrical functions

Chapter 21   Coordinate geometry

Chapter 22   Further topics in coordinate geometry

Chapter 23   Variation and experimental laws

Chapter 24   Iterative methods for solving equations

Preface

The original version of *Backhouse & Houldsworth* was one of the classics among school mathematics textbooks. Generations of students and many of today's mathematics teachers grew up on it.

The aim of the 1985 edition was to reconcile 'traditional' A-level mathematics with the newer material which appeared during the 1970s.

Since the introduction of the GCSE and the emergence of the National Curriculum a need has arisen for this new shorter version of *Pure Mathematics* which is designed to cater, within the covers of one book, for the needs of students following what is usually called 'single subject' mathematics at A-level, and also for those taking AS-level.

Readers familiar with the earlier editions will notice some important changes. A new introductory chapter called 'Preparatory work' gives the student practice in the basic algebraic skills which are needed to study the subject successfully.

A particularly important innovation is the introduction of the revision exercises. These, with the exception of 'Revision Exercise 5', are sets of questions selected from recent A- and AS-level papers. Some of them are specimen questions supplied by various examination boards to illustrate changes which are imminent. 'Revision Exercise 5' is different; this concentrates on all the techniques of integration explained elsewhere in the book.

Some of the questions from the earlier editions, which involved very heavy algebraic manipulation, have been deleted, since this type of work is understandably out of favour in current examinations. Where appropriate, more straightforward questions have replaced them and, in other places, the text has been modified or rewritten to make it more suitable for today's students.

Otherwise the style of *Pure Mathematics books 1 & 2* is retained. There is explanatory text with worked examples and, at suitable intervals, sets of exercises. There are also individual questions in the text, marked **Qu.**, which help the reader to check that important new concepts have been fully grasped. These questions are especially valuable to any student who is working from the book without the aid of a regular teacher. Each chapter ends with a 'Miscellaneous exercise' which sums up the whole chapter.

It is expected that most readers will be using a scientific calculator.

There has been widespread concern in recent years about the standard of written English in schools, and mathematics teachers will be well aware how difficult it is to persuade students to use the language correctly when answering mathematical questions. I have done my best to follow the good example set in this respect by John Backhouse and Peter Houldsworth when they wrote the original text, and I hope that all students using this book will try to do likewise.

As before I am indebted to the original authors for trusting me with the task of this further development of their original work; I hope the end product will please them.

I am also extremely grateful to my colleague, John Wood, who has given me invaluable assistance in preparing the manuscript, checking the answers and proof reading. My thanks are also due to Andrew Ransom and his team at Longman for their encouragement and professional advice. Last, but not least, I thank my wife Pamela for her help and patience over the months spent on the project.

P.J.F. HORRIL
Nottingham
1991

Note on degree of accuracy of answers

In order to avoid tedious repetition in the wording of questions the following conventions are observed throughout the book, unless there are specific instructions to the contrary:

(a) When possible an exact answer is given. To this end it is normally appropriate to retain surds and π in the answers where they occur. (The word *exact* is used here in the rather limited sense of being derived from the data without any intervening approximation.)

(b) When an answer is not exact, it is usually given correct to three significant figures, or, if it is an angle measured in degrees, to the nearest tenth of a degree.

Acknowledgements

We are grateful to the following examination boards for permission to reproduce copyright material;

The Associated Examining Board (AEB) for questions from past AS level Mathematics examination papers & AS level specimen Mathematics examination papers; Joint Matriculation Board (JMB) for questions from past A level Mathematics examination papers; Oxford & Cambridge (O & C) Schools Examination Board for questions from past A level Mathematics examination papers & questions from A level specimen Mathematics examination papers; University of Cambridge Local Examinations Syndicate (C) for questions from past AS, AO & A level Mathematics examination papers & AS level specimen Mathematics examination papers; University of London School Examination Board (L) for questions from past AS & A level Mathematics examination papers & questions from AS level specimen Mathematics examination papers; University of Oxford Delegacy of Local Examinations (O) for questions from past A level Mathematics examination papers; Welsh Joint Education Committee (W) for a question from a past AS level Mathematics examination paper & questions from AS level specimen Mathematics examination papers. (SUJB is now covered by the University of Cambridge Local Examinations Syndicate.)

Questions from the above bodies are indicated by the letters shown in parentheses.

Front cover: Theo van Doesburg *Counter Composition*, 1924.
Oil on canvas, 39⅜ × 39⅜ in.
Amsterdam, Stedelijk Museum.

Mathematical notation

The following notation is used in this book. It follows the conventions employed by most GCE Examining Boards.

1. Set notation

$\in$	is an element of
$\notin$	is not an element of
$\{a, b, c, \ldots\}$	the set with elements $a, b, c, \ldots$
$\{x: \ldots\}$	the set of elements x, such that $\ldots$
$n(A)$	the number of elements in set A
$\varnothing$	the empty set
$\mathscr{E}$	the universal set
A'	the complement of set A
$\mathbb{N}$	the set of natural numbers (including zero) 0, 1, 2, 3, ...
$\mathbb{Z}$	the set of integers 0, ± 1, ± 2, ± 3, ...
$\mathbb{Z}^+$	the set of positive integers $+1$, $+2$, $+3$, ...
$\mathbb{Q}$	the set of rational numbers
$\mathbb{R}$	the set of real numbers
$\mathbb{C}$	the set of complex numbers
$\subseteq$	is a subset of
$\subset$	is a proper subset of
$\cup$	union
$\cap$	intersection
$[a, b]$	the closed interval $\{x \in \mathbb{R}: a \leqslant x \leqslant b\}$
(a, b)	the open interval $\{x \in \mathbb{R}: a < x < b\}$

2. Miscellaneous symbols

$=$	is equal to
$\neq$	is not equal to
$>, <$	is greater than, is less than
$\geqslant, \leqslant$	is greater than or equal to, is less than or equal to
$\approx$	is approximately equal to

3. Operations

$a + b$	a plus b
$a - b$	a minus b
$a \times b$, ab, $a.b$	a multiplied by b
$a \div b$, $\dfrac{a}{b}$, a/b	a divided by b
$\displaystyle\sum_{i=1}^{i=n} a_i$	$a_1 + a_2 + a_3 + \ldots + a_n$

4. Functions

$f(x)$	the value of the function f at x
$f: A \to B$	f is a function which maps each element of set A onto a member of set B
$f: x \mapsto y$	f maps the element x onto an element y
f^{-1}	the inverse of the function f
gf or $g \circ f$	the composite function $g(f(x))$
$\lim_{x \to a} f(x)$	the limit of $f(x)$ as x tends to a
δx	an increment of x
$\dfrac{dy}{dx}$	the derivative of y with respect to x
$\dfrac{d^n y}{dx^n}$	the nth derivative of y with respect to x
$f'(x)$, $f''(x)$, $\ldots f^{(n)}(x)$	the first, second, $\ldots$ nth derivatives of $f(x)$
$\int y \, dx$	the indefinite integral of y with respect to x
$\displaystyle\int_a^b y \, dx$	the definite integral, with limits a and b
$[F(x)]_a^b$	$F(b) - F(a)$

5. Exponential and logarithmic functions

e^x or $\exp x$	the exponential function
$\log_a x$	logarithm of x in base a logarithms
$\ln x$	$\log_e x$
$\lg x$	$\log_{10} x$

6. Circular functions

$\sin x$, $\cos x$, $\tan x$	the circular functions sine, cosine, tangent
$\operatorname{cosec} x$, $\sec x$, $\cot x$	the reciprocals of the above functions
$\sin^{-1} x$ or $\arcsin x$	the inverse of the function $\sin x$ (with similar abbreviations for the inverses of the other circular functions)

7. Other functions

$\sqrt{a}$	the positive square root of a
$\lvert a\rvert$	the modulus of a
$n!$	n factorial; $n! = n \times (n-1) \times (n-2) \times \ldots \times 3 \times 2 \times 1$ $(0! = 1)$

$\dbinom{n}{r}$ or $^{n}C_{r}$ $\qquad \dfrac{n!}{r!(n-r)!} \quad$ when $n, r \in \mathbb{N}$ and $0 \leqslant r \leqslant n$

$\dbinom{n}{r}$ $\qquad \dfrac{n(n-1)\ldots(n-r+1)}{r!} \quad$ when $n \in \mathbb{Q}$ and $r \in \mathbb{N}$

8. Complex numbers

i	the square root of -1
z or w	a typical complex number, e.g. $x + iy$, where $x, y \in \mathbb{R}$
$\mathrm{Re}(z)$	the real part of z; $\mathrm{Re}(x+iy) = x$
$\mathrm{Im}(z)$	the imaginary part of z; $\mathrm{Im}(x+iy) = y$
$\lvert z\rvert$	the modulus of z; $\lvert x+iy\rvert = \sqrt{(x^2+y^2)}$
$\arg z$	the argument of z
z^{*}	the complex conjugate of z

9. Matrices

$\mathbf{M}$	a typical matrix $\mathbf{M}$
$\mathbf{M}^{-1}$	the inverse of a matrix $\mathbf{M}$ (provided it exists)
$\mathbf{M}^{\mathrm{T}}$	the transpose of matrix $\mathbf{M}$
$\det \mathbf{M}$	the determinant of a square matrix $\mathbf{M}$
$\mathbf{I}$	the identity matrix

10. Vectors

$\mathbf{a}$	the vector $\mathbf{a}$
$\lvert\mathbf{a}\rvert$ or a	the magnitude of vector $\mathbf{a}$
$\hat{\mathbf{a}}$	the unit vector with the same direction as $\mathbf{a}$
$\mathbf{i}, \mathbf{j}, \mathbf{k}$	unit vectors parallel to the Cartesian coordinate axes
$\overrightarrow{AB}$	the vector represented by the line segment AB
$\lvert\overrightarrow{AB}\rvert$ or AB	the length of the vector $\overrightarrow{AB}$
$\mathbf{a}.\mathbf{b}$	the scalar product of $\mathbf{a}$ and $\mathbf{b}$

Formulae

Most examination boards issue a list of formulae, similar to this one, for use in their examinations. Readers will need to check which of the formulae in the list below are allowed in the examination they are taking.

Algebra

The quadratic formula for solving $ax^2 + bx + c = 0$:

$$x = \frac{-b \pm \sqrt{(b^2 - 4ac)}}{2a}$$

The sum of an AP:

$$a + (a + d) + (a + 2d) + \ldots + (a + (n - 1)d)$$
$$= \tfrac{1}{2}(a + l), \quad \text{where} \quad l = a + (n - 1)d$$

The sum of a GP:

$$a + ar + ar^2 + \ldots + ar^{n-1} = \frac{a(r^n - 1)}{r - 1}$$

$$a + ar + ar^2 + \ldots = \frac{a}{1 - r}, \quad \text{provided} \quad |r| < 1$$

Binomial theorem for $n \in \mathbb{Z}^+$:

$$(a + b)^n = a^n + \frac{n}{1}a^{n-1}b + \frac{n(n-1)}{1 \times 2}a^{n-2}b^2 + \ldots + \frac{n!}{(n-r)!\,r!}a^{n-r}b^r + \ldots + b^n$$

Other standard series:

$$1 + 2 + 3 + \ldots + n = \tfrac{1}{2}n(n + 1)$$
$$1^2 + 2^2 + 3^2 + \ldots + n^2 = \tfrac{1}{6}n(n + 1)(2n + 1)$$
$$1^3 + 2^3 + 3^3 + \ldots + n^3 = \tfrac{1}{4}n^2(n + 1)^2$$

Combinations:

$$^nC_r = \frac{n!}{(n - r)!\,r!}$$

Trigonometry

The sine rule:

$$\frac{a}{\sin A} = \frac{b}{\sin B} = \frac{c}{\sin C}$$

The cosine rule:

$$a^2 = b^2 + c^2 - 2bc \cos A$$

The addition formulae:

$$\sin (A + B) = \sin A \cos B + \cos A \sin B$$
$$\sin (A - B) = \sin A \cos B - \cos A \sin B$$
$$\cos (A + B) = \cos A \cos B - \sin A \sin B$$
$$\cos (A - B) = \cos A \cos B + \sin A \sin B$$

$$\tan (A + B) = \frac{\tan A + \tan B}{1 - \tan A \tan B}$$

$$\tan (A - B) = \frac{\tan A - \tan B}{1 + \tan A \tan B}$$

The double angle formulae:

$$\sin 2A = 2 \sin A \cos A$$
$$\cos 2A = \cos^2 A - \sin^2 A$$
$$= 2 \cos^2 A - 1$$
$$= 1 - 2 \sin^2 A$$

$$\tan 2A = \frac{2 \tan A}{1 - \tan^2 A}$$

The factor formulae:

$$\sin P + \sin Q = 2 \sin \tfrac{1}{2}(P + Q) \cos \tfrac{1}{2}(P - Q)$$
$$\sin P - \sin Q = 2 \cos \tfrac{1}{2}(P + Q) \sin \tfrac{1}{2}(P - Q)$$
$$\cos P + \cos Q = 2 \cos \tfrac{1}{2}(P + Q) \cos \tfrac{1}{2}(P - Q)$$
$$\cos P - \cos Q = -2 \sin \tfrac{1}{2}(P + Q) \sin \tfrac{1}{2}(P - Q)$$

Calculus

Differentiation:

$f(x)$	$f'(x)$
x^n	nx^{n-1}
$\sin x$	$\cos x$
$\cos x$	$-\sin x$
$\tan x$	$\sec^2 x$
$\csc x$	$-\csc x \cot x$
$\sec x$	$\sec x \tan x$
$\cot x$	$-\csc^2 x$

$f(x)$	$f'(x)$
e^x	e^x
$\ln x$	$1/x$
$\sin^{-1} x$	$(1-x^2)^{-\frac{1}{2}}$
$\tan^{-1} x$	$(1+x^2)^{-1}$

Integration:

$f(x)$	$\int f(x)\,dx$ (constants omitted)
$x^n,\ (n \neq -1)$	$\dfrac{x^{n+1}}{n+1}$
$1/x$	$\ln|x|$
$\sin x$	$-\cos x$
$\cos x$	$\sin x$
$\tan x$	$\ln|\sec x|$
$\sec^2 x$	$\tan x$
$\sec x$	$\ln|\sec x + \tan x|$
$\dfrac{1}{(a^2+x^2)}$	$\dfrac{1}{a}\tan^{-1}\left(\dfrac{x}{a}\right)$
$\dfrac{1}{\sqrt{(a^2-x^2)}}$	$\sin^{-1}\left(\dfrac{x}{a}\right)$

General rules

Product rule:
$$\frac{d(uv)}{dx} = u\frac{dv}{dx} + v\frac{du}{dx}$$

Quotient rule:
$$\frac{d}{dx}\left(\frac{u}{v}\right) = \frac{v\frac{du}{dx} - u\frac{dv}{dx}}{v^2}$$

Integration by parts:
$$\int u\frac{dv}{dx}\,dx = uv - \int v\frac{du}{dx}\,dx$$

Numerical methods

The Newton-Raphson method for solving $f(x) = 0$:
$$a_{n+1} = a_n - \frac{f(a_n)}{f'(a_n)}$$

The trapezium rule:
$$\tfrac{1}{2}d(y_1 + 2y_2 + 2y_3 + \dots + 2y_{n-1} + y_n)$$

Simpson's rule:
$$\tfrac{1}{3}d(y_1 + 4y_2 + 2y_3 + 4y_4 + \dots + 4y_{n-1} + y_n)$$

Geometry

Equations

straight line
  through $(0, c)$ with gradient m:

$$y = mx + c$$

  through (x_1, y_1) with gradient m:

$$(y - y_1) = m(x - x_1)$$

circle, centre (a, b), radius r:

$$(x - a)^2 + (y - b)^2 = r^2$$

parabola:

$$y^2 = 4ax$$

hyperbola:

$$xy = c^2$$

plane in three dimensions:

$$ax + by + cz = d$$

plane perpendicular to vector **n**:

$$\mathbf{r}.\mathbf{n} = d$$

line in three dimensions:

$$\frac{x - a}{l} = \frac{y - b}{m} = \frac{z - c}{n}$$

line, through a point with position vector **a**, parallel to vector **b**:

$$\mathbf{r} = \mathbf{a} + t\mathbf{b}$$

Parametric form

circle, centre (a, b), radius r:

$$x = a + r \cos \theta, \qquad y = b + r \sin \theta$$

parabola:

$$x = at^2, \qquad y = 2at$$

rectangular hyperbola:

$$x = ct, \qquad y = c/t$$

The scalar product of two vectors:

$$\mathbf{a}.\mathbf{b} = ab \cos \theta$$

Chapter 1

Preparatory work

The object of this chapter is to give the reader practice in the basic algebraic techniques which will be encountered in this book.

Some readers may already have a strong command of algebra, if so they can skip this preparatory chapter. Even they however may find it helpful to return to parts of it in order to brush up specific techniques.

1.1 Simplification

Example 1

Simplify $(x + h)^2 - (x - h)^2$.

$$(x + h)^2 - (x - h)^2 = (x^2 + 2xh + h^2) - (x^2 - 2xh + h^2)$$
$$= x^2 + 2xh + h^2 - x^2 + 2xh - h^2$$
$$= 4xh$$

Exercise 1a

Simplify:

1 $4(x + 3) - (x - 5)$ 2 $x(5x + y) - y(x + y)$
3 $x(1 + x^2) + x^2(2 - x)$ 4 $5(y - 3) - 2(x + 5)$
5 $(2y - 1) - 3(3 - y)$ 6 $2(x + 3) - 5(x + 7) + 7(x - 2)$
7 $9 - (x - 3)^2$ 8 $(x + h)^2 + (x - h)^2$
9 $x(x + 3) - 3(x - 4)$ 10 $(t + 1/t)^2$

1.2 Factorisation

The ability to factorise algebraic expressions is an essential skill for any one wishing to succeed with advanced mathematics. As a general rule any expression which has factors should be factorised. We shall deal here with four important techniques (a) using common factors, (b) the difference of two squares, (c) perfect squares and (d) quadratics.

1

Using common factors

This is perhaps the most important technique. If an algebraic expression has got a common factor then it should be dealt with before considering anything else.

Example 2

(a) $2t^2 + 10$

This has a common factor of 2

$$2t^2 + 10 = 2(t^2 + 5)$$

(b) $ax + bx$

Here the common factor is x

$$ax + bx = x(a + b)$$

(c) $ax + bx + ap + bp$

In this expression the first two terms have a common factor x, and the second two have a common factor p

$$ax + bx + ap + bp = x(a + b) + p(a + b)$$

and each of the terms on the right has a common factor $(a + b)$. Hence

$$ax + bx + ap + bp = (x + p)(a + b)$$

Exercise 1b

Factorise:

1 $12x^2 + 8xy$	2 $ab^2 - a^2b$	3 $2x^2y + 8xy^2$
4 $xyz + uxy$	5 $\pi r^2 + 2\pi rh$	6 $p(a + b) - q(a + b)$
7 $ax + bx - ay - by$	8 $hp - hq - kp + kq$	9 $x^2 + 2xy + 3xy + 6y^2$
10 $4ab^3 + 4a^3b$		

The difference of two squares

This important method depends on the identity

$$\boxed{A^2 - B^2 = (A + B)(A - B)}$$

Example 3

(a) $x^2 - 25 = (x + 5)(x - 5)$
(b) $4a^2 - 9b^2 = (2a + 3b)(2a - 3b)$
(c) $7x^2 - 63 = 7(x^2 - 9) = 7(x + 3)(x - 3)$

Exercise 1c

Factorise, where possible:

1 $p^2 - 36$ 2 $100x^2 - 49$ 3 $t^2 - \frac{1}{4}$
4 $2x^2 - 50$ 5 $p^2 + 25$ 6 $75x^2 - 48$
7 $(x+7)^2 - 64$ 8 $16 - 81y^4$ 9 $(3x+1)^2 - (3x-1)^2$
10 $(a+b)^2 - (b+c)^2$

Perfect squares

Perfect squares depend on the following identities:

$$(A + B)^2 = A^2 + 2AB + B^2$$

and

$$(A - B)^2 = A^2 - 2AB + B^2$$

Example 4

(a) $x^2 + 8x + 16 = (x+4)^2$
(b) $4x^2 - 20x + 25 = (2x - 5)^2$
(c) $25a^2 + 70ab + 49b^2 = (5a + 7b)^2$

Quadratics

Many of the above expressions are quadratics. The general quadratic

$$ax^2 + bx + c$$

cannot always be factorised, e.g. $x^2 + 1$ has no factors. Simple cases, however, can be factorised by trial and error, as in the example below.

Example 5

Factorise $2t^2 + 15t + 7$.

The first term $2t^2$ can only be the result of $2t \times t$ and the constant term can only be 7×1. So the only factors worth considering are

either $(2t + 1)(t + 7)$ or $(2t + 7)(t + 1)$

By trial and error we can see that only the first pair give $15t$ as the middle term. Hence:

$$2t^2 + 15t + 7 = (2t + 1)(t + 7)$$

The second pair of factors would be the correct factors of $2t^2 + 9t + 7$. If the middle term is neither $9t$ nor $15t$, then the quadratic cannot be factorised by trial and error.

Exercise 1d

Factorise where possible:

1 $x^2 - 9x + 14$	**2** $2y^2 + 11y - 21$	**3** $8t^2 - 2t - 3$
4 $25p^2 + 4$	**5** $9 - 6s + s^2$	**6** $m^2 + 7m + 20$
7 $2x^2 - 11x + 14$	**8** $16y^2 + 24y + 9$	**9** $x^2 + 4x + 10$
10 $25 + 20c + 4c^2$	**11** $4x^2 + 10x + 6$	**12** $p^2 - 9pq + 8q^2$
13 $2A^2 + 7AB + 3B^2$	**14** $21 - 45n + 6n^2$	**15** $4x^4 + 12x^2 + 9$
16 $100a^6 - 60a^3 b^3 + 9b^6$		

Exercise 1e (Miscellaneous factors)

Factorise:

1 $35x^2 + x - 6$	**2** $2x^2 - 98$
3 $2x^2 - xy - y^2$	**4** $xy + ay + xb + ab$
5 $xy + 3y - 2x - 6$	**6** $x(x + 1)^2 + (x + 1)(x^2 - 3)$
7 $(x + 3)(x^2 + 3) + x(x + 3)^2$	**8** $5(x + 1)^2 + 7x(x + 1)$
9 $(x + 3)^2 - (x - 7)^2$	**10** $(x - 2)^3 + 5x(x - 2)^2$

1.3 Fractions

Let us first summarise some of the main facts about fractions. The top line of a fraction is called the **numerator** and the bottom line is the **denominator**.

If we multiply the numerator and the denominator by the same number, the value of the fraction is unchanged e.g. $2/3 = 8/12$. The fractions are said to be **equivalent**. Conversely, if the numerator and the denominator have a common factor, then we may divide both numbers by it. It is usual to say the common factor has been **cancelled** and the fraction has been **simplified**. In algebra this takes the form:

$$\frac{ax}{bx} = \frac{a}{b}$$

Be careful, however, *not* to cancel the x if it is not a factor:

$$\frac{a + x}{b + x} \quad \textit{does not equal} \quad \frac{a}{b}$$

Fractions which have the same denominator are added (or subtracted) by adding (or subtracting) their numerators, e.g. $2/7 + 3/7 = 5/7$. If their denominators are not the same, we first change the fractions into equivalent fractions:

$$\frac{2}{5} + \frac{3}{7} = \frac{14}{35} + \frac{15}{35}$$

$$= \frac{29}{35}$$

In algebra, we use a similar method:

$$\frac{a}{x} + \frac{b}{y} = \frac{ay}{xy} + \frac{bx}{xy}$$

$$= \frac{ay + bx}{xy}$$

Multiplication is simply a matter of multiplying the numerators to form the new numerator, and multiplying the denominators to form the new denominator:

$$\frac{a}{x} \times \frac{b}{y} = \frac{ab}{xy}$$

To divide one fraction by another, invert the second one (called the **divisor**) and multiply by it:

$$\frac{a}{x} \div \frac{b}{y} = \frac{a}{x} \times \frac{y}{b}$$

$$= \frac{ay}{bx}$$

Example 6

(a) $\dfrac{4x}{6x^2} = \dfrac{2}{3x}$

(b) $\dfrac{5x}{6} - \dfrac{3x}{8} = \dfrac{20x}{24} - \dfrac{9x}{24}$

$$= \dfrac{11x}{24}$$

(c) $\dfrac{15x^2}{4y} \div \dfrac{3x}{8} = \dfrac{15x^2}{4y} \times \dfrac{8}{3x}$

$$= \dfrac{10x}{y}$$

Example 7

Express as a single fraction:

(a) $\dfrac{1}{2+x} + \dfrac{2}{1-3x}$ (b) $\dfrac{1}{a^3 b} + \dfrac{1}{ab^3}$

(a) $\dfrac{1}{2+x} + \dfrac{2}{1-3x} = \dfrac{1}{2+x} \times \dfrac{1-3x}{1-3x} + \dfrac{2}{1-3x} \times \dfrac{2+x}{2+x}$

$$= \dfrac{(1-3x) + 2(2+x)}{(2+x)(1-3x)}$$

$$= \dfrac{1-3x+4+2x}{(2+x)(1-3x)}$$

$$= \dfrac{5-x}{(2+x)(1-3x)}$$

(b) $\dfrac{1}{a^3 b} + \dfrac{1}{ab^3} = \dfrac{b^2}{a^3 b^3} + \dfrac{a^2}{a^3 b^3}$

$$= \dfrac{a^2 + b^2}{a^3 b^3}$$

(In this part, notice that $a^3 b^3$ is the lowest common multiple of the original denominators $a^3 b$ and ab^3.)

Exercise 1f

Simplify:

1 $\dfrac{a+b}{4a+4b}$ **2** $\dfrac{ax^2}{a^2 x}$ **3** $\dfrac{a+b}{a^2 - b^2}$

4 $\dfrac{a-b}{b-a}$ **5** $\dfrac{x+2}{x^2 + 5x + 6}$

Express as a single fraction:

6 $\dfrac{5x^2}{y} \times \dfrac{y^2}{10x}$ **7** $\dfrac{a-b}{c} \times \dfrac{c^2}{a^2 - b^2}$ **8** $\dfrac{x^4}{y^4} \times \left(\dfrac{y}{x}\right)^2$

9 $\dfrac{5x}{4y} \div \dfrac{10x^2}{8y^2}$ **10** $\dfrac{1}{3x-y} \div \dfrac{1}{5y-15x}$

Exercise 1g

Express as a single fraction:

1 $\dfrac{1}{x} - \dfrac{1}{y}$ **2** $\dfrac{x}{y} + \dfrac{y}{x}$ **3** $\dfrac{1}{a^2} + \dfrac{1}{a}$

4 $\dfrac{1}{ab^2} + \dfrac{1}{a^2 b}$ **5** $\dfrac{1}{x-h} + \dfrac{1}{x+h}$ **6** $\dfrac{1}{(x+h)^2} - \dfrac{1}{x^2}$

7 $\dfrac{1}{1-x} - \dfrac{2}{2+x}$ **8** $\dfrac{x}{x^2 + 2} - \dfrac{2}{2+x}$ **9** $\dfrac{n}{n+1} + \dfrac{1}{(n+1)(n+2)}$

10 $\dfrac{1}{(x+1)^2} + \dfrac{1}{(x+1)} + 1$

Exercise 1h

Simplify:

1 $\dfrac{2T - 2t}{T^2 - t^2}$

2 $x - 1 + \dfrac{1}{1 + x}$

3 $\dfrac{1 - 1/t}{1 - t}$

4 $\dfrac{T - t}{1/T - 1/t}$

5 $\dfrac{N(4N^2 - 1) + 3(2N + 1)^2}{N + 1}$

6 $\dfrac{a}{\sqrt{(a + b)}} + \dfrac{b}{\sqrt{(a + b)}}$

7 $\dfrac{a/b + c/d}{1 + ac/(bd)}$

8 $\dfrac{(x + h)^3 - x^3}{h}$

9 $\dfrac{1}{\sqrt{(1 + x^2)}} - \dfrac{x^2}{\sqrt{(1 + x^2)}(1 + x^2)}$

10 $\sqrt{\left\{\dfrac{1 - 2t/(1 + t^2)}{1 + 2t/(1 + t^2)}\right\}}$

1.4 Completing the square

Completing the square is a very useful technique which appears in several different contexts. It depends on the identity

$$(A + B)^2 = A^2 + 2AB + B^2$$

as the following example illustrates.

Example 8

Complete: $(\Box x + \Box)^2 = 25x^2 + 70x + \Box$.

Comparing this incomplete statement with the identity above and, in particular, comparing the term $25x^2$ with A^2 in the identity, we see that $A = 5x$. Comparing the middle terms, namely $70x$ and $2AB$, and bearing in mind that $A = 5x$, we can see that $B = 7$. Lastly, the final term on the right-hand side should be B^2 and so the missing number in the last box is 49. The complete statement is

$$(5x + 7)^2 = 25x^2 + 70x + 49$$

Exercise 1i

In each of the questions below, there is a number missing wherever a box has been printed. Find the missing numbers.

1 $(x + 3)^2 = x^2 + \Box x + 9$

2 $(x - 5)^2 = x^2 - \Box x + \Box$

3 $(3x + 2)^2 = 9x^2 + \Box x + 4$

4 $(x + \Box)^2 = x^2 + 10x + \Box$

5 $(x - \Box)^2 = x^2 - 14x + \Box$

6 $(2x + \Box)^2 = \Box x^2 + 12x + \Box$

7 $(x + \tfrac{1}{2})^2 = x^2 + \Box x + \Box$

8 $(\tfrac{1}{2}x - \Box)^2 = \Box x^2 - x + \Box$

9 $(\Box x^2 + 3)^2 = 100x^4 + 60x^2 + \Box$

10 $(\tfrac{1}{3}x + \Box y)^2 = \Box x^2 + \tfrac{1}{3}xy + \Box y^2$

Quadratics which are not perfect squares can be expressed in the form

$$a(x + p)^2 + q$$

as follows:

(a) $x^2 + 6x + 20 = x^2 + 6x + 9 + 11$
$= (x + 3)^2 + 11$
(b) $x^2 - 5x + 8 = x^2 - 5x + 6.25 + 1.75$
$= (x - 2.5)^2 + 1.75$
(c) $4x^2 + 12x + 7 = 4x^2 + 12x + 9 - 2$
$= (2x + 3)^2 - 2$
(d) $2x^2 + 8x + 9 = 2(x^2 + 4x) + 9$
$= 2[(x + 2)^2 - 4] + 9$
$= 2(x + 2)^2 - 8 + 9$
$= 2(x + 2)^2 + 1$

A quadratic arranged like this is said to be in **completed square form**. We shall return to this topic in Chapter 11.

Exercise 1j

Express in completed square form:

1 $x^2 + 14x + 50$ 2 $x^2 + 10x + 40$ 3 $t^2 - 6t + 13$
4 $p^2 - 4p + 3$ 5 $q^2 + 20q + 80$ 6 $4x^2 + 12x + 10$
7 $25z^2 + 70z + 60$ 8 $9v^2 - 6v - 4$ 9 $2x^2 + 28x - 2$
10 $5w^2 - 20w + 12$

1.5 Changing the subject of a formula

Example 9

(a) Make y the subject of $\dfrac{y - k}{a} = \dfrac{x - h}{b}$.

(b) Make x the subject of $m = \dfrac{x + a}{b - x}$.

(a) $\dfrac{y - k}{a} = \dfrac{x - h}{b}$

Multiply both sides by a:

$$y - k = a \times \dfrac{(x - h)}{b}$$

$$= \dfrac{a}{b}(x - h)$$

Add k to both sides:

$$y = \frac{a}{b}(x - h) + k$$

(b) (This is slightly harder because x appears more than once. The purpose of the first few steps is to rearrange the equation so that x appears once only.)

$$m = \frac{x + a}{b - x}$$

Multiply both sides by $b - x$:

$$m(b - x) = x + a$$
$$\therefore \ mb - mx = x + a$$

Add mx to both sides and subtract a from both sides:

$$mb - a = x + mx$$
$$= x(1 + m)$$

(This has achieved the first objective; x now appears once only.)

Now, divide both sides by $(1 + m)$:

$$\frac{mb - a}{1 + m} = x$$

i.e. $x = \dfrac{mb - a}{1 + m}$

Exercise 1k

In each question, the letter which is to be made the subject is printed (in brackets) at the end of the equation.

1 $y = mx + c$ (m)

2 $b = a(1 - e)$ (e)

3 $y^2 = (x + a)^2 - (x - a)^2$ (x)

4 $\dfrac{y - k}{K - k} = \dfrac{x - h}{H - h}$ (y)

5 $3mc = (4 + 3m)(c - 4)$ (c)

6 $ax - x + 1 - b = 0$ (x)

7 $T = 2\pi \sqrt{\dfrac{l}{g}}$ (l)

8 $T = 2\pi \sqrt{\dfrac{l}{g}}$ (g)

9 $2x + 2y + 2mx - 4my + 1 = 0$ (m)

10 $2x - 3y - 3mx + 2my - 2m + 4 = 0$ (m)

1.6 Linear and quadratic equations

Example 10

Solve the equation $\frac{1}{2}(2x - 3) - \frac{1}{3}(x - 2) = \frac{7}{6}$.

$\frac{1}{2}(2x-3) - \frac{1}{3}(x-2) = \frac{7}{6}$

Multiply both sides by 6:

$$3(2x-3) - 2(x-2) = 7$$
$$6x - 9 - 2x + 4 = 7$$

(Be very careful over the $+$ sign in front of the 4: this is a very common source of error!)

Simplifying the left-hand side gives

$$4x - 5 = 7$$
$$\therefore \quad 4x = 12$$

and hence $x = 3$

[It is a wise precaution to check the answer by substituting $x = 3$ in the original equation. The left-hand side gives:

$$\frac{1}{2}(2x-3) - \frac{1}{3}(x-2) = \frac{1}{2}(6-3) - \frac{1}{3}(3-2)$$
$$= \frac{1}{2} \times 3 - \frac{1}{3} \times 1$$
$$= 1\frac{1}{2} - \frac{1}{3}$$
$$= \frac{7}{6}]$$

Example 11

Solve the equation $tx - t^2 = Tx - T^2$, expressing x in terms of t and T.

$$tx - t^2 = Tx - T^2$$
$$\therefore \quad tx - Tx = t^2 - T^2$$

Factorising this gives

$$x(t - T) = (t - T)(t + T)$$

Dividing both sides by $(t - T)$ we have

$$x = (t + T)$$

(However, it should be noted that the final step, namely dividing by $(t - T)$, is only permissible if $t \neq T$, because one must never divide by zero. If t *does* equal T, the original equation is true for all values of x.)

Example 12

Solve the quadratic equation

$$2x^2 = 11x + 21$$

First arrange the equation in the form $ax^2 + bx + c = 0$ and then factorise the left-hand side:

$$2x^2 - 11x - 21 = 0$$
$$(2x + 3)(x - 7) = 0$$

A product can only be zero if one of its factors is zero, so

either $2x + 3 = 0$ or $x - 7 = 0$
$2x = -3$ $x = 7$
$x = -1.5$

Hence $x = -1.5$ or $x = 7$.

We shall consider quadratic equations which cannot be factorised in Chapter 11.

Example 13

Solve the quadratic equation

$$tx^2 + c(1 - t^2)x - c^2t = 0$$

giving your answer in terms of c and t.

Removing the brackets and factorising gives

$$tx^2 + cx - ct^2x - c^2t = 0$$
$$x(tx + c) - ct(tx + c) = 0$$

Hence

$$(tx + c)(x - ct) = 0$$

giving

either $tx + c = 0$ or $x - ct = 0$

Hence $x = -c/t$ or $x = ct$.

Exercise 1I

Solve the following equations:

1 $2x + 1 = 16 - 3x$ **2** $\dfrac{2x-1}{3} - \dfrac{x-7}{5} = 2$ **3** $\dfrac{x}{x+1} - \dfrac{1}{x-2} = 1$

4 $\dfrac{x-5}{x+1} = \dfrac{x-7}{x-2}$ **5** $2x^2 - 17x + 21 = 0$ **6** $x^2 = 5x + 14$

7 $x^2 + 2x = 99$ **8** $2x^2 = 77 + 3x$ **9** $5x^2 + 4x = 0$

10 $4x^2 - 25 = 0$ **11** $x = 5 - 6/x$ **12** $\dfrac{1}{x} - \dfrac{1}{x+1} = \dfrac{1}{x+4}$

Express x in terms of the other letters:

13 $\dfrac{x-ct}{2} = \dfrac{cT-x}{3}$ **14** $5x^2 - 16tx + 3t^2 = 0$

15 $tx^2 + (tT - 1)x - T = 0$

1.7 Simultaneous equations

The reader will have solved simultaneous equations before, but the method of substitution may be new. In Example 14 substitution is merely an alternative to other possible methods, but in Example 16 it is the only way the equation can be solved.

Example 14

Solve the simultaneous equations

$$7x + 2y = 11 \qquad \qquad \qquad \ldots \text{ (1)}$$
$$4x + y = 7 \qquad \qquad \qquad \ldots \text{ (2)}$$

Equation (2) can be rearranged to give

$$y = 7 - 4x$$

Substituting $(7 - 4x)$ for y in equation (1):

$$7x + 2(7 - 4x) = 11$$

Removing the brackets:

$$7x + 14 - 8x = 11$$
$$\therefore \qquad 14 - x = 11$$
$$\therefore \qquad x = 3$$

Hence the solution is $x = 3, y = -5$.

(This should be checked by substituting these values into equation (1).)

Example 15

Solve the simultaneous equations

$$x + y + z = 6 \qquad \qquad \ldots \text{ (1)}$$
$$2x + y - z = 1 \qquad \qquad \ldots \text{ (2)}$$
$$4x - 3y + 2z = 4 \qquad \qquad \ldots \text{ (3)}$$

Here we have three equations in three unknowns, x, y and z. As with two simultaneous equations in two unknowns, they can be solved by 'elimination'. First we eliminate z.

Add equations (1) and (2)

$$3x + 2y = 7 \qquad \qquad \ldots \text{ (4)}$$

Multiply equation (2) by 2 and add it to equation (3)

$$8x - y = 6 \qquad \qquad \ldots \text{ (5)}$$

y can be eliminated by multiplying equation (5) by 2 and adding it to equation (4)

$$19x = 19$$

Hence $x = 1$. Substituting this into equation (4) gives

$$3 + 2y = 7$$
$$\therefore \qquad y = 2.$$

and substituting these values for x and y in equation (1) gives $z = 3$.

Hence the solution is $x = 1$, $y = 2$ and $z = 3$.

Example 16

Solve the simultaneous equations

$$x^2 + y^2 = 25r^2$$
$$2y + x = 10r$$

giving the answers in terms of r.

From the second equation we have

$$x = 10r - 2y$$

Substituting this into the first equation gives

$$(10r - 2y)^2 + y^2 = 25r^2$$

Removing the brackets

$$100r^2 - 40ry + 4y^2 + y^2 = 25r^2$$

i.e. $\quad 100r^2 - 40ry + 5y^2 = 25r^2$

$\therefore \qquad 5y^2 - 40ry + 75r^2 = 0$

After dividing both sides by 5, this becomes

$$y^2 - 8ry + 15r^2 = 0$$
$$\therefore \quad (y - 3r)(y - 5r) = 0$$

Therefore, either $\quad y - 3r = 0 \quad$ or $\quad y - 5r = 0$

$\therefore \quad y = 3r \quad$ or $\quad 5r$

Substituting these values into the equation $2y + x = 10r$, gives

either $\quad 6r + x = 10r \qquad$ i.e. $\quad x = 4r$

or $\qquad 10r + x = 10r \qquad$ i.e. $\quad x = 0$

Hence the solution is

$$x = 0 \quad \text{and} \quad y = 5r$$

or

$$x = 4r \quad \text{and} \quad y = 3r$$

(It should be carefully noted that each solution consists of a value of x and a value of y.)

Exercise 1m

Solve the equations:

1 $7x + 4y = 10$
$5x + 3y = 7$

2 $6x + y = 9$
$4x - y = 11$

3 $5x + 2y + 1 = 0$
$y = 7x + 3$

4 $1.7x + 2.3y = 3.5$
$2.8x - 3.2y = -9.5$

5 $x + y + 2z = 4$
$2x + 4y - 2z = 1$
$3x + 8y + 4z = 1$

6 $y^2 = 4x$
$y = x$

7 $xy = 64$
$4x - y = 60$

8 $y^2 = 4x + 1$
$y = x + 1$

9 $4x + y = 30$
$y^2 + xy = 18$

10 $y = 2 - 4x^2 + x^3$
$y = -5x + 4$

Express x and y (and z in no. 15) in terms of the other letters:

11 $2y = x + 4c$
$5y = x + 25c$

12 $ty = x + t^2$
$Ty = x + T^2$, (where $t \neq T$)

13 $xy = 1$
$t^2 x - y = t^3 - 1/t$

14 $x^2 - y^2 = 16a^2$
$y = 3x - 12a$

15 $2x + y + z = 6a$
$5x + 4y - z = 3a$
$x - y - z = 0$

1.8 Equations of higher degree

Equations of degree more than two can be very troublesome to solve unless they can be factorised. However, when factors can be found, the same idea which is used in the solution of quadratic equations by factorisation may be used, namely that a product of real numbers (see Section 3.1) can only be zero if one of the factors is zero.

Example 17

Solve the equation $x^3 - 5x^2 + 6x = 0$.

Since x is a factor of each term in the equation, we can re-write it as

$$x(x^2 - 5x + 6) = 0$$

and on factorising the quadratic, we have

$$x(x - 2)(x - 3) = 0$$

Hence

$$x = 0 \quad \text{or} \quad x - 2 = 0 \quad \text{or} \quad x - 3 = 0$$

Therefore $x = 0$, or 2, or 3.

(Notice that although it is tempting to 'divide through' by x, if we do so, we lose the solution $x = 0$.)

Example 18

Solve the equation $x^4 - 5x^2 - 36 = 0$.

(Although this is an equation of degree 4, we may treat it as a quadratic in x^2.)

$$X^2 - 5X - 36 = 0, \quad \text{where } X = x^2$$

Factorising:

$$(X - 9)(X + 4) = 0$$
i.e. $\quad (x^2 - 9)(x^2 + 4) = 0$

The factor $(x^2 + 4)$ cannot be zero (not, that is, unless we use complex numbers, see Section 11.6), so if x is a real number we must deduce that

$$x^2 - 9 = 0$$
$$\therefore \qquad x^2 = 9$$

Therefore $x = +3$, or -3.

Exercise 1n

Solve the following equations. In nos. 6–10 express x in terms of the other letters:

1 $x^3 - 4x = 0$ 2 $x^3 = 7x^2$ 3 $x^3 - x^2 - 20x = 0$
4 $x^4 - 17x^2 + 16 = 0$ 5 $9x^4 + 5x^2 - 4 = 0$ 6 $x^3 + kx^2 = 0$
7 $(x - a)^3 - b^2(x - a) = 0$ 8 $x^3 + a^2 x = 0$ 9 $x^4 - a^4 = 0$
10 $(x - p)^3 = q^3$

Exercise 1o (Miscellaneous)

1 Simplify:
  (a) $\sqrt{\{(a - b)^2 + 4ab\}}$ (b) $(a + b)^3 - 3ab(a + b)$
2 Factorise:
  (a) $K^2(K + 1)^2 + 4(K + 1)^3$ (b) $N(N + 1)(2N + 7) + 6(N + 1)(N + 3)$
3 Express as a single fraction:

  (a) $\dfrac{1}{(x - h)^2} - \dfrac{1}{(x + h)^2}$ (b) $\dfrac{2}{(N + 1)(N + 3)} - \dfrac{2N + 3}{(N + 1)(N + 2)}$

4 Simplify:

(a) $\dfrac{2n+1}{n^2(n+1)^2} - \dfrac{1}{n^2}$ (b) $N\{(N+1)(2N+1) + 9(N+1) + 12\}$

5 Complete the following:

(a) $(7x + \square)^2 = 49x^2 + 42x + \square$ (b) $(x + \square)^2 + \square = x^2 + 7x + 13$

6 Make x the subject:

(a) $u = \sqrt{(3x+3)}$ (b) $u = 5x^2 + 1$

7 Solve the following equations, expressing x in terms of a:

(a) $\dfrac{1}{2}(x-a) + \dfrac{1}{5}(2x+a) = \dfrac{3a}{10}$ (b) $7x^2 + 4ax - 3a^2 = 0$

8 Solve the following equations, expressing x in terms of c and t:

(a) $c/t = (x - ct)/t^2$ (b) $x - c/t = -t^2(x + ct)$

9 Solve the following simultaneous equations, giving the answers in terms of a:

(a) $7x - 4y + 5a = 0$ (b) $y^2 = 4ax$
    $9x - 5y - a = 0$ $4y = 3(x - a)$

10 Solve the following equations, giving the answers in terms of k:

(a) $x^5 + k^2 x = 0$ (b) $x^6 - 7k^3 x^3 - 8k^6 = 0$

Chapter 2

Coordinates and the straight line

2.1 Coordinates

One of the most fundamental and fruitful concepts in mathematics is the idea that the position of a point in a plane can be specified by giving its distances from a pair of fixed, perpendicular lines, called **the axes**. The point where the axes intersect is called **the origin** and it is always denoted by the letter O. Most readers will have met this idea when following an earlier course of study.

The **x-axis** is drawn across the page, and the **y-axis** is drawn up the page; units of distance are marked off on them, positive in one direction, negative in the other (Figure 2.1). The plane containing these axes is called the **Cartesian** plane, after René Descartes (1588–1648) who did much to lay the foundations of the subject we now call Coordinate Geometry. When the axes are drawn in a

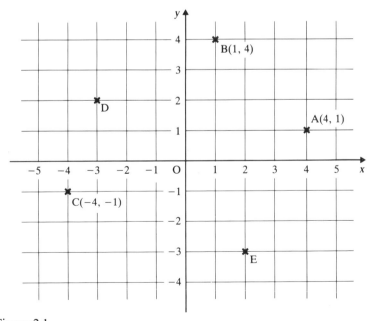

Figure 2.1

17

vertical plane (for instance, when a teacher draws them on a board, fixed to a vertical wall), the x-axis is always drawn as a horizontal line and the y-axis as a vertical line; for this reason, they are often called the **horizontal axis**, and the **vertical axis**, respectively (even though when they are drawn on the page of a book, lying on a horizontal table, both axes are horizontal!).

Consider the point A in Figure 2.1. To reach A from O we travel 4 units in the direction of Ox, and then 1 unit in the direction of Oy.

The **x-coordinate** (or *abscissa*) of A is $+4$.
The **y-coordinate** (or *ordinate*) of A is $+1$.

We say that the **coordinates** of A are (4, 1), or that A is the point (4, 1). The x-coordinate is always given first, thus we distinguish between the points A(4, 1) and B(1, 4). By use of the sign of the coordinates we distinguish between the points A(4, 1) and C(-4, -1).

Qu. 1 Write down the coordinates of the points D, E, O in Figure 2.1.
Qu. 2 Sketch your own axes and plot the points P(2, 4), Q(-5, 7), R(4, -2), S(0, 3), T(2, 0).

2.2 The length of a straight line

Example 1

Find the length of the straight line joining A(2, 1) and B(5, 5).

AC and CB are drawn parallel to the x-axis and y-axis respectively (Figure 2.2). Applying Pythagoras' theorem to the right-angled triangle ABC,

$$AB^2 = AC^2 + CB^2$$
$$= (5-2)^2 + (5-1)^2$$
$$= 9 + 16$$
$$\therefore \quad AB = \sqrt{25} = 5$$

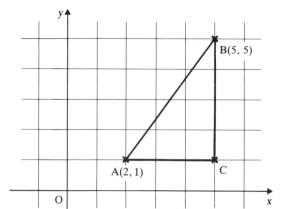

Figure 2.2

Notice that, if A had been the point $(-2, 1)$ in the above example, the length of AC would still be the *difference* between the x-coordinates of A and B, since it would be $5 - (-2) = 5 + 2 = 7$.

Qu. 3 Find the lengths of the straight lines joining the following pairs of points:
(a) A(3, 2) and B(8, 14)
(b) C(-1, 3) and D(4, 7)
(c) E(p, q) and F(r, s)

2.3 The mid-point of a straight line

Example 2

Find the mid-point of the straight line joining A(2, 1) and D(6, 5).

Let M, the mid-point of AD, have coordinates (p, q). FM and ED are drawn parallel to Oy; AFE is drawn parallel to Ox (Figure 2.3).

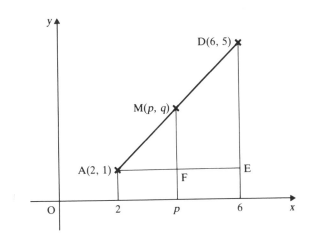

Figure 2.3

In the triangle ADE, applying the mid-point theorem, since M is the mid-point of AD, and MF is parallel to DE, F is the mid-point of AE. Thus

$$AF = FE$$
$$\therefore \quad p - 2 = 6 - p$$
$$\therefore \quad p = \frac{6 + 2}{2}$$
$$\therefore \quad p = 4$$

The x-coordinate of M is seen to be the average of those of A and D.

The y-coordinate of M may be found similarly.

$$q = \frac{5+1}{2}$$

$$\therefore \quad q = 3$$

$\therefore$ the mid-point of AD is $(4, 3)$.

In practice, of course, the working would be presented in shortened form thus:

the mid-point of AD is $\left(\dfrac{6+2}{2}, \dfrac{5+1}{2}\right)$, i.e. $(4, 3)$

Qu. 4 Find the coordinates of the mid-points of the straight lines joining the following pairs of points:
(a) A(4, 2) and B(6, 10)   (b) C(−5, 6) and D(3, 2)
(c) E(−6, −1) and F(3, −4)   (d) G(p, q) and H(r, s)

Exercise 2a

1 Find the lengths of the straight lines joining the following pairs of points:
  (a) A(1, 2) and B(5, 2)   (b) C(3, 4) and D(7, 1)
  (c) E(−2, 3) and F(4, 3)   (d) G(−6, 1) and H(6, 6)
  (e) J(−4, −2) and K(3, −7)   (f) L(−2, −4) and M(−10, −10)
2 Find the coordinates of the mid-points of the lines AB, CD, etc., in no. 1.
3 Find the distance of the point (−15, 8) from the origin.
4 P, Q, R are the points (5, −3), (−6, 1), (1, 8) respectively. Show that triangle PQR is isosceles, and find the coordinates of the mid-point of the base.
5 Repeat no. 4 for the points L(4, 4), M(−4, 1), N(1, −4).
6 A and B are the points (−1, −6) and (5, −8) respectively. Which of the following points lie on the perpendicular bisector of AB?
  (a) P(3, −4)   (b) Q(4, 0)   (c) R(5, 2)   (d) S(6, 5)
7 Three of the following four points lie on a circle whose centre is at the origin. Which are they, and what is the radius of the circle?

  A(−1, 7), B(5, −5), C(−7, 5), D(7, −1)

8 A and B are the points (12, 0) and (0, −5) respectively. Find the length of AB, and the length of the median, through the origin O, of the triangle OAB.

2.4 The gradient of a straight line

Consider the straight line passing through A(1, 1) and B(7, 2) (Figure 2.4). If we think of the x-axis as horizontal, and the line through A and B as a road, then someone walking from A to B would rise a vertical distance CB whilst at the same time moving a horizontal distance AC.

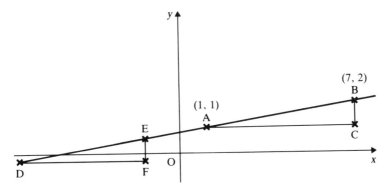

Figure 2.4

The gradient of the road is $CB/AC = (2-1)/(7-1) = 1/6$. Instead of the two points A and B we might just as well have taken any other two points on the line, D and E; the gradient would then be expressed as FE/DF, which is the same as CB/AC, since the triangles ABC and DEF are similar.

Definition

> The gradient of a straight line is $\dfrac{\text{the increase in } y}{\text{the increase in } x}$ in moving from one point on the line to another.

In moving from A to B, since both x and y increase by positive amounts, the gradient is positive.

But now consider the gradient of PQ (Figure 2.5). In moving from P to Q, the increase in x is $+2$, but since y decreases, we may say the increase in y is -3. Thus the gradient of PQ is $-\frac{3}{2}$.

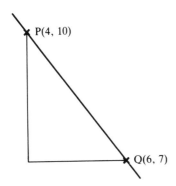

Figure 2.5

Until the reader is accustomed to the idea of positive and negative gradient it may help to think of it this way. In travelling along a line with x increasing, (i.e. moving from left to right across the page) if going *uphill* the gradient is *positive*: whereas if going *downhill* the gradient is *negative*. In calculating gradients a figure should not be necessary, but one similar to Figure 2.5 will help in the first few examples.

Example 3

Find the gradient of the line joining R(4, 8) and S(5, -2).

$$\text{The gradient of RS} = \frac{y\text{-coord. of R} - y\text{-coord. of S}}{x\text{-coord. of R} - x\text{-coord. of S}}$$

$$= \frac{8 - (-2)}{4 - 5}$$

$$= \frac{10}{-1} = -10$$

Remember that the coordinates of R must appear first in the denominator *and* numerator (or second in both). In this case $\{8 - (-2)\}/(4 - 5)$ and $(-2 - 8)/(5 - 4)$ both give the correct gradient.

The gradient of the line joining A(2, 1) and B(2, 9) presents us with a problem. Proceeding as in Example 3, above, we might say that

$$\text{the gradient of AB} = \frac{y\text{-coord. of A} - y\text{-coord. of B}}{x\text{-coord. of A} - x\text{-coord. of B}}$$

$$= \frac{1 - 9}{0}$$

$$= \frac{-8}{0}$$

On the other hand we might also say that

$$\text{the gradient of AB} = \frac{y\text{-coord. of B} - y\text{-coord. of A}}{x\text{-coord. of B} - x\text{-coord. of A}}$$

$$= \frac{9 - 1}{0}$$

$$= \frac{+8}{0}$$

Now, what meaning should we attach to expressions like $-8/0$ and $+8/0$ and how can the line AB have two apparently different gradients? This illustrates just one of the difficulties which can arise when we attempt to divide by zero. Because it gives rise to many insuperable problems, division by zero is never allowed in mathematics; mathematicians say that an expression like 8/0 'does not exist'. So what are we to do about the gradient of the line AB? We have to accept that for a 'vertical line' such as AB, no numerical value can be given to its gradient; however, we can still say that 'AB is parallel to the y-axis'.

Qu. 5 Find the gradients of the lines joining the following pairs of points:
(a) $(4, 3)$ and $(8, 12)$ (b) $(-2, -3)$ and $(4, 6)$ (c) $(5, 6)$ and $(10, 2)$
(d) $(-3, 4)$ and $(8, -6)$ (e) $(-5, 3)$ and $(2, 3)$ (f) (p, q) and (r, s)
(g) $(0, a)$ and $(a, 0)$ (h) $(0, 0)$ and (a, b)
Qu. 6 A and B are the points $(3, 4)$ and $(7, 1)$ respectively. Use Pythagoras' theorem to prove that OA is perpendicular to AB. Calculate the gradients of OA and AB, and find their product.
Qu. 7 Repeat Qu. 6 for the points A$(5, 12)$ and B$(17, 7)$.

2.5 Parallel and perpendicular lines

The gradient of a straight line was defined in Section 2.4; it may be proved that it is also the tangent of the angle between the line and the positive direction of the x-axis.

In Figure 2.6 the gradient of AB is CB/AC, which is tan θ. The reader familiar with the tangent of an obtuse angle will appreciate that this covers negative gradient as well.

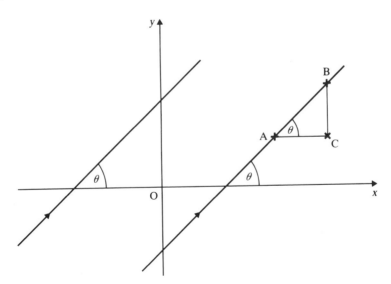

Figure 2.6

Since parallel lines make equal corresponding angles with the x-axis, **parallel lines have equal gradients**.

Qu. 6 and 7 of Section 2.4 will have led the reader to discover a useful property of the gradients of perpendicular lines. This we will now prove.

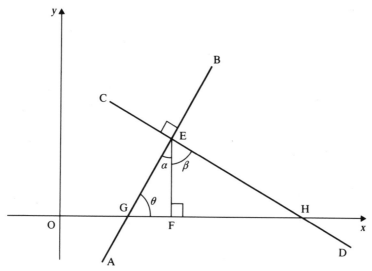

Figure 2.7

Consider the two straight lines AB and CD which cut at right angles at E. EF is drawn perpendicular to the x-axis (Figure 2.7).

$$\alpha + \theta = 90°$$
$$\alpha + \beta = 90°$$
$$\therefore \qquad \theta = \beta$$

Let the gradient of AB be m, then

$$m = \frac{FE}{GF} = \tan \theta$$

The gradient of $CD = -\frac{FE}{FH}$

$$= -\frac{1}{\tan \beta}$$

$$\therefore = -\frac{1}{\tan \theta}$$

$$= -\frac{1}{m}$$

$\therefore$ the gradient of AB $\times$ the gradient of $CD = m \times \left(-\frac{1}{m}\right) = -1$

In general, if two lines are perpendicular, the product of their gradients is -1.

Or in other words, if the gradient of one is m, the gradient of the other is $-1/m$.

Qu. 8 Write down the gradients of lines perpendicular to lines of gradient:
(a) 3   (b) $\frac{1}{4}$ (c) -6 (d) $-\frac{2}{3}$ (e) $2m$ (f) $-b/a$ (g) $-m/2$

Qu. 9 Find if AB is parallel or perpendicular to PQ in the following cases:
(a) A(1, 4), B(6, 6), P(2, -1), Q(12, 3)
(b) A(-1, -1), B(0, 4), P(-4, 3), Q(6, 1)
(c) A(0, 3), B(7, 2), P(6, -1), Q(-1, -2)

2.6 The meaning of equations

The bare statement 'P is the point (x, y)' means that P can be anywhere in the plane. Previously, if we have been asked to find P, we have been given some data which enabled us to find one pair of numerical values for x and y, and so to fix the position of P.

Suppose however that the data is in the form of the equation $y = x^2 - 2x$. This does not give one pair of values for x and y, it gives as many as we like to find. But P is not now free to be anywhere in the plane, since for any chosen value of x there is only one corresponding value of y; P is now restricted to positions whose coordinates (x, y) satisfy the relationship $y = x^2 - 2x$.

The reader will be familiar with the process of making a table of values as shown below, in which certain suitable values of x are chosen, and the corresponding values of y calculated.

Table of values for $y = x^2 - 2x$

x	-1	$-\frac{1}{2}$	0	$\frac{1}{2}$	1	$\frac{3}{2}$	2	$\frac{5}{2}$	3
x^2	1	$\frac{1}{4}$	0	$\frac{1}{4}$	1	$2\frac{1}{4}$	4	$6\frac{1}{4}$	9
$-2x$	2	1	0	-1	-2	-3	-4	-5	-6
y	3	$1\frac{1}{4}$	0	$-\frac{3}{4}$	-1	$-\frac{3}{4}$	0	$1\frac{1}{4}$	3

From this we find that the points $(-1, 3)$, $(-\frac{1}{2}, 1\frac{1}{4})$, $(0, 0)$ etc., have coordinates which satisfy the relationship $y = x^2 - 2x$, and by plotting these points and drawing a smooth curve through them (Figure 2.8), we obtain all the possible positions of P corresponding to the values of x from $x = -1$ to $x = 3$.

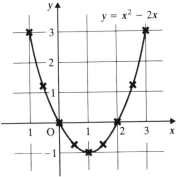

Figure 2.8

Just as coordinates are used to name a point, so an equation is used to name a curve, and we refer to 'the curve $y = x^2 - 2x$'.

It must be stressed that the equation is the condition that the point (x, y) should lie on the curve.

Thus, only if $b = a^2 - 2a$ does the point (a, b) lie on the curve $y = x^2 - 2x$, and in that case we say that the coordinates of the point *satisfy* the equation.

If $q \neq p^2 - 2p$, the point (p, q) does *not* lie on the curve $y = x^2 - 2x$.

Example 4

Do the points $(-3, 9)$ and $(14, 186)$ lie on the curve $y = x^2$?

(a) The point $(-3, 9)$:
When $x = -3$, $y = x^2 = (-3)^2 = +9$,

$\therefore (-3, 9)$ does lie on the curve $y = x^2$.

(b) The point $(14, 186)$:
When $x = 14$, $y = x^2 = 14^2 = 196$,

$\therefore (14, 186)$ does *not* lie on the curve $y = x^2$.

The next example illustrates another way of presenting this idea.

Example 5

Does the point $(-7, 6)$ lie on the curve $x^2 - y^2 = 14$?

[We use L.H.S. as an abbreviation for 'the left-hand side' of the equation and R.H.S. for 'the right-hand side'.]

$$x^2 - y^2 = 14$$

When $x = -7$ and $y = +6$,

$$\text{L.H.S.} = (-7)^2 - 6^2 = 49 - 36 = 13$$
$$\text{R.H.S.} = 14$$

The coordinates of the point do not satisfy the equation. Therefore $(-7, 6)$ does *not* lie on the curve $x^2 - y^2 = 14$.

Qu. 10 Find the coordinates of the points on the curve $y = 2x^2 - x - 1$ for which $x = 2, -3, 0$.

Qu. 11 Find the x-coordinates of the points on the curve $y = 2x + 3$ for which the y-coordinates are $7, 3, -2$.

Qu. 12 Find the points at which the curve in Qu. 10 cuts
(a) the x-axis   (b) the y-axis.

Qu. 13 Determine whether the following points lie on the given curves:
(a) $y = 6x + 7$, $(1, 13)$ (b) $y = 2x + 2$, $(13, 30)$
(c) $3x + 4y = 1$, $(-1, \frac{1}{2})$ (d) $y = x^3 - 6$, $(2, -2)$
(e) $xy = 36$, $(-9, -4)$ (f) $x^2 + y^2 = 25$, $(3, -4)$

The relationship between a curve and its equation gives rise to two main groups of problems.

Firstly there are those problems in which we are given the equation, and from it we are required to find the curve. With this type the reader will already be familiar, in such work as the graphical solution of quadratic and other equations.

Secondly there are those problems in which we are given some purely geometrical facts about the curve, and from these we are required to discover the equation. It is this second type of problem with which we are now mainly concerned, but first we shall discuss a few more simple equations, to see what they represent.

$y = x$.   This equation is satisfied by the coordinates of the points $(0, 0)$, $(1, 1)$, $(2, 2)$, $(3, 3)$, etc., and it is readily seen to represent a straight line through the origin. Its gradient is 1.

$x = 2$.   Whatever the value of its y-coordinate, provided that its x-coordinate is 2, a point will lie on this curve. The points $(2, 0)$, $(2, 1)$, $(2, 2)$, $(2, 3)$, etc., lie on the curve, which is a straight line parallel to the y-axis, 2 units from it, on the side on which x is positive.

Qu. 14 Make a rough sketch of the lines represented by the following equations. Write down the gradient of each:
(a) $y = 3$ (b) $y = 2x$ (c) $y = 3x$ (d) $y = \frac{1}{2}x$ (e) $y = -x$

2.7 The equation $y = mx + c$

We come now to the second type of problem mentioned above, in which from some geometrical facts about a curve we discover its equation. And the examples we do will, in turn, help us to interpret straight line equations more skilfully.

Example 6

Find the equation of the straight line of gradient 4 which passes through the origin.

If $P(x, y)$ is any point on the line, other than O, the gradient of the line may be written y/x (Figure 2.9).

$$\therefore \frac{y}{x} = 4$$

Hence $y = 4x$ is the required equation.

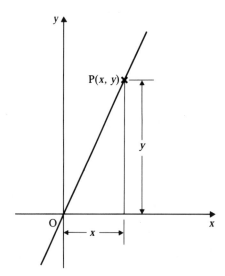

Figure 2.9

Qu. 15 Write down the equations of the straight lines through the origin having gradients:
(a) $\frac{1}{3}$ (b) -2 (c) m

Qu. 16 Rearrange the following equations in the form $y = mx$, and hence write down the gradients of the lines they represent:

(a) $4y = x$ (b) $5x + 4y = 0$ (c) $3x = 2y$ (d) $\dfrac{x}{4} = \dfrac{y}{7}$ (e) $\dfrac{x}{p} - \dfrac{y}{q} = 0$

Example 7

Find the equation of the straight line of gradient 3 which cuts the y-axis at $(0, 1)$.

Let $P(x, y)$ be any point on the line other than $(0, 1)$.

The gradient of the line may be written $(y - 1)/x$ (Figure 2.10).

$$\therefore \frac{y-1}{x} = 3$$

Hence $y = 3x + 1$ is the required equation.

Qu. 17 By the method of Example 7, find the equations of the straight lines of given gradients cutting the y-axis at the named points:
(a) gradient 3, $(0, 2)$ (b) gradient 3, $(0, 4)$ (c) gradient 3, $(0, -1)$
(d) gradient $\frac{1}{3}$, $(0, 2)$ (e) gradient $\frac{1}{3}$, $(0, 4)$

If a straight line cuts the y-axis at the point $(0, c)$, the distance of this point from the origin is called the **intercept** on the y-axis.

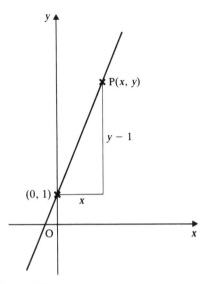

Figure 2.10

Then the equation of a straight line of gradient m, making an intercept c on the y-axis (Figure 2.11) is

$$\frac{y - c}{x} = m$$

i.e.

$$\boxed{y = mx + c}$$

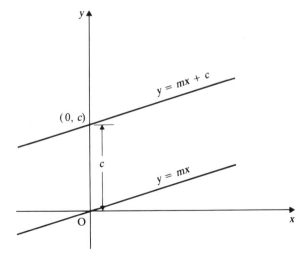

Figure 2.11

This line is parallel to $y = mx$, which passes through the origin, and it is m, the coefficient of x, which in each case determines the gradient. The effect of altering the value of the number c (c being the intercept on the y-axis) is to raise or lower the line, without altering its gradient; the sign of c determines whether the line cuts the y-axis above or below the origin.

We might be tempted to think at this stage that in $y = mx + c$ we have found the form in which all straight line equations may be written. But remember that on page 22 we ran into trouble trying to find the gradient of a line parallel to the y-axis; for such a line it is impossible to find a numerical value for m, and the equation is $x = k$, where k is a constant.

The various straight line equations we have met are summarised below. It should be noted that only terms of the first degree in x and y and a constant term occur; this, in fact, is how we may recognise a straight line, or *linear*, equation.

$y = mx + c$	is a line of gradient m, passing through $(0, c)$.
$y = mx$	is a line of gradient m, passing through the origin.
$y = c$	is a line of zero gradient (i.e. parallel to the x-axis).
$x = k$	is a line parallel to the y-axis.

Example 8

Find the gradient of the straight line $7x + 4y + 2 = 0$, and its intercepts on the axes.

The equation may be written

$$4y = -7x - 2$$
$$\text{or} \quad y = -\tfrac{7}{4}x - \tfrac{1}{2}$$

This is now in the form $y = mx + c$, where $m = -\tfrac{7}{4}$, and $c = -\tfrac{1}{2}$, and we see that the gradient is $-\tfrac{7}{4}$, and that the intercept on the y-axis is $-\tfrac{1}{2}$. In fact, to find the intercepts on each axis it is better to go back to the original equation

$$7x + 4y + 2 = 0$$

To find the intercept on the y-axis:
putting $x = 0$, $4y + 2 = 0$, $\therefore y = -\tfrac{1}{2}$.

To find the intercept on the x-axis:
putting $y = 0$, $7x + 2 = 0$, $\therefore x = -\tfrac{2}{7}$.

The intercepts on the x-axis and y-axis are $-\tfrac{2}{7}$ and $-\tfrac{1}{2}$ respectively.

Qu. 18 Arrange the following equations in the form $y = mx + c$, hence write down the gradient of each line; also find the intercepts on the y-axis:
(a) $3y = 2x + 6$ (b) $x - 4y + 2 = 0$ (c) $3x + y + 6 = 0$
(d) $7x = 3y + 5$ (e) $y + 4 = 0$ (f) $lx + my + n = 0$

Qu. 19 Write down the equation of (a) the x-axis, (b) the y-axis, (c) a straight line parallel to the y-axis through $(4, 0)$, (d) a straight line parallel to the x-axis making an intercept of -7 on the y-axis.

Exercise 2b

1 Find the gradients of the straight lines joining the following pairs of points:
   (a) $(4, 6)$ and $(9, 15)$ (b) $(5, -11)$ and $(-1, 3)$
   (c) $(-2\frac{1}{2}, -\frac{1}{2})$ and $(4\frac{1}{2}, -1)$ (d) $(7, 0)$ and $(-3, -2)$
2 Show that the three given points are in each case collinear, i.e. they lie on the same straight line:
   (a) $(0, 0)$, $(3, 5)$, $(21, 35)$ (b) $(-3, 1)$, $(1, 2)$, $(9, 4)$
   (c) $(-3, 4)$, $(1, 2)$, $(7, -1)$ (d) $(1, 2)$, $(0, -1)$, $(-2, -7)$
3 Find the gradients of the straight lines which make the following angles with the x-axis, the angle in each case being measured anti-clockwise from the positive direction of the x-axis:
   (a) $45°$ (b) $135°$ (c) $60°$ (d) $150°$
4 Find if AB is parallel or perpendicular to PQ in the following cases:
   (a) A(4, 3)   B(8, 4)   P(7, 1)   Q(6, 5)
   (b) A(-2, 0)   B(1, 9)   P(2, 5)   Q(6, 17)
   (c) A(8, -5)   B(11, -3)   P(1, 1)   Q(-3, 7)
   (d) A(-6, -1)   B(-6, 3)   P(2, 0)   Q(2, -5)
   (e) A(4, 3)   B(-7, 3)   P(5, 2)   Q(5, -1)
   (f) A(3, 1)   B(7, 3)   P(-3, 2)   Q(1, 0)
5 Show that A(-3, 1), B(1, 2), C(0, -1), D(-4, -2) are the vertices of a parallelogram.
6 Show that P(1, 7), Q(7, 5), R(6, 2), S(0, 4) are the vertices of a rectangle. Calculate the lengths of the diagonals, and find their point of intersection.
7 Show that D(-2, 0), E($\frac{1}{2}$, $1\frac{1}{2}$), F($3\frac{1}{2}$, $-3\frac{1}{2}$) are the vertices of a right-angled triangle, and find the length of the shortest side, and the mid-point of the hypotenuse.
8 Find the y-coordinates of the points on the curve $y = x^2 + 1$ for which the x-coordinates are -3, 0, 1, 5. Find the coordinates of points on the curve whose y-coordinates are 5, and 17. Sketch the curve.
9 Find the coordinates of the points on the curve $y = x^3$ for which $x = -3$, -1, 1, 3; and also of the points for which $y = -8$, 0, $+8$. Sketch the curve.
10 Determine whether the following points lie on the given curve:
   (a) $y = 3x - 5$, $(-1, -8)$ (b) $5x - 2y + 7 = 0$, $(1, -1)$
   (c) $y = x^3$, $(-4, 64)$ (d) $x^2y = 1$, $(-2, \frac{1}{4})$
11 Find the intercepts on the axes made by the straight line $3x - 2y + 10 = 0$. Hence find the area of the triangle enclosed by the axes and this line.
12 Find the coordinates of the points at which the following curves cut the axes:
   (a) $y = x^2 - x - 12$ (b) $y = 6x^2 - 7x + 2$
   (c) $y = x^2 - 6x + 9$ (d) $y = x^3 - 9x^2$
   (e) $y = (x + 1)(x - 5)^2$ (f) $y = (x^2 - 1)(x^2 - 9)$

13 Plot the following points on squared paper, and write down the equations of the straight lines passing through them, in the form $y = mx + c$:

(a) $(-1, -1)$, $(0, 0)$, $(4, 4)$ (b) $(-1, 1)$, $(0, 0)$, $(1, -1)$

(c) $(-4, -2)$, $(0, 0)$, $(8, 4)$ (d) $(0, -4)$, $(4, -2)$, $(6, -1)$

(e) $(-5, 2)$, $(-5, 0)$, $(-5, -2)$ (f) $(-3, 7)$, $(3, 3)$, $(6, 1)$

14 Write down the equation of the straight line

(a) through $(5, 11)$ parallel to the x-axis

(b) which is the perpendicular bisector of the line joining $(2, 0)$ and $(6, 0)$

(c) through $(0, -10)$ parallel to $y = 6x + 3$

(d) through $(0, 2)$ parallel to $y + 8x = 0$

(e) through $(0, -1)$ perpendicular to $3x - 2y + 5 = 0$

15 Find the equation of the straight line joining the origin to the mid-point of the line joining A$(3, 2)$ and B$(5, -1)$.

2.8 The use of suffixes

When we wish to refer to points whose coordinates are not given, it is convenient to write them as:

(x_1, y_1) read as   'x one, y one'

(x_2, y_2) read as   'x two, y two', etc.

It is important to write the number (the suffix) at the bottom of the letter, so as to avoid confusion between x_2 and x^2, x_3 and x^3, and so on. This is a suitable point at which to summarise some of the early results of this chapter, using this notation.

If A and B are the points (x_1, y_1) and (x_2, y_2) respectively,

the length of AB is $\sqrt{\{(x_1 - x_2)^2 + (y_1 - y_2)^2\}}$

the mid-point of AB is $\left(\dfrac{x_1 + x_2}{2}, \dfrac{y_1 + y_2}{2} \right)$

the gradient of AB is $\dfrac{y_1 - y_2}{x_1 - x_2}$ or $\dfrac{y_2 - y_1}{x_2 - x_1}$

the condition for A to lie on $ax + by + c = 0$ is

$$ax_1 + by_1 + c = 0$$

2.9 Finding the equation of a straight line

The method of Example 7 in Section 2.7 can of course be used to find the equation of any straight line provided (a) that we know one point through which the line passes, and (b) that we know, or can calculate, the gradient. Two examples will illustrate this.

Example 9

Find the equation of the straight line of gradient $-\frac{2}{3}$, which passes through $(-4, 1)$.

Let $P(x, y)$ be any point on the line other than $(-4, 1)$ (Figure 2.12). The gradient of the line may be written

$$\frac{y-1}{x-(-4)} = \frac{y-1}{x+4}$$

But the gradient is given as $-\frac{2}{3}$,

$$\therefore \qquad \frac{y-1}{x+4} = -\frac{2}{3}$$

$$\therefore \qquad 3(y-1) = -2(x+4)$$

$$\therefore \qquad 3y-3 = -2x-8$$

Hence the required equation is $2x + 3y + 5 = 0$.

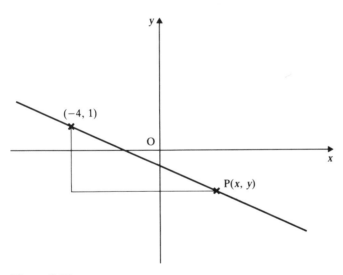

Figure 2.12

Example 10

Find the equation of the straight line joining the points $(-5, 2)$ and $(3, -4)$

The gradient of the line $= \dfrac{2-(-4)}{-5-3} = \dfrac{6}{-8} = -\dfrac{3}{4}.$

If P(x, y) is any point on the line other than (3, -4), the gradient may be written

$$\frac{y - (-4)}{x - 3} = \frac{y + 4}{x - 3}$$

$$\therefore \quad \frac{y + 4}{x - 3} = -\frac{3}{4}$$

$$\therefore \quad 4(y + 4) = -3(x - 3)$$

$$\therefore \quad 4y + 16 = -3x + 9$$

Hence the required equation is $3x + 4y + 7 = 0$.

Since we shall frequently need to write down the equation of a line with a given gradient, m, through a given point, (x_1, y_1), it is helpful to reduce this process to a formula. Proceeding as in Examples 9 and 10, we have:

$$\frac{y - y_1}{x - x_1} = m$$

and hence

$$\boxed{y - y_1 = m(x - x_1)}$$

Using this formula in Example 9, enables us to write down

$$y - 1 = (-\tfrac{2}{3})(x - (-4))$$

and hence

$$3(y - 1) = -2(x + 4) \text{ etc.}$$

Qu. 20 Find the equations of the straight lines:
(a) through (4, -3), of gradient $\tfrac{5}{2}$ (b) joining $(-3, 8)$ and (1, -2)
Qu. 21 Find the equations of the straight lines:
(a) through (5, -2), of gradient $\tfrac{3}{2}$ (b) joining $(-2, 5)$ and (3, -7)

2.10 Points of intersection

If the two straight lines $x + y - 1 = 0$ and $2x - y - 8 = 0$ cut at the point P(a, b) then the coordinates of P satisfy the equation of each line, and we may write

$$a + b - 1 = 0$$
$$2a - b - 8 = 0$$

The solution of these equations is $a = 3$, $b = -2$, which tells us that the given lines cut at (3, –2). In practice we obtain the results by solving the equations simultaneously for x and y.

Qu. 22 Find the points of intersection of the following pairs of straight lines:
(a) $2x - 3y = 6$ and $4x + y = 19$ (b) $y = 3x + 2$ and $2x + 3y = 17$
(c) $y = c$ and $y = mx + c$ (d) $x = -a$ and $y = mx + c$

Qu. 23 Can you find the point of intersection of

$$3x - 2y - 10 = 0 \quad \text{and} \quad 4y = 6x - 7?$$

Qu. 24 Find the points of intersection of the curve $y = 12x^2 + x - 6$ and the x-axis.

Exercise 2c

1 Find the equations of the straight lines of given gradients, passing through the points named:
   (a) $4, (1, 3)$ (b) $3, (-2, 5)$ (c) $\frac{1}{3}, (2, -5)$
   (d) $-\frac{3}{4}, (7, 5)$ (e) $\frac{1}{2}, (\frac{1}{3}, -\frac{1}{2})$ (f) $-\frac{5}{3}, (\frac{1}{4}, -3)$
2 Find the equations of the straight lines joining the following pairs of points:
   (a) $(1, 6)$ and $(5, 9)$ (b) $(3, 2)$ and $(7, -3)$
   (c) $(-3, 4)$ and $(8, 1)$ (d) $(-1, -4)$ and $(4, -3)$
   (e) $(\frac{1}{2}, 2)$ and $(3, \frac{1}{3})$ (f) $(-\frac{1}{2}, 0)$ and $(5, 11)$
3 Find the points of intersection of the following pairs of straight lines:
   (a) $x + y = 0, \; y = -7$
   (b) $y = 5x + 2, \; y = 3x - 1$
   (c) $3x + 2y - 1 = 0, \; 4x + 5y + 3 = 0$
   (d) $5x + 7y + 29 = 0, \; 11x - 3y - 65 = 0$
4 Find the equation of the straight line:
   (a) through $(5, 4)$, parallel to $3x - 4y + 7 = 0$
   (b) through $(-2, 3)$, parallel to $5x - 2y - 1 = 0$
   (c) through $(4, 0)$, perpendicular to $x + 7y + 4 = 0$
   (d) through $(-2, -3)$, perpendicular to $4x + 3y - 5 = 0$
5 Find the equation of the perpendicular bisector of AB, where A and B are the points $(-4, 8)$ and $(0, -2)$ respectively.
6 Repeat no. 5 for the points A$(7, 3)$ and B$(-6, 1)$.
7 Find the equation of the straight line joining A$(10, 0)$ and B$(0, -7)$. Also find the equation of the median through the origin, O, of the triangle OAB.
8 P, Q, R are the points $(3, 4), (7, -2), (-2, -1)$ respectively. Find the equation of the median through R of the triangle PQR.
9 Calculate the area of the triangle formed by the line $3x - 7y + 4 = 0$ and the axes.
10 Find the equation of the straight line through P$(7, 5)$ perpendicular to the straight line AB whose equation is $3x + 4y - 16 = 0$. Calculate the length of the perpendicular from P to AB.

Exercise 2d (Miscellaneous)

1 Find the equation of the line joining the points $(6, 3)$ and $(5, 8)$. Show also that these two points are equidistant from the point $(-2, 4)$.
2 What is the equation of the straight line joining the points A$(7, 0)$ and B$(0, 2)$? Obtain the equation of the straight line AC such that the x-axis bisects the angle BAC.
3 Find the equations of the following straight lines, giving each in the form
   $$ax + by + c = 0:$$

(a) the line joining the points $(2, 4)$ and $(-3, 1)$

(b) the line through $(3, 1)$ parallel to the line $3x + 5y = 6$

(c) the line through $(3, -4)$ perpendicular to the line $5x - 2y = 3$

4 Write down the condition that the straight lines

$$y = m_1 x + c_1 \quad \text{and} \quad y = m_2 x + c_2$$

should be at right angles. Find the equations of the straight lines through the point $(3, -2)$ which are (a) parallel, and (b) perpendicular to the line $2y + 5x = 17$.

5 The points A, B, C have coordinates $(7, 0)$, $(3, -3)$, $(-3, 3)$ respectively. Find the coordinates of D, E, F, the mid-points of BC, CA, AB respectively. Find the equations of the lines AD, BE, and the coordinates of K, their point of intersection. Prove that C, K, F are in a straight line.

6 Find the equation of the straight line

(a) joining the points $(-3, 2)$ and $(1, -4)$

(b) through $(-1, 3)$ parallel to the line $2x + 7y - 8 = 0$

(c) through $(2, -3)$ perpendicular to the line $5x - 2y - 11 = 0$

7 Find the equations of the lines passing through the point $(4, -2)$ and respectively (a) parallel, (b) perpendicular to the line $2x - 3y - 4 = 0$. Find also the coordinates of the foot of the perpendicular from $(4, -2)$ to $2x - 3y - 4 = 0$.

8 A line is drawn through the point $(2, 3)$ making an angle of $45°$ with the positive direction of the x-axis, and it meets the line $x = 6$ at P. Find the distance of P from the origin O, and the equation of the line through P perpendicular to OP.

9 Prove that the points $(-5, 4)$, $(-1, -2)$, $(5, 2)$ lie at three of the corners of a square. Find the coordinates of the fourth corner, and the area of the square.

10 The vertices of a quadrilateral ABCD are $A(4, 0)$, $B(14, 11)$, $C(0, 6)$, $D(-10, -5)$. Prove that the diagonals AC, BD bisect each other at right angles, and that the length of BD is four times that of AC.

11 The coordinates of the vertices A, B, C of the triangle ABC are $(-3, 7)$, $(2, 19)$, $(10, 7)$ respectively.

(a) Prove that the triangle is isosceles.

(b) Calculate the length of the perpendicular from B to AC, and use it to find the area of the triangle.

12 A triangle ABC has A at the point $(7, 9)$, B at $(3, 5)$, C at $(5, 1)$. Find the equation of the line joining the mid-points of AB and AC; and find also the area of the triangle enclosed by the line and the axes.

13 One side of a rhombus is the line $y = 2x$, and two opposite vertices are the points $(0, 0)$ and $(4\frac{1}{2}, 4\frac{1}{2})$. Find the equations of the diagonals, the coordinates of the other two vertices, and the length of the side.

14 Prove that the four points $(4, 0)$, $(7, -3)$, $(-2, -2)$, $(-5, 1)$ are the vertices of a parallelogram and find the equations of its diagonals.

15 Find the equation of the line which is parallel to the line $x + 4y - 1 = 0$, and which passes through the point of intersection of the lines $y = 2x$ and $x + y - 3 = 0$.

Chapter 3

Functions

3.1 Real numbers

Any student of mathematics who has progressed this far will be thoroughly familiar with the **real numbers**; they are the bricks and mortar of arithmetic. All the weighing, measuring and calculating that are used in commerce and science require the use of the real numbers. To the mathematician, they are the numbers, both positive and negative, which can be represented by points on the 'real number line'. Some of them are illustrated in Figure 3.1.

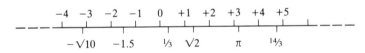

Figure 3.1

3.2 Integers

One of the earliest mathematical skills that a child has to learn is the skill of counting ... 'one, two, three, ...'. In mathematics these numbers are called the **counting** numbers. However, in order to develop mathematical ideas beyond very elementary arithmetic, it is necessary to extend the concept of counting numbers in two important directions. One of these is the extension to negative, as well as positive, numbers. Mathematicians refer to the positive and negative whole numbers, together with zero, as **integers**. An integer then is any number of the form ..., -4, -3, -2, -1, 0, $+1$, $+2$, $+3$, ...

3.3 Rational numbers

The other important extension of the counting numbers is the idea of fractions, e.g. $\frac{1}{4}$, $\frac{1}{2}$, $\frac{3}{4}$, ... In mathematics we extend this idea still further to include fractions which are bigger than one, e.g. 7/5, 22/7 (these are often called improper fractions), and we also allow them to be positive or negative. The collective name for all such numbers is **rational numbers** (rational is the adjective derived from the noun 'ratio').

Unfortunately, but for mathematicians rather interestingly, that is not the end of the story; the rational numbers do not 'fill' the number line. There are points on the number line, that representing $\sqrt{2}$ for example, which do not represent rational numbers. In other words, some real numbers are not rational numbers. In the next section we shall prove that $\sqrt{2}$ is not rational.

Before we can do this, we must state clearly and unambiguously what we mean by a rational number. **A rational number is a number of the form a/b, in which a and b are integers with no common factor**. (If there is a common factor, it should be cancelled, e.g. 12/15 should be simplified to 4/5.) *The number b must not be zero.* Notice however that b can be 1; this enables us to regard any integer, including zero itself, as a rational number. An integer is simply a rational number whose denominator b is equal to 1. Notice that a can be larger than b; 5/3 is a perfectly acceptable rational number.

3.4 The irrationality of $\sqrt{2}$

The Greek mathematicians of the 4th century BC knew all about the theorem of Pythagoras so they knew that the hypotenuse of a right-angled triangle, whose other two sides have a length of 1 unit, would have a length of $\sqrt{2}$ units. They discovered the proof that $\sqrt{2}$ is irrational, which is expressed in modern terms below.

Firstly we assume that $\sqrt{2}$ *can* be expressed as a rational number. That is, we assume that two integers, a and b, with no common factor, can be found such that

$$\sqrt{2} = \frac{a}{b}$$

Multiplying both sides by b gives

$$\sqrt{2}b = a$$

and squaring both sides we have

$$2b^2 = a^2$$

This equation tells us that a^2 is a multiple of 2, that is, it is an even number. Now, the squares of even numbers are even and the squares of odd numbers are odd, so we can deduce that a itself is an even number. Consequently it can be written as $2c$, where c is a natural number. Substituting $2c$ for a in the last equation, we have

$$2b^2 = (2c)^2 = 4c^2$$

and dividing through by 2 gives

$$b^2 = 2c^2$$

As before we can now deduce that b^2, and hence b itself, is an even number.

Thus the initial assumption that $\sqrt{2}$ is a rational number has led to the conclusion that both a and b are even numbers, that is, they have a common factor of 2. But a and b have *no* common factor, so we have contradicted ourselves. Now there are only two possible ways out of this *impasse*; either the argument is faulty (the reader should go through it again to check that this is not the case) or the original assumption is false. Hence $\sqrt{2}$ is not a rational number.

This proof is an example of a very important type of argument called *reductio ad absurdum*.

With only minor amendments it can be adapted to prove that the square root of any prime number is irrational. If such a square root is multiplied by a rational number, the result is also irrational. Numbers such as $\sqrt{2}$, $\sqrt{3}$, $\sqrt{6}$ are often called **surds**; we shall return to these in Chapter 10.

There are other irrational numbers, π for example, but we shall not go into the details here. Readers who wish to know more should consult a more advanced mathematics book. In particular, they should look for the names Cantor (1845–1918) and Dedekind (1831–1916) who were largely responsible for investigating irrational numbers.

Qu. 1 Are the following statements true or false? If you think they are false explain clearly why you have come to this conclusion.
(a) All prime numbers are odd numbers.
(b) Any natural number can be expressed as a rational number.
(c) The square root of a natural number is an irrational number.
(d) $\pi = 22/7$, so π is a rational number.

3.5 Infinity

If you have a calculator, work out the value of $1/n$ for $n = 0.1$, 0.001, 0.0001, 0.000 0001. (Even if you do not have a calculator it is easy to find the answers!) You should find that $1/n$ gets bigger and bigger as n gets smaller and smaller; we say that $1/n$ 'tends to infinity as n tends to zero'. The symbol ∞ is normally used for infinity. However, the idea of 'infinity' is a very risky one for the unwary. Consider, for example the two lists

    1, 2, 3,   4,   5,   6, ...
    1, 4, 9, 16, 25, 36, ...

How many terms are there in each of these lists? One might say 'infinity', but look carefully; since each number in the second list is the square of the corresponding number in the first, one could claim that each list contains the same number of terms. Yet the second list clearly omits many of the terms which are in the first, so one could also claim that the second list contains fewer terms than the first. 'Infinity' then is a dangerous concept and should be handled with great care. Mathematicians, unless they are very brave or very foolish, usually try to dodge it. In particular they never divide by zero; instead they usually say that an expression like $1/0$ does not exist. Infinity itself is not a number.

Example 1

Find the values of x for which the expression $\dfrac{2x+5}{x^2-x-6}$ does not exist.

The expression does not exist if

$$x^2 - x - 6 = 0$$
$$(x-3)(x+2) = 0$$

i.e.   either $x - 3 = 0$ or $x + 2 = 0$

The expression does not exist when $x = 3$ or -2.

Qu. 2 Find the values of x for which the following expressions do not exist:

(a) $\dfrac{x}{2x+5}$ (b) $\dfrac{1}{x^2+8x+15}$ (c) $\dfrac{x}{x^2-25}$ (d) $\dfrac{10}{x^2-3}$

3.6 Sets

In the previous sections we have already encountered the need to refer to particular collections, or **sets**, of numbers. For the benefit of any reader who has not met the idea of a set in mathematics before, a set is any clearly defined collection of objects (in this chapter the objects will always be numbers, but in later chapters you will meet sets of other mathematical objects or **elements**). The members of a set may be defined by listing them, or by describing them carefully in words. It is usual to enclose the list of members of a set in curly brackets, e.g.

$\{2, 4, 6, 8\}$ is the set of even numbers less than ten
$\{2, 3, 5, 7\}$ is the set of prime numbers less than ten
$\{3, 6, 9, ..., 99\}$ is the set of multiples of three, less than a hundred

Notice that when the pattern has been clearly established, as in the last case, the three dots indicate that the pattern continues until the last term is reached. In some cases there may be no last term, for example, the set of square numbers,

$\{1, 4, 9, 16, 25, 36, ...\}$

When listing the members of a set, an individual member is never repeated. Thus the set of prime factors of 1200 is $\{2, 3, 5\}$.

When we wish to indicate that a particular number belongs to a certain set, the symbol $\in$ is used. Thus if P is the set of prime numbers we may write

$37 \in P$

and this means '37 is a member of the set of prime numbers'. In contrast,

$$36 \notin P$$

means '36 is not a member of the set of prime numbers'.

The symbol : is often used in this context to mean 'such that'. Thus if we use $\mathbb{N}$ to indicate the set of natural numbers $\{0, 1, 2, 3, ...\}$, the mathematical statement

$$A = \{x^3 : x \in \mathbb{N}\}$$

means 'A is the set whose members have the form x^3, where x is such that it belongs to the set of natural numbers'. Thus $A = \{0, 1, 8, 27, 64, ...\}$. Or again,

$$B = \{3n^2 : n \in \mathbb{N}\}$$

means 'B is the set whose members have the form $3n^2$, where n is a member of the set of natural numbers', i.e. $B = \{0, 3, 12, 27, 48, 75, ...\}$.

$$C = \{x : x \in \mathbb{R}, \ -3 \leqslant x \leqslant +3\}$$

means that C is the set which contains any real number x between -3 and $+3$, inclusive.

Some very important sets have standard symbols:

$\mathbb{N}$ is used for the set of natural numbers, $\mathbb{N} = \{0, 1, 2, 3, 4, 5, ...\}$,
$\mathbb{Z}$ is the set of integers, positive or negative, $\mathbb{Z} = \{..., -3, -2, -1, 0, +1, +2, +3, ...\}$,
$\mathbb{Z}^+$ is the set of positive integers, $\mathbb{Z}^+ = \{+1, +2, +3, +4, +5, +6, ...\}$,
$\mathbb{Q}$ is the set of rational numbers, (see Section 3.3),
$\mathbb{R}$ is the set of real numbers.

In a later chapter you will meet $\mathbb{C}$, the set of complex numbers.

3.7 The algebra of sets

(Readers who have studied this in an elementary course may wish to omit this section; on the other hand readers who have not met it before may need to supplement the section with further exercises from a more elementary textbook.)

Given two sets A and B, the set consisting of all those elements which belong both to A and B is called the **intersection of A and B**. The symbol for it is $A \cap B$. Thus if

$$A = \{2, 4, 6, 8, 10, 12\} \quad \text{and} \quad B = \{3, 6, 9, 12\}$$

the intersection of A and B is the set $\{6, 12\}$ and we write

$$A \cap B = \{6, 12\}$$

The set consisting of those elements which belong to A or B, or *both*, is called the **union of A and B** and the symbol for it is $A \cup B$. (The symbol $\cup$ can be remembered as the initial letter of union.) It is important to remember that when we list the members of a set we never repeat any individual element. Thus in the case of the sets A and B in the previous paragraph,

$$A \cup B = \{2, 3, 4, 6, 8, 9, 10, 12\}$$

Example 2

Given that A is the set of odd numbers less than 20, and B is the set of prime numbers less than 20, list the members of A, B, $A \cap B$, $A \cup B$.

$$A = \{1, 3, 5, 7, 9, 11, 13, 15, 17, 19\}$$
$$B = \{2, 3, 5, 7, 11, 13, 17, 19\}$$
$$A \cap B = \{3, 5, 7, 11, 13, 17, 19\}$$
$$A \cup B = \{1, 2, 3, 5, 7, 9, 11, 13, 15, 17, 19\}$$

Notice that if P is the set of odd numbers and Q is the set of multiples of 2 then there would be no number which belongs to $P \cap Q$. Such a set, that is a set with no members, is called an **empty set**; the symbol for it is $\emptyset$. Thus in the example above we write $P \cap Q = \emptyset$. ($\emptyset$ is pronounced 'ur', as in hurt.)

Sometimes it is convenient to have a special symbol for *all* the elements which are involved in a particular topic, or in a particular question. The normal symbol used for this is $\mathscr{E}$; it is called the **universal set**. In this context, it is also frequently useful to have a symbol for all the elements of the universal set $\mathscr{E}$ which are not in a given set A. The symbol used for this is A' and this set is called the **complement of set** A. For example, given that

$$\mathscr{E} = \{1, 2, 3, 4, 5, 6, 7, 8, 9, 10\} \quad \text{and that} \quad X = \{4, 8\}$$

the complement of X is the set

$$X' = \{1, 2, 3, 5, 6, 7, 9, 10\}$$

Notice that for any set P,

$$P \cap P' = \emptyset \quad \text{and} \quad P \cup P' = \mathscr{E}$$

If every member of a certain set H is also a member of a set K, then H is called a **subset** of K. For example, $\{2, 4, 6, 8\}$ is a subset of $\{1, 2, 3, 4, 5, 6, 7, 8\}$ and the symbol used for this purpose is $\subset$. Thus $H \subset K$ reads 'H is a subset of K'.

Finally, the notation $n(A)$ is used to denote 'the number of elements in set A'. Thus in Example 2 above, $n(A) = 10$, $n(B) = 8$, $n(A \cap B) = 7$ and $n(A \cup B) = 11$. Notice that

$$n(A \cup B) = n(A) + n(B) - n(A \cap B)$$

The reader should think carefully about this equation and should be able to see that it is true for *any* sets A and B.

Exercise 3a

1 Given that $A = \{1, 2, 3, 4, 5\}$, list the members of the following sets:
   (a) $\{x^2: x \in A\}$ (b) $\{1/x: x \in A\}$ (c) $\{2x: x \in A\}$
   (d) $\{4x + 1: x \in A\}$

2 Given that $A = \{-3, -2, -1, 0, +1, +2, +3\}$ list the members of the following sets:
   (a) $\{x^2: x \in A\}$ (b) $\{x^3 - x: x \in A\}$ (c) $\{x^4: x \in A\}$
   (d) $\{1/(x + 5): x \in A\}$

3 In this question, $x \in \mathbb{Z}^+$. List the members of the following sets:
   (a) $\{x^2: x < 10\}$ (b) $\{10x - x^2: x < 10\}$ (c) $\{10 - x: x < 10\}$
   (d) $\{x/2: x < 10\}$

4 Are the following statements true or false? If you think a statement is false, give a clear reason for your conclusion.
   (a) All factors of an even integer are even.
   (b) All factors of an odd integer are odd.
   (c) $\mathbb{Z} \subset \mathbb{Q}$.
   (d) Any odd square number can be expressed in the form $4m + 1$, where $m \in \mathbb{Z}^+$.

5 List the members of the set of real numbers for which the expression
$$\frac{1}{(x - 1)(x - 2)(x - 3)} \text{ does not exist.}$$

6 In this question, $\mathscr{E}$ is the set of positive integers less than 100 and the sets A and B are subsets of $\mathscr{E}$. A is the set of multiples of 5, and B is the set of multiples of 7.
   (a) List the members of A, B, $A \cap B$, $A \cup B$.
   (b) Describe in words the members of set $A \cap B$.
   (c) Write down the values of $n(A)$, $n(B)$, $n(A \cap B)$ and $n(A \cup B)$. Verify that $n(A \cup B) = n(A) + n(B) - n(A \cap B)$.

7 Given that $\mathscr{E}$ is the set of natural numbers less than or equal to 20, list the members of the following subsets of $\mathscr{E}$:
   (a) A, the multiples of 3   (b) B, the multiples of 4
   (c) A', the complement of A (d) B'
   (e) $(A \cup B)'$ (f) $A' \cap B'$
   Comment on your answers.

8 Express as recurring decimals the rational numbers:
   (a) $1/3$ (b) $2/7$ (c) $3/11$

9 Express the recurring decimal $0.\dot{7}$ as a rational number. (Hint: let $x = 0.\dot{7}$ and consider $10x$.)

10 Express the following recurring decimals as rational numbers:
   (a) $0.\dot{1}\dot{2}$ (b) $0.6\dot{5}\dot{7}$ (c) $0.\dot{4}2857\dot{1}$

3.8 Functions

Consider the two exercises (1) and (2) below.

(1) A stone is projected vertically upwards. Its height, h metres, after t seconds,

is given approximately by the formula $h = 20t - 5t^2$. Use the formula to calculate its height after 0, 1, 2, 3, 4 seconds.

The answers to this exercise are shown in the table below:

t	0	1	2	3	4
h	0	15	20	15	0

(2) Given that $x \in \{1, 2, 3, 4, 5\}$ find the corresponding set of values of y, where y is given by the rule:

(a) $y = x^2$ (b) $y = 1/x$ (c) $y = \sqrt{(5 - x)}$

The three answers to this exercise are

(a) $\{1, 4, 9, 16, 25\}$ (b) $\{1, \frac{1}{2}, \frac{1}{3}, \frac{1}{4}, \frac{1}{5}\}$ (c) $\{2, \sqrt{3}, \sqrt{2}, 1, 0\}$

All exercises like these have certain features in common. In each case, a set of values is given for one of the variables. Then a rule is given and this is applied to the given set of numbers, to produce a set of values of the other variable. In mathematics there are standard terms which are used to describe these features. The variable for which the values are given (t in exercise (1), x in (2)) is called the **independent variable** and the set of values of the independent variable is called the **domain**. The rule which is applied to the independent variable is called the **function** and the variable which is produced by the rule is called the **dependent variable**. (In (1) h is the dependent variable and in (2) y is the dependent variable.) The set of values of the dependent variable is called the **range** of the function. In exercise (2) part (a), the range is the set $\{1, 4, 9, 16, 25\}$.

When these standard terms are used there are some important restrictions which must be observed in order to avoid certain difficulties and possible misunderstandings. In many instances the domain will be $\mathbb{R}$, the set of real numbers. However, it may be necessary to restrict $\mathbb{R}$, to exclude numbers to which the rule cannot be applied. For instance in exercise (2) part (b), x must not be zero, and in part (c) x must not be greater than 5 since this would require us to find the square root of a negative number. The other restriction, which must be observed, is that the rule must provide one and *only one* value of the dependent variable. There is no difficulty over this point in the exercises above, but suppose that the rule is 'y is the angle whose sine is x'. In this case, if $x = 0.5$, then y could be 30°, 150°, 390°, ...; in fact this particular rule would produce infinitely many values of y for a given value of x. This difficulty has to be faced by the manufacturer of a pocket calculator. Since a calculator has a single display for showing numbers, it is only possible for a calculator to show *one* answer to a given calculation. In the case of finding an angle whose sine is given, the designer must use a standard convention for deciding which answer should appear in the display. Similarly, when we define a function, we must define it carefully so that it produces just one value of the dependent variable. Another example in which this difficulty could arise would be the rule

'y is the square root of x', because any positive value of x would yield *two* values of y (both $+5$ and -5 are square roots of 25). It should be noted however that there is a convention in mathematics that the square root sign $\sqrt{}$ is reserved for the positive square root only, that is $\sqrt{25} = +5$ (not -5). With this convention it is perfectly in order to regard $y = \sqrt{x}$ as a function.

The member of the range which corresponds to a certain member of the domain is usually called the **image** of that member, e.g. in (2) (a) above, 25 is the image of 5. Notice that there is no objection to having two distinct members of the domain with the same image, see (1) above, in which both $t = 1$ and $t = 3$ have the image 15. The converse however is not allowed; a member of the domain must not have more than one image. When each member of the range has exactly one corresponding member of the domain the function is called a 'one-to-one function'. Thus if the domain is $\mathbb{R}$, the set of all real numbers, $y = x^3$ represents a one-to-one function, but $y = x^2$ does not. A function which is not one-to-one is said to be 'many-to-one'.

Qu. 3 For each of the rules below, state carefully the largest possible subset of $\mathbb{R}$ which would be a suitable domain. In each case describe the corresponding range.

(a) $y = 1/(x - 3)$ (b) $y = \sqrt{(10 - x)}$ (c) $y = \sqrt{(25 - x^2)}$
(d) $y = 1/(25 - x^2)$ (e) $y = 1/(25 + x^2)$

Qu. 4 Which of the rules below represent functions (distinguish between one-to-one functions and many-to-one functions)? In each part, the domain is $\mathbb{R}$.

(a) $y = x^4$ (b) $y = x^5$ (c) $y^2 + x^2 = 25$ (d) $y = x^3 - x$

3.9 The function notation

Sometimes we may need to discuss several functions simultaneously and consequently a notation which enables us to distinguish between them can be very convenient. Suppose we have two functions, both having $\mathbb{R}$ as the domain, and suppose one of them squares each member of the domain and the other doubles each member of the domain. We write $f(x)$ to represent the image of x under the function f; our first function would be represented by $f(x) = x^2$ and the second by $g(x) = 2x$. The usual letters to use for this purpose are f, g, h and their corresponding capital letters, but other letters may be used if desired. In the illustration above, $f(5) = 25$ and $g(5) = 10$. We can also write $f(a) = a^2$, $f(a + h) = (a + h)^2$, $g(k) = 2k$, and so on.

Example 3

Given that $h(x) = x^2 - x$, find the values of $h(10)$, $h(-3)$, $h(\frac{1}{2})$, $h(t + 1)$, $h(5k)$.

$h(10) = 10^2 - 10 = 100 - 10 = 90$
$h(-3) = (-3)^2 - (-3) = 9 + 3 = 12$
$h(\frac{1}{2}) = (\frac{1}{2})^2 - (\frac{1}{2}) = \frac{1}{4} - \frac{1}{2} = -\frac{1}{4}$
$h(t + 1) = (t + 1)^2 - (t + 1) = t^2 + 2t + 1 - t - 1 = t^2 + t$
$h(5k) = (5k)^2 - 5k = 25k^2 - 5k$

There is an alternative to this notation, which can also be quite useful. In this notation the function $f(x) = x^3$ is written

$$f: x \mapsto x^3$$

This statement should be read 'f is a function which **maps** x onto x^3'. The function $g(x) = 2x$ now becomes g: $x \mapsto 2x$. When $x = 5$, we write $f: 5 \mapsto 125$ and g: $5 \mapsto 10$.

3.10 Composite functions

In this section f and g will be used to represent the functions $f(x) = x^2$ and $g(x) = x + 5$. The domain of both functions will be $\mathbb{R}$.

Notice that $f(3) = 9$ and $g(9) = 14$. Thus if we start with $x = 3$ and apply to it first function f and then function g, we shall obtain the number 14. This could be written $g(f(3)) = g(9) = 14$, but it is usually abbreviated to $gf(3) = 14$ (alternatively, the notation $g \circ f(3) = 14$ may be used). Similarly $gf(10) = 100 + 5 = 105$. In general

$$gf(x) = x^2 + 5$$

The function $gf(x)$ is called a **composite function**. Notice that the order of the functions which make up a composite function is very important. With f and g defined as above,

$$fg(x) = (x + 5)^2 = x^2 + 10x + 25$$

Remember that when a composite function is written down, the individual functions must be applied from right to left.

Example 4

Given that F: $x \mapsto (10 + x)$, G: $x \mapsto x^3$ and H: $x \mapsto x/2$, write down the functions (a) FG (b) GF (c) FGH.

(a)   FG: $x \mapsto (10 + x^3)$
(b)   GF: $x \mapsto (10 + x)^3$
(c)   H: $x \mapsto (x/2)$
        GH: $x \mapsto (x/2)^3$,   hence GH: $x \mapsto x^3/8$
        FGH: $x \mapsto 10 + x^3/8$

Example 5

Given that $f(x) = 25 - x^2$ and that $g(x) = \sqrt{x}$, find, where possible, the values of (a) gf(0) (b) gf(4) (c) gf(13)

(a) $f(0) = 25$, $gf(0) = g(25) = 5$,
(b) $f(4) = 9$, $gf(4) = g(9) = 3$,
(c) $f(13) = 25 - 169 = -144$, but we cannot evaluate $g(-144)$ because a negative number does not have a real square root.

Example 5(c) illustrates a difficulty which can arise when forming a composite function. If the domain of the function f(x), above, is ℝ then its range is {y, y ∈ ℝ, y ⩽ 25} and this includes negative numbers, which are not in the domain of the function $g(x) = \sqrt{x}$. This can only be avoided if we restrict the domain of f(x) to {x: x ∈ ℝ, −5 ⩽ x ⩽ +5}. In general, when a composite function gf(x) is formed, the range of the function f(x) must be a subset of the domain of the function g(x).

Some mathematicians insist that whenever a function is defined its domain should be explicitly stated and, strictly speaking, they are correct. However this soon becomes rather tedious and most people adopt the less rigid convention that, unless the domain has some special features that need comment, it may be assumed that the domain is intended to be ℝ; the reader is normally expected to use common-sense to exclude any members of the domain which give rise to obvious difficulties (e.g. square roots of negative numbers, fractions with a zero denominator). This is the convention which will generally be employed in this book, although in *this* chapter, the domain will be described in full.

The term **codomain** is sometimes used for any set which contains the range. For example, the function $f(x) = x^2$ maps real numbers onto real numbers and so one can say the domain is ℝ and the codomain is ℝ, but since all the images are positive (or, to be precise, non-negative) the range is the set of non-negative real numbers.

Exercise 3b

1 Given that $g(x) = x^3 + 1$, find the values of:
   (a) g(0)   (b) g(5)   (c) g($\frac{3}{4}$)   (d) g(−2)
2 The domain of the function $g(x) = 5x + 1$ is {0, 1, 2, 3, 4, 5}. Find its range.
3 The domain of the function $f(x) = x^2 + 1$ is ℝ. Find its range.
4 The domain of the function $f(x) = 1/(1 + x^2)$ is ℝ. Find its range.
5 The domain of the function $f(x) = 1/\sqrt{(25 - x)}$ is a subset of ℝ. Write down the largest possible set which is a suitable domain.

In nos. 6–10 the domain is ℝ.

6 Given that f: $x \mapsto 5x + 1$ and that g: $x \mapsto x^2$, express the composite functions fg and gf in their simplest possible forms.
7 Given that $f(x) = x^2$, express as simply as possible:

   (a) f(5 + h)   (b) $\dfrac{f(5 + h) - f(5)}{h}$ $(h \neq 0)$

8 If $f(x) = x^2$ express as simply as possible:

   $\dfrac{f(a + h) - f(a)}{h}$ $(h \neq 0)$

9 Given that $f(x) = x^3$ find:
(a) $f(2)$ (b) $f(-10)$
(c) $f(\frac{1}{2})$ (d) $f(5a)$
(e) $f(a/3)$ (f) $f(a+h)$

(g) $f(a+h) - f(a-h)$ (h) $\dfrac{f(a+h) - f(a-h)}{2h}$ $(h \neq 0)$

10 If $f(x) = 7x$ and $g(x) = x + 3$ and fg: $x \mapsto y$, express as simply as possible the rule which maps x onto y. Find the values of p, q, r such that:
(a) fg: $5 \mapsto p$ (b) fg: $10 \mapsto q$ (c) fg: $r \mapsto 35$
Find also the function, F, which reverses the function fg, that is, it maps y onto x.

3.11 Graphs of functions

When the domain is the set of real numbers $\mathbb{R}$, it is always represented by the horizontal axis, and the corresponding values of the dependent variable are represented by points on the vertical axis. When x and y are used to represent typical members of the domain and the codomain, these axes are called the x-axis and the y-axis respectively. Figure 3.2 shows the graph of a function $y = f(x)$. A typical member a of the domain and its image $f(a)$ are shown.

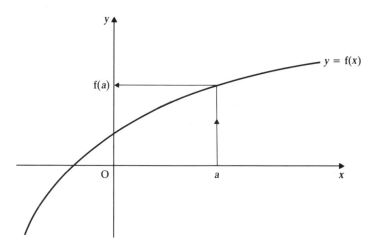

Figure 3.2

Bearing in mind that each member of the domain has exactly one image in the codomain, a graph like the one shown in Figure 3.3 does not represent the graph of a function. In this diagram, a has three possible images in the codomain.

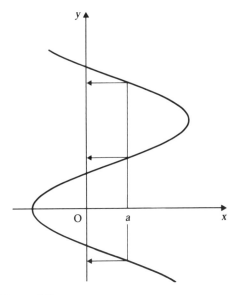

Figure 3.3

Although this is an artificial example, made up to illustrate the point, consider the circle, centre $(0, 0)$, radius 10. The coordinates of any point P on the circle satisfy the equation $x^2 + y^2 = 100$, so a relation exists between the values of x and y at each point, and a graph can be drawn, but this is not the graph of a function because there are values of x for which there are two possible values of y, e.g. when $x = 6$, $y = +8$ or $y = -8$ (see Figure 3.4).

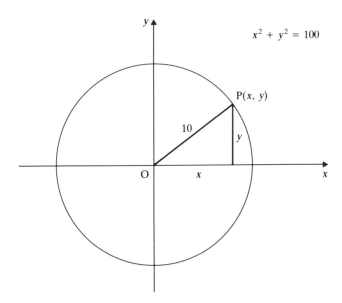

Figure 3.4

3.12 Graphs of some common functions

Figure 3.5 illustrates the graphs of $y = x^2$, $y = x^3$ and $y = x^4$; any reader who is not familiar with these already is advised to draw and save graphs of these functions. (Start by plotting the values of y corresponding to values of x from $x = -2$ to $+2$, at intervals of $\frac{1}{4}$ of a unit.) Note that all these graphs pass through the point $(1, 1)$; $y = x^2$ and $y = x^4$ also pass through $(-1, 1)$, while $y = x^3$ passes through $(-1, -1)$. Notice also that the graphs 'flatten out' between $x = -1$ and $x = +1$, as the power increases. (Try plotting $y = x^{10}$: a calculator may be needed for some of the calculations.)

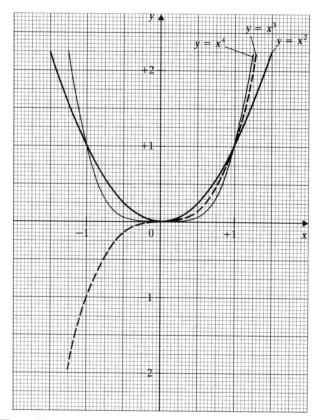

Figure 3.5

Figure 3.6 shows the graphs of $y = 1/x$, $(x \neq 0)$ and $y = \sqrt{x}$, $(x \geqslant 0)$. (Remember that the square-root sign means the positive square root.)

Any reader who is not familiar with these graphs is advised to make careful copies, using a calculator where necessary, and to save the graphs for future reference. Notice also that if the functions are changed to $y = 1/(x-2)$, $(x \neq 2)$, and $y = \sqrt{(x-2)}$, $(x \geqslant 2)$, then the shape of the graphs is unaltered but the graph is translated 2 units to the right. In general, the graph of $y = f(x-a)$ will have the same shape as $y = f(x)$ but it will be translated a units to the right.

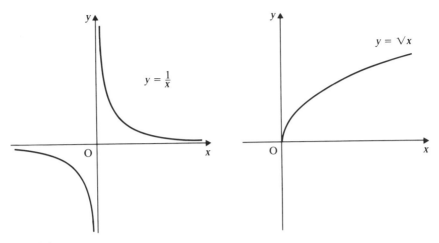

Figure 3.6

The modulus of x, written $|x|$, is probably new to many readers; *the modulus of x is the magnitude of x*, thus $|+5| = +5$ and $|-7| = +7$. A table of values of $|x|$ for $x = -4$ to $x = +4$ is shown below:

x	-4	-3	-2	-1	0	$+1$	$+2$	$+3$	$+4$
$|x|$	$+4$	$+3$	$+2$	$+1$	0	$+1$	$+2$	$+3$	$+4$

and the graph of $y = |x|$ is shown in Figure 3.7.

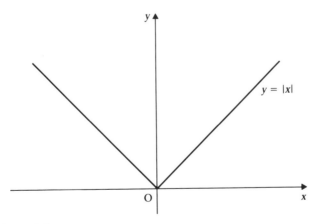

Figure 3.7

The instructions 'plot the graph of ...' and 'sketch the graph of ...' have very definite, but distinct, meanings in mathematics. The instruction 'plot the graph of $y = x^2$, for $x = 0$ to 5' means that the necessary values of y should be calculated, the points should be accurately plotted on graph paper and the points should be joined with a neat smooth curve. In contrast, a *sketch* of a curve should not be done on graph paper; plain, or ordinary lined paper should be used. Only a few points need to be plotted, but points which have special importance should be marked. The sketch should not be limited to a small part of the domain. Instead, every effort should be made to convey the overall appearance of the graph throughout its domain.

Example 6

Sketch the graph of $y = \dfrac{1}{x-3} + 2 \qquad (x \neq 3)$.

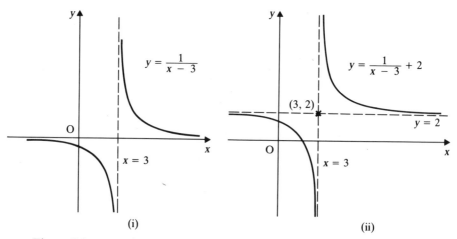

Figure 3.8

The graph of $y = 1/x$ is one of the standard graphs; a sketch of it is shown in Figure 3.6. Replacing x by $x - 3$ translates the graph 3 units to the right, and so a sketch of $y = 1/(x - 3)$ would be like Figure 3.8(i). When the final 2 is added to $1/(x - 3)$ the graph is translated 2 units vertically upwards. Hence the sketch graph of $y = 1/(x - 3) + 2$ should look like Figure 3.8(ii).

Exercise 3c

Sketch (detailed plotting is not required) the graphs of the following functions. Where possible, the sketch should be obtained by modifying one of the standard graphs in the preceding section.

1 $y = 2x + 1$

2 $y = (x + 2)^3$

3 $y = x^2 + 5$

4 $y = 1/(x + 4) \qquad (x \neq -4)$

5 $y = -x^2$

6 $y = 5x^2$

7 $y = \sqrt{(10 - x)} \qquad (x \leqslant 10)$

8 $y = 1/x^2 \qquad (x \neq 0)$

So far x has always been used for the independent variable and y for the dependent variable, but x and y are not the only letters which may be used. In nos. 9–15, t is used for the independent variable, hence the t-axis is horizontal, and z is used for the dependent variable.

9 $z = (t - 4)^3$ **10** $z = 100 - t^2$ $(-10 \leqslant t \leqslant +10)$
11 $z = |t - 3|$ **12** $z = |(t + 4)(t - 4)|$
13 $z = |1/(1 + t)|$ **14** $z = 1/(1 + |t|)$
15 $z = |t| - |t + 1|$
16 Figure 3.9 shows the graph of an unspecified function $y = f(x)$. Trace the diagram and use the tracing to show, on a single diagram, sketch graphs of:
(a) $y = f(x - 6)$ (b) $y = f(x + 3)$ (c) $y = f(x) + 2$

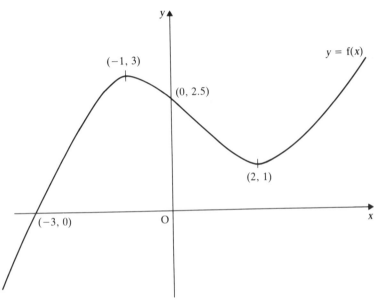

Figure 3.9

17 Use the tracing from no. 16 to draw the graph of $y = f(x)$ and superimpose on it sketches of the following graphs, showing clearly their relationship to the graph of $y = f(x)$:
(a) $y = 5f(x)$ (b) $y = f(5x)$ (c) $y = -f(x)$ (d) $y = f(-x)$
18 Describe, in words, the appearance of the following graphs, relative to the graph of $y = f(x)$:
(a) $y = f(x - a)$ (b) $y = f(x) + a$ (c) $y = k \times f(x)$
(d) $y = -f(x)$ (e) $y = f(-x)$

3.13 Further functions

Example 7

In 1990 the cost of posting a parcel, weighing not more than 10 kg, was given by the table overleaf. Explain why this table expresses the cost of the parcel as a function of its weight and draw a graph of the function.

Not over	Cost	Not over	Cost
1 kg	£1.85	6 kg	£3.60
2 kg	£2.30	7 kg	£3.80
3 kg	£2.85	8 kg	£3.95
4 kg	£3.10	9 kg	£4.20
5 kg	£3.30	10 kg	£4.40

The table expresses the cost as a function of the weight because if the weight is known, the table indicates the cost of postage. A function is any rule which enables the dependent variable to be found, when the independent variable is known. It is not necessary to express the rule as a formula. The graph is shown in Figure 3.10.

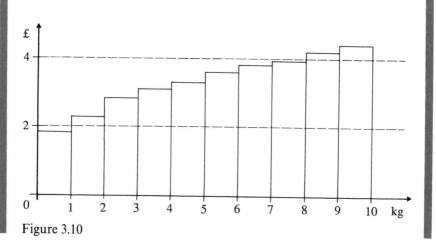

Figure 3.10

The function in Example 7 differs from the functions discussed earlier in the chapter, in that different rules apply to different parts of the domain. Many of the functions which arise from real life problems are like this. When a multistage rocket is fired, the function which expresses its velocity in terms of time will have different mathematical formulae corresponding to each stage of the rocket motor. Examples 8 and 9 illustrate further functions which display this characteristic.

Example 8

The domain of function f is $\mathbb{R}$.

$$f: x \mapsto 1 \quad \text{when } x < 0, \quad \text{and}$$
$$f: x \mapsto x^2 + 1 \quad \text{when } x \geq 0.$$

Sketch the graph of this function. (See Figure 3.11.)

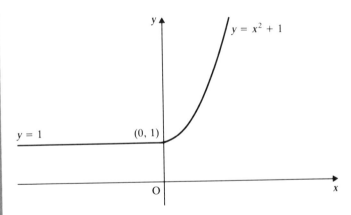

Figure 3.11

Example 9

The domain of the function f is $\mathbb{R}$.

$$f: x \mapsto 1 \quad \text{if } x \in \mathbb{Z}, \quad \text{and}$$
$$f: x \mapsto 2 \quad \text{if } x \notin \mathbb{Z}.$$

Write down $f(+5)$, $f(-1)$, $f(0)$, $f(3.4)$, $f(\sqrt{2})$ and $f(\pi)$.
Sketch the graph of $y = f(x)$.

$f(+5) = 1$, because $+5$ is an integer, i.e. $+5 \in \mathbb{Z}$. Similarly $f(-1) = 1$ and $f(0) = 1$.

But 3.4, $\sqrt{2}$ and π are not members of $\mathbb{Z}$, so $f(3.4) = f(\sqrt{2}) = f(\pi) = 2$.

The graph of this function consists of the points ... $(-2, 1), (-1, 1)$, $(0, 1), (1, 1), (2, 1)$ ... and the straight line $y = 2$, with 'holes' in it whenever x is an integer (Figure 3.12). In the diagram, the 'holes' have been exaggerated for the sake of clarity.

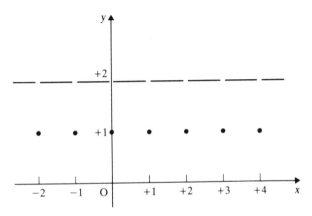

Figure 3.12

3.14 Odd and even functions

Functions whose graphs are symmetrical about the vertical axis (i.e. the y-axis in Figure 3.13) are called **even functions**.

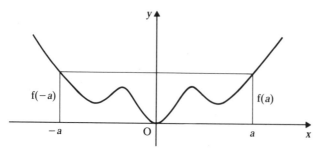

Figure 3.13

In terms of the algebra, this means that for any value of a, $f(a) = f(-a)$. Obvious examples of even functions are functions of the form $f(x) = x^n$, where n is an even integer, hence the name, even function. Another important even function is $f(x) = \cos x$ (see Chapter 17).

A function with the property $f(-a) = -f(a)$, for every member a of the domain, is called an **odd function**. The graph of an odd function will have rotational symmetry of order 2 about the origin, that is, after a 180° rotation about the origin the graph will be superimposed upon itself (Figure 3.14).

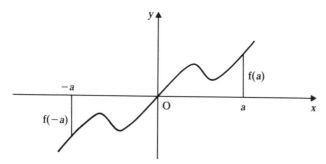

Figure 3.14

Functions of the form $f(x) = x^n$, where n is an odd number, will be odd functions. Another important odd function is $f(x) = \sin x$ (see Chapter 17).

Example 10

Prove that the sum of two even functions is an even function and that the sum of two odd functions is an odd function.

Let $f(x)$ and $g(x)$ be two even functions. Then $f(x)$ and $g(x)$ have the property $f(-a) = f(a)$ and $g(-a) = g(a)$, for any member a of the domain.

Let $F(x)$ be the sum of $f(x)$ and $g(x)$, that is $F(x) = f(x) + g(x)$. Then, if a is any member of the domain:

$$\begin{aligned} F(-a) &= f(-a) + g(-a) \\ &= f(a) + g(a) \\ &= F(a) \end{aligned}$$

hence $F(x)$ is an even function.

Similarly, if $f(x)$ and $g(x)$ are odd functions, then:

$$\begin{aligned} F(-a) &= f(-a) + g(-a) \\ &= -f(a) - g(a) \\ &= -F(a) \end{aligned}$$

hence $F(x)$ is an odd function.

Qu. 5 Prove that the product of two even functions is an even function.
Qu. 6 Prove that the product of two odd functions is an even function.
Qu. 7 Is the product of an even function and an odd function odd or even?

3.15 Periodic functions

A function whose graph repeats itself at regular intervals is called a **periodic function** (see Figure 3.15). Such functions are especially important in science. The sound wave of a note of constant pitch, for example, is periodic.

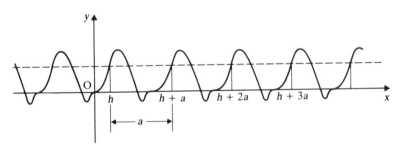

Figure 3.15

The length of the interval between repeats is called the **period** of the function. If the period is a, then for any value of h in the domain of the function,

$$f(h + a) = f(h)$$

The most common periodic functions are the trigonometric functions (see Chapter 17) $\sin x$ and $\cos x$; they have a period of $360°$, because

$$\sin (x + 360)° = \sin x° \quad \text{and} \quad \cos (x + 360)° = \cos x°$$

Example 11

Sketch the graph of the periodic function such that $f(x) = x$, for $-1 < x \leqslant +1$, where the period of $f(x)$ is 2.

Between $x = -1$ and $x = +1$, the graph is the ordinary straight line $y = x$. Outside this interval, the graph repeats itself every 2 units (Figure 3.16).

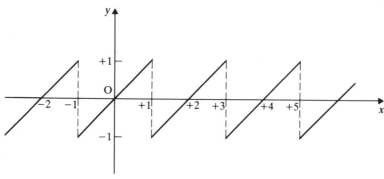

Figure 3.16

Example 12

Sketch the graph of $y = f(x)$ where $f(x) = \sqrt{(1 - x^2)}$, when $0 \leqslant x \leqslant 1$, and $f(x)$ is an even function with a period of 2.

The equation $y = \sqrt{(1 - x^2)}$ produces an arc of a circle between $x = 0$ and $x = +1$. Because the function is even, the graph is symmetrical about the vertical axis. Thus between $x = -1$ and $x = +1$, the graph is a semicircle, and this is then repeated at regular intervals of 2 units (Figure 3.17).

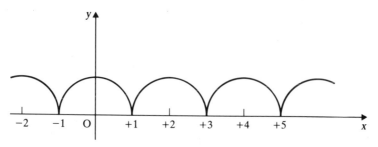

Figure 3.17

3.16 The inverse of a function

Consider the function $y = f(x)$, where $f(x) = \frac{1}{8}x^3 + 1$. A sketch of its graph is shown in Figure 3.18.

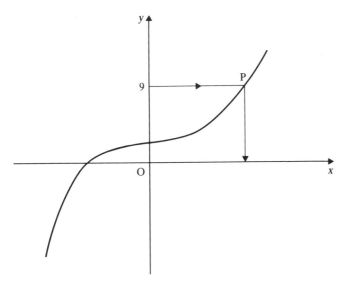

Figure 3.18

If we are given a member of the range, say $y = 9$, is it possible to find the corresponding member of the domain? On the graph this would mean starting from $y = 9$ on the vertical axis, drawing a line horizontally to the point P on the curve and then drawing a vertical line down to the x-axis. The point where the line meets the axis gives the value of x which is required. In this particular example it is fairly easy to solve the problem algebraically. The value of x required is found by solving the equation:

$$\tfrac{1}{8}x^3 + 1 = 9$$
$$\tfrac{1}{8}x^3 = 8$$
$$x^3 = 64$$
$$\therefore \quad x = 4$$

Indeed it is quite simple to generalise this. Starting with the given value from the range of function f, we first subtract 1, then we multiply by 8 and finally we find the cube root. The whole operation is called the inverse of function f and it is written f^{-1}. Following the usual convention of writing x for a typical member of the domain of function f^{-1}, we can write our inverse function as follows:

$$f^{-1}(x) = \sqrt[3]{\{8(x-1)\}}$$

Thus:

$$f^{-1}(9) = \sqrt[3]{\{8(9-1)\}} = \sqrt[3]{(8 \times 8)} = \sqrt[3]{64} = 4$$

There is however one problem; when we draw the horizontal line from the given number to the graph of $y = f(x)$, this line must meet the curve *once only*. Otherwise there will be more than one possible answer and we are not allowed to use the word function to describe such a situation. For example, $f(x) = x^2$ is a perfectly acceptable function, but it maps both $+5$ and -5 onto the same image, namely 25. There is no objection to this, we simply agree to call it a many-to-one function. However if we attempt to find $f^{-1}(25)$, there are two possible answers, namely $+5$ and -5. So $f(x)$ does not have an inverse function. This difficulty can be by-passed if we agree in advance to limit the domain of $f(x) = x^2$ to the non-negative real numbers; in that case we shall not be applying it to -5 and the difficulty of having two possible answers will not arise.

To sum up then, we can only have an inverse function if the original function is a one-to-one function. (However the fact that an inverse function exists does not necessarily mean we shall be able to write down the rule which gives the inverse.)

In general, if (a, b) is a point on the graph of $y = f(x)$, then (b, a) will be a point on the graph of $y = f^{-1}(x)$, and consequently the graph of $y = f^{-1}(x)$ will be the reflection of the graph of $y = f(x)$ in the line $y = x$ (see Figure 3.19).

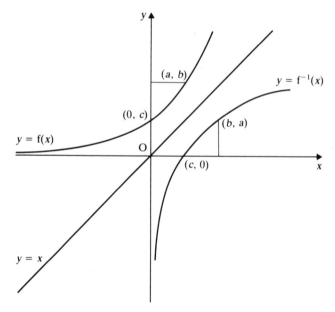

Figure 3.19

Here are some examples of common functions and their inverses:
(a) $f(x) = x + a$ $f^{-1}(x) = x - a$
(b) $f(x) = kx$ $f^{-1}(x) = x/k$
(c) $f(x) = x^2$ $(x \geqslant 0)$ $f^{-1}(x) = \sqrt{x}$
(d) $f(x) = a - x$ $f^{-1}(x) = a - x$
(e) $f(x) = 1/x$ $f^{-1}(x) = 1/x$

Functions, like (d) and (e), which are the same as their inverses are called **self-inverse functions**.

If a function f is applied to a number a, and then f^{-1} is applied, the final result will be the original number a. For example using function (c) above, $f(3) = 9$

and $f^{-1}(9) = 3$. (This can be clearly observed on a pocket calculator. First key in any number a, then press a function button, say x^2, and then the button of the inverse function $\sqrt{x}$, and the original number a should be displayed. Although the following functions are as yet unknown to you, you can observe the same phenomenon by pressing the buttons representing the following pairs of functions and their inverses: $\log x$, 10^x; $\ln x$, e^x.)

We have already seen that $fg(x)$ is the composite function, in which the function g is applied first and then function f is applied to the result. The inverse of this composite function is $g^{-1}f^{-1}(x)$. (This is rather like packing and unpacking a parcel. Suppose you wrap the parcel in paper and then tie it up with string. When the parcel is unpacked, first the string must be untied and, after that, the paper removed.)

Example 13

Given that $f(x) = 10x$ and $g(x) = x + 3$, find $fg(x)$ and $(fg)^{-1}(x)$. Verify that if $b = fg(a)$, then $(fg)^{-1}(b) = a$.

$$g(x) = x + 3$$

$$fg(x) = 10(x + 3)$$

The inverse of g and f are $g^{-1}(x) = x - 3$ and $f^{-1}(x) = x/10$. Hence

$$(fg)^{-1}(x) = g^{-1}f^{-1}(x)$$

$$= g^{-1}\left(\frac{x}{10}\right)$$

$$= \frac{x}{10} - 3$$

In the general case, we are given $b = fg(a)$,

$$\therefore \quad b = 10(a + 3)$$

and hence,

$$(fg)^{-1}(b) = \frac{10(a + 3)}{10} - 3$$

$$= a + 3 - 3$$

$$= a$$

In some cases the inverse function can be found by regarding $y = f(x)$ as an equation in which y is *known*, and solving the equation for the *unknown* x. For instance, if

$$y = \frac{5x + 7}{3x + 2}$$

then

$$y(3x + 2) = 5x + 7$$
$$3xy + 2y = 5x + 7$$
$$3xy - 5x = 7 - 2y$$
$$x(3y - 5) = 7 - 2y$$

$$x = \frac{7 - 2y}{3y - 5}$$

So the inverse of $f(x) = (5x + 7)/(3x + 2)$ is $g(y) = (7 - 2y)/(3y - 5)$. However, since we need to emphasise that g is the inverse of f and since the letter x is normally used to represent the independent variable, we express this result as

$$f^{-1}(x) = \frac{7 - 2x}{3x - 5}$$

A result such as this can be checked by verifying that $f^{-1}(f(x)) = x$. In this case:

$$f^{-1}(f(x)) = \frac{7 - 2(5x + 7)/(3x + 2)}{3(5x + 7)/(3x + 2) - 5}$$

$$= \frac{7(3x + 2) - 2(5x + 7)}{3(5x + 7) - 5(3x + 2)}$$

$$= \frac{21x + 14 - 10x - 14}{15x + 21 - 15x - 10}$$

$$= \frac{11x}{11}$$

$$= x$$

Exercise 3d

1 Given that $f(x) = 5x + 1$, find the values of:
    (a) $f^{-1}(36)$ (b) $f^{-1}(-14)$ (c) $f^{-1}(0)$ (d) $f^{-1}(a)$
2 Given that $g(t) = 1/(t - 5)$, $(t \neq 5)$, find the values of:
    (a) $g^{-1}(\frac{1}{2})$ (b) $g^{-1}(2)$ (c) $g^{-1}(-1)$ (d) $g^{-1}(a)$
3 Find the inverses of the following functions:
    (a) $f(x) = 12 - \frac{1}{2}x$ (b) $f(x) = \frac{1}{2}(x - 3)$
    (c) $f(x) = (2x + 1)/5$ (d) $f(x) = (7 - 3x)/10$
4 Find the inverses of the following functions:
    (a) $f: x \mapsto \frac{5}{9}(x - 32)$ (b) $f: x \mapsto 180(x - 2)$
    (c) $f: x \mapsto 2\pi x$ (d) $f: x \mapsto 5(x + 7)/3 - 9$
5 Find the inverses of the following functions:
    (a) $F: t \mapsto t^2 + 5$ $(t \geqslant 0)$ (b) $F: t \mapsto 5\sqrt{t}$ $(t \geqslant 0)$
    (c) $F: t \mapsto (t - 5)^3$ (d) $F: t \mapsto \sqrt[3]{(t + 1)}$

6 Find the inverses of the following functions:

(a) g: $x \mapsto \dfrac{1}{x-3}$ $(x \neq 3)$ (b) g: $x \mapsto \dfrac{1}{2x+1}$ $(x \neq -\frac{1}{2})$

(c) g: $x \mapsto \dfrac{3}{4-x}$ $(x \neq 4)$ (d) g: $x \mapsto \dfrac{2x}{1+x}$ $(x \neq -1)$

7 Show that the function $f(x) = 1/(1-x)$, $(x \neq 1)$, is the inverse of the function $g(x) = (x-1)/x$, $(x \neq 0)$.
8 Show that the function $H(x) = x/(x-1)$ is a self-inverse function.
9 Sketch the graph of the function $y = f(x)$, where $f(x) = x^3 + 1$ and, on the same diagram, sketch the graph of the inverse function $y = f^{-1}(x)$.
10 Figure 3.20 shows the graph of a function $y = f(x)$. Copy the diagram carefully, using tracing paper if necessary, and on the same diagram, sketch the graph of the inverse function.

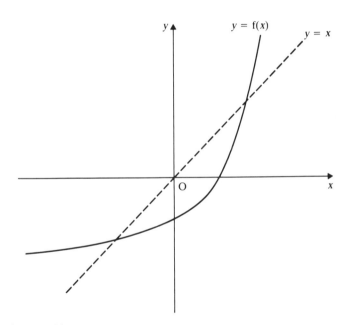

Figure 3.20

3.17 Investigating limits, using a calculator

In this section we shall investigate the limits of some functions using a calculator. It is important to understand that our investigations will only tell us the value of the function at the points we examine. To prove that the limits are what we think they are, we must turn to algebra, which we shall do in the next section. Nevertheless, the calculator can give us some very strong clues to the behaviour of certain functions.

The phrase 'x tends to zero', which is written '$x \to 0$', means that x can be made as small as we please. If any prearranged small number is chosen, then it must be possible to make x smaller than that number.

Example 14

Investigate the function $f(x) = x/\sin x$ as $x \to 0$, using your calculator in degree mode.

(Notice that this function does not exist at $x = 0$, since when $x = 0$, the function would give $0/0$.)

x	1.0	0.5	0.1	0.01
$f(x)$	57.299	57.297	57.296	57.296

This function seems pretty determined to approach 57.296 (to five significant figures) as x tends to zero.

When we say 'x tends to a', where a is a fixed real number, we mean that x can be made as close to a as we please; or, to put it another way, $|x - a| \to 0$. In the following example, x tends to 2.

Example 15

Investigate the function $f(x) = \dfrac{x^3 - 8}{x - 2}$ as $x \to 2$.

(First it should be noticed that $f(x)$ does not exist when $x = 2$; with this value of x the function gives $0/0$.)

Set out below are two tables; the first shows the values of $f(x)$ when x approaches 2 from below, and the second shows the values of $f(x)$ when x approaches 2 from above.

x	1.9	1.99	1.999	1.9999
$f(x)$	11.41	11.940	11.994	11.999

x	2.1	2.01	2.001	2.0001
$f(x)$	12.61	12.060	12.006	12.000

This suggests that $f(x)$ approaches 12, as x tends to 2.

A function $f(x)$ is said to tend to a **limit** L, if $|f(x) - L| \to 0$, as $x \to a$. The *same* number L must be reached whether x approaches the fixed number a from above or below. The function itself may, in some cases, be undefined at $x = a$. (In Example 15, opposite, we say that the limit of f(x) is 12, as $x \to 2$.)

The phrase 'x tends to infinity', means that x gets bigger and bigger, without any limit on its size. If we choose a large number N, then it must be possible for x to exceed N. (Infinity itself is not a real number, see Section 3.5.) Thus we can say that $1/n$ tends to zero as n tends to infinity. In other words $1/n$ gets smaller and smaller as n gets bigger and bigger. If we choose a very small number, say 10^{-6}, and ask whether we can make $1/n$ smaller than this number, the answer is 'yes'; all we have to do is to make n bigger than 10^{+6}. In writing, this statement is abbreviated to '$1/n \to 0$, as $n \to \infty$'.

Example 16

Investigate the function $f(x) = \dfrac{2x}{1+x}$ as $x \to \infty$.

The table below shows some values of f(x) for some increasingly large values of x. (The values of f(x) are given to five significant figures.)

x	10	100	1000	10 000
f(x)	1.8182	1.9802	1.9980	1.9998

From this table it seems reasonable to suppose that $f(x) \to 2$, as $x \to \infty$.

Example 17

Investigate $f(n) = (1 + 1/n)^n$ as $n \to \infty$.

The table below shows the values of f(n), for some increasingly large values of n. (The values of f(n) have been corrected to four significant figures.)

n	1	5	10	100	1000	1 000 000
f(n)	2	2.488	2.594	2.705	2.717	2.718

The table suggests that the limit of this function is 2.718. (It is difficult to investigate the limit of this function rigorously, but it can be shown that it is a number called e. We will meet e again in Chapter 26; like π, it plays a very important role in higher mathematics.)

In Qu. 8–12, use your calculator to investigate each function, as x tends to the number stated.

Qu. 8 $\dfrac{2x - 7}{x - 4}$ $x \to \infty$.   **Qu. 9** $\dfrac{x^2 + 5x - 14}{x - 2}$ $x \to 2$.

Qu. 10 $\left(1+\dfrac{2}{x}\right)^x$ $x \to \infty$.

Qu. 11 $\dfrac{x}{\sin x}$ $x \to 0$, using your calculator in radian mode.

Qu. 12 $\dfrac{1-\cos x}{x^2}$ $x \to 0$, using your calculator in radian mode.

3.18 Finding limits algebraically

Some of the functions which you have investigated in the preceding sections can be examined more rigorously using algebra.

In Example 16, on p. 65, if we divide the numerator and the denominator by x, the function can be written

$$f(x) = \frac{2}{1/x + 1}$$

If we now let $x \to \infty$, the term $1/x$ will tend to zero and we can see that $f(x)$ will tend to 2. Notice that, since x is positive, the denominator will always be slightly bigger than 1, so $f(x)$ will always be slightly less than 2. We say that $f(x)$ tends to 2 from below. On the other hand, when $x \to -\infty$, the denominator will be slightly less than 1 and so $f(x)$ will approach 2 from above.

In Example 15, put $x = 2 + h$, where h is small (in due course, we shall let h tend to zero).

$$x^3 = (2+h)^3 = 8 + 12h + 6h^2 + h^3$$

hence

$$\frac{x^3 - 8}{x - 2} = \frac{12h + 6h^2 + h^3}{h}$$
$$= 12 + 6h + h^2 \qquad (h \neq 0)$$

Although we must not put h *equal* to zero, we can let h *tend* to zero, that is, we can let it get smaller and smaller. As it does so, the terms $6h$ and h^2 tend to zero and we see that the function tends to 12. This confirms the result of our investigation by calculator.

If $f(x)$ tends to L as x tends to a, we frequently say that the limit of $f(x)$, as x tends to a, is L. This is usually abbreviated to

$$\lim_{x \to a} f(x) = L$$

Thus the outcome of Example 15 could be written

$$\lim_{x \to 2} \left(\frac{x^3 - 8}{x - 2} \right) = 12$$

3.19 Continuity

Looking back at Examples 7 and 8 (Section 3.13), the reader will notice that there is an important difference between them. The graph of Example 8 could, at least in our imagination, be drawn with a single sweep of the pencil, whereas in Example 7 the pencil must be lifted off the page at each integer point of the domain. We say that the function in Example 8 is **continuous**, but the function in Example 7 is **discontinuous** at 1, 2, 3, ...

Figure 3.21 shows sketches of the graphs of $y = x^2$, $y = 1/x$ and $y = 1/x^2$.

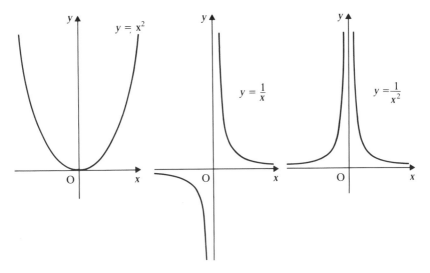

Figure 3.21

$f(x) = x^2$ is plainly a continuous function, but the other two are discontinuous at $x = 0$ (they are, of course, both undefined at this point).

The function given by

$$f(x) = +1, \quad \text{when} \quad x \geqslant 0$$
$$f(x) = -1, \quad \text{when} \quad x < 0$$

is defined at every point of $\mathbb{R}$, but it is discontinuous at $x = 0$. A sketch of its graph is shown in Figure 3.22 overleaf.

In all these cases the break in the graph has been pretty obvious, but a discontinuity can be more subtle than this. Consider for example the function

$$F(x) = \frac{x^2 - 4}{x - 2} \quad (x \neq 2)$$

For all values of x, except $x = 2$, this function is equal to $(x + 2)$, and consequently its graph is the straight line $y = x + 2$, with a 'hole' in it at $x = 2$ (Figure 3.23).

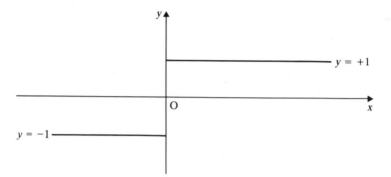

Figure 3.22

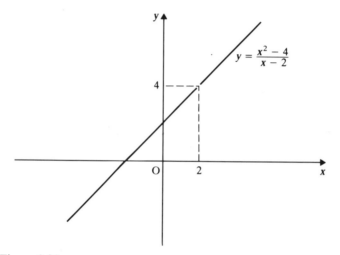

Figure 3.23

It is perfectly legitimate to say that $\lim_{x \to 2} F(x) = 4$, but we must not actually put x *equal* to 2. At the moment the graph is undefined at this point. Now, if we wish, we can 'plug the gap' by *defining* $F(2)$ as 4. In doing so we shall have made $F(x)$ continuous at $x = 2$. But, if we wish to be difficult, we could choose to define $F(2)$ as something else, say $F(2) = 0$; in this case $F(x)$ is discontinuous at $x = 2$.

Notice that in the case of $f(x) = 1/x$ and $f(x) = 1/x^2$, we can decide to define the function at $x = 0$, if we wish, but there is no number which we could assign to it which would make these functions continuous at $x = 0$.

We can express this more formally by saying that, if

$$\lim_{x \to a} f(x) \neq f(a)$$

then $f(x)$ is discontinuous at $x = a$. But if

$$\lim_{x \to a} f(x) = f(a)$$

then the function is continuous at $x = a$. A function which is continuous at every point in its domain is called a continuous function.

Exercise 3e

1 Find the limits of the following expressions as $x \to \infty$:

(a) $\dfrac{5x + 1}{10 + 2x}$ (b) $\dfrac{x + 1}{x^2}$ (c) $\dfrac{x^2 + 1}{x}$ (d) $\dfrac{5}{1 + x}$

2 Find the limits of the following expressions as $x \to 5$:

(a) $\dfrac{x^2 - 4x - 5}{x - 5}$ (b) $\dfrac{x^2 - 25}{x - 5}$ (c) $\dfrac{x^3 - 125}{x - 5}$ (d) $\dfrac{x^2 - 25}{(x - 5)^2}$

3 The following functions are not defined at $x = 0$. Define them, if possible, so that each function is continuous at $x = 0$.

(a) $f(x) = \dfrac{x^2 + x}{x}$ (b) $f(x) = x^2 + \dfrac{5}{x}$

(c) $f(x) = \dfrac{|x|}{x}$ (d) $f(x) = \dfrac{10 + 6/x}{5 + 2/x}$

4 Which of the following functions are continuous at $x = 0$? Sketch the graph in each case.

(a) $f(x) = x$ when $x \geqslant 0$ (b) $f(x) = x$ when $x \geqslant 0$
           $= 0$ when $x < 0$ $= 1$ when $x < 0$

(c) $f(x) = x + 1$ when $x \geqslant 0$ (d) $f(x) = 2^x$ when $x \geqslant 0$
           $= 0$ when $x < 0$ $= 1$ when $x < 0$

5 The function $f(x) = \dfrac{x^3 + x^2 - 9x - 9}{x^2 - 9}$ does not exist for two members of $\mathbb{R}$.

Find these two members of $\mathbb{R}$ and define $f(x)$ at each of these points, so that it becomes a continuous function.

Exercise 3f (Miscellaneous)

1 The domain of the function $f(x)$ is $\{1, 2, 3, 4, 5\}$. Find the range if:
(a) $f(x) = 5x^2 + 3$ (b) $f(x) = x/(x + 1)$
2 Given that $F(t) = 30/(t + 2)$, find:
(a) $F(3)$ (b) $F(\frac{1}{2})$ (c) $F(-1)$ (d) $F(-2.5)$
3 Given that $g(x) = 5 + x/2$, find the values of:
(a) $g^{-1}(6)$ (b) $g^{-1}(0)$ (c) $g^{-1}(-1)$ (d) $g^{-1}(a)$
4 The domain of the function $h(t) = |t| - t$ is $\mathbb{Z}$. Describe its range. Describe in words the set of numbers $\{a : h(a) = 0\}$.
5 The domain of the functions $f(x) = 5x$, $g(x) = x^2$, and $h(x) = x + 1$, is $\mathbb{R}$. Write down as simply as possible, the composite functions:
(a) $fgh(x)$ (b) $hgf(x)$

6 The domain of the functions $f(x) = x/5$ and $g(x) = 7 - x$ is $\mathbb{R}$. Write down, as simply as possible:

(a) $f^{-1}(x)$ (b) $g^{-1}(x)$ (c) $fg(x)$ (d) $(fg)^{-1}(x)$

7 The domain of the function $f(x) = 1/(1 + x^2)$ is $\mathbb{R}$. Explain why the denominator is never zero. Find the range of the function. Sketch the graph of $y = f(x)$.

8 Given than $f(x) = x + 2 - 15/x$ and that $g(x) = 1/x$, $(x \neq 0)$, write down the composite function $gf(x)$, in its simplest form, stating clearly any restrictions on the domain which are necessary.

9 State, with reasons, whether the following functions are one-to-one or many-to-one:

(a) $f: \mapsto 10x + 2$ $x \in \mathbb{R}$,

(b) $g: \mapsto 1/(x + 4)$ $x \in \mathbb{R}, x \neq -4$,

(c) $h: \mapsto x^2 + 1$ $x \in \mathbb{R}$.

Find the composite function $fgh(x)$ in its simplest possible form. Is $\mathbb{R}$ a suitable domain for $fgh(x)$? Find the range of the function $fgh(x)$ and sketch the graph of $y = fgh(x)$.

10 Show that the function $g(x) = (2x - 1)/(x - 3)$ can be expressed in the form

$$g(x) = \frac{a}{x - 3} + b$$

where a and b are real numbers and $x \neq 3$. Hence, or otherwise, find $\lim_{x \to \infty} g(x)$.

Show, also, that the graph of $g(x)$ can be obtained from the graph of $y = a/x$, by suitably chosen translations parallel to the axes. Sketch the graph of $y = g(x)$, showing clearly how it can be obtained by translating the graph of $y = a/x$.

11 Functions f and g, whose domain is the set of real numbers, are defined as follows:

$$f: x \mapsto x^3 + 2 \qquad g: x \mapsto x - 3$$

Find (a) $gf(2)$ (b) $(fg)^{-1}(-6)$ (O & C: SMP)

12 (a) Sketch the graph of the function $f: x \mapsto ||x + 2| - |x||$, where x is real. State the range of f.

(b) The function g is defined by $g: x \mapsto 4/(1 + x^2)$. Give a suitable domain for x so that g is a one-to-one function and state the range of g for this domain. Define an inverse function g^{-1} stating its domain and the corresponding range.   (C)

Chapter 4

The gradient of a curve

4.1 The gradient of a curve

So far we have only discussed the gradient of a straight line. A man walking up the ramp AB (Figure 4.1) is climbing a gradient of $\frac{2}{7}$.

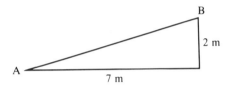

Figure 4.1

Let us now consider a man walking up the slope represented by the curve CPD (Figure 4.2). Between C and D the gradient is steadily increasing. If, when he had reached the point P, the gradient had stopped increasing, and had remained constant from then on, he would have climbed up the slope represented by the straight line PT, the tangent to the curve at P. Thus in walking up the slope CD, when the man is at the point P (and only at that instant) he is climbing a gradient represented by the gradient of PT.

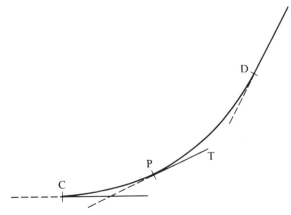

Figure 4.2

Definition

> The gradient of a curve at any point is the gradient of the tangent to the curve at that point.

4.2 The gradient at a point

If we wish to find approximately the gradient of a curve at a certain point, we could draw the curve, draw the tangent at that point by eye, and measure its gradient. But to develop our study of curves and their equations, it is important that we should discover a method of calculating exactly the gradient of a curve at any point; to do this we shall think of a tangent to a curve in the following way.

First we start with two distinct points on a curve, P and Q (Figure 4.3), and the chord PQ is drawn and produced in both directions. Now consider RPQS as a straight rod hinged at P, which is rotated clockwise about P to take up successive positions shown by PQ_1, PQ_2, PQ_3, etc. Notice that the points at which it cuts the curve, Q_1, Q_2, Q_3, are successively nearer the fixed point P. The nearer this second point of intersection approaches P, the nearer does the gradient of the chord approach the gradient of the tangent NPT. *By taking Q sufficiently close to P, we can make the gradient of the chord PQ as near as we please to the gradient of the tangent at P.*

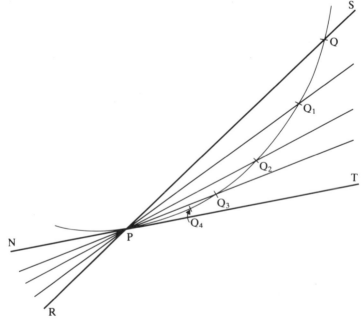

Figure 4.3

To see precisely how this happens, place the edge of a ruler along RPQS and then rotate it clockwise about P. You will see the second point of intersection approach P along the curve, until it actually coincides with P when the ruler lies along the tangent NPT. Using an arrow to denote 'tends to' or 'approaches' we may write:

as Q → P along the curve,
- the gradient of the chord PQ → the gradient of the tangent at P,
- the tangent at P is called the **limit** of the chord PQ (or more exactly of the secant RPQS), and
- the gradient of the curve at P is the limit of the gradient of the chord PQ.

Qu. 1 A regular polygon of n sides is inscribed in a circle. What is the limit of the polygon as $n \to \infty$?

Qu. 2 OP is a radius of a circle centre O. A straight line PQR cuts the circumference at Q. What is the limit of the angle QPR as Q approaches P along the circumference?

Qu. 3 P is a point on the straight line $y = \frac{1}{3}x$. Q is the foot of the perpendicular from P to the x-axis. As P approaches O, the origin, what happens to PQ and QO? What can you say about the value of PQ/QO?

4.3 The gradient of $y = x^2$ at (2, 4)

We shall now use this idea of a tangent being the limit of a chord, to find the gradient of the curve $y = x^2$ at a particular point, namely (2, 4).

P is the point (2, 4) on the curve $y = x^2$ (Figure 4.4). Q is another point on the curve, which we take first as (3, 9). Then, as the chord PQ rotates clockwise about P, Q moves along the curve to Q_1, and then nearer and nearer to P. By studying the behaviour of the gradient of PQ as this is happening we hope to be able to deduce the gradient of the tangent at P.

$$
\begin{aligned}
\text{The gradient of PQ} \quad &= \frac{\text{RQ}}{\text{PR}} \\[2mm]
&= \frac{\text{RQ}}{\text{MN}} \\[2mm]
&= \frac{\text{NQ} - \text{NR}}{\text{ON} - \text{OM}} \\[2mm]
&= \frac{9 - 4}{3 - 2} \\[2mm]
&= 5
\end{aligned}
$$

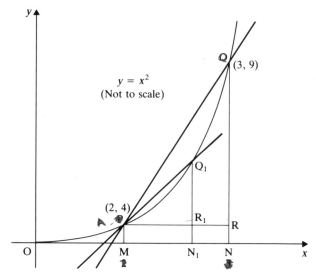

Figure 4.4

If Q now moves to the position Q_1, whose coordinates are $(2\frac{1}{2}, 6\frac{1}{4})$,

$$\text{the gradient of } PQ_1 \quad = \frac{N_1 Q_1 - N_1 R_1}{ON_1 - OM}$$

$$= \frac{6\frac{1}{4} - 4}{2\frac{1}{2} - 2}$$

$$= 4\frac{1}{2}$$

We now let Q approach yet closer to P along the curve, and the table opposite gives the gradient of the chord PQ as it approaches the gradient of the tangent at P.

Comparing the first and last columns of this table, we see that for each position of Q, the gradient of PQ exceeds 4 by the same amount as the x-coordinate of Q exceeds 2. The actual equality is not important; what is important is that these values we have taken so far suggest that by taking Q sufficiently near P (i.e. by taking the x-coordinate of Q sufficiently near 2) we can make the gradient of PQ as near 4 as we please (see Section 3.17). This suggests that the limit of the gradient of PQ is 4, and that the gradient of the tangent at P is 4.

Qu. 4 Draw a figure similar to Figure 4.4, taking P as the point $(1, 1)$. Taking the x-coordinate of Q successively as 2, $1\frac{1}{2}$, 1.1, 1.01, make out a table similar to the one opposite. What appears to be the limit of the gradient of PQ in this case?

Qu. 5 Add a last line to your table for Qu. 4 by taking the x-coordinate of Q to be $1 + h$. What happens to Q as $h \to 0$? What happens to the gradient of PQ as $h \to 0$? Deduce the gradient of $y = x^2$ at $(1, 1)$.

Qu. 6 Add a last line to the table in the book, taking the x-coordinate of Q as $(2 + h)$. Deduce the gradient of $y = x^2$ at $(2, 4)$.

ON	NQ	PR	RQ	$\dfrac{RQ}{PR}$
(x-coord. of Q)	(y-coord. of Q)	(ON − 2)	(NQ − 4)	Gradient of PQ
3	9	1	5	5
$2\frac{1}{2}$	$6\frac{1}{4}$	$\frac{1}{2}$	$2\frac{1}{4}$	$\dfrac{2\frac{1}{4}}{\frac{1}{2}} = 4\frac{1}{2}$
2.1	4.41	0.1	0.41	$\dfrac{0.41}{0.1} = 4.1$
2.01	4.0401	0.01	0.0401	$\dfrac{0.0401}{0.01} = 4.01$
2.001	4.004 001	0.001	0.004 001	$\dfrac{0.004\ 001}{0.001} = 4.001$

4.4 The gradient function of $y = x^2$

We now use the method suggested in Qu. 5 to find the gradient of $y = x^2$ at *any* point.

P is the point (a, a^2), and Q is another point on the curve whose x-coordinate is $a + h$ (Figure 4.5).

$$RQ = NQ - NR$$
$$= (a + h)^2 - a^2$$
$$= 2ah + h^2$$

and $PR = h$

The gradient of the chord PQ is

$$\frac{RQ}{PR} = \frac{2ah + h^2}{h}$$

$$= 2a + h$$

As we let the chord rotate clockwise about P, Q approaches P along the curve, and the gradient of the chord PQ → the gradient of the tangent at P, and $h \to 0$.

But as $h \to 0$, the gradient of the chord PQ, $(2a + h) \to 2a$.

If follows that the gradient of the tangent at P is $2a$.

Thus the gradient of $y = x^2$ at (a, a^2) is $2a$, and since a is the x-coordinate of the point (a, a^2), the gradient of $y = x^2$ at (x, x^2) is $2x$.

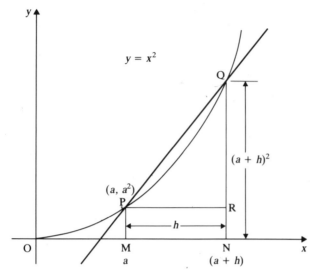

Figure 4.5

Just as x^2 is the expression in which we substitute a value of x to find the corresponding y-coordinate and plot a point on the curve $y = x^2$, so we now have another expression, $2x$, in which we can substitute the value of x to find the gradient at that point.

$2x$ is called the **gradient function** of the curve $y = x^2$.

Example 1

Find the coordinates of the points on the curve $y = x^2$, given by $x = 4$ and -10, and find the gradient of the curve at these points.

$$y = x^2$$

When $x = 4$, $y = 4^2 = 16$.

    The gradient function $= 2x$

    $\therefore$ the gradient $= 8$,   when $x = 4$

    $\therefore$ the point is (4, 16), and the gradient is 8.

When $x = -10$, $y = x^2 = +100$.

    The gradient function $= 2x = -20$

    $\therefore$ the point is $(-10, 100)$, and the gradient is -20.

Qu. 7 Calculate the gradients of the tangents to $y = x^2$ at the points given by $x = -1\frac{1}{2}, -1, +\frac{1}{2}, +2$.

Qu. 8 Use the method of Section 4.4 to find the gradient functions of the following curves, making a sketch in each case, and compare each result with the gradient function of $y = x^2$: (a) $y = 3x^2$, (b) $y = 5x^2$, (c) $y = \frac{1}{2}x^2$, (d) $y = cx^2$, where c is a constant, (e) $y = x^2 + 3$, (f) $y = x^2 + k$, where k is a constant.

Clearly we need an abbreviation for the statement 'the gradient function of $y = x^2$ is $2x$'. A convenient way of writing this is

'if $y = x^2$

grad $y = 2x$'

The process of finding the gradient function of a curve is known as **differentiation**, and it is useful if we understand 'grad' also to be an instruction to differentiate. Thus,

grad $x^2 = 2x$

4.5 The differentiation of x^3

P is any point (a, a^3) on the curve $y = x^3$. Q is another point on the curve with x-coordinate $(a + h)$ (Figure 4.6).

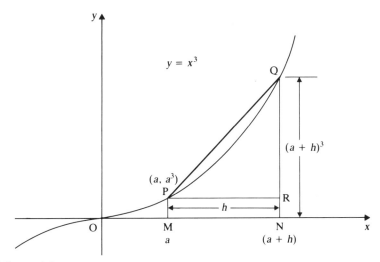

Figure 4.6

$$RQ = NQ - NR$$
$$= (a + h)^3 - a^3$$
$$= a^3 + 3a^2h + 3ah^2 + h^3 - a^3$$
$$= 3a^2h + 3ah^2 + h^3$$
$$PR = h$$

The gradient of $PQ = \dfrac{RQ}{PR}$

$$= \frac{3a^2h + 3ah^2 + h^3}{h}$$

$$= 3a^2 + 3ah + h^2$$

As Q approaches P along the curve, $h \to 0$, and then the terms $3ah$ and h^2 each tend to zero; therefore the gradient of $PQ \to 3a^2$.

It follows that the gradient of $y = x^3$ at (a, a^3) is $3a^2$, or

$$\text{grad } x^3 = 3x^2$$

Qu. 9 Use the method of Section 4.5 to find grad x^4.
[Hint: $(a + h)^4 = a^4 + 4a^3 h + 6a^2 h^2 + 4ah^3 + h^4$.]
Qu. 10 Differentiate $2x^3$ by the same method.

4.6 Summary of results

We have now confirmed the following:

$$\text{grad } x^2 = 2x$$
$$\text{grad } x^3 = 3x^2$$
$$\text{grad } x^4 = 4x^3$$

The form of these results suggests that the rule for differentiating a power of x is: *multiply by the index, and reduce the index by* 1; this means that grad x^5 would be $5x^4$, grad x^6 would be $6x^5$, and so on.

At this stage we must dispense with a formal proof of the validity of this process in general, and we shall assume that

$$\boxed{\text{grad } x^n = nx^{n-1}}$$

when $n \in \mathbb{Z}^+$.

It is now time to link up these ideas with our earlier work on a straight line, and to extend them further.

$y = c$

Straight lines of this form, such as $y = 4$ and $y = -2$, are parallel to the x-axis, and have zero gradient. It follows that grad $4 = 0$ and grad $-2 = 0$. Thus, *if we differentiate a constant we get* 0.

[Note that this does agree with the general result, grad $x^n = nx^{n-1}$. Since $x^0 = 1$ (see Section 10.4), we may write grad $4 = \text{grad } 4x^0 = 0 \times 4x^{-1} = 0$.]

$y = kx, \quad y = kx^n$

We know that the straight line $y = mx + c$ has gradient m, e.g. $y = x$ has gradient 1, and $y = 3x$ has gradient 3. Thus

$$\text{grad } x = 1$$

[Again, this agrees with the general result, since grad $x^1 = 1 \times x^0 = 1$.] Also,

$$\text{grad } 3x = 3 \times \text{grad } x = 3 \times 1 = 3$$

and as Qu. 8 showed,

$$\text{grad } 3x^2 = 3 \times \text{grad } x^2 = 3 \times 2x = 6x$$

This illustrates the general property that *if a function has a constant factor, that constant remains unchanged as a factor of the gradient function* (Figure 4.7).

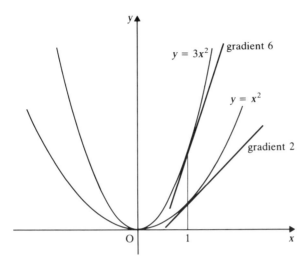

Figure 4.7

Qu. 11 Differentiate:
(a) $4x^3$ (b) $5x^4$ (c) ax^2 (d) $4x^n$ (e) Kx^{n+1}

4.7 The differentiation of a polynomial

So far we have differentiated functions with one term only. What happens if there are two or more terms?

$y = mx + c$

The straight lines $y = 3x$, $y = 3x + 4$, and $y = 3x - 2$ all have gradient 3. Thus

$$\text{grad } 3x = 3$$
$$\text{grad } (3x + 4) = 3$$
$$\text{grad } (3x - 2) = 3$$

The above lines are parallel, and as we discovered in Section 2.7, the effect of giving the different values $c = 0$, $+4$ and -2, is to raise or lower the line, but not to alter its gradient.

Clearly the same applies to the curves $y = x^2$, $y = x^2 + 4$ and $y = x^2 - 2$ (Figure 4.8). At the point on each curve for which $x = a$, the tangents are parallel, each having gradient $2a$.

$$\text{grad } x^2 = 2x$$
$$\text{grad } (x^2 + 4) = 2x$$
$$\text{grad } (x^2 - 2) = 2x$$

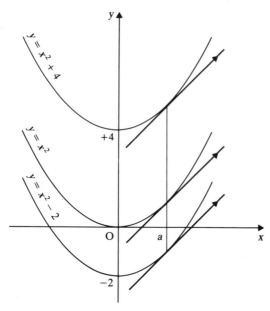

Figure 4.8

In the above cases where the function consists of two terms, we should get the same result by differentiating each term separately. Thus,

$$\text{grad}\,(x^2 + 4) = \text{grad}\,x^2 + \text{grad}\,4$$
$$= 2x + 0$$
$$= 2x$$

This leads us to investigate whether this method is valid in general.

$$y = x^2 + 3x - 2$$

To find the gradient function of this curve, let P be any point $(a, a^2 + 3a - 2)$ on it. Q is another point on the curve with x-coordinate $(a + h)$ (Figure 4.9).

$$RQ = NQ - NR$$
$$= \{(a + h)^2 + 3(a + h) - 2\} - \{a^2 + 3a - 2\}$$
$$= a^2 + 2ah + h^2 + 3a + 3h - 2 - a^2 - 3a + 2$$
$$= 2ah + h^2 + 3h$$

$$PR = h$$

The gradient of $PQ = \dfrac{RQ}{PR}$

$$= \dfrac{2ah + h^2 + 3h}{h}$$

$$= 2a + h + 3$$

As Q approaches P along the curve, $h \to 0$ and the gradient of $PQ \to 2a + 3$.

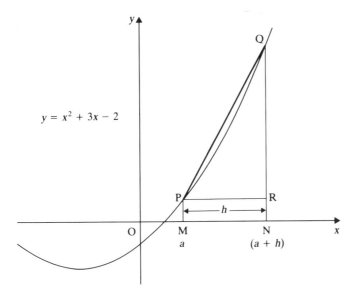

Figure 4.9

It follows that the gradient of $y = x^2 + 3x - 2$ at $(a, a^2 + 3a - 2)$ is $2a + 3$, or

$$\text{grad } (x^2 + 3x - 2) = 2x + 3$$

Now, if we try differentiating each term separately,

$$\text{grad } (x^2 + 3x - 2) = \text{grad } x^2 + \text{grad } 3x + \text{grad } -2$$
$$= 2x + 3 + 0$$
$$= 2x + 3$$

This illustrates the general property that *the gradient function of the sum of a number of terms is obtained by differentiating each term separately.*

Qu. 12 Differentiate:
(a) $x^3 + 2x^2 + 3x$ (b) $4x^4 - 3x^2 + 5$ (c) $ax^2 + bx + c$

A special method of dealing with products and quotients will be met later, but for the present we must reduce a function in this form to the sum of a number of terms before differentiating. (The reader may check that to differentiate each factor separately in the following examples does *not* lead to the correct result.)

$$\text{grad } \{x^2(2x + 3)\} = \text{grad } (2x^3 + 3x^2) = 6x^2 + 6x$$

$$\text{grad } \left\{ \frac{x^3 + 4x^2}{x} \right\} = \text{grad } (x^2 + 4x) = 2x + 4$$

Qu. 13 Differentiate:

(a) $x^2(4x - 2)$ (b) $(x + 3)(x - 4)$ (c) $\dfrac{5x^3 + 3x^2}{x^2}$

4.8 Differentiation and the function notation

In the preceding sections we have considered a variety of functions and we have found their corresponding gradient functions. The gradient function is often called the **derived function**, or **derivative**.

If we have a given function f(x) it is very convenient to have a standard notation for its corresponding gradient function; the normal way of doing this is to write f'(x). Thus if $f(x) = x^3 + 5x^2 + 3x - 7$ then we write its derivative $f'(x) = 3x^2 + 10x + 3$. Alternatively

$$f: x \mapsto x^3 + 5x^2 + 3x - 7$$
$$f': x \mapsto 3x^2 + 10x + 3$$

The process of finding the derived functions in the case of $f(x) = x^2$ and $f(x) = x^3$, has been written out in full in Sections 4.4 and 4.5 respectively. The general case is set out below.

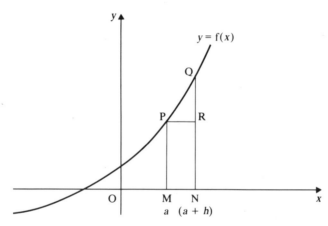

Figure 4.10

Figure 4.10 shows the graph of a general function $y = f(x)$; M and N are the points $(a, 0)$ and $(a + h, 0)$ respectively. P and Q are points on the curve given by $x = a$ and $x = a + h$. So $MP = f(a)$ and $NQ = f(a + h)$.

$$RQ = NQ - NR$$
$$= NQ - MP$$
$$= f(a + h) - f(a)$$

The gradient of PQ

$$= \frac{RQ}{PR}$$

$$= \frac{f(a + h) - f(a)}{h}$$

Hence the gradient of the tangent at $P = \lim\limits_{h \to 0} [f(a+h) - f(a)]/h$, and hence the derived function $f'(x)$ is given by

$$f'(x) = \lim_{h \to 0} \frac{f(x+h) - f(x)}{h}$$

. . . . (1)

In saying this, we are assuming that this limit exists and that it is the same whether h tends to zero from above or from below (see Section 3.17).

If you are ever required to differentiate a given function from first principles, you should start the proof by quoting the formula marked (1).

Example 2

Find, from first principles, the derivative of the function $f(t) = kt^4$, where k is a constant.

$$f'(t) = \lim_{h \to 0} \frac{f(t+h) - f(t)}{h}$$

$$f(t+h) = k(t+h)^4$$
$$= k(t^4 + 4t^3 h + 6t^2 h^2 + 4th^3 + h^4)$$

$$\therefore \quad f(t+h) - f(t) = kt^4 + 4kt^3 h + 6kt^2 h^2 + 4kth^3 + kh^4 - kt^4$$
$$= 4kt^3 h + 6kt^2 h^2 + 4kth^3 + kh^4$$

$$\frac{f(t+h) - f(t)}{h} = 4kt^3 + 6kt^2 h + 4kth^2 + kh^3$$

and hence

$$f'(t) = \lim_{h \to 0} (4kt^3 + 6kt^2 h + 4kth^2 + kh^3)$$

$$= 4kt^3$$

Example 3

Find, from first principles, $f'(x)$ when $f(x) = |x|$.

$$f'(x) = \lim_{h \to 0} \frac{f(x+h) - f(x)}{h}$$

$$= \lim_{h \to 0} \frac{|x+h| - |x|}{h}$$

Now if x and $x + h$ are both positive, then $|x + h| = x + h$ and $|x| = x$.

Consequently in this case

$$f'(x) = \lim_{h \to 0} \frac{x+h-x}{h}$$

$$= \lim_{h \to 0} \left(\frac{h}{h}\right)$$

$$= +1$$

But, if x and $x+h$ are both negative, $|x+h| = -(x+h)$ and $|x| = -x$. In this case

$$f'(x) = \lim_{h \to 0} \left(\frac{-x-h-(-x)}{h}\right)$$

$$= \lim_{h \to 0} \left(\frac{-h}{h}\right)$$

$$= -1$$

The remaining case, namely $f'(0)$, is rather tricky!

$$f'(0) = \lim_{h \to 0} \frac{|0+h|-0}{h}$$

$$= \lim_{h \to 0} \left(\frac{|h|}{h}\right)$$

But $|h|/h = +1$ if $h > 0$, or -1 if $h < 0$. Consequently, the limit as $h \to 0$ from above is $+1$, but it is -1 when h tends to 0 from below. Hence $f'(0)$ cannot be found. This may seem rather strange, but it makes sense if we consider the graph of $y = |x|$ (Figure 4.11).

It is clear from the graph that when $x > 0$, the gradient is $+1$, while if $x < 0$ the gradient is -1. At $x = 0$, however, the graph comes to a point and its gradient here does not exist.

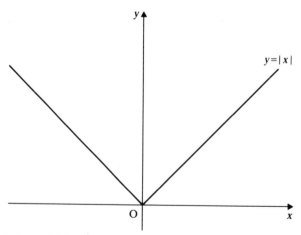

Figure 4.11

Exercise 4a

Write down the gradient functions of the following curves:

1 $y = x^{12}$ **2** $y = 3x^7$ **3** $y = 5x$
4 $y = 5x + 3$ **5** $y = 3$ **6** $y = 5x^2 - 3x$

Write down the derived function f'(x), for each of the following functions:

7 $f(x) = 3x^4 - 2x^3 + x^2 - x + 10$ **8** $f(x) = 2x^4 + \frac{1}{3}x^3 - \frac{1}{4}x^2 + 2$
9 $f(x) = ax^3 + bx^2 + cx$ **10** $f(x) = 2x(3x^2 - 4)$

11 $f(x) = \dfrac{10x^5 + 3x^4}{2x^2}$

Differentiate the following functions:

12 $-x$ **13** $+10$ **14** $4x^3 - 3x + 2$
15 $\frac{1}{2}ax^2 - 2bx + c$ **16** $2(x^2 + x)$ **17** $3x(x - 1)$
18 $\frac{1}{3}(x^3 - 3x + 6)$ **19** $(x + 1)(x - 2)$

Find the derivatives of the following functions:

20 $f: x \mapsto 3(x + 1)(x - 1)$ **21** $f: x \mapsto \dfrac{(x + 3)(2x + 1)}{4}$

22 $f: x \mapsto \dfrac{2x^3 - x^2}{3x}$ **23** $f: x \mapsto \dfrac{x^4 + 3x^2}{2x^2}$

Find the y-coordinate, and the gradient, at the points on the following curves corresponding to the given values of x:

24 $y = x^2 - 2x + 1$, $x = 2$ **25** $y = x^2 + x + 1$, $x = 0$
26 $y = x^2 - 2x$, $x = -1$ **27** $y = (x + 2)(x - 4)$, $x = 3$
28 $y = 3x^2 - 2x^3$, $x = -2$ **29** $y = (4x - 5)^2$, $x = \frac{1}{2}$

Find the coordinates of the points on the following curves at which the gradient has the given values:

30 $y = x^2$,   8   **31** $y = x^3$,   12
32 $y = x(2 - x)$,   2   **33** $y = x^2 - 3x + 1$,   0
34 $y = x^3 - 2x + 7$,   1   **35** $y = x^3 - 6x^2 + 4$, -12
36 $y = x^4 - 2x^3 + 1$,   0   **37** $y = x^2 - x^3$, -1
38 $y = x(x - 3)^2$,   0

4.9 Tangents and normals

Definition

A normal to a curve at a point is the straight line through the point at right angles to the tangent at the point (Figure 4.12 overleaf).

We are now able to find the equations of tangents and normals.

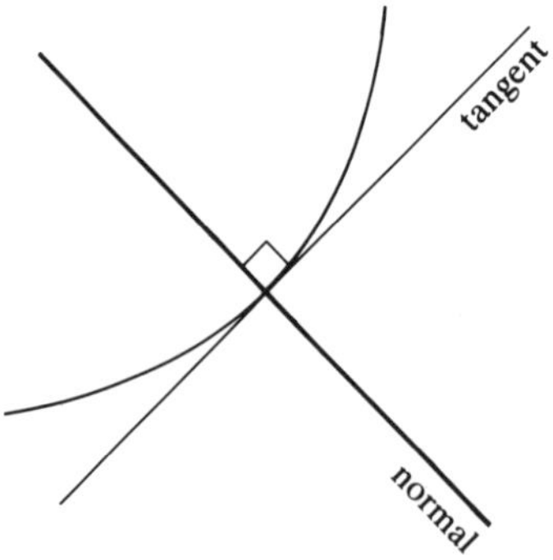

Figure 4.12

Example 4

Find the equation of the tangent to the curve $y = x^3$ at the point (2, 8).

$$y = x^3$$
$$\therefore \quad \text{grad } y = 3x^2$$

When $x = 2$,

$$\text{grad } y = 12$$

Thus the gradient of the tangent at (2, 8) is $+12$. Using the formula (see Section 2.9)

$$(y - y_1) = m(x - x_1)$$

its equation is:

$$y - 8 = 12(x - 2)$$
$$\therefore \quad y - 8 = 12x - 24$$
$$\therefore \text{ the equation of the tangent is } 12x - y - 16 = 0.$$

We can generalise Example 4 as follows.

Example 5

Find the equation of the tangent to the curve $y = f(x)$ at the point (a, b).

Putting $x = a$ in the equation gives

$$b = f(a)$$

The gradient at the given point is obtained by differentiating and putting $x = a$. Hence the gradient required is $f'(a)$.

The equation of the tangent has the form

$$y - b = m(x - a)$$

where m is the gradient. Hence the equation of the tangent is

$$y - f(a) = f'(a)(x - a)$$

Example 6

Find the equation of the normal to the curve $y = (x^2 + x + 1)(x - 3)$ at the point where it cuts the x-axis.

$$y = (x^2 + x + 1)(x - 3)$$

The first task is to find where the curve meets the x-axis.

When $y = 0$,

$$(x^2 + x + 1)(x - 3) = 0$$

But $x^2 + x + 1 = 0$ has no real roots,

$$\therefore \quad x = +3$$

$\therefore$ the curve cuts the x-axis at $(3, 0)$.

Now we must find the gradient at this point.

$$y = x^3 - 2x^2 - 2x - 3$$
$$\therefore \quad \text{grad } y = 3x^2 - 4x - 2$$

When $x = 3$,

$$\text{grad } y = 27 - 12 - 2 = 13$$

The gradient of the tangent at $(3, 0)$ is $+13$, therefore the gradient of the normal at $(3, 0)$ is $-\frac{1}{13}$ (see Section 2.5) and its equation is

$$y - 0 = -\tfrac{1}{13}(x - 3)$$
$$\therefore \quad 13y = -x + 3$$

$\therefore$ the equation of the normal is $x + 13y - 3 = 0$.

Exercise 4b

1 Find the equations of the tangents to the following curves at the points corresponding to the given values of x:
(a) $y = x^2$, $x = 2$
(b) $y = 3x^2 + 2$, $x = 4$
(c) $y = 3x^2 - x + 1$, $x = 0$
(d) $y = 3 - 4x - 2x^2$, $x = 1$
(e) $y = 9x - x^3$, $x = -3$

2 Find the equations of the normals to the curves in no. 1 at the given points.

3 Find the equation of the tangent and the normal to the curve $y = x^2(x - 3)$ at the point where it cuts the x-axis. Sketch the curve.

4 Repeat no. 3 for the curve $y = x(x - 4)^2$.

5 Find the equation of the tangent to the curve $y = 3x^3 - 4x^2 + 2x - 10$ at the point of intersection with the y-axis.

6 Repeat no. 5 for the curve $y = x^2 - 4x + 3$.

7 Find the values of x for which the gradient function of the curve

$$y = 2x^3 + 3x^2 - 12x + 3$$

is zero. Hence find the equations of the tangents to the curve which are parallel to the x-axis.

8 Repeat no. 7 for the curve $y = 2x^3 - 9x^2 + 10$.

Exercise 4c (Miscellaneous)

1 Find the gradient of the curve $y = 9x - x^3$ at the point where $x = 1$. Find the equation of the tangent to the curve at this point. Where does this tangent meet the line $y = x$?

2 Find the equation of the tangent at the point $(2, 4)$ to the curve $y = x^3 - 2x$. Also find the coordinates of the point where the tangent meets the curve again.

3 Find the equation of the tangent to the curve $y = x^3 - 9x^2 + 20x - 8$ at the point $(1, 4)$. At what points of the curve is the tangent parallel to the line $4x + y - 3 = 0$?

4 Find the equation of the tangent to the curve $y = x^3 + \frac{1}{2}x^2 + 1$ at the point $(-1, \frac{1}{2})$. Find the coordinates of another point on the curve where the tangent is parallel to that at the point $(-1, \frac{1}{2})$.

5 Find the points of intersection with the x-axis of the curve $y = x^3 - 3x^2 + 2x$, and find the equation of the tangent to the curve at each of these points.

6 Find the equations of the normals to the parabola $4y = x^2$ at the points $(-2, 1)$ and $(-4, 4)$. Show that the point of intersection of these two normals lies on the parabola.

7 Find the equation of the tangent at the point $(1, -1)$ to the curve

$$y = 2 - 4x^2 + x^3$$

What are the coordinates of the point where the tangent meets the curve again? Find the equation of the tangent at this point.

8 Find the coordinates of the point P on the curve $8y = 4 - x^2$ at which the gradient is $\frac{1}{2}$. Write down the equation of the tangent to the curve at P. Find also the equation of the tangent to the curve whose gradient is $-\frac{1}{2}$, and the coordinates of its point of intersection with the tangent at P.

9 Find the equations of the tangents to the curve $y = x^3 - 6x^2 + 12x + 2$ which are parallel to the line $y = 3x$.

10 Find the coordinates of the points of intersection of the line $x - 3y = 0$ with the curve $y = x(1 - x^2)$. If these points are in order P, O, Q, prove that the tangents to the curve at P and Q are parallel, and that the tangent at O is perpendicular to them.

Chapter 5

Velocity and acceleration

5.1 Gradient and velocity

It is assumed that the reader will already have met 'travel graphs'. One such graph is shown in Figure 5.1, representing a girl walking to see a friend who lives 5 km away, staying 2 hours, and then returning home. On her outward journey, represented by OA, she travels 5 km in 2 hours, and her velocity, $\frac{5}{2}$ km h^{-1}, is represented by DA/OD, the gradient of OA.

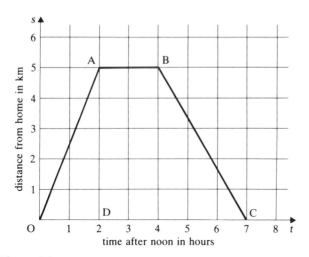

Figure 5.1

Whilst with her friend her velocity is zero; this is represented by the gradient of AB.

On her return journey, the gradient of BC gives her velocity as $-\frac{5}{3}$ km h^{-1}. The negative sign denotes that she is now travelling in the opposite direction; she is *decreasing* the distance from home.

This type of graph in which the distance, s, is plotted against the time, t, is called a **space–time graph**.

89

5.2 Velocity and speed

In mathematics and science, a distinction is made between the words **distance** and **displacement**. The latter term is used when we wish to refer to the change in the position of a point giving the distance *and the direction*. In this book, we shall only be concerned with motion along a straight line, and we shall often use the x-axis for reference. A displacement in the positive direction will have a plus sign, and a displacement in the opposite direction, a minus sign. For example, the *distance* between the point A (8, 0) and the point B (20, 0), where the units are measured in centimetres, is twelve centimetres. But we describe the move from A to B as a *displacement of +12 cm*, whilst the move from B to A is said to be −12 cm.

A similar distinction is made between the words **speed** and **velocity**. The word 'speed' is used for the rate at which an object is moving, and the term 'velocity' is used when the speed *and the direction of motion* are required. For example, when describing the motion of a ship sailing in a straight line, we might say that its *speed* is 20 knots, but for its *velocity* we must include the direction, e.g. 20 knots due east.

Suppose a point P moves along the x-axis at constant speed, and travels from A (8, 0) to B (20, 0) in 3 seconds, we say that its speed is 4 cm s^{-1} but we describe its *velocity* as $+4 \text{ cm s}^{-1}$. However if P moves from B to A in the same time interval we say its velocity is -4 cm s^{-1} (but its speed is still 4 cm s^{-1}).

For a point moving in a straight line, its average velocity is defined as follows:

$$\text{average velocity} = \frac{\text{increase in displacement}}{\text{total time taken}}$$

This definition can be used even if the velocity is changing. We examine this in the next section.

5.3 Variable speed and variable velocity

When we go on a journey we often refer to the 'average speed'. By this we mean:

$$\frac{\text{the total distance travelled}}{\text{the total time taken}}$$

Suppose a train travelled 160 km in 2 hours, we would say that the average speed was 80 km h^{-1}. However, the train's speed may not have been constant; there may have been times when the speed was well above 80 km h^{-1}, and others when it was well below (it might even have been zero, e.g. while the train stopped at a station).

The speed of a vehicle at any particular instant is indicated on the vehicle's speedometer.

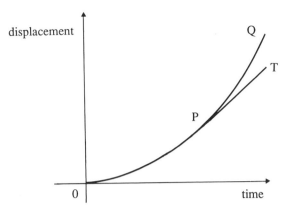

Figure 5.2

Suppose the curve OPQ in Figure 5.2 represents the displacement–time graph of a car as it accelerates from 0 to 80 km h^{-1}.

Let point P on the curve be the point which corresponds to the instant when the speed is 60 km h^{-1}. If, from this moment onwards, the car's speed had remained at a constant 60 km h^{-1}, then its motion would have been represented by the straight line PT instead of the curve PQ. The gradient of PT would be 60, and PT would be a tangent to the curve at P.

This illustrates an important concept, namely that on a displacement–time graph, the gradient of the tangent at a point P on the graph represents the velocity at that moment.

Now let us consider the motion of a small stone falling vertically from an initial velocity of zero. It can be verified by experiment that, provided air resistance is neglected, it will be s m below its starting point t seconds after the start, where s is given by the formula $s = 4.9t^2$. From this we may make a table of values giving the position of the stone at different times.†

Value of t	0	0.5	1.0	1.5	2.0	2.5	3.0
Value of s	0	1.2	4.9	11.0	19.6	30.6	44.1

Part of the space-time graph is given in Figure 5.3 (over the page).

From $t = 1$ to $t = 2$, the *average velocity* is represented by the gradient of the chord PQ.

$$\frac{RQ}{PR} = \frac{19.6 - 4.9}{2 - 1} = 14.7$$

∴ the average velocity is 14.7 m s^{-1}.

---

† Throughout Section 5.3, including Qu. 1 to 5, we work to one decimal place.

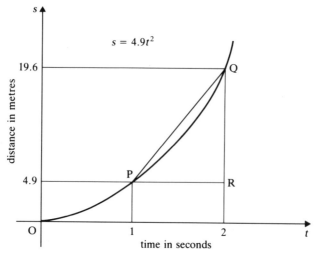

Figure 5.3

Qu. 1 How far does the stone move in the interval $t = 1$ to $t = 1.5$? What is the average velocity during this interval?

Qu. 2 Repeat Qu. 1 for the intervals (a) $t = 1$ to $t = 1.1$ and (b) $t = 1$ to $t = 1 + h$.

The smaller we make the time interval (letting $Q \rightarrow P$ along the curve), the nearer the average velocity (the gradient of PQ) approaches the velocity given by the gradient of the curve at P.

Now we have seen that the gradient of the curve at P is the limit of the gradient of PQ as $Q \rightarrow P$ (Section 4.2); this leads to the following definition.

Definition

> The velocity at an instant is the limit of the average velocity for an interval following that instant, as the time interval tends to zero.

Qu. 3 From your answer to Qu. 2(b) determine the actual velocity at the instant when $t = 1$.

Qu. 4 Calculate the distance moved, and the average velocity during the following intervals:
(a) $t = 2$ to $t = 3$ (b) $t = 2$ to $t = 2.5$
(c) $t = 2$ to $t = 2.1$ (d) $t = 2$ to $t = 2 + h$
Deduce the velocity when $t = 2$.

The definition given above identifies the velocity at an instant with the gradient of the space–time graph for the corresponding value of t. If we are given s in terms of t we can therefore find an expression for the velocity of the stone at any instant by differentiation, that is, if $s = f(t)$, then the velocity v is given by

$$v = f'(t)$$

In the case we considered above, $f(t) = 4.9t^2$ and so the velocity, v m s^{-1}, is given by

$$v = f'(t) = 9.8t$$

Thus when $t = 0$, $v = 0$
      when $t = 1$, $v = 9.8$
      when $t = 2$, $v = 19.6$ etc.

Qu. 5 A stone is thrown vertically downwards from the top of a cliff, and the depth below the top, s m, after t s, is given by the formula $s = 2t + 4.9t^2$.
(a) Where is the stone after 1, 2, 3, 4 s?
(b) What is its velocity at these times?
(c) What is the average velocity during the 3rd second (from $t = 2$ to $t = 3$)?

5.4 The symbols δs and δt

The idea of gradient helped us to arrive at the definition of velocity at an instant. It is instructive to take the definition as our starting point; and now, without reference to graphical ideas, we shall again demonstrate that velocity is found by differentiating the expression for s in terms of t. To do this it is convenient to introduce some new symbols, which will be of great use from now onwards.

Again we deal with the stone which falls s metres from rest in t seconds. Suppose that it falls a further small distance δs metres in the additional small interval of time δt seconds.

[In general, the symbol δt, read as 'delta t', is used to denote a small increase, or *increment*, in time. Note that δt is a single symbol; it does not mean δ multiplied by t. Similarly δs is the corresponding *increment* in the displacement.]

The average velocity for the time interval δt (i.e. from t to $t + \delta t$) is $\delta s/\delta t$ m s^{-1}, and we now obtain an expression for this in terms of t.

Since the stone falls $(s + \delta s)$ metres in $(t + \delta t)$ seconds

$$s + \delta s = 4.9(t + \delta t)^2$$
i.e. $s + \delta s = 4.9t^2 + 9.8t \times \delta t + 4.9 \times (\delta t)^2$
But $s \quad\quad = 4.9t^2$

and subtracting,

$$\delta s = 9.8t \times \delta t + 4.9 \times (\delta t)^2$$

To find the average velocity between time t and time $(t + \delta t)$ we divide each side by δt, giving

$$\frac{\delta s}{\delta t} = 9.8t + 4.9 \times \delta t$$

As $\delta t \to 0$, the R.H.S. $\to 9.8t$.

By the definition of velocity at an instant, the velocity, v m s^{-1}, at time t, is the limit of $\delta s/\delta t$ as $\delta t \rightarrow 0$, hence

$v = 9.8t$

The fact that this process is identical with that of finding the gradient function of $s = 4.9t^2$ is readily seen from Figure 5.4.

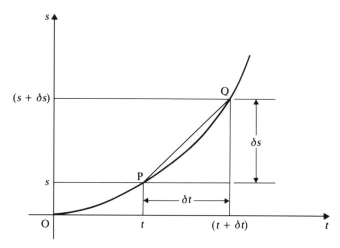

Figure 5.4

Exercise 5a

1 A stone is thrown vertically upwards at 35 m s^{-1}. It is s m above the point of projection t s later, where $s = 35t - 4.9t^2$.
   (a) What is the distance moved, and the average velocity during the 3rd second (from $t = 2$ to $t = 3$)?
   (b) Find the average velocities for the intervals $t = 2$ to $t = 2.5$, $t = 2$ to $t = 2.1$, $t = 2$ to $t = 2 + h$.
   (c) Deduce the actual velocity at the end of the 2nd second.
2 A stone is thrown vertically upwards at 24.5 m s^{-1} from a point on the level with but just beyond a cliff ledge. Its height above the ledge t s later is $4.9t(5 - t)$ m. If its velocity is v m s^{-1}, differentiate to find v in terms of t.
   (a) When is the stone at the ledge level?
   (b) Find its height and velocity after 1, 2, 3, and 6 s.
   (c) What meaning is attached to a negative value of s? A negative value of v?
   (d) When is the stone momentarily at rest? What is its greatest height?
   (e) Find the total distance moved during the 3rd second.
3 A particle moves along a straight line so that it is s m from a fixed point O on the line t s after a given instant, where $s = 3t + t^2$. After $(t + \delta t)$ s it is $(s + \delta s)$ m from O. Find the average velocity during the time interval t to $(t + \delta t)$ as was done in Section 5.4, and deduce an expression for the velocity v m s^{-1} at time t. Check by differentiation.

(a) Where is the particle and what is its velocity at the instant from which time is measured (i.e. when $t = 0$)?
(b) When is the particle at O?
(c) When is the particle momentarily at rest? Where is it then?
(d) What is the velocity the first time the particle is at O?

4 A particle moves along a straight line OA in such a way that it is s m from O t s after the instant from which time is measured, where $s = 6t - t^2$. A is to be taken as being on the positive side of O.
(a) Where is the particle when $t = 0, 2, 3, 4, 6, 7$? What is the meaning of a negative value of s?
(b) Differentiate the given expression to find the velocity, v m s^{-1}, in terms of t. Find the value of v when $t = 0, 2, 4, 6$. What is the meaning of a negative value of v?
(c) When and where does the particle change its direction of motion?

5.5 Constant acceleration

Earlier in this chapter we used the formula $s = 4.9t^2$ for a stone falling from rest. On differentiation $v = $ grad $s = 9.8t$. The stone's velocity is 9.8, 19.6, 29.4, 39.2, ... m s^{-1} at the end of successive seconds, and it is steadily increasing by 9.8 m s^{-1} in each second. This *rate* at which the stone's velocity increases is called its **acceleration**. This particular formula is based on the assumption that gravity is producing a *constant* acceleration of 9.8 m per second per second, written usually as 9.8 m/s^2 or 9.8 m s^{-2}.

Figure 5.5 shows the corresponding **velocity–time graph**. The equation $v = 9.8t$ (being of the form $y = mx$) represents graphically a straight line through the origin of gradient 9.8. In this case then, the acceleration is represented by the gradient of the velocity–time graph.

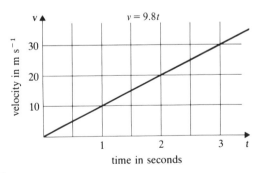

Figure 5.5

Qu. 6 A stone is thrown vertically downwards with a velocity of 10 m s^{-1}, and gravity produces on it an acceleration of 9.8 m s^{-2}.
(a) What is the velocity after 1, 2, 3, t s?
(b) Sketch the velocity–time graph.

If a particle has an initial velocity u m s^{-1} and a constant acceleration a m s^{-2}, then its velocity after t s is $(u + at)$ m s^{-1} and the equation $v = u + at$ (being of the form $y = mx + c$) represents a straight line of gradient a.

Thus when acceleration is constant, it is represented by the *gradient* of the straight-line *velocity–time graph*.

Exercise 5b

In this exercise, acceleration is constant.

1 At the start and end of a two-second interval, a particle's velocity is observed to be 5 m s^{-1} and 10 m s^{-1}. What is its acceleration?
2 A body starts with velocity 15 m s^{-1}, and at the end of the 11th second its velocity is 48 m s^{-1}. What is its acceleration?
3 Express an acceleration of 5 m s^{-2} in (a) km h^{-1} per s, (b) km h^{-2}.
4 A car accelerates from 5 km h^{-1} to 41 km h^{-1} in 10 s. Express this acceleration in (a) km h^{-1} per s, (b) m s^{-2}, (c) km h^{-2}.
5 A car can accelerate at 4 m s^{-2}. How long will it take to reach 90 km h^{-1} from rest?
6 Sketch the velocity–time graph for a cyclist who, starting from rest, reaches 3 m s^{-1} in 5 s, travels at that speed for 20 s, and then comes to rest in a further 2 s. What is the acceleration when braking? What is the gradient of the corresponding part of the graph?
7 An express train reducing its velocity to 40 km h^{-1}, has to apply the brakes for 50 s. If the retardation is 0.5 m s^{-2}, find its initial velocity in km h^{-1}.

5.6 Variable acceleration

A car starts from rest and moves a distance s m in t s, where $s = \frac{1}{6}t^3 + \frac{1}{4}t^2$. If its velocity after t s is v m s^{-1}, then $v = \text{grad } s = \frac{1}{2}t^2 + \frac{1}{2}t$. The following table gives some corresponding values of v and t:

t	0	1	2	3	4
v	0	1	3	6	10

The increases in velocity during the first four seconds are 1 m s^{-1}, 2 m s^{-1}, 3 m s^{-1}, 4 m s^{-1} respectively. Since the rate of increase of the velocity is not constant in this case, we shall first investigate the average rate of increase over a given time interval.

Definition

$$\text{average acceleration} = \frac{\text{increase in } v}{\text{increase in } t}$$

Thus from $t = 0$ to $t = 2$, the average acceleration $= \dfrac{3-0}{2} = 1\frac{1}{2}$ m s^{-2} and from

$t = 2$ to $t = 4$, the average acceleration $= \dfrac{10-3}{2} = 3\frac{1}{2}$ m s^{-2}.

Clearly the acceleration itself is increasing with the time, and the next step is to define what is meant by the acceleration at an instant.

Definition

> The acceleration at an instant is the limit of the average acceleration for an interval following that instant, as the interval tends to zero.

Using the notation of Section 5.4, if δv is the small increase in velocity which occurs in time δt, then the average acceleration for that interval is $\delta v / \delta t$, and the acceleration at time t is the limit of this as $\delta t \to 0$.

Reference to the velocity–time graph given in Figure 5.6 shows that the average acceleration $\delta v / \delta t$ is the gradient of the chord PQ, and the limit is the gradient of the graph at P.

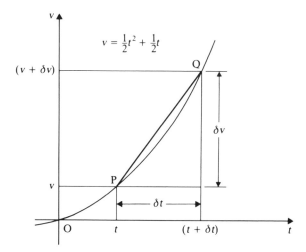

Figure 5.6

Thus an expression for the acceleration at time t may be found by differentiating the expression for v, that is, if $v = g(t)$, then a the acceleration is given by $a = g'(t)$.

Notice that if we start with the displacement given by $s = f(t)$, then we differentiate once to obtain the velocity v and we differentiate again to find the acceleration a. We are already familiar with the symbol $f'(t)$ for the derivative of f(t); when this in turn is differentiated we write f"(t). Thus we can sum up the preceding statement as follows:

$$s = f(t)$$
$$v = f'(t)$$
$$a = f''(t)$$

Example 1

A car starts from rest and its displacement s m after t s is $s = \frac{1}{6}t^3 + \frac{1}{4}t^2$. What is the initial acceleration, and the acceleration at the end of the second second?

$$s = f(t) = \tfrac{1}{6}t^3 + \tfrac{1}{4}t^2$$
$$v = f'(t) = \tfrac{1}{2}t^2 + \tfrac{1}{2}t$$
$$a = f''(t) = t + \tfrac{1}{2}$$

When $t = 0$, $a = \frac{1}{2}$ and when $t = 2$, $a = 2\frac{1}{2}$.

Hence the required accelerations are $\frac{1}{2}$ m s^{-2}, and $2\frac{1}{2}$ m s^{-2}.

Before reading Example 2 the reader should refer once again to the definitions of *average velocity* and *average acceleration*. In particular it should be noted that (a) average velocity is not the same as the average of the initial and final velocities (unless the acceleration is constant) and (b) average acceleration is not necessarily the same as the average of the initial and final accelerations.

Example 2

A particle moves along a straight line in such a way that its displacement from a fixed point O on the line after t s is s m, where $s = \frac{1}{6}t^4$. Find (a) its velocity after 3 s, and after 4 s, (b) its average velocity during the fourth second, (c) its acceleration after 2 s, and after 4 s, and (d) its average acceleration from $t = 2$ to $t = 4$.

$$s = f(t) = \tfrac{1}{6}t^4$$
$$v = f'(t) = \tfrac{2}{3}t^3$$
$$a = f''(t) = 2t^2$$

(a) When $t = 3$, $v = \frac{2}{3} \times 3^3 = 18$ m s^{-1} and when $t = 4$, $v = \frac{2}{3} \times 4^3 = 42\frac{2}{3}$ m s^{-1}. Hence after 3 s and 4 s, the velocity is 18 m s^{-1} and $42\frac{2}{3}$ m s^{-1} respectively.

(b) When $t = 3$, $s = \frac{81}{6} = 13\frac{1}{2}$ m and when $t = 4$, $s = \frac{256}{6} = 42\frac{2}{3}$ m.

∴ the average velocity during the fourth second is

$$\frac{42\frac{2}{3} - 13\frac{1}{2}}{1} = 29\frac{1}{6} \text{ m s}^{-1}$$

(c) When $t = 2$, $a = 2 \times 2^2 = 8$ m s^{-2} and when $t = 4$, $a = 2 \times 4^2 = 32$ m s^{-2}.

(d) When $t = 2$, $v = \frac{2}{3} \times 2^3 = 5\frac{1}{3}$ m s^{-1} and when
$t = 4$, $v = \frac{2}{3} \times 4^3 = 42\frac{2}{3}$ m s^{-1}.

The change in velocity $= 37\frac{1}{3}$ m s^{-1}.

$\therefore$ the average acceleration from $t = 2$ to $t = 4$ is

$$\frac{37\frac{1}{3}}{2} \text{ m s}^{-2} = 18\frac{2}{3} \text{ m s}^{-2}$$

Exercise 5c

1 A stone is thrown vertically upwards, and after t s its height is h m, where $h = 10.5t - 4.9t^2$. Determine, with particular attention to the signs, the height, velocity and acceleration of the stone (a) when $t = 1$, (b) when $t = 2$, and (c) when $t = 3$. Also state clearly in each case whether the stone is going up or down, and whether its speed is increasing or decreasing.

2 A stone is thrown downwards from the top of a cliff, and after t s it is s m below the top, where $s = 20t + 4.9t^2$. Find how far it has fallen, its velocity, and its acceleration at the end of the first second.

3 A ball is thrown vertically upwards and its height after t s is s m where $s = 25.2t - 4.9t^2$. Find:
   (a) its height and velocity after 3 s,
   (b) when it is momentarily at rest,
   (c) the greatest height reached,
   (d) the distance moved in the third second,
   (e) the acceleration when $t = 2\frac{4}{7}$.

4 A particle moves in a straight line so that after t s it is s m from a fixed point O on the line, where $s = t^4 + 3t^2$. Find:
   (a) the acceleration when $t = 1$, $t = 2$, and $t = 3$,
   (b) the average acceleration between $t = 1$ and $t = 3$.

5 At the instant from which time is measured a particle is passing through O and travelling towards A, along the straight line OA. It is s m from O after t s where $s = t(t - 2)^2$.
   (a) When is it again at O?
   (b) When and where is it momentarily at rest?
   (c) What is the particle's greatest displacement from O, and how far does it move, during the first 2 s?
   (d) What is the average velocity during the third second?
   (e) At the end of the first second where is the particle, which way is it going, and is its speed increasing or decreasing?

6 Repeat no. 5(e) for the instant when $t = -1$.

7 A particle moves along a straight line so that after t s its distance from O, a fixed point on the line, is s m where $s = t^3 - 3t^2 + 2t$.
   (a) When is the particle at O?
   (b) What is its velocity and acceleration at these times?
   (c) What is its average velocity during the first second?
   (d) What is its average acceleration between $t = 0$ and $t = 2$?

Exercise 5d (Miscellaneous)

1 The distance of a moving point from a fixed point in its straight line of motion is s m, at a time t s after the start. If $s = \frac{1}{10}t^2$, find the distances travelled from rest by the end of the 1st, 2nd, 3rd, 4th, and 5th seconds.

Draw a graph plotting distance against time, taking 2 cm to represent both 1 m and 1 s. Draw a tangent to your graph at the point where $t = 3.5$ and measure its gradient; deduce the velocity of the moving point when $t = 3.5$.

2 A point moves along a straight line so that, at the end of t s, its distance from a fixed point on the line is $t^3 - 2t^2 + t$ m. Find the velocity and acceleration at the end of 3 s.

3 A particle moves along the x-axis in such a way that its distance x cm from the origin after t s is given by the formula $x = 27t - 2t^2$. What are its velocity and acceleration after 6.75 s? How long does it take for the velocity to be reduced from 15 cm s^{-1} to 9 cm s^{-1}, and how far does the particle travel meanwhile?

4 A point moves along the x-axis so that its distance x cm from the point O at time t s is given by the formula $x = t^3 - 6t^2 + 9t$. Find:

(a) at what times and in what positions the point will have zero velocity,

(b) its acceleration at those instants,

. (c) its velocity when its acceleration is zero.

5 A particle moves in a straight line so that its distance x cm from a fixed point O on the line is given by $x = 9t^2 - 2t^3$ where t is the time in seconds measured from O. Find the speed of the particle when $t = 3$. Also find the distance from O of the particle when $t = 4$, and show that it is then moving towards O.

6 A particle moves along the x-axis in such a way that its distance x cm from the origin after t s is given by the formula $x = 7t + 12t^2$. What distance does it travel in the nth second? What are its velocity and acceleration at the end of the nth second?

Chapter 6

Maxima and minima

6.1 The symbols δ*x*, δ*y* and $\dfrac{\mathrm{d}y}{\mathrm{d}x}$

In Chapter 5, we met the symbols δ*s* and δ*t* and, to extend the scope of differentiation, it is convenient to denote small increases in *x* and *y* as δ*x* and δ*y* in the same way. If P is the point (*x*, *y*) on a curve, and Q is another point, and if the increase in *x* in moving from P to Q is δ*x*, then the corresponding increase in *y* is δ*y*; thus Q is the point (*x* + δ*x*, *y* + δ*y*) (Figure 6.1).

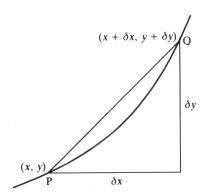

Figure 6.1

The gradient of the chord PQ is $\dfrac{\delta y}{\delta x}$, and the gradient of the curve at P is the limit of $\dfrac{\delta y}{\delta x}$, as δ*x*→0. Up to now, we have denoted this limit as grad *y* to keep in mind the fundamental idea of gradient in relation to differentiation. We will in future adopt the usual practice of writing this limit as $\dfrac{\mathrm{d}y}{\mathrm{d}x}$, the symbol

101

$\dfrac{d}{dx}$ being an instruction to differentiate.† Thus, if $y = x^2$, $\dfrac{dy}{dx} = 2x$; or we may write $\dfrac{d}{dx}(x^2) = 2x$. The gradient function will also be referred to in future as the *derived function*, or *derivative* (see Section 4.8).

Qu. 1 Find $\dfrac{dy}{dx}$ when

(a) $y = x^2 - 4x$ (b) $y = 3x^2 - 3$ (c) $y = 2x^3 - 5x^2 + 1$
(d) $y = x(x - 2)$ (e) $y = x(x + 1)(x - 3)$

The notation $\dfrac{dy}{dx}$ is often called *Leibnitz notation*, after Gottfried Leibnitz (1646–1716), who invented it.

6.2 Greatest and least values

Figure 6.2 represents the path of a stone thrown from O, reaching its greatest height AB, and striking the ground at C. Between O and A, when the stone is climbing, the gradient is positive but steadily decreases to zero at A. Past A the stone is descending, and the path has a negative gradient.

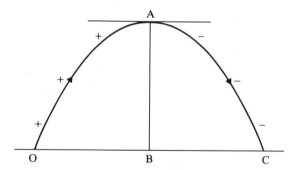

Figure 6.2

The curve $y = x^2$ of which we made much use earlier on, is called a parabola. A more general equation of this type of curve is of the form $y = ax^2 + bx + c$. When a is positive, we get a curve like a valley, such as DEF in Figure 6.3, on which y has a least value (GE); when a is negative, we get a curve like a mountain top, such as OAC in Figure 6.3, on which y has a greatest value (BA).

---

† This notation $\dfrac{d}{dx}$ serves to indicate that we are differentiating with respect to x. Thus $\dfrac{d}{dy}(y^3) = 3y^2$ and $\dfrac{d}{dt}(2t^2) = 4t$.

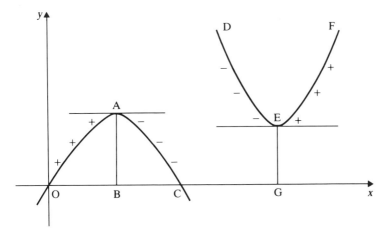

Figure 6.3

If we allow our eye to travel along each curve in Figure 6.3 from left to right (the direction in which x increases), we notice that in passing through A, where y has a greatest value, the gradient is zero and is changing sign *from positive to negative*; on the other hand in passing through E, where y has a least value, the gradient is zero and is changing sign *from negative to positive*. This distinction enables us to investigate the highest or lowest point on a parabola without going to the length of plotting the curve in detail.

Example 1

Find the greatest or least value of y on the curve $y = 4x - x^2$. Sketch the curve.

$$y = 4x - x^2$$
$$\frac{dy}{dx} = 4 - 2x$$
$$= 2(2 - x)$$

The gradient is zero when

$$2(2 - x) = 0$$
$$x = 2$$
and $\qquad y = 4 \times 2 - 2^2 = 4$

We must now investigate the sign of the gradient on either side of the point (2, 4) to discover whether it is a highest (Figure 6.4) or lowest (Figure 6.5) point on the curve. We look back to the gradient in the form $2(2 - x)$.

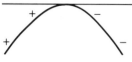

Figure 6.4

Figure 6.5

Just to the left of (2, 4), x is just less than 2, and $\frac{dy}{dx}$ is positive.

Just to the right of (2, 4), x is just greater than 2, and $\frac{dy}{dx}$ is negative.

Thus Figure 6.4 gives the shape of the curve at (2, 4), and the greatest value of y is $+4$.

To make a sketch of the curve, we find where it cuts the axes.

$$y = 4x - x^2$$

When $x = 0$,

$$y = 0$$

∴ the curve passes through (0, 0).

When $y = 0$,

$$4x - x^2 = 0$$
$$x(4 - x) = 0$$
$$x = 0 \text{ or } 4$$

∴ the curve passes through (0, 0) and (4, 0).

From this information we can make the sketch (Figure 6.6).

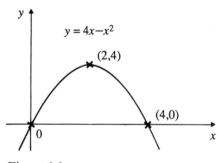

Figure 6.6

Qu. 2 Find the coordinates of the points on the following curves where the gradient is zero:

(a) $y = 4x - 2x^2$ (b) $y = 3x^2 + 2x - 5$ (c) $y = 4x^2 - 6x + 2$

At this stage the reader must be clear about the meaning of 'greater than' and 'less than' in respect of negative numbers. For example, -3.1 is *less* than -3, and -2.9 is *greater* than -3.

In Qu. 3 and Example 2, we use the notation $f'(x)$ for the derived function; it is a useful alternative to the $\dfrac{dy}{dx}$ notation and the reader should be prepared to use it.

Qu. 3 Find the values of x for which the following derived functions are zero, and determine whether the corresponding graphs have a highest or lowest point for these values of x:

(a) $f'(x) = 5 - 3x$ (b) $f'(x) = 6x - 7$
(c) $f'(x) = 2x + 3$ (d) $f'(x) = -4 - 5x$

The investigation of the sign of the gradient may be conveniently laid out in the way shown in the following example.

Example 2

Find the greatest or least value of the function $f(x) = x^2 + 4x + 3$ and the value of x for which it occurs.

$$f(x) = x^2 + 4x + 3$$
$$f'(x) = 2x + 4$$
$$= 2(x + 2)$$

The gradient is zero when $f'(x) = 0$, i.e. when $x = -2$ and

$$f(-2) = (-2)^2 + 4(-2) + 3 = -1$$

Value of x	L	-2	R	[L for 'left', R for 'right']
Sign of $f'(x)$	$-$	0	$+$	

When $x = -2$, $x^2 + 4x + 3$ has the least value -1.

This method can be used to solve some practical problems, as in the following example.

Example 3

1000 m of fencing is to be used to make a rectangular enclosure. Find the greatest possible area, and the corresponding dimensions.

If the length is x m, the width will be $(500 - x)$ m, and the area, A m^2, is given by

$$A = x(500 - x)$$
or $$A = 500x - x^2$$

[This problem could now be solved by drawing accurately the graph of area plotted against length (Figure 6.7), and reading off the greatest

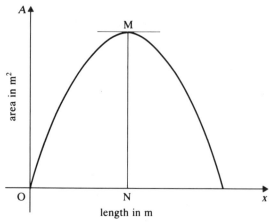

Figure 6.7

area (NM) and the corresponding length (ON). In practice it is, of course, much quicker to continue, along the lines of Example 2, by finding the greatest value of $500x - x^2$, without plotting a graph.]

$$\frac{dA}{dx} = 500 - 2x$$

$$= 2(250 - x)$$

which is zero when

$$x = 250$$
and $A = 250(500 - 250) = 62\ 500$

Value of x	L	250	R
Sign of $\dfrac{dA}{dx}$	+	0	−

The greatest area is 62 500 m², when the length is 250 m, and the width is 250 m.

Exercise 6a

1 Find $\dfrac{dy}{dx}$ when

(a) $y = 3x^2 - 2x + 5$ (b) $y = 5x^2 + 4x - 6$ (c) $y = 2x(1 - x)$
(d) $y = (x + 1)(3x - 2)$ (e) $y = 3(2x - 1)(4x + 3)$

2 Find the coordinates of the points on the following curves where the gradient is zero:

(a) $y = x^2 + 5x - 2$ (b) $y = 5 + 9x - 7x^2$
(c) $y = x(3x - 2)$ (d) $y = (2 + x)(3 - 4x)$

3 Find the values of x for which the following derived functions are zero, and determine whether the corresponding graphs have a highest or a lowest point for these values of x:

(a) $f'(x) = 2x - 5$ (b) $f'(x) = \frac{1}{2}x + 3$
(c) $f'(x) = \frac{1}{3} - \frac{1}{4}x$ (d) $f'(x) = -5 - \frac{1}{5}x$

4 Find the greatest or least values of the following functions:

(a) $x^2 - x - 2$ (b) $x(4 - x)$
(c) $15 + 2x - x^2$ (d) $(2x + 3)(x - 2)$

5 Sketch the graphs of the functions in no. 4.

6 A ball is thrown vertically upwards from ground level and its height after t s is $(15.4t - 4.9t^2)$ m. Find the greatest height it reaches, and the time it takes to get there.

7 A farmer has 100 m of metal railing with which to form two adjacent sides of a rectangular enclosure, the other two sides being two existing walls of the yard, meeting at right angles. What dimensions will give him the maximum possible area?

8 A stone is thrown into a mud bank and penetrates $(1200t - 36\,000t^2)$ cm in t s after impact. Calculate the maximum depth of penetration.

9 A rectangular sheep pen is to be made out of 1000 m of fencing, using an existing straight hedge for one of the sides. Find the maximum area possible, and the dimensions necessary to achieve this.

10 An aeroplane flying level at 250 m above the ground suddenly swoops down to drop supplies, and then regains its former altitude. It is h m above the ground t s after beginning its dive, where $h = 8t^2 - 80t + 250$. Find its least altitude during this operation, and the interval of time during which it was losing height.

11 Figure 6.8 represents the end view of the outer cover of a match box, AB and EF being gummed together, and assumed to be the same length. If the total length of edge (ABCDEF) is 12 cm, calculate the lengths of AB and BC which will give the maximum possible cross-section area.

Figure 6.8

6.3 To differentiate the function $f(x) = x^{-1}$

In Section 4.6 we reached the conclusion that if $f(x) = x^n$, where $n \in \mathbb{Z}^+$, then $f'(x) = nx^{n-1}$, although we only *proved* that this was so for $n = 1, 2, 3$ and 4. In this section we shall prove that it is also true when $n = -1$, that is, we shall prove that if $f(x) = 1/x = x^{-1}$, then $f'(x) = -x^{-2} = -1/x^2$. We start by quoting the expression for $f'(x)$ in Section 4.8,

$$f'(x) = \lim_{h \to 0} \frac{f(x+h) - f(x)}{h}$$

Now, in this case,

$$
\begin{aligned}
f(x+h) - f(x) &= \frac{1}{x+h} - \frac{1}{x} \\
&= \frac{x - (x+h)}{(x+h)x} \\
&= \frac{-h}{x(x+h)}
\end{aligned}
$$

Hence

$$\frac{f(x+h) - f(x)}{h} = \frac{-1}{x(x+h)}$$

and thus

$$
\begin{aligned}
f'(x) &= \lim_{h \to 0} \frac{-1}{x(x+h)} \\
&= -\frac{1}{x^2} \\
&= -x^{-2}
\end{aligned}
$$

We have proved that if $f(x) = x^{-1}$, then $f'(x) = -x^{-2}$ and this verifies that the general result, namely that if $f(x) = x^n$, then $f'(x) = nx^{n-1}$, is true when $n = -1$. We shall now assume that it is true for $n \in \mathbb{Z}$, that is when n is a positive or negative integer, or zero.†

Qu. 4 Write down the derivative of

(a) x^{-4} (b) $\dfrac{3}{x^2}$ (c) $\dfrac{2}{x^3}$ (d) $\dfrac{1}{2x^3}$ (e) $\dfrac{1}{x^m}$

(f) $2x^2 - 3x + 4 + \dfrac{5}{x}$ (g) $\dfrac{x^3 + 3x - 4}{x^2}$

---

† $n = 0$ is a special case. The rule suggests that the gradient of $y = x^0$ is zero. Now $x^0 = 1$, (see Section 10.4) so the graph of $y = x^0$ is a straight line parallel to the x-axis, i.e. its gradient is zero. Consequently the result predicted by the rule is correct.

6.4 Maxima and minima

In Section 6.2 we were dealing with a type of curve whose gradient was zero only at one point. With a more complicated curve (Figure 6.9) the gradient may be zero at a number of points, and the possible shapes fall into three categories. In this case, moving along the curve from left to right, that is with x increasing,

(a) at A and D, the gradient is changing from negative to positive, and these are called **minimum points**; FA and HD are **minimum values** of y (or **minima**),
(b) at B and E, the gradient is changing from positive to negative, and these are called **maximum points**; GB and JE are **maximum values** of y (or **maxima**).

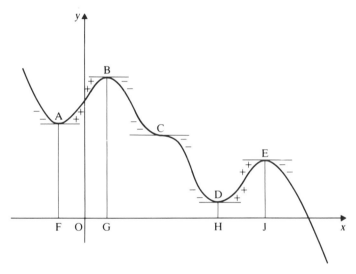

Figure 6.9

The reader will note that the words maximum and minimum are used in the sense of greatest and least only in the immediate vicinity of the point; this local meaning is brought out clearly in this curve, since a maximum value, JE, is in fact less than a minimum value, FA, and for this reason the expressions *local* maximum and *local* minimum are often used.

(c) At C the gradient is zero, but is *not* changing sign; this is a **point of inflexion**, which may be likened to the point on an S-bend at which a road stops turning left and begins to turn right, or vice versa. The gradient of a curve at a point of inflexion need not be zero (the reader should be able to spot four more in Figure 6.9); however at this stage we are concerned only with searching for maxima and minima, and we need to bear in mind points of inflexion only as a third possibility at points where the gradient is zero.

At any point where the gradient of a curve is zero, y is said to have a **stationary value**. Any maximum or minimum point is called a **turning point**, and y is said to have a **turning value** there.

Qu. 5 Copy Figures 6.10–6.12, and on each draw the tangents at all points where the gradient is zero, and mark in the sign of the gradient for each segment of the curve. State whether the points marked are maxima, minima, or points of inflexion.

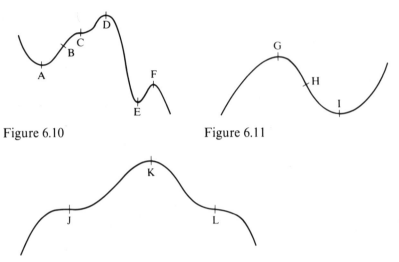

Figure 6.10   Figure 6.11

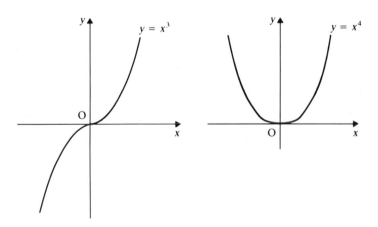

Figure 6.12

Consider the functions $f(x) = x^3$ and $g(x) = x^4$; sketches of their graphs are shown in Figure 6.13.

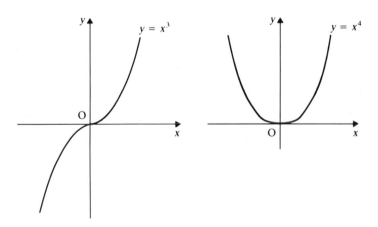

Figure 6.13

The derived functions are $f'(x) = 3x^2$ and $g'(x) = 4x^3$ and, in both cases, the derivative is zero when $x = 0$; this is confirmed by the graphs which both have zero gradient at the origin. Notice, however, that $f'(x) = 3x^2$ is never negative, which is in accordance with the observation that the graph of $y = x^3$ (see Figure 6.13) always slopes upwards to the right, and has a point of inflexion at $(0, 0)$. On the other hand, $g'(x)$ is negative for $x < 0$ and positive for $x > 0$. This also is in accordance with the graph of $y = x^4$ (see Figure 6.13) which slopes downwards on the left and upwards on the right, and has a local minimum at $(0, 0)$.

Example 4

Investigate the stationary values of the function $x^4 - 4x^3$.†

Let $y = x^4 - 4x^3$

$$\frac{dy}{dx} = 4x^3 - 12x^2$$

$$= 4x^2(x - 3)$$

which is zero when $x = 0$ or $+3$.

When $x = 0$, $y = 0$, and when $x = 3$, $y = -27$. Thus the stationary values of the function occur at $(0, 0)$ and at $(+3, -27)$.

[We now find the shape of the curve at these points by investigating the sign of the gradient just to the left and just to the right of each. Looking back to the factorised form of $\frac{dy}{dx}$, we see that $4x^2$ is positive for all values of x other than zero, so we are concerned with the sign of the factor $x - 3$ only.

When x is just less than 0, $x - 3$ is negative, and when x is just greater than 0, $x - 3$ is negative. When x is just less than $+3$, $x - 3$ is negative, and when x is just greater than $+3$, $x - 3$ is positive.

These signs are entered in the table.]

Value of x	L	0	R	L	$+3$	R
Sign of $\dfrac{dy}{dx}$	$-$	0	$-$	$-$	0	$+$

                          infl.   min.

The stationary values of $x^4 - 4x^3$ are 0 and -27; $(0, 0)$ is a point of inflexion; $(3, -27)$ is a minimum point.

---

† The wording of this example illustrates that questions will often not specify the symbol for the dependent variable. The solution to such a question should normally start with a phrase like 'Let $y = x^4 - 4x^3$', as in this example, or, alternatively, 'Let $f(x) = \dots$'.

The following example further illustrates the advisability of arranging the gradient function in a convenient factorised form, and brings out an important point in the investigation of the sign of the gradient for negative values of x.

Example 5

Find the turning values of y on the graph $y = f(x)$, where

$$f(x) = 5 + 24x - 9x^2 - 2x^3$$

and distinguish between them.

$$f(x) = 5 + 24x - 9x^2 - 2x^3$$
$$f'(x) = 24 - 18x - 6x^2 = -6(x^2 + 3x - 4)$$
$$= -6(x + 4)(x - 1)$$

which is zero when $x = -4$ or 1.
When $x = -4$:

$$y = 5 + 24 \times (-4) - 9 \times (-4)^2 - 2 \times (-4)^3 = -107$$

and when $x = 1$:

$$y = 5 + 24 - 9 - 2 = 18$$

Thus the stationary values of y occur at $(-4, -107)$ and $(1, 18)$.

[In completing the gradient table we must remember the negative factor -6, and find the sign of each factor $(x + 4)$ and $(x - 1)$; we shall then see if there are one, two or three negative factors, and so determine the sign of $f'(x)$.

Let us pay particular attention to the point $(-4, -107)$, and the sign of the factor $(x + 4)$. To the *left*, when x is just *less* than -4 (e.g. -4.1), $(x + 4)$ is negative, $(x - 1)$ is also negative, thus $f'(x)$ has three negative factors and is negative. To the *right*, when x is just greater than -4 (e.g. -3.9), $(x + 4)$ is now positive, $(x - 1)$ is still negative, thus $f'(x)$ has two negative factors, and is positive.]

Value of x	L	-4	R	L	1	R
Sign of $f'(x)$	$-$	0	$+$	$+$	0	$-$

                    min.   max.

The turning values of y are -107 and 18; -107 is a minimum value; 18 is a maximum value.

Exercise 6b

1 Write down the values of x for which the following derived functions are zero, and prepare in each case a gradient table as in the foregoing examples, showing whether the corresponding points on the graph are maxima, minima or points of inflexion:

(a) $f'(x) = 3x^2$ (b) $f'(x) = -4x^3$
(c) $f'(x) = (x - 2)(x - 3)$ (d) $f'(x) = (x + 3)(x - 5)$
(e) $f'(x) = (x + 1)(x + 6)$ (f) $f'(x) = -(x - 1)(x - 3)$
(g) $f'(x) = -x^2 + x + 12$ (h) $f'(x) = -x^2 - 5x + 6$
(i) $f'(x) = 15 - 2x - x^2$ (j) $f'(x) = 5x^4 - 27x^2$
(k) $f'(x) = 1 - 4/x^2$

2 Find any maximum or minimum values of the following functions:

(a) $f(x) = 4x - 3x^3$ (b) $f(x) = 2x^3 - 3x^2 - 12x - 7$
(c) $f(x) = x^2(x - 4)$ (d) $f(x) = x + 1/x$
(e) $f(x) = x(2x - 3)(x - 4)$

3 Find the turning points on the following curves, and state whether y has a maximum or minimum value at each:

(a) $y = x(x^2 - 12)$ (b) $y = x^3 - 5x^2 + 3x + 2$
(c) $y = x^2(3 - x)$ (d) $y = 4x^2 + 1/x$
(e) $y = x(x - 8)(x - 15)$

4 Investigate the stationary values of y on the following curves:

(a) $y = x^4$ (b) $y = 3 - x^3$
(c) $y = x^3(2 - x)$ (d) $y = 3x^4 + 16x^3 + 24x^2 + 3$

5 Figure 6.14 represents a rectangular sheet of metal 8 cm by 5 cm. Equal squares of side x cm are removed from each corner, and the edges are then turned up to make an open box of volume V cm³. Show that $V = 40x - 26x^2 + 4x^3$. Hence find the maximum possible volume, and the corresponding value of x.

Figure 6.14

6 Repeat no. 5 when the dimensions of the sheet of metal are 8 cm by 3 cm, showing that in this case $V = 24x - 22x^2 + 4x^3$.

7 The size of a parcel despatched through the post used to be limited by the fact that the sum of its length and girth (perimeter of cross-section) must not exceed 6 feet. What was the volume of the largest parcel of square cross-section which was acceptable for posting? (Let the cross-section be a square of side x feet.)

8 Repeat no. 7 for a parcel of circular cross-section, leaving π in your answer.

9 A chemical factory wishes to make a cylindrical container, of thin metal, to hold 10 m³, using the least possible area of metal. If the outside surface is S m², and the radius is r m, show that $S = 2\pi r^2 + 20/r$ and hence find the required radius and height for the container. (Leave π in your answer.)

10 Repeat no. 9 showing that whatever may be the given volume, the area of metal will always be least when the height is twice the radius.

6.5 Curve sketching

We have seen in Section 6.4 how maxima and minima problems may be solved without direct use of the relevant graph. Frequently however the determination of maximum and minimum points is a valuable aid in sketching a curve. (See Section 3.12 for a note on the difference between *sketching* and *plotting* a curve.)

Example 6

Sketch the curve $y = 4x^3 - 3x^4$.

(a) To find where the curve meets the x-axis, put $y = 0$, then:

$$4x^3 - 3x^4 = 0$$
$$\therefore \quad x^3(4 - 3x) = 0$$

Therefore the curve meets the x-axis at the points $(0, 0)$ and $(\frac{4}{3}, 0)$.

(b) To find where the curve meets the y-axis, put $x = 0$. The curve meets the y-axis at the origin.

(c) To find stationary points:

$$y = 4x^3 - 3x^4$$
$$\therefore \quad \frac{dy}{dx} = 12x^2 - 12x^3$$
$$= 12x^2(1 - x)$$

which is zero when $x = 0$ or 1.

Therefore $(0, 0)$ and $(1, 1)$ are stationary points.

Value of x	L	0	R	L	1	R
Sign of $\dfrac{dy}{dx}$	+	0	+	+	0	−

infl.   max.

Hence $(0, 0)$ is a point of inflexion and $(1, 1)$ is a maximum.

These results may now be used to sketch the curve, as in Figure 6.15.

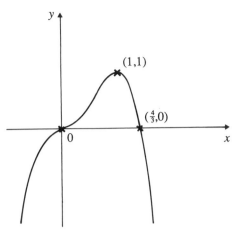

Figure 6.15

Exercise 6c

Find where the following curves meet the axes. Find, also, the coordinates of their stationary points and use these results to sketch the curves.

1 $y = 3x^2 - x^3$ **2** $y = x^3 - 6x^2$ **3** $y = x^3 - 2x^2 + x$
4 $y = (x + 1)^2(2 - x)$ **5** $y = x^2(x - 2)^2$ **6** $y = x^4 - 8x^3$
7 $y = x^4 - 10x^2 + 9$ **8** $y = x^4 + 32x$ **9** $y = 4x^5 - 5x^4$
10 $y = 3x^5 - 5x^3$

Another useful approach to curve sketching is shown in the next example.

Example 7

Sketch the curve $y = (x + 1)(x - 1)(2 - x)$.

(a) To find where the curve meets the x-axis, put $y = 0$, then

$$(x + 1)(x - 1)(2 - x) = 0$$

Therefore the curve meets the x-axis at $(-1, 0), (1, 0), (2, 0)$.

(b) To find where the curve meets the y-axis, put $x = 0$. Thus the curve meets the y-axis at $(0, -2)$.

(c) To examine the behaviour of the curve 'at infinity', expand the RHS of the equation:

$$y = (x^2 - 1)(2 - x) = -x^3 + 2x^2 + x - 2$$

Now, if x is large, the sign of y will be determined by the term of highest degree, $-x^3$. (If $x = 100$, $y = -1\,000\,000 + 20\,000 + 100 - 2$; or if $x = -100$, $y = 1\,000\,000 + 20\,000 - 100 - 2$. In either case the term in x^3 predominates.)

If x is large and positive, y is large and negative, and if x is large and negative, y is large and positive. Thus the behaviour of the curve as $x \rightarrow +\infty$ and $x \rightarrow -\infty$ is illustrated by Figure 6.16.

The curve is then sketched, as in Figure 6.17.

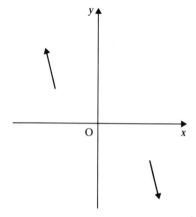

Figure 6.16   Figure 6.17

6.6 Displacement, velocity and acceleration graphs

Useful physical interpretations of the graphical ideas discussed in Section 6.4 are obtained from the displacement–time, velocity–time, and acceleration–time graphs for the motion of a particle, if we plot one above the other as in the following example.

Example 8

O is a point on a straight line. A particle moves along the line so that it is s m from O, t s after a certain instant, where $s = t(t-2)^2$. Describe the motion before and after $t = 0$.

The *displacement–time graph* has the equation $s = t(t-2)^2$. By the methods of Section 6.5 we may determine that the graph has a maximum point $(\frac{2}{3}, \frac{32}{27})$, a minimum point $(2, 0)$, and passes through $(0, 0)$. We thus arrive at the upper sketch in Figure 6.18.

The equation may be written $s = t^3 - 4t^2 + 4t$.

$$\therefore \quad \frac{ds}{dt} = 3t^2 - 8t + 4 = (3t-2)(t-2)$$

Hence the *velocity–time graph* has the equation $v = (3t-2)(t-2)$. This graph has a minimum point $(1\frac{1}{3}, -1\frac{1}{3})$, and passes through $(\frac{2}{3}, 0)$, $(2, 0)$, and $(0, 4)$; it is the middle sketch in Figure 6.18.

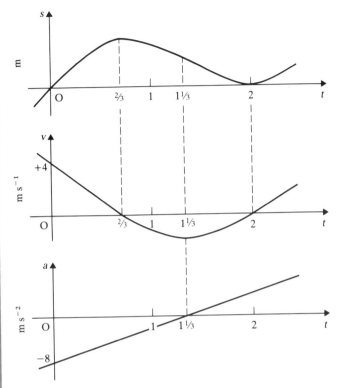

Figure 6.18

Differentiating once again, $\dfrac{dv}{dt} = 6t - 8$, and so the *acceleration–time*

graph has the equation $a = 6t - 8$, and is the bottom sketch in Figure 6.18.

Notice that the local maximum and minimum values of s occur

when v $\left(\text{i.e. } \dfrac{ds}{dt}\right)$ is zero, and that the local minimum value of v occurs

when a $\left(\text{i.e. } \dfrac{dv}{dt}\right)$ is zero.

It is easy to visualise the motion of the particle as being along the Os axis of the displacement–time graph, its displacement from O at any instant being given by the height of the graph for the corresponding value of t. Before $t = 0$, the particle is approaching O from the negative side; at $t = 0$, it is passing through O with velocity 4 m s^{-1}, and acceleration -8 m s^{-2}, hence its speed is decreasing. It comes momentarily to rest $\frac{32}{27}$ m from O (on the positive side) when $t = \frac{2}{3}$; it returns to O, where it is momentarily at rest when $t = 2$, and thereafter it moves away from O in the positive direction.

Some further points regarding the sign and direction of the velocity and acceleration deserve emphasis. Consider the three graphs between $t = 0$ and

$t = 1\frac{1}{3}$; throughout this interval the acceleration is negative, and the velocity decreases from $+4 \text{ m s}^{-1}$ to $-1\frac{1}{3} \text{ m s}^{-1}$. The effect of the negative acceleration is to *decrease* the speed when the velocity is positive ($t = 0$ to $t = \frac{2}{3}$), and to *increase* the speed when the velocity is negative ($t = \frac{2}{3}$ to $t = 1\frac{1}{3}$). The reader should note the distinction between the *speed* and the *velocity*, the speed being the numerical value of the velocity, irrespective of direction. See section 5.2.

Qu. 6 In Example 8, give the signs of the velocity, and acceleration, and state if the speed is increasing or decreasing, when
(a) $t = 1\frac{1}{2}$ (b) $t = 3$ (c) $t = 1\frac{1}{3}$

Exercise 6d

1 Make a sketch of each of the following curves by finding the points of intersection with the axes, and by investigating the behaviour of y as $x \to +\infty$ and as $x \to -\infty$. (Do *not* find maximum and minimum points.)
(a) $y = (x + 2)(x - 3)$ (b) $y = (5 + x)(1 - x)$
(c) $y = x(x + 1)(x + 2)$ (d) $y = (2 + x)(1 + x)(3 - x)$
(e) $y = (x - 1)(x - 3)^2$ (f) $y = (x + 4)^2(x - 3)$
(g) $y = -x(x - 7)^2$ (h) $y = x^2(5 - x)$
(i) $y = (x - 2)^3$ (j) $y = (x - 3)^4$
(k) $y = -x(x - 4)^3$

2 A particle moves along a straight line OB so that t s after passing O it is s m from O, where $s = t(2t - 3)(t - 4)$. Deduce expressions for the velocity and acceleration in terms of t, and sketch the displacement–, velocity–, and acceleration–time graphs as in Figure 6.18. Briefly describe the motion, and when $t = 2$ find
(a) where the particle is,
(b) if it is going towards or away from B,
(c) its speed,
(d) if its speed is increasing or decreasing,
(e) the rate of change of the speed.

3 Answer the questions in no. 2 for the instant when $t = 1$.

4 With the data of no. 2, when is the particle moving at its greatest speed away from B, and where is it then?

5 A particle is moving along a straight line OA is such a way that t s after passing through O for the first time it is s m from O where

$$s = -t(t - 8)(t - 15)$$

A is taken to be on the positive side of O. Deduce expressions for the velocity and acceleration in terms of t, and sketch the three graphs as in Figure 6.18. Briefly describe the motion.
(a) Describe in detail the motion and position of the particle when $t = 10$.
(b) When is it moving towards A?
(c) When is it travelling at its greatest speed towards A?

6 A car in a traffic jam starts from rest with constant acceleration 2 m s^{-2}, and when its velocity reaches 6 m s^{-1} it remains constant at that figure for

4 s, and it is then reduced to zero in 6 s at a constant retardation. Sketch the displacement–, velocity–, and acceleration–time graphs for this motion.

Exercise 6e (Miscellaneous)

1 Find the coordinates of the points on the following curves at which y is a local maximum or a local minimum:

(a) $y = x^3 - 6x^2 + 9x + 2$ (b) $y = 2x^3 - 3x^2 - 12x + 8$
(c) $y = x^3 - 3x$ (d) $y = 4x^3 - 3x^2 - 6x + 4$
(e) $y = x^2(x^2 - 8)$ (f) $y = 2(x + 1)(x - 1)^2 + 1$

2 Find the turning points of the graph $y = 2x^3 + 3x^2 - 12x + 7$, distinguishing between maximum and minimum values. Show that the graph passes through $(1, 0)$ and one other point on the x-axis. Draw a sketch of the curve.

3 If $y = x^4 - 2x^2 + 1$, find the values of x for which y is a minimum and draw a sketch of the curve.

4 The equation of a curve is $y = x^3 - x^4 - 1$. Has y a maximum or a minimum value when

(a) $x = \frac{3}{4}$ (b) $x = 0$?

5 Prove that there are two points on the curve $y = 2x^2 - x^4$ at which y has a maximum value, and one point at which y has a minimum value. Give the equations of the tangents to the curve at these three points.

6 A point P, whose x-coordinate is a, is taken on the line $y = 3x - 7$. If Q is the point $(4, 1)$ show that $PQ^2 = 10a^2 - 56a + 80$. Find the value of a which will make this expression a minimum. Hence show that the coordinates of N, the foot of the perpendicular from Q to the line, are $(2\frac{4}{5}, 1\frac{2}{5})$. Find the equation of QN.

7 The tangent to the curve $y = ax^2 + bx + c$ at the point where $x = 2$ is parallel to the line $y = 4x$. Given that y has a minimum value of -3 where $x = 1$ find the values of a, b and c.

8 Find the equation of the tangent to the curve $xy = 4$ at the point P whose coordinates are $(2t, 2/t)$. If O is the origin and the tangent at P meets the x-axis at A and the y-axis at B, prove

(a) that P is the mid-point of AB,
(b) that the area of the triangle OAB is the same for all positions of P.

9 Find the equations of the normals to the curve $xy = 4$ which are parallel to the line $4x - y - 2 = 0$.

10 A solid rectangular block has a square base. Find its maximum volume if the sum of the height and any one side of the base is 12 cm.

11 A man wishes to fence in a rectangular enclosure of area 128 m². One side of the enclosure is formed by part of a brick wall already in position. What is the least possible length of fencing required for the other three sides?

12 The angle C of triangle ABC is always a right angle.

(a) If the sum of CA and CB is 6 cm, find the maximum area of the triangle.
(b) If, on the other hand, the hypotenuse AB is kept equal to 4 cm, and the sides CA, CB allowed to vary, find the maximum area of the triangle.

13 A piece of wire of length l is cut into two parts of lengths x and $l - x$. The former is bent into the shape of a square, and the latter into a rectangle of which the base is double the height. Find an expression for the sum of the areas of these two figures. Prove that the only value of x for which this sum is a maximum or a minimum is $x = 8l/17$, and find which it is.

14 A farmer has a certain length of fencing and uses it all to fence in two square sheep-folds. Prove that the sum of the areas of the two folds is least when their sides are equal.

15 Prove that, if the sum of the radii of two circles remains constant, the sum of the areas of the circles is least when the circles are equal.

16 An open tank is to be constructed with a horizontal square base and four vertical rectangular sides. It is to have a capacity of 32 m^3. Find the least area of sheet metal of which it can be made.

17 A sealed cylindrical jam tin is of height h cm and radius r cm. The area of its total outer surface is $A \text{ cm}^2$ and its volume is $V \text{ cm}^3$. Find an expression for A in terms of r and h. Taking $A = 24\pi$, find
  (a) an expression for h in terms of r, and hence an expression for V in terms of r,
  (b) the value of r which will make V a maximum.

18 (a) A variable rectangle has a constant perimeter of 20 cm. Find the lengths of the sides when the area is a maximum.
  (b) A variable rectangle has a constant area 36 cm^2. Find the lengths of the sides when the perimeter is a minimum.

19 A cylinder is such that the sum of its height and the circumference of its base is 5 m. Express the volume $(V \text{ m}^3)$ in terms of the radius of the base $(r \text{ m})$. What is the greatest volume of the cylinder?

20 An open tank is to be constructed with a square base and vertical sides so as to contain 500 m^3 of water. What must be the dimensions if the area of sheet metal used in its construction is to be a minimum?

Chapter 7

Integration

7.1 The reverse of differentiation — geometrical interpretation

Suppose that instead of an equation of a curve, we take as our starting point a gradient function. For example, what is represented geometrically by the equation $\frac{dy}{dx} = \frac{1}{3}$?

The constant gradient $\frac{1}{3}$ indicates a straight line; $y = \frac{1}{3}x$ is the equation of the straight line of this gradient through the origin, and, on differentiation, it leads to $\frac{dy}{dx} = \frac{1}{3}$. But $y = \frac{1}{3}x$ is not the only possibility; any straight line of gradient $\frac{1}{3}$ may be written as $y = \frac{1}{3}x + c$, where c is a constant, and this is the most general equation which gives $\frac{dy}{dx} = \frac{1}{3}$.

Thus the equation $\frac{dy}{dx} = \frac{1}{3}$ represents the same as the equation $y = \frac{1}{3}x + c$, namely *all straight lines of gradient* $\frac{1}{3}$ (Figure 7.1).

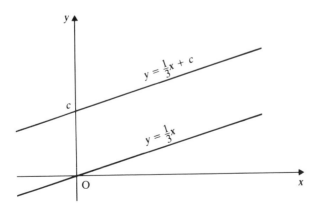

Figure 7.1

Let us take another example, $\dfrac{dy}{dx} = 2x$. We know that $y = x^2$ is a curve with this gradient function; but the most general equation leading to $\dfrac{dy}{dx} = 2x$ on differentiation is $y = x^2 + c$, where c is a constant.

Thus the equation $\dfrac{dy}{dx} = 2x$ represents the same as the equation $y = x^2 + c$, namely the family of curves 'parallel' to $y = x^2$ (see Figure 4.8 on page 80).

We have found that

if $\dfrac{dy}{dx} = \frac{1}{3}$ then $y = \frac{1}{3}x + c$

Also

if $\dfrac{dy}{dx} = 2x$ then $y = x^2 + c$

This process of finding the expression for y in terms of x when given the gradient function – in other words, the reverse of differentiation – is called **integration**.

$x^2 + c$ is called the **integral** of $2x$ with respect to x

The constant c, which, unless further data is given, cannot be determined, is called the **arbitrary constant** of integration.

We know that when we differentiate a power of x, the index is reduced by 1, since $\dfrac{d}{dx}(x^n) = nx^{n-1}$. In this reverse process of integration we must therefore increase the index by 1, thus

if $\dfrac{dy}{dx} = x$ then $y = \dfrac{x^2}{2} + c$

and

if $\dfrac{dy}{dx} = 5x^2$ then $y = 5 \times \dfrac{x^3}{3} + c$

The reader should check these by differentiating, and it will then be clear why the denominators 2 and 3 arise. The rule for integrating a power of x is seen to be: 'increase the index by 1 and divide by the new index'.

Qu. 1 Integrate with respect to x:
(a) 2   (b) m (c) $3x^2$ (d) $3x$
(e) $3x^4$ (f) $3 + 2x$ (g) $x - x^2$ (h) $ax + b$

Just as we have assumed that the rule for differentiating x^n is valid for $n \in \mathbb{Z}$, i.e. when n is any integer, positive or negative, so we shall make a similar assumption about the rule for integrating x^n, with the notable exception of x^{-1}.

In other words, for all positive and negative integral values of n, other than -1,

$$\text{if } \frac{dy}{dx} = x^n \text{ then } y = \frac{x^{n+1}}{n+1} + c$$

Thus if $\frac{dy}{dx} = 1/x^2 = x^{-2}$ then:

$$y = \frac{x^{-2+1}}{-2+1} + c = \frac{x^{-1}}{-1} + c = -\frac{1}{x} + c$$

The reader should check this last result by differentiating, and in fact should make a habit of doing this always. It is important to remember that the arbitrary constant is an essential part of each integral.

Qu. 2 Integrate with respect to x:

(a) $\dfrac{1}{x^3}$ (b) x^{-4} (c) $\dfrac{2}{x^2}$

Qu. 3 Why is the rule for integrating not valid when $n = -1$?

Reverting to our earlier examples, $\frac{dy}{dx} = \frac{1}{3}$ and $\frac{dy}{dx} = 2x$ are called **differential equations**, and $y = \frac{1}{3}x + c$ and $y = x^2 + c$ respectively are the **general solutions**. We saw that the differential equation $\frac{dy}{dx} = \frac{1}{3}$ represents all straight lines of gradient $\frac{1}{3}$; to be able to find the equation of a particular straight line of gradient $\frac{1}{3}$, we must find the appropriate value of c in the general solution $y = \frac{1}{3}x + c$, and to do this we need to know one point through which the line passes.

Qu. 4 $\dfrac{dy}{dx} = 4$. Find y in terms of x, given that $y = 10$ when $x = -2$. What does the solution represent graphically?

Exercise 7a

1 Integrate:

(a) with respect to x: $\frac{1}{2}$, $\frac{1}{2}x^2$, $x^2 + 3x$, $(2x+3)^2$, x^{-5}, $\dfrac{-2}{x^4}$

(b) with respect to t: at, $\frac{1}{3}t^3$, $(t+1)(t-2)$, $\dfrac{1}{t^{n+1}}$, $\dfrac{1}{t^2} + 3 + 2t$

(c) with respect to y: $-ay^{-2}$, $\dfrac{k}{y^2}$, $\dfrac{(y^2+2)(y^2-3)}{y^2}$

2 Solve the following differential equations:

(a) $\dfrac{dy}{dx} = 3ax^2$ (b) $\dfrac{ds}{dt} = 3t^3$

(c) $\dfrac{ds}{dt} = u + at$ (d) $\dfrac{dx}{dt} = \left(1 + \dfrac{1}{t}\right)\left(1 - \dfrac{1}{t}\right)$

(e) $\dfrac{dy}{dt} = \dfrac{t^3 - 3t + 4}{t^3}$ (f) $\dfrac{dA}{dx} = \dfrac{(1 + x^2)(1 - 2x^2)}{x^2}$

3 What is the gradient function of a straight line passing through $(-4, 5)$ and $(2, 6)$? Find the equation of the line.

4 A curve passes through the point $(3, -1)$ and its gradient function is $2x + 5$. Find its equation.

5 A curve passes through the point $(2, 0)$ and its gradient function is $3x^2 - 1/x^2$. Find its equation.

6 The gradient of a curve at the point (x, y) is $3x^2 - 8x + 3$. If it passes through the origin, find the other points of intersection with the x-axis.

7 The gradient of a curve at the point (x, y) is $8x - 3x^2$, and it passes through the origin. Find where it cuts the x-axis, and find the equation of the tangent parallel to the x-axis.

8 Find s in terms·of t if $\dfrac{ds}{dt} = 3t - 8/t^2$, given that $s = 1\frac{1}{2}$ when $t = 1$.

9 Find A in terms of x if $\dfrac{dA}{dx} = (3x + 1)(x^2 - 1)/x^5$. What is the value of A when $x = 2$, if $A = 0$ when $x = 1$?

7.2 Velocity and acceleration

In Chapter 5 we used the formula $s = 4.9t^2$ for a stone falling from rest, and it was explained that this is based on the assumption that the acceleration of the stone is 9.8 metres per second per second, or $9.8\ \text{m s}^{-2}$. We are now in a position to see how the formula is deduced from this assumption by the process of integration.

If the acceleration is given by

$$\frac{dv}{dt} = 9.8$$

then

$$v = 9.8t + c$$

Now if the stone falls from rest at the instant from which we measure the time, $v = 0$ when $t = 0$, and substituting these values in the last equation we get $c = 0$.

$$\therefore \quad v = 9.8t$$

This may be written

$$\frac{ds}{dt} = 9.8t$$

from which

$$s = 4.9t^2 + k$$

If s measures the distance below the initial position of the stone, $s = 0$ when $t = 0$, and substituting these values in the last equation, we get $k = 0$.

$$\therefore \quad s = 4.9t^2$$

Qu. 5 A stone is thrown vertically downwards from the top of a cliff at 15 m s^{-1}. Assuming that its acceleration due to gravity is 9.8 m s^{-2}, find expressions for its velocity and position t s later, by solving the differential equation $\frac{dv}{dt} = 9.8$.

It again needs emphasising that displacement, velocity and acceleration in a straight line are positive in one direction, negative in the other (see Section 5.2), and it is important to decide at the outset which is to be taken as the positive direction. The reader should take upwards as positive in Qu. 6.

Qu. 6 A stone is thrown vertically upwards from the edge of a cliff at 19.6 m s^{-1}. Assuming that gravity produces a downwards acceleration of 9.8 m s^{-2}, deduce the velocity and position of the stone after 1, 3 and 5 s. Explain the sign of each answer, taking upwards as positive.

Example 1

Figure 7.2 represents part of a conveyor belt, the dots being small articles on it at 1 m spacing. Initially the belt is at rest with the article R 7 m short of O, a fixed mark on a wall. The belt is accelerated from rest so that its velocity is $0.1t$ m s^{-1}, t s after starting. Find (a) the position of R when $t = 10$ and (b) the distance moved by R between $t = 3$ and $t = 5$.

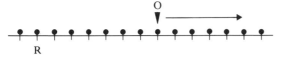

O

R

Figure 7.2

(a) If the distance from O at time t s is s m (positive to the right of O, negative to the left), then it is true of each article that its velocity, $\frac{ds}{dt} = 0.1t$, and also, by integration, that

$$s = 0.05t^2 + c$$

However, this last equation does not give us the distance of any particular article from O, until we have discovered the appropriate value of c. Since when $t = 0$, $s = c$, the arbitrary constant of integration in this case represents the initial position of an article.

In the case of R, when $t = 0$,

$$s = -7$$

Substituting in the last equation, $-7 = 0 + c$,

$$\therefore \quad c = -7$$

Therefore the distance of R from O at time t s is s m where

$$s = 0{\cdot}05t^2 - 7$$

When $t = 10$,

$$s = 0.05 \times 100 - 7 = -2$$

$\therefore$ R is 2 m short of O at this instant.

(b) The distance moved by each article in any given interval is the same, therefore we are not concerned with any particular numerical value for the constant of integration, and we shall leave c in our working.

As before, since $\dfrac{ds}{dt} = 0.1t$,

$$s = 0.05t^2 + c$$

When $t = 3$,

$$s = 0.05 \times 3^2 + c$$

When $t = 5$,

$$s = 0.05 \times 5^2 + c$$

The distance moved between $t = 3$ and $t = 5$ is

$$(0.05 \times 5^2 + c) - (0.05 \times 3^2 + c)$$
$$= 0.05 \times 25 + c - 0.05 \times 9 - c$$
$$= 0.8 \text{ m}$$

Notation

Square brackets are frequently used in integration to mean:

$$[F(x)]_a^b = F(b) - F(a)$$

e.g. $\left[x^2 \right]_3^5 = 25 - 9 = 16$

Using this notation, the solution to (b) can be written

$$\frac{ds}{dt} = 0.1t$$

$$\therefore \quad s = 0.05t^2 + c$$

The distance moved between $t = 3$ and $t = 5$ is

$$\left[0.05t^2 + c \right]_3^5 = (0.05 \times 25 + c) - (0.05 \times 9 + c)$$

$$= 1.25 + c - 0.45 - c$$

$$= 0.8 \text{ m}$$

Qu. 7 Evaluate:

(a) $\left[3t + 8 \right]_2^5$ (b) $\left[3t^2 - t + k \right]_1^4$

(c) $\left[t^2 - t \right]_{-2}^{+1}$ (d) $\left[t^3 - 3t^2 + t \right]_{-3}^{-2}$

Qu. 8 A particle moves in a straight line with velocity $2t^2$ m s^{-1}, t s after the start. Find the distance moved in the third second.

Qu. 9 With the data of Example 1, answer the following questions.

(a) Find the position of R when $t = 20$.

(b) Find the position when $t = 10$ of the article initially at O.

(c) An article N is 2.2 m past O when $t = 2$; find its position when $t = 10$.

(d) An article T is 99.95 m short of O when $t = 1$; find its initial position.

Exercise 7b

1 A stone is thrown vertically downwards at 20 m s^{-1} from the top of a cliff. Assuming that gravity produces on it an acceleration of 9.81 m s^{-2}, deduce, from the differential equation $\dfrac{dv}{dt} = 9.81$, expressions for its velocity and position t s later.

2 A stone is thrown vertically upwards from ground level at 12 m s^{-1}, at a point immediately above a well. Taking the downwards direction as positive, deduce, from the differential equation $\dfrac{dv}{dt} = 9.8$, expressions for the stone's velocity and position t s later. Find the velocity and position after 1, 2, 3 s, explaining the sign of each answer.

3 Find the displacement (s) in terms of time (t) from the following data:

(a) $\dfrac{ds}{dt} = 3$ $s = 3$ when $t = 0$

(b) $v = 4t - 1$ $s = 0$ when $t = 2$

(c) $v = (3t - 1)(t + 2)$ $s = 1$ when $t = 2$

(d) $v = t^2 + 5 - \dfrac{2}{t^2}$ $s = \frac{1}{3}$ when $t = 1$

4 Evaluate:

(a) $\left[8t + c \right]_1^5$

(b) $\left[3t^2 + 5t \right]_2^{10}$

(c) $\left[t^2 - 4t \right]_{-3}^0$

(d) $\left[2t^3 - t^2 - t \right]_{-2}^{-1}$

5 Find s in terms of t, and the distance moved in the stated interval (the units being metres and seconds), given that

(a) $\dfrac{ds}{dt} = 4t + 3$ $t = 0$ to $t = 2$

(b) $v = t^2 - 3$ $t = 2$ to $t = 3$

(c) $v = (t - 1)(t - 2)$ $t = -1$ to $t = 0$

(d) $v = t + 3 - \dfrac{1}{t^2}$ $t = 10$ to $t = 20$

6 If a particle moves in a straight line so that its acceleration in terms of the time is At (A being a constant), deduce expressions for the velocity and displacement at time t.

7 Deduce expressions for v and s from the following data, determining the constants of integration whenever possible:
(a) $a = 3t$, $s = 0$ and $v = 3$ when $t = 0$
(b) $a = 2 + t$, $s = -3$ and $v = 0$ when $t = 0$
(c) $a = 10 - t$, $v = 2$ when $t = 1$, $s = 0$ when $t = 0$
(d) $a = \frac{1}{2}t$, $v = 5$ when $t = 0$
(e) $a = t^2$, $s = 10$ when $t = 1$

8 A system of particles moves along a straight line OA so that t s after a certain instant their velocity is v m s^{-1} where $v = 3t$.
(a) One of the particles is at O when $t = 0$. Find its position when $t = 3$.
(b) A second particle is 4 m past O when $t = 1$. Find its position when $t = 0$.
(c) A third particle is 10 m short of O when $t = 2$. Find its position when $t = 4$.
(d) Find the distance moved by the particles during the third second.

9 A particle moves along a straight line OA with velocity $(6 - 2t)$ m s^{-1}. When $t = 1$ the particle is at O.
(a) Find an expression for its distance from O in terms of t, and deduce the net change in position which takes place between $t = 0$ and $t = 5$.
(b) By finding the time at which it is momentarily at rest, calculate the actual distance through which it moves during the same interval.
(c) Sketch the space–time and velocity–time graphs from $t = 0$ to $t = 6$.

10 A stone is thrown vertically upwards from ground level with a velocity of 12.6 m s^{-1}. If the acceleration due to gravity is 9.8 m s^{-2}, deduce, from the differential equation $\dfrac{dv}{dt} = -9.8$, expressions for its velocity and its height t s later. Find:

(a) the time to the highest point
(b) the greatest height reached
(c) the distance moved through by the stone during each of the first two
   seconds of motion.

7.3 The area under a curve

Another important aspect of integration is that it enables us to calculate exactly
the areas enclosed by curves.

Let us consider the area enclosed by the axes, the line $x = 3$, and part of the
curve $y = 3x^2 + 2$. This is the area TUVO in Figure 7.3.

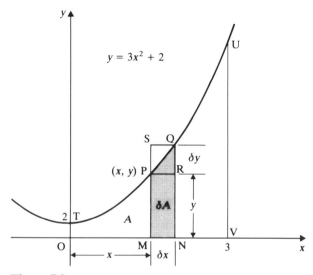

Figure 7.3

P is the point (x, y) on the curve, MP is its y-coordinate, and the area TPMO
we shall call A. Now if we move P along the curve, A increases or decreases
as x increases or decreases; clearly the size of A depends upon the value of x,
i.e. A is a function of x, and our present aim is to find an expression for A in
terms of x.

With the usual notation Q is the point $(x + \delta x, y + \delta y)$ adjacent to P, and NQ
is its y-coordinate. If we move the right-hand boundary of A from MP to NQ,
we increase x by δx, and the resulting increase in A, the shaded area PQNM,
we call δA. In other words δA is the increment in A corresponding to the
increment δx in x. It can be seen from Figure 7.3 that δA lies between the areas
of the two rectangles PRNM, $y\,\delta x$, and SQNM, $(y + \delta y)\delta x$. This may be
written†

$$y\,\delta x < \delta A < (y + \delta y)\delta x$$

† This statement is called an inequality. $<$ means 'is less than'; $>$ means 'is greater than'. The
reader should note in passing that an inequality is reversed by changing the sign of each term.
Thus $1 < 2 < 3$, but $-1 > -2 > -3$; this explains the reference to δx being positive.

and dividing by δx, which is positive,

$$y < \frac{\delta A}{\delta x} < (y + \delta y)$$

Now as $\delta x \to 0$, $\delta y \to 0$, and so $(y + \delta y) \to y$. Thus we find that $\frac{\delta A}{\delta x}$ lies between y and something which we can make as near to y as we please, by making δx sufficiently small. Therefore the limit of $\frac{\delta A}{\delta x}$ is y, and writing the limit of $\frac{\delta A}{\delta x}$ as $\frac{dA}{dx}$, we get

$$\frac{dA}{dx} = y$$

$$\therefore \quad \frac{dA}{dx} = 3x^2 + 2$$

and by integration,

$$A = x^3 + 2x + c$$

If we were to bring in the right-hand boundary of the area A from MP to OT, we should reduce A to zero; that is to say, when $x = 0$, $A = 0$. Substituting these values in the last equation we find that $c = 0$.

$$\therefore \quad A = x^3 + 2x$$

and we have achieved our immediate aim of expressing A in terms of x; now to find the area TUVO. In this case, the right-hand boundary of A has been pushed out from MP to VU, and x is increased to 3.

When $x = 3$,

$$A = 3^3 + 2 \times 3 = 33$$

$\therefore$ the area TUVO $= 33$.

Example 2

Find the area enclosed by the x-axis, the curve $y = 3x^2 + 2$ and the straight lines $x = 3$ and $x = 5$.

The required area is UWZV in Figure 7.4, and it may be found as the difference between the areas TWZO and TUVO. Using A as above,

$$\frac{dA}{dx} = y = 3x^2 + 2$$

$$\therefore \quad A = x^3 + 2x$$

(We have shown above that the constant of integration is zero.)

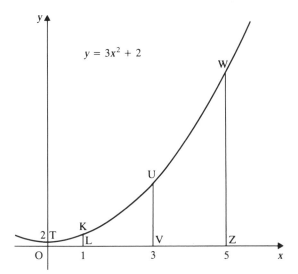

Figure 7.4

When $x = 5$,

$$A = 5^3 + 2 \times 5 = 135 \quad \text{(Area TWZO)}$$

and when $x = 3$,

$$A = 3^3 + 2 \times 3 = 33 \quad \text{(Area TUVO)}$$

∴ the area $\text{UWZV} = 135 - 33 = 102$.

Qu. 10 Find the area enclosed by the x-axis, the curve $y = 3x^2 + 2$, and the following straight lines:
(a) the y-axis and $x = 4$ (b) $x = 1$ and $x = 2$
(c) $x = -1$ and $x = 3$ (d) $x = -3$ and $x = -2$

In all the working so far in this chapter we have used the symbol A to denote an area having the y-axis as its left-hand boundary. Suppose that instead we had, in Figure 7.3, defined a similar area A' having the line $x = 1$ as its left-hand boundary. By the same process of reasoning we should arrive at the result

$$\frac{\mathrm{d}A'}{\mathrm{d}x} = y = 3x^2 + 2$$

∴ $A' = x^3 + 2x + k$

But $A' = 0$ when $x = 1$, and substituting these values we get $k = -3$.

∴ $A' = x^3 + 2x - 3$

Now A' is measured to the right from the line LK $(x = 1)$ in Figure 7.4, and Example 2 might just as well be done using A' instead of A, finding the area

UWZV as the difference between the areas KWZL and KUVL. Thus, when $x = 5$,

$$A' = 5^3 + 2 \times 5 - 3 = 135 - 3$$

and when $x = 3$,

$$A' = 3^3 + 2 \times 3 - 3 = 33 - 3$$

$\therefore$ the area $\text{UWZV} = (135 - 3) - (33 - 3) = 102$.

In each solution we have determined the constant of integration; using A, it is zero, and using A', it is -3. But as is clear from the second solution, the constant drops out on subtraction. We could in fact have measured A from any convenient left-hand boundary, and found the area UWZV by subtraction, without evaluating the constant of integration.

We shall from now onwards assume the relationship $\dfrac{dA}{dx} = y$ to calculate areas of this nature, and the square bracket notation introduced in Section 7.2 may now be put to further use, as is illustrated in the next example.

Example 3

Find the area enclosed by the x-axis, $x = 1$, $x = 3$ and the graph $y = x^3$ (Figure 7.5).

$$\frac{dA}{dx} = y = x^3$$

$$\therefore \quad A = \tfrac{1}{4}x^4 + c$$

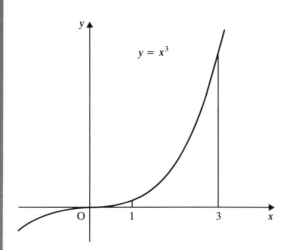

Figure 7.5

The required area $= \left[\frac{1}{4}x^4 + c \right]_1^3,$

$$= (\frac{81}{4} + c) - (\frac{1}{4} + c)$$
$$= \frac{81}{4} + c - \frac{1}{4} - c$$
$$= 20$$

The area evaluated in Example 3 is called *the area under the curve* $y = x^3$ *from* $x = 1$ *to* $x = 3$.

1 and 3 are called, respectively, the *lower* and *upper limits of integration*.

The integral $\frac{1}{4}x^4 + c$, involving the arbitrary constant of integration, is called an **indefinite integral**.

When limits are given, and the integral may be evaluated, e.g. $\left[\frac{1}{4}x^4 + c \right]_1^3$, it is called a **definite integral**. Since the constant of integration drops out in a definite integral, it is not necessary to write it in the bracket.

Qu. 11 Evaluate the following definite integrals:

(a) $\left[3x^2 + 2x \right]_{1/2}^1$ (b) $\left[x^4 - 2x^2 \right]_{-1}^2$

(c) $\left[x^3 - 3x \right]_{-2}^0$ (d) $\left[2x^2 + 4x \right]_{-3}^{-1}$

(e) $\left[x^4 - 2x^3 + x^2 - x \right]_{-2}^0$ (f) $\left[x^2 + 3x - \frac{1}{x^3} \right]_{+1/2}^{+1}$

Qu. 12 Find the area under $y = \frac{1}{2}x$ from $x = 0$ to $x = 10$ by integration. Check by another method.

Qu. 13 Find the area under
(a) $y = x^2$ from $x = 0$ to $x = 3$ (b) $y = 2x^2 + 1$ from $x = 2$ to $x = 5$

Two further examples will illustrate the advisability of making a sketch in this work if the reader is in doubt as to the shape and position of any curve; they also bring out two important points.

Example 4

Find the area under the curve $y = x^2(x - 2)$ (a) from $x = 0$ to $x = 2$, and (b) from $x = 2$ to $x = \frac{8}{3}$.

Consideration of the sign of the highest degree term, and the points of intersection with the x-axis, enables an adequate sketch to be made (Figure 7.6).

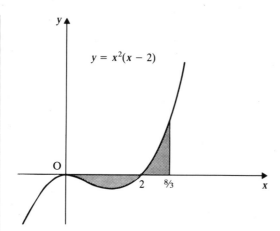

Figure 7.6

$$\frac{dA}{dx} = y = x^3 - 2x^2$$

$$\therefore \quad A = \tfrac{1}{4}x^4 - \tfrac{2}{3}x^3 + c$$

(a) The required area

$$= \left[\tfrac{1}{4}x^4 - \tfrac{2}{3}x^3\right]_0^2$$

$$= (\tfrac{1}{4} \times 2^4 - \tfrac{2}{3} \times 2^3) - (0)$$

$$= -1\tfrac{1}{3}$$

(b) The required area

$$= \left[\tfrac{1}{4}x^4 - \tfrac{2}{3}x^3\right]_2^{8/3}$$

$$= \left(\frac{1}{4} \times \frac{8^4}{3^4} - \frac{2}{3} \times \frac{8^3}{3^3}\right) - \left(\frac{1}{4} \times 2^4 - \frac{2}{3} \times 2^3\right)$$

$$= (0) - (-1\tfrac{1}{3})$$

$$= +1\tfrac{1}{3}$$

Part (a) of this example illustrates that *the area under a curve is negative below the x-axis*. The reader should verify that $\left[\tfrac{1}{4}x^4 - \tfrac{2}{3}x^3\right]_0^{8/3}$ is zero, and now that we have the convention about the sign of an area, we see that this is because it represents the sum of the two areas we have evaluated, numerically equal but of opposite sign.

The reader should now appreciate that a sketch of the relevant curve may help to avoid misleading results arising from perfectly correct calculation.

Qu. 14 Confirm that the total area enclosed by $y = x^2(x-2)$, the x-axis, $x = 1$ and $x = 3$ is $4\frac{1}{2}$.

What is the value of $\left[\frac{1}{4}x^4 - \frac{2}{3}x^3\right]_1^3$?

Qu. 15 Sketch the curve $y = x(x-1)(x-2)$. Find the total area enclosed between this curve and the x-axis.

Example 5

(a) Find the area under $y = 1/x^2$ from $x = 1$ to $x = 2$.
(b) Can any meaning be attached to the phrase 'the area under $y = 1/x^2$ from $x = -1$ to $x = +2$'?

(a) $\dfrac{\mathrm{d}A}{\mathrm{d}x} = y = \dfrac{1}{x^2} = x^{-2}$

$\therefore \quad A = -x^{-1} + c$

The required area

$$= \left[-\frac{1}{x}\right]_1^2$$
$$= \left(-\frac{1}{2}\right) - (-1)$$
$$= -\frac{1}{2} + 1$$
$$= \frac{1}{2}$$

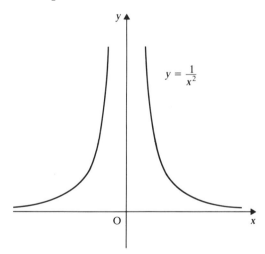

Figure 7.7

(b) Figure 7.7 is a sketch of $y = \dfrac{1}{x^2}$, and we see that if we try to find the area under the graph from $x = -1$ to $x = 2$, between these limits is the value $x = 0$ for which y has no value, and the curve consists of two separate branches. It is possible to go through the motions of evaluating $\left[-\dfrac{1}{x}\right]_{-1}^{+2}$ but the result, $-1\frac{1}{2}$, is meaningless. If we break up the area into two parts and integrate from -1 to 0 and from 0 to 2, in each case we get the meaningless term $\dfrac{1}{0}$. (See Section 3.5.)

The second part of Example 5 illustrates that in order that we may calculate the area under a curve, the curve must have no breaks between the limits of x involved, i.e. the function must be continuous (see Section 3.19) for all values of x between these limits.

Exercise 7c

1 Evaluate:

(a) $\left[\dfrac{x^4}{4}\right]_{1/2}^{2}$

(b) $\left[3x^3 - 4x\right]_{-1}^{+1}$

(c) $\left[\frac{1}{6}x^3 - 3x^2 + \frac{1}{2}x\right]_{-2}^{-1}$

(d) $\left[x^3 - \dfrac{1}{x^2}\right]_{-4}^{-3}$

2 Find the area enclosed by $x + 4y - 20 = 0$ and the axes, by integration. Check by another method.

3 Find the areas enclosed by the x-axis, and the following curves and straight lines:
(a) $y = 3x^2$, $x = 1$, $x = 3$
(b) $y = x^2 + 2$, $x = -2$, $x = 5$
(c) $y = x^2(x-1)(x-2)$, $x = -2$, $x = -1$
(d) $y = 3/x^2$, $x = 1$, $x = 6$

4 Find the area under $y = 4x^3 + 8x^2$ from $x = -2$ to $x = 0$.

5 Sketch the curve $y = x^2 - 5x + 6$ and find the area cut off below the x-axis.

6 Sketch the curve $y = x(x+1)(2-x)$, and find the area of each of the two segments cut off by the x-axis.

7 Sketch the following curves and find the areas enclosed by them, and by the x-axis, and the given straight lines:
(a) $y = x(4-x)$, $x = 5$ (b) $y = -x^3$, $x = -2$
(c) $y = x^3(x-1)$, $x = 2$ (d) $y = 1/x^2 - 1$, $x = 2$

8 Find the area of the segment cut off from $y = x^2 - 4x + 6$ by the line $y = 3$.

9 Repeat no. 8 for the curve $y = 7 - x - x^2$, and $y = 5$.

10 Find the points of intersection of the following curves and straight lines, and find the area of the segment cut off from each curve by the corresponding straight line:
(a) $y = \frac{1}{2}x^2$, $y = 2x$
(b) $y = 3x^2$, $3x + y - 6 = 0$
(c) $y = (x+1)(x-2)$, $x - y + 1 = 0$

Exercise 7d (Miscellaneous)

1 If $\dfrac{dy}{dx} = (3x - 2)/x^3$ find y in terms of x, if $y = 1$ when $x = 1$.

2 If $f'(x) = 2x - 1/x^2$ and if $f(1) = 1$, find $f(x)$.

3 The curve $y = 6 - x - x^2$ cuts the x-axis in two points A and B. By integration find the area enclosed by the x-axis and that portion of the curve which lies between A and B.

4 Sketch the curve $y = x^2 - x - 2$ from $x = -2$ to $x = 3$. Find the area bounded by the curve and the x-axis.

5 Sketch the curve $y = x^2(3 - x)$ between $x = -1$ and $x = 4$. Calculate the area bounded by the curve and the x-axis.

6 For the curve $y = 12x - x^3$, find the area bounded by the curve and the positive x-axis.

7 The velocity v of a point moving along a straight line is given in terms of the time t by the formula $v = 2t^2 - 9t + 10$, the point being at the origin when $t = 0$. Find expressions in terms of t for the distance from the origin, and the acceleration. Show that the point is at rest twice, and find its distances from the origin at those instants.

8 The velocity v of a point moving along a straight line is connected with the time t by the formula $v = t^2 - 3t + 2$, the units being metres and seconds. If the distance of the point from the origin is 5 m when $t = 1$, find its position and acceleration when $t = 2$.

9 A particle moves in a straight line with a velocity of v m s^{-1} after t s, where $v = 3t^2 + 2t$. Find the acceleration at the end of 2 s, and the distance it travels in the fourth second.

10 Find the equation of the curve which passes through the point $(-1, 0)$ and whose gradient at any point (x, y) is $3x^2 - 6x + 4$. Find the area enclosed by the curve, the axis of x and the lines $x = 1$ and $x = 2$.

11 Draw in the same figure, for values of x from 0 to 6, a sketch of the curve $y = 6x - x^2$ and the line $y = 2x$. Calculate the area enclosed by them.

12 The parabola $y = 6x - x^2$ meets the x-axis at O and A. The tangents at O and A meet at T. Show that the curve divides the area of the triangle OAT into two parts in the ratio $2:1$.

13 The curve $y = x(x - 1)^2$ touches the x-axis at the point A. B is the point $(2, 2)$ on the curve and N is the foot of the perpendicular from B to the x-axis. Prove that the tangent at B divides the area between the arc AB, NB, and AN in the ratio $11:24$.

14 The point P moves in a straight line with an acceleration of $(2t - 4)$ m s^{-2} after t s. When $t = 0$, P is at O and its velocity is 3 m s^{-1}. Find
   (a) the velocity of P after t s,
   (b) the value of t when P starts to return to O,
   (c) the distance of P from O at this moment.

15 A train starts from rest and its acceleration t s after the start is $0.1(20 - t)$ m s^{-2}. What is its speed after 20 s? Acceleration ceases at this instant and the train proceeds at this uniform speed. What is the total distance covered 30 s after the start from rest, to the nearest metre?

Further differentiation

8.1 To differentiate the function $f(x) = x^n \ (n \in \mathbb{Q})$

In this chapter we shall use fractional and negative indices, and any reader not prepared for this should first read Sections 10.2–10.4. We are already familiar with the rule that the derivative of x^n is nx^{n-1}, but so far we have used it only when n has been a positive or negative integer or zero, i.e. for $n \in \mathbb{Z}$. We now need to extend this rule. First we shall prove its validity for the special case $n = \frac{1}{2}$.

Figure 8.1 shows the graphs of the function $f(x) = x^{1/2} = \sqrt{x}$ and its inverse function $f^{-1}(x) = x^2$, $x \geqslant 0$. We saw in Chapter 3 that the graph of the inverse function is the reflection of the graph of $y = f(x)$ in the line $y = x$. The point $Q(b, a)$ on the graph $y = x^2$ is the reflection of the point $P(a, b)$ on the graph $y = x^{1/2}$. Notice, in particular, that the tangent at P to $y = x^{1/2}$ is inclined at an angle α to the x-axis, whereas the tangent at Q to $y = x^2$ is inclined at an angle α to the y-axis. Thus, in Figure 8.1 (ii), α is equal to $(90° - \beta)$. Also notice that, since $P(a, b)$ is on $y = \sqrt{x}$, and $Q(b, a)$ is on $y = x^2$, $a = b^2$, or $\sqrt{a} = b$.

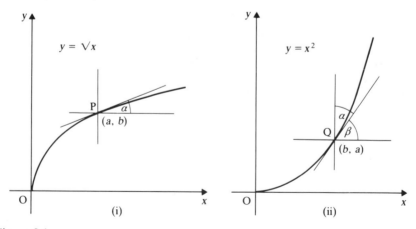

Figure 8.1

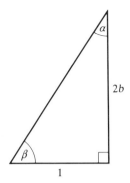

Figure 8.2

The gradient of $y = \sqrt{x}$ at P, $f'(a)$, is equal to tan α, but at the moment we do not know how to find $f'(x)$. However if we consider the graph of $y = x^2$, we know that tan β is given by the derivative of $y = x^2$ when $x = b$, and this we can find. In fact the derivative is $2x$ and hence

$$\tan \beta = 2b$$

But tan $\alpha = \tan (90° - \beta) = 1/(2b)$, (see Figure 8.2), therefore

$$f'(a) = \frac{1}{2b} = \frac{1}{2\sqrt{a}} = \tfrac{1}{2}a^{-1/2}$$

So we have proved that, for the function $f(x) = x^{1/2}$, the derivative

$$f'(x) = \tfrac{1}{2}x^{-1/2}$$

and this is in accordance with the general rule we have previously been using for differentiating x^n. From now on we shall assume that

$$\boxed{\text{if } f(x) = x^n, \ f'(x) = nx^{n-1} \text{ when } n \in \mathbb{Q}}$$

i.e. when n is any rational number. It is important that the reader should bear in mind that, although this assumption is indeed valid, we have on each occasion so far justified the use of a general rule for differentiation simply by demonstrating its truth for particular values of n. At a more advanced level of study a proof can be provided.

Example 1

Differentiate (a) $\dfrac{2}{x^3}$ (b) $\dfrac{1}{\sqrt{x}}$.

(a) Let $y = \dfrac{2}{x^3} = 2x^{-3}$

$\therefore \qquad \dfrac{\mathrm{d}y}{\mathrm{d}x} = 2(-3)x^{-4}$

$\qquad \qquad = -6x^{-4}$

(b) Let $y = \dfrac{1}{\sqrt{x}} = x^{-1/2}$

$\therefore \qquad \dfrac{\mathrm{d}y}{\mathrm{d}x} = -\dfrac{1}{2}x^{-3/2}$

Example 2

Integrate $\dfrac{3}{\sqrt[3]{x}}$.

If $\dfrac{dy}{dx} = \dfrac{3}{\sqrt[3]{x}} = 3x^{-1/3}$

$$y = \frac{3x^{-1/3+1}}{-1/3+1} + c$$

$$= \frac{3x^{2/3}}{2/3} + c$$

$$= \tfrac{9}{2}x^{2/3} + c$$

Qu. 1 Differentiate:

(a) x^{-4} (b) $2x^{-3}$ (c) $\dfrac{1}{x^2}$ (d) $\dfrac{4}{x}$ (e) $-\dfrac{2}{x^2}$ (f) $\dfrac{1}{3x^3}$ (g) $-\dfrac{1}{x^4}$ (h) $\dfrac{3}{5x^5}$

Integrate:

(i) x^{-3} (j) $2x^{-2}$ (k) $\dfrac{1}{x^2}$ (l) $\dfrac{2}{x^3}$ (m) $\dfrac{1}{3x^3}$ (n) $\dfrac{2}{5x^4}$

Qu. 2 Differentiate:

(a) $x^{1/2}$ (b) $2x^{-1/3}$ (c) $\sqrt{x}$ (d) $\sqrt[3]{x}$ (e) $\dfrac{1}{\sqrt[3]{x}}$ (f) $\dfrac{-2}{\sqrt[3]{x}}$ (g) $2\sqrt{x^3}$ (h) $\dfrac{2}{3\sqrt{x}}$

Integrate:

(i) $x^{-1/4}$ (j) $2x^{3/2}$ (k) $\sqrt{x}$ (l) $\sqrt[3]{x}$ (m) $\dfrac{1}{\sqrt{x}}$ (n) $\dfrac{1}{\sqrt{x^3}}$

8.2 The chain rule

The process of differentiating a function has already been dealt with in this book and the reader faced with a simple expression will differentiate it term by term after expansion and know that this is quite in order. If

$$y = (x+3)^2 = x^2 + 6x + 9$$

then

$$\frac{dy}{dx} = 2x + 6 = 2(x+3)$$

Quite obviously this expansion process leads to laborious multiplication when something like $(x + 3)^7$ is met. The more venturesome reader might hazard a guess that $7(x + 3)^6$ would be its derivative – and this would be right merely because $x + 3$ has the same derivative as x. Guessing is rather apt to grow indiscriminate, however, and is entirely untrustworthy!

The derivative of $(3x + 2)^4$ is *not* $4(3x + 2)^3$.
The derivative of $(x^2 + 3x)^7$ is *not* $7(x^2 + 3x)^6$.

Qu. 3 In each part of this question, find $\dfrac{dy}{dx}$ by removing the brackets and then differentiating. Factorise each answer and try to guess its relationship to the original expression.

(a) $y = (x + 4)^2$ (b) $y = (x + 2)^3$ (c) $y = (3x + 1)^2$
(d) $y = (5 - 2x)^2$ (e) $y = (x + 4)^3$ (f) $y = (x^3 + 1)^2$
(g) $y = (5 + x^2)^3$ (h) $y = (2 + 1/x)^2$ (i) $y = (1 - x^3)^2$
(j) $y = (\tfrac{1}{2}x - 7)^3$

Suppose y is a function of t, and t is itself a function of x. If δy, δt, and δx are corresponding small increments in the variables y, t, and x, then

$$\frac{\delta y}{\delta x} = \frac{\delta y}{\delta t} \times \frac{\delta t}{\delta x} \qquad\qquad \text{. . . (1)}$$

When δy, δt, and δx tend to zero,

$$\frac{\delta y}{\delta x} \to \frac{dy}{dx}, \qquad \frac{\delta y}{\delta t} \to \frac{dy}{dt}, \qquad \frac{\delta t}{\delta x} \to \frac{dt}{dx}$$

and equation (1) becomes:

$$\boxed{\frac{dy}{dx} = \frac{dy}{dt} \times \frac{dt}{dx}}$$

This important result is known as the **chain rule**. It will affect almost every exercise in differentiation which the reader will meet from here onwards, so it is most important to master it. The following examples are intended to give the reader some practice in its use.

Example 3

Differentiate $(3x + 2)^4$.

Let $y = (3x + 2)^4$ and $t = 3x + 2$ then $y = t^4$

$$\frac{dt}{dx} = 3 \qquad \frac{dy}{dt} = 4t^3$$

But, by the chain rule,

$$\frac{dy}{dx} = \frac{dy}{dt} \times \frac{dt}{dx}$$

$$\therefore \quad \frac{dy}{dx} = 4t^3 \times 3$$

$$= 12(3x + 2)^3$$

Example 4

Differentiate $(x^2 + 3x)^7$.

Let $\quad y = (x^2 + 3x)^7 \quad$ and $\quad t = x^2 + 3x \quad$ then $\quad y = t^7$

$$\frac{dt}{dx} = 2x + 3 \qquad \frac{dy}{dt} = 7t^6$$

$$\therefore \quad \frac{dy}{dx} = 7t^6(2x + 3)$$

$$\therefore \quad \frac{d}{dx}\{(x^2 + 3x)^7\} = 7(2x + 3)(x^2 + 3x)^6$$

In the very simple instance of Example 3 a similar method will apply for integration, i.e. $\int (3x + 2)^4 \, dx$ does equal $\frac{1}{5}(3x + 2)^5 \times \frac{1}{3}$, but this is a special case. A corresponding division rule in integration does *not* apply. The integration of these awkward composite functions is dealt with in Chapter 25.

It is not necessary to show the actual substitution, as has been done in the examples above, but it is advisable, until practice has made perfect this art of substitution. The bracket is really treated as a single term – the t of our formula – and then the reader must remember to 'multiply by the derivative of the bracket'. Differentiation of reciprocals and roots of functions is pure chain rule technique.

In the function notation, the chain rule becomes $(fg)'(x) = f'(g(x)) \times g'(x)$, but this lacks the elegant simplicity of the statement

$$\frac{dy}{dx} = \frac{dy}{dt} \times \frac{dt}{dx}$$

$\Big($ This may be remembered as 'differentiate y with respect to t and then multiply

by $\frac{dt}{dx}$.$\Big)$

Example 5

Differentiate $\dfrac{1}{1+\sqrt{x}}$.

Let $y = (1 + \sqrt{x})^{-1}$

$\therefore \quad \dfrac{dy}{dx} = -1 \times (1 + \sqrt{x})^{-2} \times \left\{\dfrac{d}{dx}(1 + \sqrt{x})\right\}$

$\qquad = -1 \times (1 + \sqrt{x})^{-2} \times (\tfrac{1}{2}x^{-1/2})$

$\therefore \quad \dfrac{d}{dx}\left(\dfrac{1}{1+\sqrt{x}}\right) = \dfrac{-1}{2\sqrt{x}(1+\sqrt{x})^2}$

Example 6

Differentiate $\sqrt{(1 + x^2)}$.

Let $y = (1 + x^2)^{1/2}$

$\therefore \quad \dfrac{dy}{dx} = \tfrac{1}{2}(1 + x^2)^{-1/2} \times 2x$

$\therefore \quad \dfrac{d}{dx}\{\sqrt{(1 + x^2)}\} = \dfrac{x}{\sqrt{(1 + x^2)}}$

Exercise 8a

1 Differentiate:
(a) $(2x + 3)^2$ (b) $2(3x + 4)^4$ (c) $(2x + 5)^{-1}$
(d) $(3x - 1)^{2/3}$ (e) $(3 - 2x)^{-1/2}$ (f) $(3 - 4x)^{-3}$

2 Integrate:
(a) $(3x + 2)^3$ (b) $(2x + 3)^2$ (c) $(3x - 4)^{-2}$ (d) $(2x + 3)^{1/2}$

3 Differentiate:
(a) $\dfrac{1}{(3x + 2)}$ (b) $\dfrac{1}{(2x + 3)^2}$ (c) $\dfrac{1}{\sqrt{(3x + 1)}}$ (d) $\dfrac{1}{(2x - 1)^{2/3}}$

4 Integrate:
(a) $\dfrac{1}{(2x - 3)^2}$ (b) $\dfrac{1}{\sqrt{(3x + 2)}}$ (c) $\dfrac{1}{(2x - 1)^{3/4}}$

5 Differentiate:
(a) $(3x^2 + 5)^3$ (b) $(3x^3 + 5x)^2$ (c) $(7x^2 - 4)^{1/3}$
(d) $(6x^3 - 4x)^{-2}$ (e) $(3x^2 - 5x)^{-2/3}$

6 Differentiate:
(a) $\dfrac{1}{(3x^2 + 2)}$ (b) $\dfrac{3}{\sqrt{(2 + x^2)}}$

7 Differentiate:

(a) $(3\sqrt{x} - 2x)^3$ (b) $\left(\dfrac{2}{\sqrt{x}} - 1\right)^{-1}$

8 Differentiate:

(a) $\dfrac{1}{x^{3/2} - 1}$ (b) $\sqrt{\left(1 - \dfrac{1}{x}\right)}$

9 Differentiate:

(a) $\dfrac{1}{(x^2 - 7x)^3}$ (b) $\dfrac{1}{(x^2 - \sqrt{x})^2}$

10 Differentiate:

(a) $\sqrt{\left(x^2 - \dfrac{1}{x^2}\right)}$ (b) $\dfrac{2}{x + 2\sqrt{x}}$

8.3 Rates of change

The chain rule can be used to investigate related rates of change. Suppose a spherical balloon is inflated at the rate of 2 cm³ every second. What is the rate of growth of the radius?

The solution of this type of problem has obvious calculus possibilities because $\dfrac{dy}{dx}$ is the rate of change of y with respect to x, and with the formula of the preceding section we have a ready means of connecting rates of change of dependent variables.

If the radius of the balloon is r, then the volume, $V = \frac{4}{3}\pi r^3$.

The fact we are given is that $\dfrac{dV}{dt}$, the rate of change of the volume with respect to time, t, is 2 cm³ s⁻¹, but, by the chain rule,

$$\frac{dV}{dt} = \frac{dV}{dr} \times \frac{dr}{dt} \quad \text{and} \quad \frac{dV}{dr} = 4\pi r^2$$

which leads to

$$\frac{dr}{dt} = \frac{2}{4\pi r^2}$$

i.e. the rate of change of the radius is $1/(2\pi r^2)$ cm s⁻¹. Any reader will surely at some time have blown up a balloon and noticed that the radius grows much more quickly at the beginning than near the end – sudden though the latter may sometimes be! The rate of change of the radius at any particular time could be calculated when the value of r is known. In the problem chosen, the radius after t s could be calculated from $\frac{4}{3}\pi r^3 = 2t$. The arithmetic is harder than the calculus.

Example 7

A container in the shape of a right circular cone of height 10 cm and base radius 1 cm is catching the drips from a tap leaking at the rate of 0.1 cm³ s⁻¹. Find the rate at which the surface area of water is increasing when the water is half-way up the cone.

Suppose the height of the water at any time is h cm, and that the radius of the surface of water at that time is r cm (Figure 8.3).

Figure 8.3

By similar triangles,

$$\frac{r}{1} = \frac{h}{10}$$

$$\therefore \quad r = \tfrac{1}{10}h$$

The surface area of water, $A = \pi r^2 = \pi h^2/100$ and we wish to find $\dfrac{\mathrm{d}A}{\mathrm{d}t}$ when $h = 5$. By the chain rule,

$$\frac{\mathrm{d}A}{\mathrm{d}t} = \frac{\mathrm{d}A}{\mathrm{d}h} \times \frac{\mathrm{d}h}{\mathrm{d}t} = \frac{2\pi h}{100} \times \frac{\mathrm{d}h}{\mathrm{d}t} \qquad \qquad \text{. . . (1)}$$

The volume of water, $V = \tfrac{1}{3}\pi r^2 h = \pi h^3/300$ and, using the chain rule again,

$$\frac{\mathrm{d}V}{\mathrm{d}t} = \frac{\mathrm{d}V}{\mathrm{d}h} \times \frac{\mathrm{d}h}{\mathrm{d}t} = \frac{3\pi h^2}{300} \times \frac{\mathrm{d}h}{\mathrm{d}t}$$

But we are given that $\dfrac{\mathrm{d}V}{\mathrm{d}t} = 0.1$,

$$\therefore \quad \frac{\mathrm{d}h}{\mathrm{d}t} = \frac{\mathrm{d}V}{\mathrm{d}t} \times \frac{300}{3\pi h^2} = 0.1 \times \frac{100}{\pi h^2} = \frac{10}{\pi h^2} \qquad \qquad \text{. . . (2)}$$

From (1) and (2)

$$\frac{\mathrm{d}A}{\mathrm{d}t} = \frac{2\pi h}{100} \times \frac{10}{\pi h^2} = \frac{1}{5h}$$

and, when $h = 5$,

$$\frac{dA}{dt} = \frac{1}{25} = 0.04$$

∴ when the water is half-way up, the rate of change of the surface area is equal to $0.04 \text{ cm}^2 \text{ s}^{-1}$.

Exercise 8b

1 The side of a cube is increasing at the rate of 6 cm s^{-1}. Find the rate of increase of the volume when the length of a side is 9 cm.

2 The area of surface of a sphere is $4\pi r^2$, r being the radius. Find the rate of change of the area in square cm per second when $r = 2$ cm, given that the radius increases at the rate of 1 cm s^{-1}.

3 The volume of a cube is increasing at the rate of $2 \text{ cm}^3 \text{ s}^{-1}$. Find the rate of change of the side of the base when its length is 3 cm.

4 The area of a circle is increasing at the rate of $3 \text{ cm}^2 \text{ s}^{-1}$. Find the rate of change of the circumference when the radius is 2 cm.

5 At a given instant the radii of two concentric circles are 8 cm and 12 cm. The radius of the outer circle increases at the rate of 1 cm s^{-1} and that of the inner at 2 cm s^{-1}. Find the rate of change of the area enclosed between the two circles.

6 If $y = (x^2 - 3x)^3$, find $\dfrac{dy}{dt}$ when $x = 2$, given $\dfrac{dx}{dt} = 2$.

7 A hollow right circular cone is held vertex downwards beneath a tap leaking at the rate of $2 \text{ cm}^3 \text{ s}^{-1}$. Find the rate of rise of water level when the depth is 6 cm given that the height of the cone is 18 cm and its radius 12 cm.

8 An ink blot on a piece of paper spreads at the rate of $\frac{1}{2} \text{ cm}^2 \text{ s}^{-1}$. Find the rate of increase of the radius of the circular blot when the radius is $\frac{1}{2}$ cm.

9 A hemispherical bowl is being filled with water at a uniform rate. When the height of the water is h cm the volume is $\pi(rh^2 - \frac{1}{3}h^3) \text{ cm}^3$, r cm being the radius of the hemisphere. Find the rate at which the water level is rising when it is half way to the top, given that $r = 6$ and that the bowl fills in 1 min.

10 An inverted right circular cone of vertical angle $120°$ is collecting water from a tap at a steady rate of $18\pi \text{ cm}^3 \text{ min}^{-1}$. Find
(a) the depth of the water after 12 min,
(b) the rate of increase of the depth at this instant.

11 From the formula $v = \sqrt{(60s + 25)}$ the velocity, v, of a body can be calculated when its distance, s, from the origin is known. Find the acceleration when $v = 10$.

12 If $y = (x - 1/x)^2$, find $\dfrac{dx}{dt}$ when $x = 2$, given $\dfrac{dy}{dt} = 1$.

8.4 Products and quotients

The reader is now able to differentiate quite elaborate functions, but no method has been suggested for a product such as $f(x) = (x + 1)^7 (x - 3)^4$. We could multiply out the brackets and differentiate each term separately, but this would be extremely laborious. Although it is possible to differentiate each of the factors, we have, as yet, no method for tackling the product at it stands. (We must not simply write down the product of the two derivatives. A reader tempted to do so should consider the product $f(x) = x^3 \times x^4$, which is equal to x^7 and hence its derivative is $f'(x) = 7x^6$; but this is plainly not the same as the product of the two derivatives $3x^2$ and $4x^3$.)

A further brief return to fundamental ideas will produce a formula to help us with functions of this kind.

Let y be the product of two functions u and v of a variable x. Then $y = uv$ and

$$y + \delta y = (u + \delta u)(v + \delta v)$$

where a small increment δx in x produces increments δu in u, δv in v and δy in y.

$$y + \delta y = uv + v\delta u + u\delta v + \delta u \delta v$$

and since $y = uv$,

$$\delta y = v\delta u + u\delta v + \delta u \delta v$$

Dividing by δx,

$$\frac{\delta y}{\delta x} = v\frac{\delta u}{\delta x} + u\frac{\delta v}{\delta x} + \frac{\delta u}{\delta x} \times \delta v$$

As $\delta x \to 0$, δu, δv and δy also approach 0,

$$\frac{\delta y}{\delta x} \to \frac{dy}{dx} \qquad \frac{\delta u}{\delta x} \to \frac{du}{dx} \qquad \frac{\delta v}{\delta x} \to \frac{dv}{dx}$$

$$\therefore \quad \frac{dy}{dx} = v\frac{du}{dx} + u\frac{dv}{dx} + \frac{du}{dx} \times 0$$

$$\boxed{\therefore \quad \frac{dy}{dx} = v\frac{du}{dx} + u\frac{dv}{dx}}$$

This formula must be remembered, and this is perhaps most easily done in words:

'To differentiate the product of two factors, differentiate the first factor, leaving the second one alone and then differentiate the second, leaving the first one alone,'

and it is necessary to remember also that, should one of the factors in the product be a composite function, its derivative must be found as carefully as those in Section 8.2 before insertion in this product formula.

Qu. 4 Use this method to differentiate the following functions:
(a) $(x + 1)(x + 2)$ (b) $(x^2 + 1)x^2$
(c) $(x - 2)^2(x^2 - 2)$ (d) $(x + 1)^2(x + 2)^2$

Check your results by multiplying out and then differentiating.

The most common mistakes made in this type of question are due to careless algebra and so particular attention should be paid to details of simplification.

Example 8

Differentiate the expression $y = (x^2 - 3)(x + 1)^2$ and simplify the result.

Let $u = (x^2 - 3)$ and let $v = (x + 1)^2$, then

$$\frac{du}{dx} = 2x \quad \text{and} \quad \frac{dv}{dx} = 2(x + 1)$$

$$\therefore \quad \frac{dy}{dx} = (x + 1)^2 \times 2x + (x^2 - 3) \times 2(x + 1)$$

$$= 2(x + 1)\{x(x + 1) + (x^2 - 3)\}$$
$$= 2(x + 1)\{2x^2 + x - 3\}$$
$$= 2(x + 1)(2x + 3)(x - 1)$$

Example 9

Differentiate $y = (x^2 + 1)^3(x^3 + 1)^2$.

If $u = (x^2 + 1)^3$ and $v = (x^3 + 1)^2$, then $y = uv$.

$$\frac{du}{dx} = 3(x^2 + 1)^2 \times 2x \quad \text{and} \quad \frac{dv}{dx} = 2(x^3 + 1) \times 3x^2$$

$$\therefore \quad \frac{dy}{dx} = (x^3 + 1)^2 \times 6x(x^2 + 1)^2 + (x^2 + 1)^3 \times 6x^2(x^3 + 1)$$

$$= 6x(x^3 + 1)(x^2 + 1)^2\{(x^3 + 1) + x(x^2 + 1)\}$$

$$\therefore \quad \frac{d}{dx}\{(x^2 + 1)^3(x^3 + 1)^2\} = 6x(x^3 + 1)(x^2 + 1)^2(2x^3 + x + 1)$$

Example 10

Find the x-coordinates of the stationary points of the curve
$y = (x^2 - 1)\sqrt{(1 + x)}$.

$$y = (x^2 - 1)(x + 1)^{1/2}$$

$$\therefore \quad \frac{dy}{dx} = (x + 1)^{1/2} \times 2x + (x^2 - 1) \times \tfrac{1}{2}(x + 1)^{-1/2}$$

$$= \frac{2(x + 1) \times 2x + (x^2 - 1)}{2(x + 1)^{1/2}}$$

$$= \frac{(x + 1)(4x + x - 1)}{2(x + 1)^{1/2}}$$

$$= \frac{(5x - 1)(x + 1)}{2(x + 1)^{1/2}}$$

$$= \tfrac{1}{2}(5x - 1)(x + 1)^{1/2}$$

$\therefore$ for stationary points $x = \tfrac{1}{5}$ or -1.

There is a formula for quotients corresponding to that for products and it is proved in a similar way.

If $y = u/v$ then:

$$\frac{dy}{dx} = \frac{v\dfrac{du}{dx} - u\dfrac{dv}{dx}}{v^2}$$

Some readers may wish to ignore this formula and to deal with the quotient u/v as the product uv^{-1}.

Example 11

Differentiate $\dfrac{(x - 3)^2}{(x + 2)^2}$.

Let $y = (x - 3)^2/(x + 2)^2$ and let $u = (x - 3)^2$ and $v = (x + 2)^2$, then $y = u/v$.

$$\frac{du}{dx} = 2(x - 3) \qquad \text{and} \qquad \frac{dv}{dx} = 2(x + 2)$$

$$\therefore \quad \frac{dy}{dx} = \frac{(x + 2)^2 \times 2(x - 3) - (x - 3)^2 \times 2(x + 2)}{(x + 2)^4}$$

$$= \frac{2(x + 2)(x - 3)\{(x + 2) - (x - 3)\}}{(x + 2)^4}$$

$$= \frac{2(x - 3) \times 5}{(x + 2)^3}$$

$$\therefore \quad \frac{d}{dx}\left\{\frac{(x - 3)^2}{(x + 2)^2}\right\} = \frac{10(x - 3)}{(x + 2)^3}$$

Example 12

Differentiate $\dfrac{x}{\sqrt{(1+x^2)}}$.

Let $y = x/\sqrt{(1+x^2)}$ and let $u = x$ and $v = \sqrt{(1+x^2)}$, then $y = u/v$.

$$\frac{du}{dx} = 1 \quad \text{and} \quad \frac{dv}{dx} = \frac{2x}{2\sqrt{(1+x^2)}}$$

$$\therefore \quad \frac{dy}{dx} = \frac{\sqrt{(1+x^2)} \times 1 \; - \; x \times \dfrac{x}{\sqrt{(1+x^2)}}}{(1+x^2)}$$

$$= \frac{1 + x^2 - x^2}{(1+x^2)^{3/2}}$$

$$\therefore \quad \frac{d}{dx}\left\{ \frac{x}{\sqrt{(1+x^2)}} \right\} = \frac{1}{(1+x^2)^{3/2}}$$

Qu. 5 Prove the formula for quotients by the δu, δv method.
Qu. 6 Differentiate:

(a) $(x^2 + 1)(x + 3)^{-2}$ as a product   (b) $\dfrac{x^2 + 1}{(x+3)^2}$ as a quotient.

Simplify the results and compare them.

Simplification† was an essential part of answering the question in Example 11 and, since the gradient of a function is often needed for a specific purpose, the reader should get into the habit of factorising and simplifying as far as possible. It will be necessary, in any case, in order to check the answers with those at the back of the book!

Exercise 8c

Differentiate with respect to x:

1 $x^2(1+x)^3$	2 $x(x^2+1)^4$	3 $(x+1)^2(x^2-1)$
4 $x^3(5x+1)^2$	5 $2\sqrt{x}(x+1)^2$	6 $x^3\sqrt{(4x+1)}$
7 $x\sqrt{(x^2-1)}$	8 $(x^2+1)\sqrt{(6x+1)}$	9 $x^{-2}(1+3x)^2$
10 $x^2(1+x)^{-2}$	11 $x/(x+1)$	12 $x/(x-1)$
13 $x/(x^2+1)$	14 $(4+x)/(4-x)$	15 $(1+5x)/(5-x)$
16 $x/(1+2x)^2$	17 $(2x+1)/(x+2)^2$	18 $x/(x+3)^4$
19 $2x^2/\sqrt{(x+1)}$	20 $2\sqrt{[x/(x+3)]}$	

8.5 Implicit functions

Up to the present we have dealt only with *explicit* functions of x, such as $y = x^2 - 5x + 4/x$. Here y is given as an expression in x. If, however, y is given

---

† Practice in the algebra involved in differentiating a quotient is given in Chapter 1.

implicitly by an equation such as $x = y^4 - y - 1$, we cannot express y in terms of x.

Consider an easier case. If $x = y^2$, $y = x^{1/2}$.

$$\therefore \quad \frac{dy}{dx} = \tfrac{1}{2}x^{-1/2} = \frac{1}{2x^{1/2}} = \frac{1}{2y}$$

But $\quad \dfrac{dx}{dy} = 2y$

so in this case:

$$\frac{dy}{dx} = 1 \bigg/ \frac{dx}{dy}$$

(Strictly speaking, the equation $x = y^2$, does not define y as a *function* of x, since, for each positive value of x, there are *two* values of y, namely the positive and negative square roots of x.)

Now consider the general case.

$$\frac{\delta y}{\delta x} = 1 \bigg/ \frac{\delta x}{\delta y}$$

where δx and δy are the increments in x and y respectively.

Now as $\delta x,\ \delta y \to 0,\ \dfrac{\delta y}{\delta x} \to \dfrac{dy}{dx}$, and $\dfrac{\delta x}{\delta y} \to \dfrac{dx}{dy}$

$$\boxed{\therefore \quad \frac{dy}{dx} = 1 \bigg/ \frac{dx}{dy}}$$

When it is impracticable to express either variable explicitly in terms of the other, we can still differentiate both sides with respect to x, as in Example 13 over the page. A term like y^n can be differentiated by first differentiating with respect to y then, as the chain rule demands, multiplying by $\dfrac{dy}{dx}$. Thus

$$\frac{d}{dx}(y^n) = \frac{d}{dy}(y^n)\frac{dy}{dx} = ny^{(n-1)}\frac{dy}{dx}$$

Similarly, if we have a term of the form $x^m y^n$, then we use the product rule and obtain

$$\frac{d}{dx}(x^m y^n) = x^m \frac{d}{dx}(y^n) + y^n \frac{d}{dx}(x^m)$$

$$= nx^m y^{(n-1)}\frac{dy}{dx} + mx^{(m-1)}y^n$$

Example 13

Find the gradient of the curve

$$x^2 + 2xy - 2y^2 + x = 2$$

at the point $(-4, 1)$.

To find the gradient, differentiate with respect to x.

$$\frac{d}{dx}(x^2) + \frac{d}{dx}(2xy) - \frac{d}{dx}(2y^2) + \frac{d}{dx}(x) = \frac{d}{dx}(2)$$

$$\therefore \quad 2x + \left(2y + 2x\frac{dy}{dx}\right) - 4y\frac{dy}{dx} + 1 = 0$$

$$\therefore \quad \frac{dy}{dx}(2x - 4y) = -1 - 2x - 2y$$

When $x = -4$, $y = 1$,

$$\frac{dy}{dx}(-8 - 4) = -1 + 8 - 2$$

$$\therefore \qquad \frac{dy}{dx} = \frac{+5}{-12}$$

$\therefore$ the gradient at $(-4, 1)$ is $-\frac{5}{12}$.

Qu. 7 Differentiate with respect to x:
(a) x (b) y (c) x^2 (d) y^2 (e) xy (f) $x^2 y$ (g) xy^2

Qu. 8 Find $\dfrac{dy}{dx}$ if $x^2 + y^2 - 6xy + 3x - 2y + 5 = 0$.

8.6 Parameters

Sometimes both x and y are given as functions of another variable, a **parameter**. In such cases the gradient is given in terms of the variable parameter.

Example 14

If $x = t^3 + t^2$, $y = t^2 + t$ find $\dfrac{dy}{dx}$ in terms of t.

$$\frac{dx}{dt} = 3t^2 + 2t \qquad \frac{dy}{dt} = 2t + 1$$

Now $\dfrac{dy}{dx} = \dfrac{dy}{dt} \times \dfrac{dt}{dx}$, but $\dfrac{dt}{dx} = 1 \bigg/ \dfrac{dx}{dt}$

$$\therefore \quad \frac{dy}{dx} = \frac{dy}{dt} \div \frac{dx}{dt}$$

$$\therefore \quad \frac{dy}{dx} = \frac{2t+1}{t(3t+2)}$$

Qu. 9 Show that the parametric representation in Example 14 is of the curve $y^3 = x^2 + xy$. Find $\dfrac{dy}{dx}$ for this curve and show that it agrees with the above result.

Example 15

Find the gradient of the curve $x = \dfrac{t}{1+t}$, $y = \dfrac{t^3}{1+t}$ at the point $(\frac{1}{2}, \frac{1}{2})$.

$$\frac{dx}{dt} = \frac{(1+t) \times 1 - t \times 1}{(1+t)^2} = \frac{1}{(1+t)^2}$$

$$\frac{dy}{dt} = \frac{(1+t) \times 3t^2 - t^3 \times 1}{(1+t)^2} = \frac{3t^2 + 2t^3}{(1+t)^2}$$

$$\therefore \quad \frac{dy}{dx} = 3t^2 + 2t^3$$

At $(\frac{1}{2}, \frac{1}{2})$, $t = 1$,

$$\therefore \quad \frac{dy}{dx} = 3 + 2$$

$\therefore$ the gradient at $(\frac{1}{2}, \frac{1}{2})$ is 5.

Exercise 8d

1 Find the gradient of the ellipse $2x^2 + 3y^2 = 14$ at the points where $x = 1$.
2 Find the x-coordinates of the stationary points of the curve represented by the equation $x^3 - y^3 - 4x^2 + 3y = 11x + 4$.
3 Find the gradient of the ellipse $x^2 - 3yx + 2y^2 - 2x = 4$ at the point $(1, -1)$.
4 Find the gradient of the tangent at the point $(2, 3)$ to the hyperbola $xy = 6$.

5 Find $\dfrac{dy}{dx}$ in terms of x, y when $x^2 + y^2 - 2xy + 3y - 2x = 7$.

6 At what points are the tangents to the circle $x^2 + y^2 - 6y - 8x = 0$ parallel to the y-axis?

7 Find $\dfrac{dy}{dx}$ when (a) $x^2 y^3 = 8$ (b) $xy(x - y) = 4$.

8 Find $\dfrac{dy}{dx}$ in terms of x, y when $3(x - y)^2 = 2xy + 1$.

9 (a) If $x = t^2$, $y = t^3$ find $\dfrac{dy}{dx}$ in terms of t.   (b) If $y = x^{3/2}$ find $\dfrac{dy}{dx}$.

10 Find $\dfrac{dy}{dx}$, in terms of t, when

(a) $x = 3t^2$ $y = 6t$ (b) $x = (t+1)^2$ $y = (t^2 - 1)$.

11 If $x = t/(1 - t)$ and $y = t^2/(1 - t)$ find $\dfrac{dy}{dx}$ in terms of t.

12 If $x = 2t/(t + 2)$, $y = 3t/(t + 3)$, find $\dfrac{dy}{dx}$ in terms of t.

8.7 Small changes

We have seen that, as $\delta x \to 0$, $\dfrac{\delta y}{\delta x} \to \dfrac{dy}{dx}$. Therefore, if δx is small,

$$\frac{\delta y}{\delta x} \approx \frac{dy}{dx}$$

$$\therefore \quad \delta y \approx \frac{dy}{dx} \delta x$$

Two applications of this formula follow in Examples 16 and 17.

Example 16

The side of a square is 5 cm. Find the increase in the area of the square when the side expands 0.01 cm.

Let the area of the square be A cm^2 when the side is x cm, then $A = x^2$. Now

$$\delta A \approx \frac{dA}{dx} \delta x \quad \text{and} \quad \frac{dA}{dx} = 2x$$

$$\therefore \quad \delta A \approx 2x \delta x$$

When $x = 5$ and $\delta x = 0.01$,

$$\delta A \approx 2 \times 5 \times 0.01 = 0.1$$

$\therefore$ the increase in area ≈ 0.1 cm^2.

In this case the increase in area can be found accurately very easily:

$$\delta A = 5.01^2 - 5^2 = 0.1001$$

Note that the error by the calculus method is, *in this case*, $(0.01)^2 = (\delta x)^2$.

Example 17

A 2% error is made in measuring the radius of a sphere. Find the percentage error in surface area.

Let the surface area be S and the radius be r, then

$$S = 4\pi r^2$$

$$\therefore \quad \frac{dS}{dr} = 8\pi r$$

$$\therefore \quad \delta S \approx 8\pi r \delta r$$

But the error in r is 2%, therefore $\delta r = \frac{2}{100} \times r$.

$$\therefore \quad \delta S \approx 8\pi r \times \frac{2r}{100} = \frac{16\pi r^2}{100}$$

$$\therefore \quad \frac{\delta S}{S} \approx \frac{16\pi r^2}{100} \div 4\pi r^2 = \frac{4}{100}$$

$\therefore$ the error in the surface area $\approx 4\%$.

Exercise 8e

1 The surface area of a sphere is $4\pi r^2$. If the radius of the sphere is increased from 10 cm to 10.1 cm, what is the approximate increase in surface area?

2 An error of 3% is made in measuring the radius of a sphere. Find the percentage error in volume.

3 If l cm is the length of a pendulum and t s the time of one complete swing, it is known that $l = kt^2$. If the length of the pendulum is increased by $x\%$, x being small, find the corresponding percentage increase in time of swing.

4 If the pressure and volume of a gas are p and v then Boyle's law states $pv = $ constant. If δp and δv denote corresponding small changes in p and v express $\dfrac{\delta p}{p}$ in terms of $\dfrac{\delta v}{v}$.

5 An error of $2\frac{1}{2}\%$ is made in the measurement of the area of a circle. What is the percentage error in (a) the radius, (b) the circumference?

6 The height of a cylinder is 10 cm and its radius is 4 cm. Find the approximate increase in volume when the radius increases to 4.02 cm.

7 One side of a rectangle is three times the other. If the perimeter increases by 2% what is the percentage increase in area?

8 The radius of a closed cylinder is equal to its height. Find the percentage increase in total surface area corresponding to a 1% increase in height.

9 The volume of a sphere increases by 2%. Find the corresponding percentage increase in surface area.

10 As x increases, prove that the area of a circle of radius x and the area of a square of side x increase by the same percentage, provided that the increase in x is small.

8.8 Second derivative

We know that velocity, v, is the rate of change of displacement, s, with respect to time, t, and may be denoted by $\dfrac{ds}{dt}$. Acceleration is the rate of change of velocity with respect to time, and we have up to now denoted this by $\dfrac{dv}{dt}$; but $\dfrac{d}{dt}(v)$ may also be written as $\dfrac{d}{dt}\left(\dfrac{ds}{dt}\right)$, and thus the acceleration is seen to be the second derivative of s with respect to t.

The second derivative arises in a wide variety of contexts as well as in kinematics, of course, and we need a less cumbersome notation.

$$\frac{d}{dx}\left(\frac{dy}{dx}\right) \text{ is written as } \frac{d^2 y}{dx^2}$$

which is spoken 'd two y by d x squared'.

Remember that if $y = f(x)$, $\dfrac{dy}{dx}$ is written as $f'(x)$, and $\dfrac{d^2 y}{dx^2}$ as $f''(x)$.

Qu. 10 (a) If $y = x^2 - 1/x^2$, find $\dfrac{dy}{dx}$ and $\dfrac{d^2 y}{dx^2}$.

(b) If $f(x) = x/(x-1)$, find $f'(x)$ and $f''(x)$.

If $\dfrac{dy}{dx}$ is found in terms of a parameter t, $\dfrac{d^2 y}{dx^2}$ requires differentiation with respect to x, so

$$\frac{d^2 y}{dx^2} = \frac{d}{dt}\left(\frac{dy}{dt}\right) \times \frac{dt}{dx} = \frac{d}{dt}\left(\frac{dy}{dx}\right) \div \frac{dx}{dt}$$

Qu. 11 If $x = (t^2 - 1)$, $y = 2(t+1)$, find $\dfrac{dy}{dx}$ and $\dfrac{d^2 y}{dx^2}$ in terms of t.

Exercise 8f (Miscellaneous)

1 Differentiate:
   (a) $1/x^6$ (b) $\sqrt{(x^3)}$ (c) $1/\sqrt{x}$ (d) $(\sqrt{x})^5$
2 Integrate:
   (a) $(x^2)^3$ (b) $(x^3)^{-2}$ (c) $1/x^2$ (d) $\sqrt{x}$
3 Differentiate:
   (a) $x^{3/2}$ (b) $\sqrt{(1/x^3)}$ (c) $\sqrt{x}/x$ (d) $\sqrt{(4/x)}$
4 Differentiate:
   (a) $1/\sqrt{x^3}$ (b) $\sqrt{(2/x^3)}$ (c) $x^2/\sqrt{x}$ (d) $(x^3)^{1/6}$.

In nos. 5–12, find $\dfrac{dy}{dx}$ and simplify it.

5 (a) $y = (x^2 + 3)^4$ (b) $y = \sqrt{(2x^3 - 3)}$

6 (a) $y = \dfrac{1}{x^2 - 1}$ (b) $y = \dfrac{1}{(\sqrt{x} - 1)^2}$

7 $y = x^2(x - 1)^3$
8 $y = x\sqrt{(x^2 - 1)}$

9 $y = \dfrac{x}{\sqrt{(x - 1)}}$

10 $y = \dfrac{x^2 + 2}{(x + 2)^2}$

11 $y = \sqrt{\left(\dfrac{x + 1}{x + 2}\right)}$

12 $y = \sqrt{\dfrac{x^2 + 1}{x^2 - 1}}$

13 Find $\dfrac{dy}{dx}$ when $x^2 + 2xy + y^2 = 3$. Explain your answer.

14 Find $\dfrac{dy}{dx}$ when $x^2 - 3xy + y^2 - 2y + 4x = 0$.

15 Find $\dfrac{dy}{dx}$ when $3x^2 - 4xy = 7$.

16 If $x = 2t/(1 + t^2)$, $y = (1 - t^2)/(1 + t^2)$ find $\dfrac{dy}{dx}$ in terms of t.

17 If $x = 1/\sqrt{(1 + t^2)}$, $y = t/\sqrt{(1 + t^2)}$ find $\dfrac{dy}{dx}$ in terms of t.

18 If $x = t/(1 - t)$, $y = (1 - 2t)/(1 - t)$ find $\dfrac{dy}{dx}$.

19 When measuring the area of a circle, 2% error is made. Find the percentage error in the radius.
20 When measuring the dimensions of a cubical box 1% error was made – all measurements being too large. Find the percentage error in volume.
21 The circumference of a circle is measured with a piece of string which stretches 1%. What is the percentage error in the area of the circle?

22 If $y = 4x^3 - 6x^2 - 9x + 1$, find $\dfrac{dy}{dx}$ and hence find the values of $\dfrac{d^2y}{dx^2}$ when the gradient is zero.

23 If $x = 3t^2$, $y = 6t$, find $\dfrac{dy}{dx}$ and $\dfrac{d^2y}{dx^2}$ in terms of t.

24 If $f(x) = 8x^3 - 11x^2 - 30x + 9$ for what values of x is $f'(x) = 0$?

25 Find the equation of the tangent to the curve $x^2 - y^2 = 9$ at the point $(5, 4)$.

Revision Exercise 1

1 Show that the gradient of the curve with equation $y = x^3 + x + 6$ at the point A(1, 8) is 4.

Hence, or otherwise, find

(a) the equation of the tangent to the curve at A

(b) the x-coordinate of the point where this tangent meets the curve again. (L)

2 The curve $y = 1 + \dfrac{1}{2 + x}$ crosses the x-axis at the point A and the y-axis at the point B.

(a) Calculate the coordinates of A and of B.

(b) Find the equation of the line AB.

(c) Calculate the coordinates of the point of intersection of the line AB and the line with equation $3y = 4x$. (C)

3 Two functions f and g are defined by:

$$f\colon x \mapsto \frac{25}{3x - 2} \qquad x \in \mathbb{R} \qquad 1 < x \leqslant 9$$

$$g\colon x \mapsto x^2 \qquad x \in \mathbb{R} \qquad 1 < x \leqslant 3$$

Find

(a) the range of f,

(b) the inverse function f^{-1}, stating its domain,

(c) the composite function fg, stating its domain,

(d) the solutions of the equation $fg(x) = \dfrac{2}{x - 1}$. (L)

4 Sketch the graph which has the equation $y = x^2(x - b)$, where b is a constant, in each of the cases:

(a) $b = 0$ (b) $b > 0$. (C)

5 Sketch, on separate diagrams, the curves

(a) $y = \dfrac{x - a}{x}$ (b) $y = \dfrac{x^2 - a^2}{x^2}$

where a is a positive constant.

(The equations of any asymptotes should be stated, together with the coordinates of any intersections with the axes.)

Hence sketch the curves

(c) $y = \left| \dfrac{x - a}{x} \right|$ (d) $y = \left| \dfrac{x^2 - a^2}{x^2} \right|$. (C)

6 The diagram over the page shows the graph of $y = f(x)$. The curve passes through the origin, and has a maximum at (1, 1). Sketch, on separate diagrams, the graphs of

(a) $y = f(x) + 2$ (b) $y = f(x + 2)$ (c) $y = f(2x)$

giving the coordinates of the maximum point in each case. (C)

159

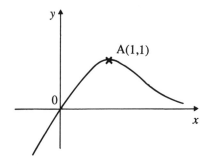

7 A manufacturer produces closed cylindrical cans of radius r cm and height h cm. Each can has a total surface area of 54π cm².

(a) Show that $\quad h = \dfrac{27 - r^2}{r}$

and hence find an expression for the volume, V cm³, of each can in terms of r.

(b) Find the value of r for which the cans have their maximum possible volume. (C)

8 The production cost per kilogram, C (in thousands of pounds) when x kilograms of a chemical are made is given by

$$C = 3x + (100/x) \qquad x > 0$$

Find the value of x for which the cost is a minimum, and the minimum cost. Show, also, that this cost is a minimum rather than a maximum. (C)

9 The rate of working, P watts, of an engine which is travelling at a speed of v m s^{-1} is given by

$$P = 10v + (4000/v) \qquad v > 0$$

Find the speed at which the rate of working is least. (L)

10 The profit, P, in thousands of pounds, made by a company t months after its launch, where $0 \leqslant t \leqslant 12$, is given by

$$P = 2t^3 - 15t^2 + 24t + 2$$

Find $\dfrac{dP}{dt}$, and hence determine the range of values of t for which the profit is decreasing. (L)

11 The diagram at the top of the next page shows a sketch of part of the curve with equation

$$y = x^3 - 12x + 16$$

Calculate
(a) the coordinates of the turning points A and B,
(b) the coordinates of C, the point where the curve crosses the x-axis,
(c) the area of the finite region enclosed by the curve and the x-axis. (L)

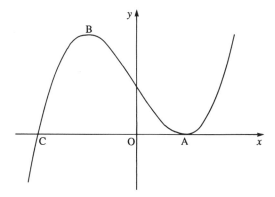

12 The normal at the point P (2, 6) to the curve $y = x^2 + 2$ meets the x-axis at the point N.

(a) Show that the x-coordinate of N is 26.

(b) The finite region R is bounded by the coordinate axes, the line segment PN and the curve $y = x^2 + 2$. Find the area of R. (L)

13 Show that the equation of the tangent to the curve $y = x^3$ at the point (t, t^3) is $y = 3t^2 x - 2t^3$.

A tangent to the curve intercepts the Ox and Oy axes at P and Q respectively. Given that the triangle OPQ has area 32/3. find the possible equations of the tangent. (W)

14

 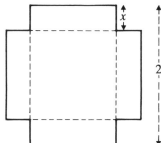 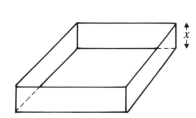

The diagrams show how an open metal box may be formed. From a square thin sheet of metal measuring 2 units by 2 units, four equal squares of side x are removed; the projecting pieces are then folded upwards to make the sides of the box, which has depth x.

Show that the volume V of the box is given by $V = 4x(1 - x)^2$.

Find the value of x for which V is a maximum, and find also the maximum value of V.

Sketch the graph of $y = 4x(1 - x)^2$, and indicate on your sketch that part of the curve where x can represent the depth of a box as described above.

(SUJB)

15 Find the gradient of the curve $y = \dfrac{x^2 + 1}{x - 1}$ when $x = 2$. (C)

16 The velocity v, in metres per second, of a particle moving on the x-axis is given in terms of the time t, in seconds, by the relation

$$v = 3t^2 - \tfrac{1}{3}t^3 + 9$$

Find (a) the values of t at which the acceleration of the particle is zero,

(b) the distance travelled by the particle between the two instants at which the acceleration is zero.   (SUJB)

17 An even function f, of period π, is defined by

$$f(x) = 4x^2 \quad \text{for} \quad 0 \leqslant x \leqslant \pi/4,$$
$$f(x) = \pi^2/4 \quad \text{for} \quad \pi/4 < x \leqslant \pi/2$$

Sketch the graph of f for $-\pi \leqslant x \leqslant \pi$.   (L)

18 Functions f and g are given by

$$f: x \mapsto 3x + 4 \quad \text{and} \quad g: x \mapsto x^2$$

(a) Find the functions f$'$ and g$'$.
(b) Calculate the values of f$'(2)$ and g$'(10)$.
(c) If h $=$ gf, find h(x) and h$'(x)$.
(d) Verify that h$'(2) = $ f$'(2)$g$'(10)$.   (O & C: SMP)

19 The real function f, defined for all $x \in \mathbb{R}$, is said to be multiplicative if, for all $x \in \mathbb{R}$, $y \in \mathbb{R}$,

$$f(xy) = f(x)f(y)$$

Prove that if f is a multiplicative function then
(a) either $f(0) = 0$ or $f(x) = 1$,
(b) either $f(1) = 1$ or $f(x) = 0$,
(c) $f(x^n) = \{f(x)\}^n$ for all positive integers n.
Give an example of a non-constant multiplicative function.   (C)

20 Functions f, g and h, with domains and co-domains

$$\mathbb{R}^+ = \{x: x \text{ real}, x > 0\}$$

are defined as follows:

$$f: x \mapsto 3x^2 \qquad g: x \mapsto \frac{1}{\sqrt{(1+x)}} \qquad h: x \mapsto (1+x)/x$$

Prove that the composite function L defined on $\mathbb{R}^+$ by L $=$ hgf is given by

$$L: x \mapsto 1 + \sqrt{(1 + 3x^2)}$$ (L)

Chapter 9

Further integration

9.1 Some standard curves

In Section 6.5 we dealt with some simple aids to curve sketching. By this stage, the reader should be thoroughly familiar with some standard curves which will be frequently occurring in the work which follows.

Figure 9.1 shows some variations on the curve $y = x^2$, which is a **parabola**. The line about which the curve is symmetrical is called the **axis**, and it cuts the curve at the **vertex**. Thus for the curve $y = x^2 + c$, the axis is the y-axis, and the vertex is $(0, c)$. Any equation of the form $y = ax^2 + bx + c$, where a, b, and c are constants (a not being zero), represents a parabola with the axis parallel to the y-axis (see Chapter 11).

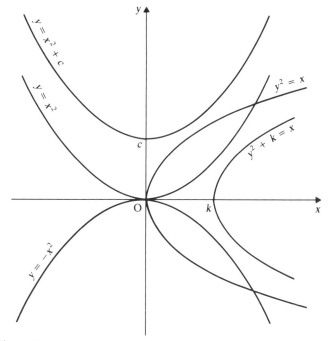

Figure 9.1

Typical shapes of curves for which y is given as a cubic function of x are shown in Figure 9.2. (i) represents $y = (x+3)(x+1)(x-2)$, the x^3 term in the expansion being positive; (ii) represents $y = (3+x)(1+x)(2-x)$, the x^3 term in the expansion being negative (see Section 6.5, Example 7).

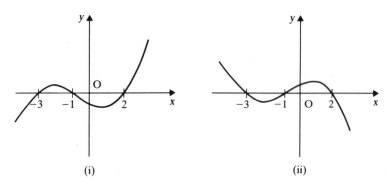

(i)   (ii)

Figure 9.2

Figure 9.3 shows (i) $y = x(x-2)^2$, and (ii) $y = -(x+1)^3$, illustrating that when the function of x has a squared factor, the curve touches the x-axis; and with a cubed factor, the curve touches *and crosses* the x-axis.

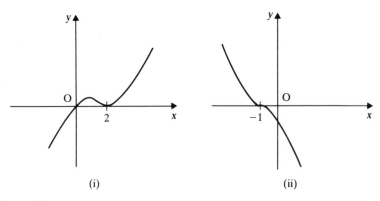

(i)   (ii)

Figure 9.3

Figure 9.4 illustrates how a sketch of the curve $y = x^2 + 1/x$ may be built up by adding the y-coordinates of the two known curves $y = x^2$ and $y = 1/x$.

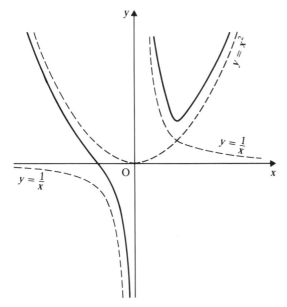

Figure 9.4

9.2 The integration of x^n $(n \in \mathbb{Q})$

In Chapter 8 the differentiation of x^n was assumed to include cases where n is a fraction, and we can integrate powers of x with fractional indices.

Thus, if

$$\frac{dy}{dx} = \sqrt{x} = x^{1/2}$$

then

$$y = \frac{x^{3/2}}{3/2} + c = \tfrac{2}{3}x^{3/2} + c$$

Exercise 9a

1 Sketch the following curves:
   (a) $y = 4x^2$ (b) $y = -x^2 + 9$ (c) $y - 1 = x^2$
   (d) $x = -y^2$ (e) $x - y^2 + 4 = 0$ (f) $2x + y^2 + 16 = 0$
2 Sketch the following curves showing where each meets the x-axis:
   (a) $y = (x - 1)(x - 2)(x - 3)$ (b) $y = (1 - x)(x - 2)(x - 3)$
   (c) $y = (x + 1)(x - 2)^2$ (d) $y = x^2(3 - x)$
   (e) $y = (x + 2)(1 - x)^2$ (f) $y^2 = x^6$
   (g) $x = y^3$ (h) $x + y^3 = 0$
   (i) $x = y(y - 3)^2$

3 Sketch the following curves:

(a) $y = -x^4$ (b) $y = \dfrac{1}{x^2}$ (c) $y = x^2 + \dfrac{1}{x^2}$ (d) $y = x^3 + \dfrac{1}{x}$

(e) $y = x^3 + \dfrac{1}{x^2}$ (f) $y = x^2 - \dfrac{1}{x}$ (g) $y = \sqrt{x} + \dfrac{1}{\sqrt{x}}$

4 Integrate with respect to x:

(a) $x^{1/3}$ (b) $\sqrt[4]{x}$ (c) $2x^{1/5}$ (d) $k\sqrt[3]{x}$ (e) $x^{-1/2}$ (f) $\dfrac{1}{\sqrt[3]{x}}$

(g) $x^{-1/6}$ (h) $\dfrac{2}{\sqrt[5]{x}}$ (i) $\sqrt[3]{x^2}$ (j) $x^{7/3}$ (k) $(\sqrt{x})^3$ (l) $x^{-4/3}$

5 Evaluate the following:

(a) $\left[x^{-1/2} \right]_1^4$ (b) $\left[x^{3/2} + 2x^{1/2} \right]_4^9$ (c) $\left[\tfrac{2}{3}(x+4)^{3/2} \right]_0^5$

9.3 Area as the limit of a sum

We have already discussed the use of integration in finding the area under a curve (Section 7.3). The word *integration* implies the putting together of parts to make up a whole, and this fundamental aspect of the process is brought out in the following alternative approach to the area under a curve.

Suppose that we wish to find the area under the curve in Figure 9.5 from $x = 0$ to $x = 3$. We divide this area into three equal strips by the lines $x = 1$ and $x = 2$.

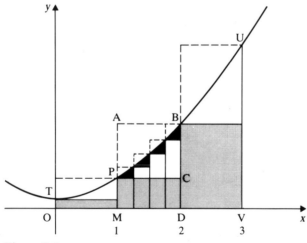

Figure 9.5

The required area TUVO lies between the sum of the areas of the three shaded 'inside' rectangles, and the sum of the three 'outside' rectangles bounded at the top by the broken lines; for example, the middle strip PBDM lies between the areas PCDM and ABDM.

We shall for the time being confine our attention to the 'inside' rectangles; the sum of these falls short of the required area by the sum of PBC and the two corresponding areas. We now divide TUVO into 12 strips (for clarity only 4 of these are shown in Figure 9.5). The sum of the 12 'inside' rectangles is clearly a better approximation to the area under the curve, since an error such as PBC has been reduced to a much smaller error represented by the 4 black roughly triangular areas. Thus by taking a sufficient number of strips (in other words, by making the width of each strip sufficiently small) we can make the sum of the areas of the 'inside' rectangles as near as we please to the area under the curve.

If we were to divide the area TUVO into a very large number of strips, then a typical one would be PQNM (Figure 9.6), where P(x, y) and Q($x + \delta x, y + \delta y$) are two points on the curve. A typical 'inside' rectangle is PRNM, of area $y\delta x$, and the process of increasing the number of strips is the same as letting $\delta x \to 0$. The required area TUVO is found by adding all the 'inside' rectangular areas $y\delta x$ between $x = 0$ and $x = 3$, and then finding the limit of this sum as $\delta x \to 0$.

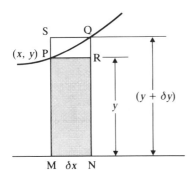

Figure 9.6

Using the symbol $\sum$ to denote 'the sum of' (see Section 14.9),

$$\text{as } \delta x \to 0 \quad \sum_{x=0}^{x=3} y\delta x \to \text{the area TUVO}$$

Hence† area TUVO = the *limit*, as $\delta x \to 0$, of $\sum_{x=0}^{x=3} y\delta x$.

Example 1

Calculate the area under $y = x + 1$ from $x = 0$ to $x = 10$.

---

† For simplicity we have confined our attention to the 'inside' rectangles. Figure 9.6 also shows a typical 'outside' rectangle SQNM of area $(y + \delta y)\delta x$; as $\delta x \to 0$, $\sum_{x=0}^{x=3} (y + \delta y)\delta x$ tends to the same limit.

Divide the area into n strips of equal width parallel to Oy (Figure 9.7); the width of each strip will be $10/n$. To find the sum of the areas of the inner shaded rectangles we must first calculate their heights.

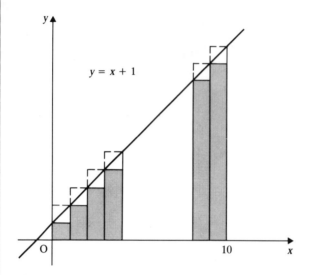

Figure 9.7

For the three smallest:

when $x = 0$ $\qquad\qquad y = x + 1 = 1$

when $x = \dfrac{10}{n}$ $\qquad\quad y = \dfrac{10}{n} + 1$

when $x = 2 \times \dfrac{10}{n}$ $\quad y = \dfrac{20}{n} + 1$

and for the largest,

when $x = 10 - \dfrac{10}{n}$ $\qquad y = 11 - \dfrac{10}{n}$

The sum of the areas of the inner rectangles is:

$$\left\{ \frac{10}{n}(1) + \frac{10}{n}\left(\frac{10}{n} + 1\right) + \frac{10}{n}\left(\frac{20}{n} + 1\right) + \dots + \frac{10}{n}\left(11 - \frac{10}{n}\right) \right\}$$

$$= \frac{10}{n}\left\{ 1 + \left(\frac{10}{n} + 1\right) + \left(\frac{20}{n} + 1\right) + \dots + \left(11 - \frac{10}{n}\right) \right\}$$

The dots have been used to signify the terms corresponding to all the intermediate rectangles; we know that there are as many terms in the curly brackets as there are strips, namely n, and they form an arithmetic progression (see Section 14.2) with common difference $10/n$.

We can now sum the terms in the brackets using the formula

$$S_n = \frac{n}{2}(a + l) \qquad \text{(see Section 14.4)}$$

$$= \frac{n}{2}\left(1 + 11 - \frac{10}{n}\right)$$

$$= \frac{n}{2}\left(12 - \frac{10}{n}\right)$$

∴ the sum of the 'inside' rectangles

$$= \frac{10}{n} \times \frac{n}{2}\left(12 - \frac{10}{n}\right)$$

$$= 60 - \frac{50}{n}$$

As $n \to \infty$, the limit of the sum is 60,
∴ the area under $y = x + 1$ from $x = 0$ to $x = 10$ is 60.

Qu. 1 Calculate the sum of the areas of the n 'outside' rectangles in Example 1, and find the limit of this sum as $n \to \infty$.

Example 2

Calculate the area under the curve $y = x^2$, from $x = 0$ to $x = a$.

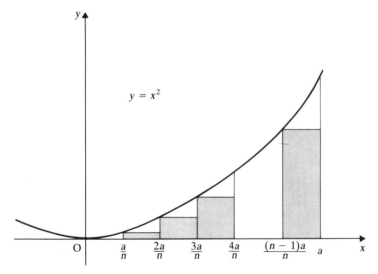

Figure 9.8

Here again we divide the interval $0 \leqslant x \leqslant a$, into n equal sub-intervals, each of length a/n (Figure 9.8). To find the area inside the shaded region, we must first calculate the heights of the $(n-1)$ rectangles. Since the equation of the curve is $y = x^2$, these heights are

$$\left(\frac{a}{n}\right)^2, \quad \left(\frac{2a}{n}\right)^2, \quad \left(\frac{3a}{n}\right)^2, \quad \dots \quad \left(\frac{(n-1)a}{n}\right)^2$$

and, since the width of each rectangle is a/n, the sum of the areas of the rectangles is

$$\frac{a}{n} \times \frac{a^2}{n^2} + \frac{a}{n} \times \frac{4a^2}{n^2} + \frac{a}{n} \times \frac{9a^2}{n^2} + \dots + \frac{a}{n} \times \frac{(n-1)^2 a^2}{n^2}$$

$$= \frac{a^3}{n^3} + \frac{4a^3}{n^3} + \frac{9a^3}{n^3} + \dots + \frac{(n-1)^2 a^3}{n^3}$$

$$= \frac{a^3}{n^3}(1 + 4 + 9 + \dots + (n-1)^2)$$

Now, it can be shown (see Section 14.8) that

$$1 + 4 + 9 + \dots + (n-1)^2 = \frac{1}{6}(n-1) \times n \times (2n-1)$$

$$= \frac{1}{6}(2n^3 - 3n^2 + n)$$

Hence the sum of the areas of these rectangles is

$$S = \frac{a^3}{n^3} \times \frac{1}{6}(2n^3 - 3n^2 + n)$$

$$= \frac{a^3}{6}\left(2 - \frac{3}{n} + \frac{1}{n^2}\right)$$

and hence, when $n \to \infty$,

$$S \to \frac{a^3}{3}$$

Hence the area under the curve $y = x^2$, from $x = 0$ to $x = a$, is $a^3/3$.

It is interesting to note that this result, proved by a similar method, was known to the ancient Greeks, long before the invention of calculus.

9.4 The integral notation

Example 1 could be done by integration. Before doing this, we introduce the symbol $\int (\dots) \, dx$ to denote integration with respect to x. The symbol $\int$, which is an elongated S, for 'sum', is a reminder that integration is essentially summation.

The area under $y = x + 1$ from $x = 0$ to $x = 10$ is

$$\int_0^{10} y \, dx = \int_0^{10} (x + 1) \, dx$$

$$= \left[\tfrac{1}{2}x^2 + x \right]_0^{10}$$

$$= (\tfrac{1}{2} \times 10^2 + 10) - (0)$$

$$= 60$$

Similarly the result of Example 2 can be obtained by integration, as follows:

$$\int_0^a x^2 \, dx = \left[\tfrac{1}{3}x^3 \right]_0^a$$

$$= \tfrac{1}{3}a^3$$

For indefinite integrals, where there are no limits, a similar notation is used. Thus:

$$\int (3x^2 + 4) \, dx = x^3 + 4x + c$$

Qu. 2 Find the following indefinite integrals:

(a) $\int (3x - 4) \, dx$ (b) $\displaystyle\int \frac{8x^5 - 3x}{x^3} \, dx$

(c) $\int \sqrt[7]{x} \, dx$ (d) $\int (2\sqrt{t} - 3)(1 - \sqrt{t}) \, dt$

Qu. 3 Evaluate the following definite integrals:

(a) $\displaystyle\int_{1/2}^1 (60t - 16t^2) \, dt$ (b) $\displaystyle\int_1^2 \frac{1}{2x^4} \, dx$ (c) $\displaystyle\int_1^4 \frac{(y + 3)(y - 3)}{\sqrt{y}} \, dy$

We have shown above that when $y = x + 1$, the limit of $\displaystyle\sum_{x=0}^{x=10} y\delta x$, as $\delta x \to 0$, is identical with, and is more readily evaluated as $\displaystyle\int_0^{10} y \, dx$.

We shall now assume that for any curve which is continuous between $x = a$ and $x = b$, the area under the curve from $x = a$ to $x = b$ is†

---

the limit, as $\delta x \to 0$, of $\displaystyle\sum_{x=a}^{x=b} y\delta x = \int_a^b y \, dx$

---

† The reader may be interested to note the parallel between this statement and that concerning gradient, namely the limit, as $\delta x \to 0$, of $\dfrac{\delta y}{\delta x} = \dfrac{dy}{dx}$.

Notice that, in general, if $f(x)$ is a continuous function and $F(x)$ is the function whose derivative is $f(x)$, i.e. $F'(x) = f(x)$, then

$$\int_a^b f(x)\,dx = \left[F(x) \right]_a^b$$
$$= F(b) - F(a)$$

This is called the **fundamental theorem of calculus**.

If, in addition, $f(x) \geqslant 0$, when $a \leqslant x \leqslant b$, then this integral gives the area under the curve $y = f(x)$, from $x = a$ to $x = b$. If, however, $f(x)$ is not always positive in this interval, then the graph of $y = f(x)$ must be consulted, in order to distinguish between the positive and negative areas.

The reader should in future think of every area bounded by a curve as a summation, first writing down the area of one of the typical strips, or *elements of area*, into which it is most conveniently divided, and then evaluating the limit of the sum of those strips by integration. A convenient way of laying out the working is shown in the following examples; these extend the work of Chapter 7 in the following ways:

(a) by using elements of area parallel to the x-axis, we may integrate with respect to y;

(b) by finding the element of area cut off between two curves we may evaluate in only one step the area enclosed between them.

Example 3

Find the area enclosed by $y = 4x - x^2$, $x = 1$, $x = 2$ and the x-axis (Figure 9.9).

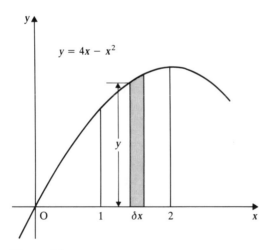

Figure 9.9

The element of area is $y\delta x = (4x - x^2)\delta x$

$\therefore$ the required area $= \displaystyle\int_1^2 (4x - x^2)\,\mathrm{d}x$

$$= \left[2x^2 - \tfrac{1}{3}x^3 \right]_1^2$$

$$= (8 - \tfrac{8}{3}) - (2 - \tfrac{1}{3})$$

$$= 3\tfrac{2}{3}$$

Example 4

Find the area enclosed by that part of $y = x^2$ for which x is positive, the y-axis, and the lines $y = 1$ and $y = 4$.

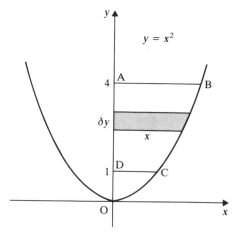

Figure 9.10

The required area is ABCD in Figure 9.10. The equation may be written $x = \pm \sqrt{y}$, and for the part of the curve with which we are concerned $x = +\sqrt{y} = y^{1/2}$.

The element of area is $x\delta y$.

$\therefore$ the required area $= \displaystyle\int_1^4 x\,\mathrm{d}y$

$$= \int_1^4 y^{1/2}\,\mathrm{d}y$$

$$= \left[\tfrac{2}{3}y^{3/2} \right]_1^4$$

$$= (\tfrac{2}{3} \times 8) - (\tfrac{2}{3})$$

$$= 4\tfrac{2}{3}$$

Example 5

Find the area enclosed between the two curves $y = 4 - x^2$ and $y = x^2 - 2x$.

We must first sketch the curves, and to find the limits of integration we must find the x-coordinates of the points of intersection.

When $x^2 - 2x = 4 - x^2$,

$$2x^2 - 2x - 4 = 0$$
$$x^2 - x - 2 = 0$$
$$(x - 2)(x + 1) = 0$$
$$x = -1 \quad \text{or} \quad +2$$

The element of area is shown shaded in Figure 9.11.

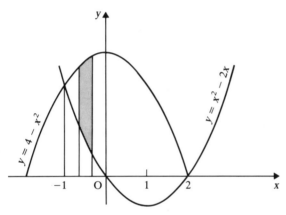

Figure 9.11

If we write $Y = 4 - x^2$ and $y = x^2 - 2x$, the element of area is $(Y - y)\delta x$.

$\therefore$ the required area $= \displaystyle\int_{-1}^{+2} (Y - y)\,dx$

$\qquad\qquad\qquad = \displaystyle\int_{-1}^{+2} \{(4 - x^2) - (x^2 - 2x)\}\,dx$

$\qquad\qquad\qquad = \displaystyle\int_{-1}^{+2} (4 + 2x - 2x^2)\,dx$

$\qquad\qquad\qquad = \left[4x + x^2 - \tfrac{2}{3}x^3 \right]_{-1}^{+2}$

$\qquad\qquad\qquad = (4 \times 2 + 2^2 - \tfrac{2}{3} \times 2^3) - (-4 + 1 + \tfrac{2}{3})$
$\qquad\qquad\qquad = 8 + 4 - 5\tfrac{1}{3} + 4 - 1\tfrac{2}{3}$
$\qquad\qquad\qquad = 9$

Exercise 9b

1 Find the following integrals:

(a) $\int x(x-3)\,dx$

(b) $\int \dfrac{2(x-1)}{x^3}\,dx$

(c) $\int \left(t^2 + 4 + \dfrac{3}{t^2}\right) dt$

(d) $\int \dfrac{t+1}{\sqrt{t}}\,dt$

2 Evaluate:

(a) $\displaystyle\int_{-2}^{+3} (v^2 + 3)\,dv$

(b) $\displaystyle\int_{1}^{4} (y^2 + \sqrt{y})\,dy$

(c) $\displaystyle\int_{0}^{1} \sqrt{x}(x+2)\,dx$

(d) $\displaystyle\int_{1}^{2} \left(3 + \dfrac{1}{t^2} + \dfrac{1}{t^4}\right) dt$

(e) $\displaystyle\int_{1}^{9} \left(\sqrt{x} + \dfrac{1}{\sqrt{x}}\right) dx$

(f) $\displaystyle\int_{4}^{11} \sqrt{(x+5)}\,dx$

3 Find the area under each of the following curves between the given limits:
(a) $y = x^2 + 3$ $x = -1$ to $x = 2$
(b) $y = x^2(3-x)$ $x = 4$ to $x = 5$
(c) $y = x^2 + 1/x^2$ $x = \frac{1}{2}$ to $x = 1$

4 Find the area enclosed by the y-axis and the following curves and straight lines:
(a) $x = y^2$, $y = 3$ (b) $y = x^3$, $y = 1$, $y = 8$
(c) $x - y^2 - 3 = 0$, $y = -1$, $y = 2$ (d) $x = 1/\sqrt{y}$, $y = 2$, $y = 3$

5 Find the area enclosed by each of the following curves and the y-axis:
(a) $x = (y-1)(y-4)$ (Why is this negative?)
(b) $x = 3y - y^2$
(c) $x = y(y-2)^2$

6 Find the area enclosed by $y^2 = 4x$ and the straight lines $x = 1$ and $x = 4$.

7 Find the area enclosed by $y^2 = x + 9$ and the y-axis, by taking an element of area (a) parallel to the y-axis, and (b) parallel to the x-axis.

8 Find the area enclosed by $9x^2 + y - 16 = 0$ and the x-axis, by integrating (a) with respect to x, and (b) with respect to y.

9 By reference to a clear diagram, show that if $f(x)$ is an odd function, then

$$\int_{-a}^{+a} f(x)\,dx = 0$$

Show also that if $g(x)$ is an even function, then

$$\int_{-a}^{+a} g(x)\,dx = 2\int_{0}^{+a} g(x)\,dx$$

10 Prove, using the method of Example 2 in the text, that

$$\int_0^a x^3 \, dx = \frac{a^4}{4}$$

[You will need to quote that $1 + 8 + 27 + \ldots + (N-1)^3 = N^2(N-1)^2/4$.]

9.5 Solids of revolution

If we take a triangular piece of cardboard ABC with a right angle at B, and rotate it through 360 degrees about AB, we sweep out the volume of a right circular cone (Figure 9.12). The cone can thus be thought of as the **solid of revolution** generated by rotating the area ABC about the line AB.

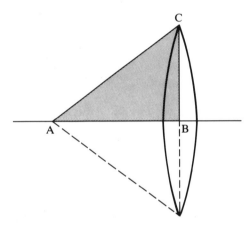

Figure 9.12

Qu. 4 State the solid generated by rotating through 360 degrees:
(a) the above triangle ABC (i) about BC, (ii) about AC
(b) the area of a semi-circle about the bounding diameter
(c) a quadrant of a circle about a boundary radius
(d) the area of a circle centre (3, 3) radius 1, about the y-axis
(e) a rectangle about one of its sides.

The method of calculating the volume of a solid of revolution is best illustrated by discussing an example; the ideas involved are the same as those of Section 9.3.

Example 6

Find the volume of the solid generated by rotating about the x-axis the area under $y = \frac{3}{4}x$ from $x = 0$ to $x = 4$.

A typical element of area under $y = \frac{3}{4}x$ is $y\delta x$, shown shaded in Figure 9.13; rotating this area about the x-axis we generate the typical *element of volume*, a cylinder of volume $\pi y^2 \delta x$. The corresponding 'slice' of the solid (Figure 9.14) has one circular face of radius y, and the other of radius $y + \delta y$, and its volume lies between that of an 'inside' cylinder $\pi y^2 \delta x$, and an 'outside' cylinder $\pi (y + \delta y)^2 \delta x$.

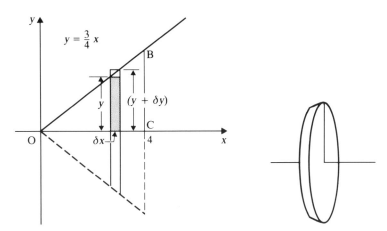

Figure 9.13   Figure 9.14

The sum of the volumes of all the 'inside' (or 'outside') cylinders is an approximation to the volume required, and, by making δx sufficiently small, we can make this sum approach as close as we please to the volume of the solid of revolution, which may therefore be written as

$$\text{the limit, as } \delta x \to 0, \text{ of } \sum_{x=0}^{x=4} \pi y^2 \delta x$$

This may be evaluated as $\displaystyle\int_0^4 \pi y^2 \, dx$; thus the solution of this example may be presented as follows.

The element of volume $= \pi y^2 \delta x = \pi \dfrac{9x^2}{16} \delta x$

$$\therefore \quad \text{the required volume} = \int_0^4 \pi \frac{9x^2}{16} \, dx$$

$$= \left[\pi \frac{3x^3}{16} \right]_0^4$$

$$= \pi \frac{3 \times 4^3}{16}$$

$$= 12\pi$$

Qu. 5 Find the volume of the solid generated by rotating about the x-axis:
(a) the area under $y = x^2$ from $x = 1$ to $x = 2$,
(b) the area under $y = x^2 + 1$ from $x = -1$ to $x = +1$.

The volumes of solids generated by rotating areas about the y-axis may be evaluated by integration with respect to y. This, and other aspects of this work, are illustrated by the following examples.

Example 7

Find the volume of the solid generated by rotating about the y-axis the area in the first quadrant enclosed by $y = x^2$, $y = 1$, $y = 4$, and the y-axis (Figure 9.15).

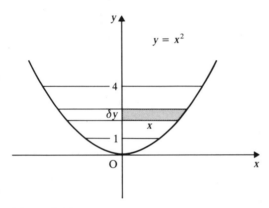

Figure 9.15

The element of volume $= \pi x^2 \delta y = \pi y \delta y$

$\therefore$ the required volume $= \displaystyle\int_1^4 \pi y \, dy$

$$= \left[\tfrac{1}{2}\pi y^2 \right]_1^4$$

$$= \tfrac{1}{2}\pi \times 16 - \tfrac{1}{2}\pi$$

$$= \frac{15\pi}{2}$$

Example 8

The area of the segment cut off by $y = 5$ from the curve $y = x^2 + 1$ is rotated about $y = 5$; find the volume generated (Figure 9.16).

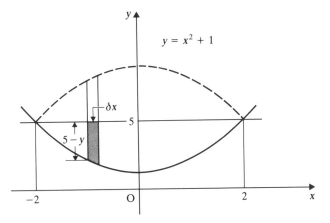

Figure 9.16

The points of intersection occur when

$$x^2 + 1 = 5$$
$$x^2 = 4$$
$$x = -2 \quad \text{or} \quad +2$$

The element of volume $= \pi(5-y)^2\,\delta x$
$$= \pi(5 - x^2 - 1)^2\,\delta x$$
$$= \pi(16 - 8x^2 + x^4)\delta x$$

$$\therefore \quad \text{the required volume} = \int_{-2}^{+2} \pi(16 - 8x^2 + x^4)\,\mathrm{d}x$$

$$= \left[\pi(16x - \tfrac{8}{3}x^3 + \tfrac{1}{5}x^5)\right]_{-2}^{+2}$$

$$= \pi(32 - 21\tfrac{1}{3} + 6\tfrac{2}{5}) - \pi(-32 + 21\tfrac{1}{3} - 6\tfrac{2}{5})$$

$$= 34\tfrac{2}{15}\pi$$

Example 9

The area of the segment cut off by $y = 5$ from the curve $y = x^2 + 1$ is rotated about the x-axis; find the volume generated (Figure 9.17).

The solid generated is a cylinder fully open at each end, but with the internal diameter decreasing towards the middle; its volume is found by subtracting the volume of the cavity from the volume of the solid cylinder of the same external dimensions.

The required volume = the volume generated by rotation, about the x-axis, of the rectangle ABDE   . . . (1)
minus   the volume generated by rotation, about the x-axis, of the area under $y = x^2 + 1$ from $x = -2$ to $x = +2$, i.e. ABCDE   . . . (2)

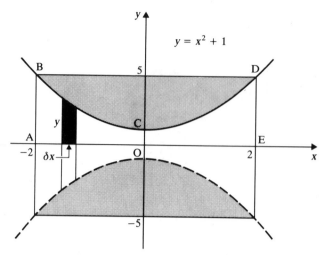

Figure 9.17

$\text{volume } (1) = \pi r^2 h = \pi \times 5^2 \times 4 = 100\pi$

$\text{element of volume } (2) = \pi y^2 \delta x$

$$= \pi(x^4 + 2x^2 + 1)\delta x$$

$\therefore \quad \text{volume } (2) = \displaystyle\int_{-2}^{+2} \pi(x^4 + 2x^2 + 1)\,dx$

$$= \left[\pi\left(\frac{x^5}{5} + \frac{2}{3}x^3 + x \right) \right]_{-2}^{+2}$$

$$= \pi(6\tfrac{2}{5} + 5\tfrac{1}{3} + 2) - \pi(-6\tfrac{2}{5} - 5\tfrac{1}{3} - 2)$$

$$= 27\tfrac{7}{15}\pi$$

$\therefore \quad \text{the required volume} = 100\pi - 27\tfrac{7}{15}\pi$

$$= 72\tfrac{8}{15}\pi$$

Exercise 9c

Leave π in the answers.

1 Find the volumes of the solids generated by rotating about the x-axis each of the areas bounded by the following curves and lines:
(a) $x + 2y - 12 = 0$, $x = 0$, $y = 0$ (b) $y = x^2 + 1$, $y = 0$, $x = 0$, $x = 1$
(c) $y = \sqrt{x}$, $y = 0$, $x = 2$ (d) $y = x(x - 2)$, $y = 0$
2 Find the volumes of the solids generated by rotating about the y-axis each of the areas bounded by the following curves and lines:
(a) $y = 2x - 4$, $y = 2$, $x = 0$ (b) $x = \sqrt{(y - 1)}$, $x = 0$, $y = 4$
(c) $x - y^2 - 2 = 0$, $x = 0$, $y = 0$, $y = 3$ (d) $y^2 = x + 4$, $x = 0$

3 Find the volumes of the solids generated when each of the areas enclosed by the following curves and lines is rotated about the given line:
 (a) $y = x$, $x = 0$, $y = 2$, about $y = 2$
 (b) $y = \sqrt{x}$, $y = 0$, $x = 4$, about $x = 4$
 (c) $y^2 = x$, $x = 0$, $y = 2$, about $y = 2$
 (d) $y = 2 - x^2$, $y = 1$, about $y = 1$
4 Repeat no. 3 for the following areas:
 (a) $x - 3y + 3 = 0$, $x = 0$, $y = 2$, about the x-axis
 (b) $x - y^2 - 1 = 0$, $x = 2$, about the y-axis
 (c) $y^2 = 4x$, $y = x$, about $y = 0$
 (d) $y = 1/x$, $y = 1$, $x = 2$, about $y = 0$
5 Obtain, by integration, the formula for the volume of a right circular cone of base radius r, height h. (Consider the area enclosed by $y = (h/r)x$, $x = 0$ and $y = h$.)
6 The equation of a circle centre the origin and radius r is $x^2 + y^2 = r^2$. By considering the area of this circle cut off in the first quadrant being rotated about either the x- or y-axis, deduce the formula for the volume of a sphere radius r.
7 A hemispherical bowl of internal radius 13 cm contains water to a maximum depth of 8 cm. Find the volume of the water.
8 A goldfish bowl is a glass sphere of inside diameter 20 cm. Calculate the volume of water it contains when the maximum depth is 18 cm.
9 The area under $y = \frac{1}{9}x^2 + 1$ from $x = 0$ to $x = 3$, and the area enclosed by $y = 0$, $y = 2$, $x = 3$, and $x = 4$, are rotated about the y-axis, and the solid generated represents a metal ash tray, the units being cm. Calculate the volume of metal.
10 The area enclosed by $y = x^2 + 1/x$, the x-axis and $x = -2$, is rotated about the x-axis; find the volume generated.

9.6 Centre of gravity

The reader who has dealt with this topic in mechanics will be familiar with the fact that, for a system of bodies whose centres of gravity lie in a plane, taking moments about any line in the plane:

the moment of their total weight acting at the centre of gravity of the system
= the sum of the moments of the weight of each body

If n bodies of weight $w_1, w_2, w_3, \ldots w_n$ have their centres of gravity at (x_1, y_1), (x_2, y_2), (x_3, y_3), ... (x_n, y_n) respectively, writing the coordinates of the centre of gravity of the system as $(\bar{x}, \bar{y})$, and taking moments about the y-axis:

$$\bar{x}(w_1 + w_2 + w_3 + \ldots + w_n) = x_1 w_1 + x_2 w_2 + x_3 w_3 + \ldots + x_n w_n$$

Using the $\sum$ notation:

$$\bar{x} \sum w = \sum xw$$

Similarly, taking moments about the x-axis,

$$\bar{y} \sum w = \sum yw$$

If, instead of separate bodies, we consider the elements of area of a uniform lamina, then $\sum xw$ and $\sum yw$ become the sums of the moments of the weights of the elements about the axes, and these can be evaluated by integration.

Example 10

Find the centre of gravity of a uniform lamina whose shape is the area bounded by $y^2 = 4x$ and $x = 9$.

By symmetry the centre of gravity lies on the x-axis, hence $\bar{y} = 0$. Consider the lamina as made up of strips parallel to the y-axis, then if the weight per unit area is ρ, a typical element (Figure 9.18) at a distance x from the y-axis has weight $\rho \times 2y \times \delta x$ and its moment about the y-axis is $x \times 2\rho y \delta x$.

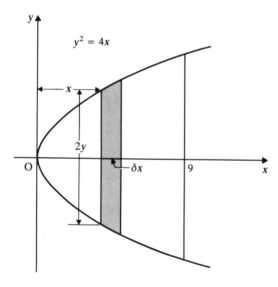

Figure 9.18

The sum of the moments of the weights of the elements

$$= \sum_{x=0}^{x=9} 2\rho xy \delta x$$

and the limit of this, as $\delta x \to 0$, is evaluated as

$$2\rho \int_0^9 xy \, dx$$

The weight of the whole lamina

$$= \rho \times \text{twice the area under } y = 2x^{1/2} \text{ from } x = 0 \text{ to } x = 9$$

$$= 2\rho \int_0^9 y \, dx$$

Since

$$\bar{x} \sum w = \sum xw$$

$$\bar{x} \times 2\rho \int_0^9 y \, dx = 2\rho \int_0^9 xy \, dx$$

∴

$$\bar{x} \int_0^9 y \, dx = \int_0^9 xy \, dx$$

But $y = 2x^{1/2}$,

∴

$$\bar{x} \int_0^9 x^{1/2} \, dx = \int_0^9 x^{3/2} \, dx$$

∴

$$\bar{x} \left[\tfrac{2}{3} x^{3/2} \right]_0^9 = \left[\tfrac{2}{5} x^{5/2} \right]_0^9$$

∴

$$\bar{x} \times \tfrac{2}{3} \times 3^3 = \tfrac{2}{5} \times 3^5$$

∴

$$\bar{x} = \tfrac{27}{5}$$

∴   the centre of gravity of the lamina is at $(\tfrac{27}{5}, 0)$.

Example 11

Find the centre of gravity of a uniform lamina whose shape is the area bounded by $y = x^2$, the x-axis and $x = 4$ (Figure 9.19).

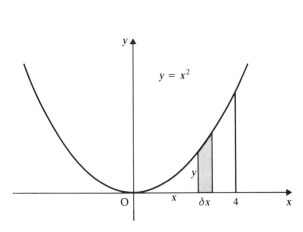

Figure 9.19

Let the weight per unit area be ρ.

Taking moments about the y-axis,

$$\bar{x} \times \rho \int_0^4 y\,dx = \rho \int_0^4 xy\,dx$$

$$\therefore \quad \bar{x} \int_0^4 y\,dx = \int_0^4 xy\,dx$$

But $y = x^2$,

$$\therefore \quad \bar{x} \int_0^4 x^2\,dx = \int_0^4 x^3\,dx$$

$$\therefore \quad \bar{x}\left[\tfrac{1}{3}x^3\right]_0^4 = \left[\tfrac{1}{4}x^4\right]_0^4$$

$$\therefore \quad \bar{x} \times \tfrac{1}{3} \times 4^3 = \tfrac{1}{4} \times 4^4$$

$$\therefore \qquad \bar{x} = 3$$

The centre of gravity of the element is at its mid-point, thus the moment of its weight about the x-axis is $\tfrac{1}{2}y \times \rho y \delta x$.

Taking moments about the x-axis,

$$\bar{y} \times \rho \int_0^4 y\,dx = \rho \int_0^4 \tfrac{1}{2}y^2\,dx$$

$$\therefore \quad \bar{y} \int_0^4 y\,dx = \int_0^4 \tfrac{1}{2}y^2\,dx$$

$$\therefore \quad \bar{y} \int_0^4 x^2\,dx = \int_0^4 \tfrac{1}{2}x^4\,dx$$

$$\therefore \quad \bar{y}\left[\tfrac{1}{3}x^3\right]_0^4 = \left[\tfrac{1}{10}x^5\right]_0^4$$

$$\therefore \quad \bar{y} \times \tfrac{1}{3} \times 4^3 = \tfrac{1}{10} \times 4^5$$

$$\therefore \qquad \bar{y} = \tfrac{24}{5}$$

$\therefore$ the centre of gravity of the lamina is at $(3, \tfrac{24}{5})$.

Qu. 6 Find the centre of gravity of the lamina whose area is bounded by
(a) $y^2 = x$ and $x = 2$ (b) $y = \sqrt{x}$, $y = 0$ and $x = 2$

The centre of gravity of a solid of revolution may be found in the same way, since the centre of gravity of each element of volume lies in the plane of the axes.

Example 12

Find the centre of gravity of the solid generated by rotating about the x-axis the area under $y = x$ from $x = 0$ to $x = 3$ (Figure 9.20).

The solid is a cone, vertex O, and axis Ox. By symmetry, the centre of gravity lies on the x-axis.

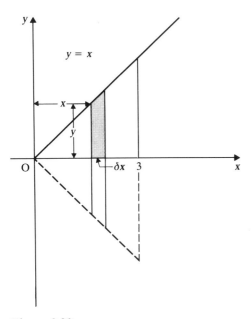

Figure 9.20

Let the weight per unit volume be ρ.

The centre of gravity of the element of volume is on the x-axis, thus the moment of its weight about the y-axis is $x \times \rho\pi y^2 \,\delta x$.

Taking moments about the y-axis,

$$\bar{x} \times \rho \int_0^3 \pi y^2 \,\mathrm{d}x = \int_0^3 x\rho\pi y^2 \,\mathrm{d}x$$

$$\therefore \qquad \bar{x} \int_0^3 y^2 \,\mathrm{d}x = \int_0^3 xy^2 \,\mathrm{d}x$$

But $y = x$,

$$\therefore \qquad \bar{x} \int_0^3 x^2 \,\mathrm{d}x = \int_0^3 x^3 \,\mathrm{d}x$$

$$\therefore \qquad \bar{x} \left[\tfrac{1}{3}x^3 \right]_0^3 = \left[\tfrac{1}{4}x^4 \right]_0^3$$

$$\therefore \qquad \bar{x} \times \tfrac{1}{3} \times 3^3 = \tfrac{1}{4} \times 3^4$$

$$\therefore \qquad \bar{x} = \tfrac{9}{4}$$

$\therefore$ the centre of gravity of the cone is at $(\tfrac{9}{4}, 0)$.

Exercise 9d

In nos. 1 to 3, find the coordinates of the centre of gravity of the uniform lamina whose area is bounded by the given straight lines and curves.

1 (a) $y^2 = 9x$, $x = 4$ (b) $y = \frac{1}{4}x^2$, $y = 1$
   (c) $y^2 = 4 - x$, the y-axis   (d) $y = 1/x^2$, $y = 1$, $y = 4$

2 (a) $x + y^2 - 1 = 0$, the y-axis
   (b) $y = x^2 + 2$, $x = -1$, $x = +1$ and $y = 0$

3 (a) $y = \frac{1}{3}x$, $y = 0$, $x = 12$ (b) $x = 2\sqrt{y}$, $y = 1$, $x = 0$
   (c) $y = x^2$, $y = 0$, $x = 3$ (d) $y = x^3$, $y = 0$, $x = 2$

4 Find the centres of gravity of the solids of revolution generated when the areas bounded by the following straight lines and curves are rotated about the given axes:
   (a) $x + 3y - 6 = 0$, $x = 0$, $y = 0$, about the x-axis
   (b) $y = 2\sqrt{x}$, $y = 0$, $x = 4$, about the x-axis
   (c) $y^2 = 4x$, $y = 4$, $x = 0$, about the y-axis
   (d) $y = x^2(2 - x)$, $y = 0$, about the x-axis

5 By considering the solid generated by rotating, about the x-axis, the area enclosed by $y = (r/h)x$, the x-axis and $x = h$, deduce the position of the centre of gravity of a right circular cone.

6 The equation of the circle, centre the origin, radius r, is $x^2 + y^2 = r^2$. By considering the solid generated by rotating about either axis the area of one quadrant, deduce the distance of the centre of gravity of a solid hemisphere from its plane surface.

7 A goldfish bowl consists of a sphere of inside radius 10 cm. If it contains water to a maximum depth of 16 cm, find the height of the centre of gravity of the water above the lowest point.

8 A uniform lamina is of the shape of the quadrant of the circle $x^2 + y^2 = r^2$ cut off by the positive axes. Find the coordinates of its centre of gravity.

Exercise 9e (Miscellaneous)

1 Calculate $\displaystyle\int_{-1}^{1} x(x^2 - 1)\,dx$.

   Find the area bounded by the curve $y = x(x^2 - 1)$ and the x-axis
   (a) between $x = -1$ and $x = 0$ (b) between $x = 0$ and $x = 1$.

2 Find the area between the curve $y = x(x - 1)^2(2 - x)$ and the portion of the x-axis between $x = 1$ and $x = 2$.

3 The line $y = \frac{1}{2}x + 1$ meets the curve $y = \frac{1}{4}(7x - x^2)$ at the points A and B. Calculate the coordinates of A and B and the length of the line AB. Prove that the upper segment of the curve cut off by the line has an area $1\frac{1}{8}$.

4 The area enclosed between the line $x = 1$, the x-axis, the line $x = 3$ and the line $3x - y + 2 = 0$, is rotated through four right angles about the x-axis. Find the volume generated.

5 Solids of revolution are generated by rotating
   (a) about the x-axis the area bounded by the arc of the curve $y = 2x^2$ between $(0, 0)$ and $(2, 8)$, the line $x = 2$ and the x-axis;
   (b) about the y-axis the area bounded by the same arc, the line $y = 8$ and the y-axis.
   Calculate the volumes of the two solids so formed.

6 The corners of a trapezium are at the points $(0, 2)$, $(2, 2)$, $(0, 4)$, $(3, 4)$. Find the volume of the solid formed by revolving the area about the y-axis.

7 Sketch the curve $y = x^2(1 - x)$. The area between the curve and the part of the x-axis from $x = 0$ to $x = 1$ is rotated about the x-axis. Find the volume swept out.

8 The portion of the parabola $y = \frac{2}{3}\sqrt{x}$ between $x = \frac{1}{4}$ and $x = 2$ is revolved about the x-axis so as to obtain a parabolic cup with a circular base and top. Show that the volume of the cup is approximately 2.75.

9 Find the equation of the tangent to the curve $y = x - 1/x$ at the point $(1, 0)$. The area between the curve, the x-axis and the ordinate $x = 2$ is rotated about the x-axis. Prove that the volume thus obtained is $\frac{5}{6}\pi$.

10 The curve $y = x^2 + 4$ meets the axis of y at the point A, and B is the point on the curve where $x = 2$. Find the area between the arc AB, the axes, and the line $x = 2$. If this area is revolved about the x-axis, prove that the volume swept out is approximately 188.

11 A cylindrical hole of radius 4 cm is cut from a sphere of radius 5 cm, the axis of the cylinder coinciding with a diameter of the sphere. Prove that the volume of the remaining portion of the sphere is 36π cm^3.

12 Find the area bounded by the curve $y = 3x^2 - x^3$ and the x-axis. Find the x-coordinate of the centre of gravity of this area.

13 Find the area bounded by the x-axis and the arc of the curve

$$y = x^2(x - 1)(3 - x)$$

from $x = 1$ to $x = 3$. Find also the x-coordinate of the centre of gravity of this area.

14 Find the area and the x-coordinate of the centre of gravity of the lamina whose edges are formed by the lines $x = 0$, $y = 0$, and the part of the curve $y = (1 - x)(5 + 4x + x^2)$ which is cut off by these lines in the first quadrant.

Chapter 10

Some useful topics in algebra

10.1 Surds

It is not immediately obvious that

$$\frac{3\sqrt5}{2\sqrt7}, \ \frac{\sqrt{45}}{\sqrt{28}}, \ \frac{3}{14}\sqrt{35}, \ \frac{15}{2\sqrt{35}}, \ \frac{3}{2}\sqrt{\frac57}, \ \frac{\sqrt{45}}{2\sqrt7}, \ \frac{3\sqrt5}{\sqrt{28}}, \ \sqrt{\frac{45}{28}}$$

all represent the same number. Again, it may not be clear on first sight that $1/(\sqrt2-1)$ and $\sqrt2+1$ are equal.

Since square roots frequently occur in trigonometry and coordinate geometry, it is useful to be able to recognise a number when it is written in different ways, and the purpose of this section is to give the reader practice in this.

The reader may have found an approximate value of $\sqrt2 \approx 1.414\,213\,562$ on a calculator and may know that this decimal does not terminate or recur. The ancient Greeks did not use decimals, but they discovered that $\sqrt2$ could not be expressed as a fraction of two integers (see Section 3.4). Such a root ($\sqrt3$, $\sqrt5$, $\sqrt[3]{6}$ are other examples) is called a **surd**. In general, a number which cannot be expressed as a fraction of two integers is called an **irrational** number.

Qu. 1 Square:
(a) $\sqrt2$ (b) $\sqrt6$ (c) $\sqrt a$ (d) $\sqrt{(ab)}$
(e) $3\sqrt2$ (f) $4\sqrt5$ (g) $2\sqrt a$ (h) $\sqrt2\times\sqrt3$
(i) $\sqrt5\times\sqrt7$ (j) $\sqrt2\times\sqrt8$ (k) $\sqrt{12}\times\sqrt3$ (l) $\sqrt a\times\sqrt b$

Note that the answers to parts (d) and (l) are the same, i.e.

$$\sqrt{(ab)}=\sqrt a\times\sqrt b$$

This result will be used in the next example.

Example 1

Write $\sqrt{63}$ as the simplest possible surd.

The factors of 63 are $3^2\times7$.

$$\therefore \quad \sqrt{63}=\sqrt{(3^2\times7)}=\sqrt{3^2}\times\sqrt7=3\sqrt7$$

188

Example 2

Express $6\sqrt{5}$ as the square root of an integer.

$$6\sqrt{5} = \sqrt{36} \times \sqrt{5} = \sqrt{(36 \times 5)} = \sqrt{180}$$

Example 3

Simplify $\sqrt{50} + \sqrt{2} - 2\sqrt{18} + \sqrt{8}$.

$$\sqrt{50} + \sqrt{2} - 2\sqrt{18} + \sqrt{8} = 5\sqrt{2} + \sqrt{2} - 2 \times 3\sqrt{2} + 2\sqrt{2}$$
$$= 8\sqrt{2} - 6\sqrt{2}$$
$$= 2\sqrt{2}$$

It is usual not to write surds in the denominator of a fraction when this can be avoided. The process of clearing *irrational* numbers is called **rationalisation**.

Example 4

Rationalise the denominators of (a) $\dfrac{1}{\sqrt{2}}$, (b) $\dfrac{1}{3 - \sqrt{2}}$.

(a) Multiply numerator and denominator by $\sqrt{2}$. Thus

$$\frac{1}{\sqrt{2}} = \frac{1}{\sqrt{2}} \times \frac{\sqrt{2}}{\sqrt{2}} = \frac{\sqrt{2}}{2}$$

(b) Multiply numerator and denominator by the denominator with the sign of $\sqrt{2}$ changed:

$$\frac{1}{3 - \sqrt{2}} = \frac{1}{3 - \sqrt{2}} \times \frac{3 + \sqrt{2}}{3 + \sqrt{2}}$$
$$= \frac{3 + \sqrt{2}}{9 - 2}$$
$$= \frac{1}{7}(3 + \sqrt{2})$$

Exercise 10a

Calculators should not be used in this exercise.

1 Square:

(a) $\sqrt{5}$
(b) $\sqrt{\frac{1}{2}}$
(c) $4\sqrt{3}$
(d) $\frac{1}{2}\sqrt{2}$
(e) $\sqrt{\dfrac{a}{b}}$

(f) $\sqrt{3} \times \sqrt{5}$
(g) $\sqrt{3} \times \sqrt{7}$
(h) $\dfrac{\sqrt{p}}{\sqrt{q}}$
(i) $\dfrac{1}{2\sqrt{p}}$
(j) $\dfrac{3\sqrt{a}}{\sqrt{(2b)}}$

2 Express in terms of the simplest possible surds:
(a) $\sqrt{8}$ (b) $\sqrt{12}$ (c) $\sqrt{27}$ (d) $\sqrt{50}$ (e) $\sqrt{45}$
(f) $\sqrt{1210}$ (g) $\sqrt{75}$ (h) $\sqrt{32}$ (i) $\sqrt{72}$ (j) $\sqrt{98}$

3 Express as square roots of integers:
(a) $3\sqrt{2}$ (b) $2\sqrt{3}$ (c) $4\sqrt{5}$ (d) $2\sqrt{6}$ (e) $3\sqrt{8}$

(f) $6\sqrt{6}$ (g) $8\sqrt{2}$ (h) $10\sqrt{10}$

4 Rationalise the denominators of the following fractions:

(a) $\dfrac{1}{\sqrt{5}}$ (b) $\dfrac{1}{\sqrt{7}}$ (c) $-\dfrac{1}{\sqrt{2}}$ (d) $\dfrac{2}{\sqrt{3}}$

(e) $\dfrac{3}{\sqrt{6}}$ (f) $\dfrac{1}{2\sqrt{2}}$ (g) $-\dfrac{3}{2\sqrt{3}}$ (h) $\dfrac{9}{4\sqrt{6}}$

(i) $\dfrac{1}{\sqrt{2}+1}$ (j) $\dfrac{1}{2-\sqrt{3}}$

5 Simplify:
(a) $\sqrt{8}+\sqrt{18}-2\sqrt{2}$ (b) $\sqrt{75}+2\sqrt{12}-\sqrt{27}$
(c) $\sqrt{28}+\sqrt{175}-\sqrt{63}$ (d) $\sqrt{1000}-\sqrt{40}-\sqrt{90}$
(e) $\sqrt{512}+\sqrt{128}+\sqrt{32}$ (f) $\sqrt{24}-3\sqrt{6}-\sqrt{216}+\sqrt{294}$

6 Express in the form $A+B\sqrt{C}$, where A, B and C are rational numbers:

(a) $\dfrac{2}{3-\sqrt{2}}$ (b) $(\sqrt{5}+2)^2$ (c) $(1+\sqrt{2})(3-2\sqrt{2})$

(d) $(\sqrt{3}-1)^2$ (e) $(1-\sqrt{2})(3+2\sqrt{2})$ (f) $\sqrt{\tfrac{1}{2}}+\sqrt{\tfrac{1}{4}}+\sqrt{\tfrac{1}{8}}$

7 Rationalise the denominators of:

(a) $\dfrac{\sqrt{3}+\sqrt{2}}{\sqrt{3}-\sqrt{2}}$ (b) $\dfrac{\sqrt{5}+1}{\sqrt{5}-\sqrt{3}}$ (c) $\dfrac{2\sqrt{2}-\sqrt{3}}{\sqrt{2}+\sqrt{3}}$

(d) $\dfrac{\sqrt{2}+2\sqrt{5}}{\sqrt{5}-\sqrt{2}}$ (e) $\dfrac{\sqrt{6}+\sqrt{3}}{\sqrt{6}-\sqrt{3}}$ (f) $\dfrac{\sqrt{10}+2\sqrt{5}}{\sqrt{10}+\sqrt{5}}$

10.2 Laws of indices

It is assumed that the reader knows the following laws of indices for positive integers:

> (1) $a^m \times a^n = a^{m+n}$
> (2) $a^m \div a^n = a^{m-n}$, $(m > n)$
> (3) $(a^m)^n = a^{mn}$
> (4) $(ab)^m = a^m b^m$

We shall now assume that these laws hold for *any* indices, and see what meaning must be assigned to fractional and negative indices as a result of this assumption.

10.3 Rational indices

We know that $4^3 = 4 \times 4 \times 4$, but so far $4^{1/2}$ has not been given any meaning. If rational indices are to be used, clearly it is an advantage if they are governed by the laws of indices. This being so, what meaning should be given to $4^{1/2}$? By the first law of indices,

$$4^{1/2} \times 4^{1/2} = 4^1 = 4$$

Therefore $4^{1/2}$ is defined as the square root of 4 (to avoid ambiguity we take it to be the positive square root) and so $4^{1/2} = 2$. Similarly, $a^{1/2} = \sqrt{a}$.

To see what value should be given to $8^{1/3}$, consider

$$8^{1/3} \times 8^{1/3} \times 8^{1/3} = 8^1 = 8$$

Therefore $8^{1/3}$ is defined as $\sqrt[3]{8}$, which is 2. Similarly, $a^{1/3} = \sqrt[3]{a}$.

In general, taking n factors of $a^{1/n}$,

$$a^{1/n} \times a^{1/n} \times \ldots \times a^{1/n} = a$$

so that

$$\boxed{a^{1/n} = \sqrt[n]{a}}$$

Next consider $8^{2/3}$. We know that $8^{1/3} = 2$, so

$$8^{2/3} = 8^{1/3} \times 8^{1/3} = 2 \times 2 = 4$$

Therefore we must take $8^{2/3}$ to be the square of the cube root of 8, and in general $a^{m/n}$ must be taken to be the mth power of $\sqrt[n]{a}$ (or the nth root of a^m), and we may write

$$\boxed{a^{m/n} = \sqrt[n]{a^m}}$$

Qu. 2 Find the values of:
(a) $9^{1/2}$ (b) $27^{1/3}$ (c) $27^{2/3}$ (d) $4^{1/2}$
(e) $4^{3/2}$ (f) $9^{5/2}$ (g) $8^{4/3}$ (h) $16^{3/4}$

10.4 Zero and negative indices

So far 2^0 has been given no meaning. Again it is desirable for it to be given a meaning consistent with the laws of indices, so we divide 2^1 by 2^1 using the second law:

$$2^1 \div 2^1 = 2^0$$

But $2^1 \div 2^1 = 1$, so 2^0 must be taken to be 1. In the same way, $a^n \div a^n = a^0$, so

$$\boxed{a^0 = 1 \quad (a \neq 0)}$$

Qu. 3 Why does the above not hold for $a = 0$?

To find what meaning must be given to 2^{-1}, divide 2^0 by 2^1, using the second law of indices:

$$2^0 \div 2^1 = 2^{-1}$$

But $2^0 \div 2^1 = 1 \div 2 = \frac{1}{2}$, therefore we must take 2^{-1} to be $\frac{1}{2}$.

Similarly:

$$2^{-3} = 2^0 \div 2^3 = \frac{1}{2^3}$$

Thus 2^{-3} is the reciprocal of 2^3.

In the same way:

$$\boxed{a^{-n} = \frac{1}{a^n}}$$

that is, a^{-n} is the reciprocal of a^n.

Example 5

Find the value of $(27/8)^{-2/3}$.

Using the last result, $(27/8)^{-2/3} = (8/27)^{2/3}$.

$$\left(\frac{8}{27}\right)^{2/3} = \left[\left(\frac{8}{27}\right)^{1/3}\right]^2$$
$$= [\tfrac{2}{3}]^2$$
$$= \tfrac{4}{9}$$

Exercise 10b

Without using a calculator, find the values of:

1 (a) $25^{1/2}$ (b) $27^{1/3}$ (c) $64^{1/6}$ (d) $49^{1/2}$ (e) $\left(\frac{1}{4}\right)^{1/2}$

(f) $1^{1/4}$ (g) $(-8)^{1/3}$ (h) $(-1)^{1/5}$ (i) $8^{4/3}$ (j) $27^{2/3}$

2 (a) 7^0 (b) 3^{-1} (c) 5^0 (d) 4^{-1} (e) 2^{-3}

(f) $\left(\frac{1}{2}\right)^{-1}$ (g) $\left(\frac{1}{3}\right)^{-2}$ (h) $\left(\frac{4}{9}\right)^0$ (i) 3^{-3} (j) $(-6)^{-1}$

3 (a) $8^{-1/3}$ (b) $8^{-2/3}$ (c) $4^{-1/2}$ (d) $4^{-3/2}$

(e) $27^{-2/3}$ (f) $\left(\frac{1}{4}\right)^{-1/2}$ (g) $\left(\frac{1}{8}\right)^{-1/3}$ (h) $\left(\frac{1}{27}\right)^{-2/3}$

(i) $\left(\frac{4}{9}\right)^{-1/2}$ (j) $\left(\frac{8}{27}\right)^{-1/3}$

4 (a) $256^{1/2}$ (b) $1296^{1/2}$ (c) $64^{1/3}$ (d) $216^{1/3}$ (e) $(2\frac{1}{4})^{1/2}$
(f) $(1\frac{7}{9})^{1/2}$ (g) $8^{-1/3}$ (h) $4^{-3/2}$ (i) $64^{-2/3}$ (j) $81^{-3/4}$

10.5 Logarithms

Definition

> If $c^x = a$, then we say that:
>
> the logarithm, base c, of a is x.

This is written

> $\log_c a = x$

For example:

$$10^3 = 1000$$

and so $\log_{10} 1000 = 3$.

Likewise:

$$2^5 = 32 \quad \text{and so} \quad \log_2 32 = 5$$

Qu. 4 What are the bases and logarithms in the following statements?
(a) $10^2 = 100$ (b) $10^{1.6021} \approx 40$ (c) $9 = 3^2$ (d) $4^3 = 64$
(e) $1 = 2^0$ (f) $8 = (1/2)^{-3}$ (g) $a^b = c$

Exercise 10c

1 Express the following statements in logarithmic notation:
(a) $2^4 = 16$ (b) $27 = 3^3$ (c) $125 = 5^3$
(d) $10^6 = 1\,000\,000$ (e) $1728 = 12^3$ (f) $64 = 16^{3/2}$
(g) $10^4 = 10\,000$ (h) $4^0 = 1$ (i) $0.01 = 10^{-2}$
(j) $\frac{1}{2} = 2^{-1}$ (k) $9^{3/2} = 27$ (l) $8^{-2/3} = \frac{1}{4}$
(m) $81 = (1/3)^{-4}$ (n) $e^0 = 1$ (o) $16^{-1/4} = \frac{1}{2}$
(p) $(1/8)^0 = 1$ (q) $27 = 81^{3/4}$ (r) $4 = (1/16)^{-\frac{1}{2}}$
(s) $c = a^5$ (t) $a^3 = b$ (u) $p^q = r$
(v) $a = b^c$
2 Express in index notation:
(a) $\log_2 32 = 5$ (b) $\log_3 9 = 2$ (c) $2 = \log_5 25$
(d) $\log_{10} 100\,000 = 5$ (e) $7 = \log_2 128$ (f) $\log_9 1 = 0$
(g) $-2 = \log_3 \frac{1}{9}$ (h) $\log_4 2 = \frac{1}{2}$ (i) $\log_e 1 = 0$
(j) $\log_{27} 3 = \frac{1}{3}$ (k) $2 = \log_a x$ (l) $\log_3 a = b$
(m) $\log_a 8 = c$ (n) $y = \log_x z$ (o) $p = \log_q r$

3 Evaluate:

(a) $\log_2 64$ (b) $\log_{10} 100$ (c) $\log_{10} 10^7$ (d) $\log_a a^2$

(e) $\log_8 2$ (f) $\log_4 1$ (g) $\log_{27} 3$ (h) $\log_5 125$

(i) $\log_e e^3$ (j) $\log_e \dfrac{1}{e}$

Given that:

$$c^x = a$$

then $\log_c a = x$

and given that:

$$c^y = b$$

then $\log_c b = y$

Using the standard rules of indices, we have:

$$ab = c^{x+y}$$

and hence:

$$\log_c (ab) = x + y$$
$$= \log_c a + \log_c b$$

Qu. 5 Prove that $\log_c (a/b) = \log_c a - \log_c b$.

The logarithm of the nth power of a number is obtained by multiplying its logarithm by n. A method of proving this rule is suggested in the next question.

Qu. 6 Write in logarithmic notation: $a = c^x$, $a^n = c^{nx}$.

Deduce that $\log_c a^n = n \log_c a$.

In Qu. 5 and Qu. 6, the suffix c has been used to denote the base of the logarithms. However, when the same base is used throughout a piece of work (for example the answer to a single question or exercise) the suffix may be omitted. Using this convention, the results we have found above can be summarised as follows:

$\log a + \log b = \log (a \times b)$	. . . . (1)
$\log a - \log b = \log (a/b)$	. . . . (2)
$n \times \log a = \log (a^n)$	. . . . (3)

These three results are used in the next example.

Example 6

Express $2 \log_{10} a + \frac{1}{2} \log_{10} b - 3$ as the logarithm of a single term.

Using rule (3) above:

$$2 \log_{10} a = \log_{10} a^2$$
and $\frac{1}{2} \log_{10} b = \log_{10} b^{1/2} = \log_{10} \sqrt{b}$
also $\qquad 3 = \log_{10} 1000$

So the given expression can be written:

$$\log_{10} a^2 + \log_{10} \sqrt{b} - \log_{10} 1000$$

$$= \log_{10} (a^2 \sqrt{b}) - \log_{10} 1000 \qquad \text{by rule (1)}$$

$$= \log_{10} \left(\frac{a^2 \sqrt{b}}{1000} \right) \qquad\qquad \text{by rule (2)}$$

The logarithm, to base *ten*, of x is frequently written $\lg x$. This abbreviation is used in the next example and in the exercise which follows.

Example 7

Simplify $\dfrac{\lg 125}{\lg 25}$

[Note that 125 and 25 are both powers of 5, so their logarithms can be expressed in terms of $\lg 5$.]

$$\frac{\lg 125}{\lg 25} = \frac{\lg 5^3}{\lg 5^2} = \frac{3 \lg 5}{2 \lg 5} = \frac{3}{2}$$

Most scientific calculators provide the user with logarithms base ten (usually indicated by a key marked *log*, or just *lg*), and also logarithms base e (indicated by *ln*). The number e is extremely important in mathematics and the reader will study it in detail in Chapter 26. For present purposes, it is sufficient to know that its approximate value is 2.718.

Example 8

Use a calculator to find an approximate value of $\log_2 7$.

Write $x = \log_2 7$, then $2^x = 7$. Since $2^x = 7$, their logarithms to the base of ten are equal, therefore

$$\lg 2^x = \lg 7$$

$$\therefore \qquad x \lg 2 = \lg 7$$

$$\therefore \qquad x = \frac{\lg 7}{\lg 2}$$

$$= 2.8074 \quad \text{(correct to five significant figures)}$$

Therefore $\log_2 7 \approx 2.8074$.

Exercise 10d

The base of the logarithms is omitted unless it has a special bearing on the question.

Note lg x means $\log_{10} x$.

1 Express in terms of $\log a$, $\log b$, $\log c$:

(a) $\log ab$

(b) $\log \dfrac{a}{c}$

(c) $\log \dfrac{1}{b}$

(d) $\log a^2 b^{3/2}$

(e) $\log \dfrac{1}{b^4}$

(f) $\log \dfrac{a^{1/3} b^4}{c^3}$

(g) $\log \sqrt{a}$

(h) $\log \sqrt[3]{b}$

(i) $\log \sqrt{(ab)}$

(j) $\lg (10a)$

(k) $\lg \dfrac{1}{100b^2}$

(l) $\log \sqrt{\left(\dfrac{a}{b}\right)}$

2 Express as single logarithms:

(a) $\log 2 + \log 3$

(b) $\log 18 - \log 9$

(c) $\log 4 + 2 \log 3 - \log 6$

(d) $3 \log 2 + 2 \log 3 - 2 \log 6$

(e) $\log c + \log a$

(f) $\log x + \log y - \log z$

(g) $2 \log a - \log b$

(h) $2 \log a + 3 \log b - \log c$

(i) $\frac{1}{2} \log x - \frac{1}{2} \log y$

(j) $\log p - \frac{1}{3} \log q$

(k) $2 + 3 \lg a$

(l) $1 + \lg a - \frac{1}{2} \lg b$

(m) $2 \lg a - 3 - \lg 2c$

(n) $3 \lg x - \frac{1}{2} \lg y + 1$

3 Simplify:

(a) $\lg 1000$

(b) $\frac{1}{2} \log_3 81$

(c) $\frac{1}{3} \log_2 64$

(d) $- \log_2 \frac{1}{2}$

(e) $\frac{1}{3} \log 8$

(f) $\frac{1}{2} \log 49$

(g) $- \frac{1}{2} \log 4$

(h) $3 \log 3 - \log 27$

(i) $5 \log 2 - \log 32$

(j) $\dfrac{\log 8}{\log 2}$

(k) $\dfrac{\log 81}{\log 9}$

(l) $\dfrac{\log 49}{\log 343}$

4 Solve the equations:

(a) $2^x = 5$

(b) $3^x = 2$

(c) $3^{4x} = 4$

(d) $2^x \times 2^{x+1} = 10$

(e) $(1/2)^x = 6$

(f) $(2/3)^x = 1/16$

5 Show that $\log_a b = 1/\log_b a$

(a) using the result $\log_a b \times \log_b c = \log_a c$

(b) from first principles

10.6 The functions $x \mapsto a^x$ and $x \mapsto \log_a x$

We can legitimately use the word function to describe $x \mapsto 10^x$ and $x \mapsto \log_{10} x$, because, in each case, for a given value of x, the rule will produce a unique result. In the case of $x \mapsto 10^x$, the domain is $\mathbb{R}$ and the range is $\mathbb{R}^+$, and for $x \mapsto \log_{10} x$, the domain is $\mathbb{R}^+$ and the range is $\mathbb{R}$. In most instances, the actual calculation of 10^x or $\log_{10} x$ will be very complicated, but this does not matter; a calculator can be used where it is appropriate (the same remarks apply to the function $x \mapsto \sqrt{x}$). More generally, if a is a fixed, positive, real number, $x \mapsto a^x$ and $x \mapsto \log_a x$, are perfectly satisfactory functions. (Note that the domains are $\mathbb{R}$ and $\mathbb{R}^+$, respectively.)

Qu. 7 If $f(x) = 10^x$ and $g(x) = \log_{10} x$, find the values of:
(a) $f(1)$ (b) $f(2)$ (c) $f(-1)$ (d) $g(10)$ (e) $g(1)$ (f) $g(\sqrt{10})$
Qu. 8 If $F(x) = a^x$ and $G(x) = \log_a x$, find:
(a) $F(1)$ (b) $F(2)$ (c) $F(-1)$ (d) $G(a)$ (e) $G(1)$ (f) $G(\sqrt{a})$

The following special cases are very common and the reader is advised to commit them to memory:

$$\begin{array}{l} \log_a 1 = 0 \\ \log_a a = 1 \\ \log_a (1/a) = -1 \end{array}$$

Remember that a logarithm is an index; the logarithm of q to base a is the power to which a must be raised to equal q, e.g. $\log_{10} 1000 = 3$, and $\log_2 (1/8) = -3$. Thus if $a^p = q$, then $\log_a q = p$, and these are equivalent statements, being simply alternative ways of stating the relationship between a, p and q. We can combine these statements in two ways:

$$\log_a (a^p) = \log_a (q) = p$$

and

$$a^{\log_a q} = a^p = q$$

So, if $f(x) = \log_a x$ and $g(x) = a^x$, then the composite functions fg and gf are given by:

$$fg(x) = f(a^x) = \log_a (a^x) = x$$

and

$$gf(x) = g(\log_a x) = a^{\log_a x} = x$$

In other words, the composite function merely gives the original value of x; the function f 'undoes' the effect of function g, and function g 'undoes' the effect of function f; that is the functions f and g are inverses of one another.

This effect can easily be observed on a pocket calculator. Enter any positive number, say 5, press the 'log' function key (the display should show 0.698 97), and then press the '10^x' function key. The display should return to the value originally entered, i.e. 5. Repeat this with other numbers; try it also with the functions in the reverse order. If your calculator is equipped with function keys for e^x and $\log_e x$ (these appear as exp and ln on some calculators) try the same routine with this pair of inverse functions.

Sketches of the graphs of $y = a^x$ and $\log_a x$ are shown in Figure 10.1. As with all inverse functions, the graphs are reflections of one another in the line $y = x$.

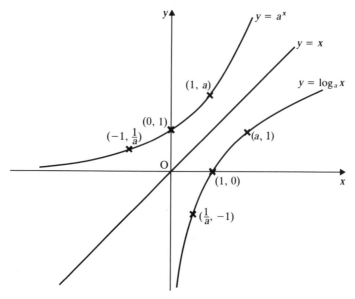

Figure 10.1

10.7 The remainder theorem

An expression of the form

$$ax^n + bx^{n-1} + \ldots + k$$

where $a, b, \ldots k$ are real numbers and n is a positive integer is called a **polynomial** of degree n. (The expression $5x^7 - 3x^2 + 1.5x - 0.3$, for example, is a polynomial of degree 7.)

If we divide the polynomial $x^3 - 3x^2 + 6x + 5$ by $x - 2$:

$$
\begin{array}{r}
x^2 - x + 4 \\
x - 2 \overline{\smash{\big)}\ x^3 - 3x^2 + 6x + 5} \\
\underline{x^3 - 2x^2} \\
-x^2 + 6x \\
\underline{-x^2 + 2x} \\
4x + 5 \\
\underline{4x - 8} \\
13
\end{array}
$$

the result may be expressed in the identity

$$x^3 - 3x^2 + 6x + 5 = (x - 2)(x^2 - x + 4) + 13$$

Here $x^2 - x + 4$ is called the **quotient** and 13 the **remainder**.

The remainder theorem gives a method of finding the remainder without going through the process of division.

Suppose it is required to find the remainder when $x^4 - 5x + 6$ is divided by $x - 2$. If the division were performed, we could write:

$x^4 - 5x + 6 = (x - 2) \times \text{quotient} + \text{remainder}$

Now if we put $x = 2$ in this identity we obtain:

$16 - 10 + 6 = 0 \times \text{quotient} + \text{remainder}$

$\therefore$ the remainder $= 12$

Applying this process to any such expression divided by $x - a$, we may write:

$\text{expression} = (x - a) \times \text{quotient} + \text{remainder}$

Putting $x = a$ in this identity, it follows that:

the remainder $=$ the value of the expression when $x = a$.

The function notation may be used to state the remainder theorem.

If a polynomial f(x) is divided by $x - a$, the remainder is f(a).

Example 9

Find the remainder when

$x^5 - 4x^3 + 2x + 3$

is divided by (a) $x - 1$, (b) $x + 2$.

Let f$(x) = x^5 - 4x^3 + 2x + 3$, then
(a) the remainder when f(x) is divided by $x - 1$ is

f$(1) = 1 - 4 + 2 + 3 = 2$

(b) the remainder when f(x) is divided by $x + 2$ is

f$(-2) = -32 + 32 - 4 + 3 = -1$

Example 10

Find the remainder when $4x^3 - 6x + 5$ is divided by $2x - 1$.

As $2x - 1$ is not in the form $x - a$, imagine the division to have been performed, then

$4x^3 - 6x + 5 = (2x - 1) \times \text{quotient} + \text{remainder}$

Putting $x = \frac{1}{2}$ in this identity:

$\frac{1}{2} - 3 + 5 = 0 \times \text{quotient} + \text{remainder}$

Therefore the remainder is $2\frac{1}{2}$.

Example 11

Factorise the expression $2x^3 + 3x^2 - 32x + 15$.

Let $f(x) = 2x^3 + 3x^2 - 32x + 15$.

$[x - a$ will be a factor of $f(x)$ only if there is no remainder on division, i.e. if $f(a) = 0$.]

$$f(1) = 2 + 3 - 32 + 15 \neq 0 \qquad \therefore \quad x - 1 \text{ is not a factor.}$$
$$f(-1) = -2 + 3 + 32 + 15 \neq 0 \qquad \therefore \quad x + 1 \text{ is not a factor.}$$

$x - 2$ and $x + 2$ cannot be factors, as 2 is not a factor of the constant term 15.

$$f(3) = 54 + 27 - 96 + 15 = 0 \qquad \therefore \quad x - 3 \text{ is a factor.}$$

On division (or by inspection):

$$2x^3 + 3x^2 - 32x + 15 = (x - 3)(2x^2 + 9x - 5)$$

Therefore the factors of $2x^3 + 3x^2 - 32x + 15$ are $(x - 3)(x + 5)(2x - 1)$.

Example 12

When the expression $x^5 + 4x^2 + ax + b$ is divided by $x^2 - 1$, the remainder is $2x + 3$. Find the values of a and b.

Suppose the division to have been performed, then

$$x^5 + 4x^2 + ax + b = (x^2 - 1) \times \text{quotient} + 2x + 3$$

Putting $x = 1$ $\qquad 1 + 4 + a + b = 2 + 3$
Putting $x = -1$ $\qquad -1 + 4 - a + b = -2 + 3$

These equations may be rewritten $a + b = 0$ and $-a + b = -2$.

Adding:
$\quad 2b = -2$
$\therefore \quad b = -1$ and $a = 1$

Exercise 10e

1 Find the values of $f(0)$, $f(1)$, $f(-1)$, $f(2)$, $f(-2)$ when:
   (a) $f(x) = x^3 + 3x^2 - 4x - 12$ (b) $f(x) = 3x^3 - 2x - 1$
   (c) $f(x) = x^5 + 2x^4 + 3x^3$ (d) $f(x) = x^4 - 4x^2 + 3$
   State one factor of each expression.
2 Find the remainders when:
   (a) $x^3 + 3x^2 - 4x + 2$ is divided by $x - 1$
   (b) $x^3 - 2x^2 + 5x + 8$ is divided by $x - 2$
   (c) $x^5 + x - 9$ is divided by $x + 1$
   (d) $x^3 + 3x^2 + 3x + 1$ is divided by $x + 2$
   (e) $4x^3 - 5x + 4$ is divided by $2x - 1$
   (f) $4x^3 + 6x^2 + 3x + 2$ is divided by $2x + 3$

3 Find the values of a in the expressions below when the following conditions are satisfied:
(a) $x^3 + ax^2 + 3x - 5$ has remainder -3 when divided by $x - 2$
(b) $x^3 + x^2 + ax + 8$ is divisible by $x - 1$
(c) $x^3 + x^2 - 2ax + a^2$ has remainder 8 when divided by $x - 2$
(d) $x^4 - 3x^2 + 2x + a$ is divisible by $x + 1$
(e) $x^3 - 3x^2 + ax + 5$ has remainder 17 when divided by $x - 3$
(f) $x^5 + 4x^4 - 6x^2 + ax + 2$ has remainder 6 when divided by $x + 2$

4 Show that $2x^3 + x^2 - 13x + 6$ is divisible by $x - 2$, and hence find the other factors of the expression.

5 Show that $12x^3 + 16x^2 - 5x - 3$ is divisible by $2x - 1$ and find the factors of the expression.

6 Factorise:
(a) $x^3 - 2x^2 - 5x + 6$ (b) $x^3 - 4x^2 + x + 6$
(c) $2x^3 + x^2 - 8x - 4$ (d) $2x^3 + 5x^2 + x - 2$
(e) $2x^3 + 11x^2 + 17x + 6$ (f) $2x^3 - x^2 + 2x - 1$

7 Find the values of a and b if $ax^4 + bx^3 - 8x^2 + 6$ has remainder $2x + 1$ when divided by $x^2 - 1$.

8 The expression $px^4 + qx^3 + 3x^2 - 2x + 3$ has remainder $x + 1$ when divided by $x^2 - 3x + 2$. Find the values of p and q.

9 The expression $ax^2 + bx + c$ is divisible by $x - 1$, has remainder 2 when divided by $x + 1$, and has remainder 8 when divided by $x - 2$. Find the values of a, b, c.

10 $x - 1$ and $x + 1$ are factors of the expression $x^3 + ax^2 + bx + c$, and it leaves a remainder of 12 when divided by $x - 2$. Find the values of a, b, c.

10.8 Inequalities

Most readers will have met this topic in an earlier course, and will be familiar with the basic rules listed below. However any reader meeting these for the first time should find it quite easy to accept them, by experimenting with a few simple numbers.

The rules most frequently used are:

if $a > b$ then $a + c > b + c$ . . . (1)
            and $a - c > b - c$ . . . (2)

and if k is a positive number, then

$$ka > kb \qquad \qquad \text{. . . (3)}$$

However, if k is negative, then

$$ka < kb \qquad \qquad \text{. . . (4)}$$

Example 13

Solve $4 - 5x > 14$.

Given that $4 - 5x > 14$

take 4 from both sides (rule (2))

$$-5x > 10$$

divide both sides by -5 and change the inequality sign (rule (4))

$$x < -2$$

Another rule which is very useful when simplifying inequalities is that if $pq > 0$, then p and q have the same sign (they are either both positive, or they are both negative). This rule is used in the following two examples.

Example 14

Find the values of x for which $x^2 + x - 6 > 0$.

Factorising the given expression, we have

$$(x + 3)(x - 2) > 0$$

Since the product of the two factors $(x + 3)$ and $(x - 2)$ is positive, they must have the same sign, i.e. either $x > 2$, or $x < -3$.

Example 15

Find the values of x for which $\dfrac{x - 2}{x - 5} > 2$.

Take 2 from both sides

$$\frac{x - 2}{x - 5} - 2 > 0$$

Put the LHS over a common denominator

$$\frac{x - 2 - 2(x - 5)}{x - 5} > 0$$

Hence

$$\frac{x - 2 - 2x + 10}{x - 5} > 0$$

that is

$$\frac{8 - x}{x - 5} > 0$$

As with a product, a quotient can only be positive when the numerator and denominator have the same sign.

In this case, the values for which the expression is positive are:

$$5 < x < 8$$

10.9 Inequalities and the modulus sign

The reader is reminded that

$$|x| = x \qquad \text{when } x \text{ is positive} \qquad \text{and}$$
$$|x| = -x \qquad \text{when } x \text{ is negative}$$

If a is a positive number, then

$$|x - a| = x - a \quad \text{when} \quad x > a \quad \text{and}$$
$$|x - a| = a - x \quad \text{when} \quad x < a$$

The graph of $y = |x - a|$, is a pair of 'half-lines' forming a shape like a letter V, as in Figure 10.2 below:

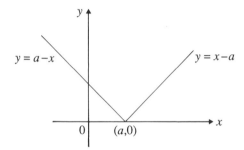

Figure 10.2

Example 16

Find the set of values of x for which $|x - 3| < 2$.

Figure 10.3 shows the graphs of $y = |x - 3|$ and $y = 2$.

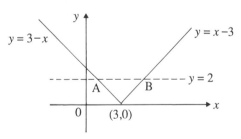

Figure 10.3

The inequality is satisfied for values of x lying between the x-coordinate of point A, and that of point B.

The x-coordinate of A is found by solving

$$3 - x = 2$$
i.e. $\qquad x = 1$

and the x-coordinate of B is found by solving

$$x - 3 = 2$$
i.e. $$x = 5$$

Hence the original inequality is satisfied when

$$1 < x < 5$$

Example 17

Solve the inequality $|x - 4| > 2|x - 7|$.

In Figure 10.4 the graph of $y = |x - 4|$ is CPAB and the graph of $y = 2|x - 7|$ is AQB.

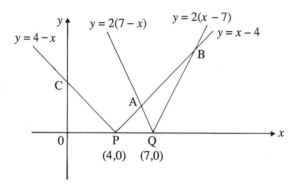

Figure 10.4

The inequality is satisfied when the first graph is above the second, i.e. for values of x lying between the x-coordinate of point A and the x-coordinate of point B.

To find the x-coordinate of point A we solve

$$2(7 - x) = x - 4$$
$$14 - 2x = x - 4$$
$$3x = 18$$
Hence $$x = 6$$

To find the x-coordinate of point B we solve

$$2(x - 7) = x - 4$$
$$2x - 14 = x - 4$$
Hence $$x = 10$$

Hence the inequality $|x - 4| > 2|x - 7|$ is satisfied when

$$6 < x < 10$$

Exercise 10f (Miscellaneous)

Calculators should not be used in this exercise.

1 Write in terms of the simplest possible surds:

(a) $\sqrt{180} + \sqrt{1125} - \sqrt{1280}$ (b) $\dfrac{3\sqrt{2}-4}{3-2\sqrt{2}}$

(c) $(\sqrt{3}+\sqrt{2})^3 + (\sqrt{3}-\sqrt{2})^3$

2 Express in the form $a + b\sqrt{2}$:

(a) $\dfrac{3+\sqrt{2}}{3-\sqrt{2}}$ (b) $(3+\sqrt{2})(5-\sqrt{2})$

3 (a) Find the values of $8^{-4/3}$, $(4/9)^{3/2}$, $512^{-2/9}$

(b) Solve the equation $x^{2/3} - 5x^{1/3} + 6 = 0$

4 Multiply $x^{2/3} + 2x^{1/3} + 1$ by $x^{1/3} - 2$. Check your answer by substituting $x = 8$.

5 Find the values of:

(a) $\dfrac{12^{3/2} \times 16^{1/8}}{27^{1/6} \times 18^{1/2}}$ (b) $\lg 75 + 2\lg 2 - \lg 3$

6 Express $\lg \dfrac{100a^2}{b^3\sqrt{c}}$ in terms of $\lg a$, $\lg b$, $\lg c$.

7 Solve the equations:

(a) $9^x = 27^{3/4}$ (b) $2^x = 9$

8 Sketch the graphs of the lines whose equations are $y = 2x + 3$ and $x + y = 5$. Shade the region for which

$y < 2x + 3$ and $x + y < 5$

9 Solve the following inequalities:

(a) $x^2 - 3x - 10 < 0$

(b) $(x-5)^2 > 3$

(c) $\dfrac{x+1}{x-2} > 3$

10 Solve the following inequalities:

(a) $|x| \leqslant 5|x-6|$

(b) $2|x+3| \leqslant x + 15$

Chapter 11

Quadratic equations and complex numbers

11.1 The quadratic equation $ax^2 + bx + c = 0$

It is assumed that readers are familiar with solving quadratic equations by factorisation, as in Example 1 below, and that some will be familiar with 'completing the square' (see Section 1.4), which is illustrated in Example 2.

Example 1

Solve $2x^2 + 7x - 15 = 0$.

$$2x^2 + 7x - 15 = 0$$
$$(2x - 3)(x + 5) = 0$$

hence:

either $\quad 2x - 3 = 0 \qquad x = 1\frac{1}{2}$
or $\qquad x + 5 = 0 \qquad x = -5$

When it is difficult to factorise, the technique of completing the square can be used. This method depends on the identity

$$(x + k)^2 = x^2 + 2kx + k^2$$

Example 2

Solve $5x^2 - 6x - 2 = 0$.

$$5x^2 - 6x - 2 = 0$$

Add 2 to both sides,

$$5x^2 - 6x \qquad = 2$$

divide through by 5,

$$x^2 - \frac{6}{5}x \qquad = \frac{2}{5}$$

complete the square, by adding $(\frac{3}{5})^2$ to both sides,

$$x^2 - \left(\frac{6}{5}\right)x + \left(\frac{3}{5}\right)^2 = \left(\frac{3}{5}\right)^2 + \frac{2}{5} = \frac{9+10}{25} = \frac{19}{25}$$

factorise the left-hand side,

$$\left(x - \frac{3}{5}\right)^2 = \frac{19}{25}$$

take the square root of both sides,

$$\left(x - \frac{3}{5}\right) = \pm\sqrt{\frac{19}{25}} = \pm\frac{\sqrt{19}}{5}$$

and finally, add $\frac{3}{5}$ to both sides,

$$x = \frac{3}{5} \pm \frac{\sqrt{19}}{5}$$
$$= \frac{3 \pm \sqrt{19}}{5}$$

[Answers to such questions should be left with surds in them, unless a specified degree of accuracy is demanded by the question.]

Notice that the roots can be used to find the factors of the original expression. Thus in Example 2,

$$5x^2 - 6x - 2 = 5(x^2 - \tfrac{6}{5}x - 2)$$
$$= 5\left(x - \frac{3+\sqrt{19}}{5}\right)\left(x - \frac{3-\sqrt{19}}{5}\right)$$

11.2 The quadratic formula

The procedure illustrated in Example 2, above, can be generalised, as follows. To solve

$$ax^2 + bx + c = 0$$

subtract c from both sides,

$$ax^2 + bx = -c$$

divide through by a,

$$x^2 + \left(\frac{b}{a}\right)x = -\left(\frac{c}{a}\right)$$

complete the square (by adding $b^2/(4a^2)$ to both sides),

$$x^2 + \left(\frac{b}{a}\right)x + \left(\frac{b}{2a}\right)^2 = \frac{b^2}{4a^2} - \frac{c}{a}$$

and factorise the left-hand side, which gives

$$\left(x + \frac{b}{2a}\right)^2 = \frac{b^2 - 4ac}{4a^2}$$

Take the square root (but note this is only possible if the right-hand side is non-negative i.e. if $b^2 - 4ac \geqslant 0$),

$$\left(x + \frac{b}{2a}\right) = \pm\sqrt{\left(\frac{b^2 - 4ac}{4a^2}\right)} = \frac{\pm\sqrt{(b^2 - 4ac)}}{2a} \qquad \ldots \ (1)$$

Now subtract $b/(2a)$ from both sides

$$x = -\frac{b}{2a} \pm \frac{\sqrt{(b^2 - 4ac)}}{2a}$$

$$\boxed{\text{So, if } \quad ax^2 + bx + c = 0 \quad \text{then} \quad x = \frac{-b \pm \sqrt{(b^2 - 4ac)}}{2a}}$$

This formula is usually the most convenient way of solving quadratic equations which cannot readily be solved by factorisation.

Example 3

Solve $2x^2 - 6x - 3 = 0$.

In this example $a = 2$, $b = -6$ and $c = -3$,

hence $b^2 - 4ac = 36 - 4 \times 2 \times (-3)$,
that is $b^2 - 4ac = 60$.

Substituting these figures into the formula

$$x = \frac{-b \pm \sqrt{(b^2 - 4ac)}}{2a}$$

gives

$$x = \frac{+6 \pm \sqrt{60}}{4}$$

$$= \frac{6 \pm 2\sqrt{15}}{4}$$

$$\therefore \quad x = \frac{3 \pm \sqrt{15}}{2}$$

Notice the importance of the step marked (1) in the proof of the quadratic formula. Three possibilities can arise:

(a) $b^2 - 4ac > 0$; a *real* value of $\sqrt{(b^2 - 4ac)}$ can be found and so the equation has two real distinct roots
(b) $b^2 - 4ac = 0$; the solution is $x = -b/(2a)$
(c) $b^2 - 4ac < 0$; there is no real value of $\sqrt{(b^2 - 4ac)}$ and so there are no real roots

In case (b), the expression $x^2 + (b/a)x + (c/a)$ is the square of $x + b/(2a)$ and it is convenient to say that the quadratic equation has 'two identical roots'. We shall return to case (c) in Section 11.6.

Because of its important role in determining the nature of the roots, the term $(b^2 - 4ac)$ is called the **discriminant** of the equation.

Qu. 1 Calculate the discriminant of each of the quadratics below and state whether the equation has (i) two distinct real roots, (ii) two identical roots, or (iii) no real roots:
(a) $3x^2 + 5x - 1 = 0$ (b) $49x^2 + 42x + 9 = 0$
(c) $2x^2 + 8x + 9 = 0$ (d) $2x^2 + 7x + 4 = 0$

11.3 The quadratic function $f(x) = ax^2 + bx + c$

Using the method of completing the square, the form $ax^2 + bx + c$ can always be reduced to the form $a(x - p)^2 + q$. This is illustrated in Example 4 below.

Example 4

Express the function $f(x) = 2x^2 - 12x + 23$ in the form $a(x - p)^2 + q$.

$$2x^2 - 12x + 23 = 2(x^2 - 6x + 11.5)$$
$$= 2[(x - 3)^2 - 9 + 11.5]$$
$$= 2[(x - 3)^2 + 2.5]$$
$$= 2(x - 3)^2 + 5$$

In this example, $a = 2$, $p = 3$ and $q = 5$. One advantage of this form is that, since $(x - 3)^2 \geq 0$, we can read off that $f(x) \geq 5$ and that the least value of the function occurs when $x = 3$.

Example 5

Find, by completing the square, the greatest value of the function $f(x) = 1 - 6x - x^2$.

$$f(x) = 1 - 6x - x^2$$
$$= 10 - (9 + 6x + x^2)$$
$$= 10 - (3 + x)^2$$

Since $(3 + x)^2$ is the square of a real number it cannot be negative; it is zero when $x = -3$, otherwise it is positive. Consequently $10 - (3 + x)^2$ is always less than or equal to 10.

∴   the greatest value of the function is 10 and this occurs when $x = -3$.

In general

$$ax^2 + bx + c = a\left(x^2 + \frac{b}{a}x + \frac{c}{a}\right)$$

$$= a\left[\left(x + \frac{b}{2a}\right)^2 - \frac{b^2}{4a^2} + \frac{c}{a}\right]$$

$$= a\left[\left(x + \frac{b}{2a}\right)^2 - \frac{b^2 - 4ac}{4a^2}\right]$$

$$= a\left(x + \frac{b}{2a}\right)^2 - \frac{b^2 - 4ac}{4a}$$

and thus $f(x) = ax^2 + bx + c$ may be written $a(x - p)^2 + q$, where

$$p = -\frac{b}{2a} \quad \text{and} \quad q = -\frac{b^2 - 4ac}{4a}$$

The least (or greatest) value of $f(x)$ is $f(p) = q$. If $a > 0$, $f(p)$ is the least value; if $a < 0$, it is the greatest value.

Qu. 2 Find, by completing the square, the range of the function

$$f(t) = 10 + 20t - 5t^2$$

11.4 The graph of $y = ax^2 + bx + c$

We have seen in Section 11.3 that this equation can be expressed in the form

$$y = a(x - p)^2 + q$$

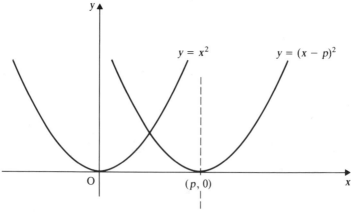

Figure 11.1

Now, we know that the graph of $y = x^2$ is a parabola and that the graph of $y = (x - p)^2$ is the same shape, but it is displaced p units to the right (Figure 11.1).

Multiplying $(x - p)^2$ by a merely 'stretches' the graph parallel to the y-axis, although if a is negative it will also turn it upside down. Adding q to $a(x - p)^2$ translates the graph q units vertically upwards. Thus the graph of

$$y = a(x - p)^2 + q$$

looks like Figure 11.2. In this diagram $a > 0$, $p > 0$ and $q > 0$ (i.e. $b^2 - 4ac < 0$).

Notice that if $q < 0$ (i.e. $b^2 - 4ac > 0$) but a and p are positive, then the graph would look like Figure 11.3.

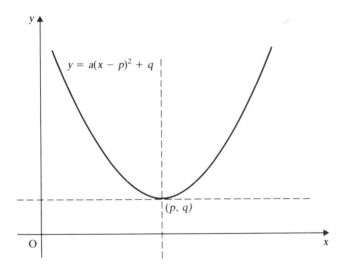

Figure 11.2

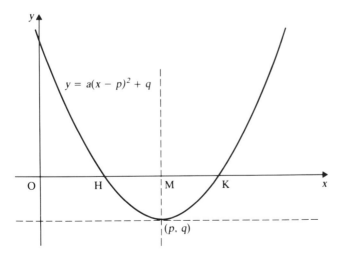

Figure 11.3

In this case, M is the point $(-b/(2a), 0)$ and H and K are the points where $ax^2 + bx + c = 0$ and, as we have seen in Section 11.2, at these points

$$x = -\frac{b}{2a} \pm \frac{\sqrt{(b^2 - 4ac)}}{2a}$$

Notice that these values of x can only be real if $b^2 - 4ac \geqslant 0$.

Qu. 3 Sketch the graph of $y = ax^2 + bx + c$, when:
(a) $b^2 > 4ac$ and $a < 0$ (b) $b^2 = 4ac$ and $a > 0$
In each diagram mark clearly the coordinates of the vertex.

Exercise 11a

Leave surds in the answers.

1 Solve, by factorisation:
   (a) $2x^2 - 5x + 3 = 0$ (b) $x^2 + 4x - 21 = 0$
   (c) $4x^2 - 25 = 0$ (d) $7x^2 + 5x = 0$
2 Solve, by completing the square:
   (a) $2x^2 - 6x - 1 = 0$ (b) $5x^2 + 12x + 6 = 0$
   (c) $x^2 + 7x - 3 = 0$ (d) $10 + 3x - 2x^2 = 0$
3 Solve, by using the formula:
   (a) $3t^2 - 7t - 1 = 0$ (b) $5z^2 + 3z - 7 = 0$
   (c) $4 + 13y + y^2 = 0$ (d) $3p^2 = 7p + 2$
4 Solve, where possible, by any suitable method:
   (a) $15 - 30x + 4x^2 = 0$ (b) $11x^2 = 48x$
   (c) $9x^2 = 8x - 2$ (d) $7x^2 - 38x + 15 = 0$
5 Using the results of no. 2, factorise:
   (a) $2x^2 - 6x - 1$ (b) $5x^2 + 12x + 6$
   (c) $x^2 + 7x - 3$ (d) $10 + 3x - 2x^2$
6 Sketch the graphs of:
   (a) $y = 2x^2 - 5x + 3$ (b) $y = 2x^2 - 6x - 1$
   (c) $y = 3x^2 - 7x - 1$ (d) $y = 3x^2 - 7x + 5$
   [Hint: use the answers to 1(a), 2(a) and 3(a).]
7 Sketch the graphs of:
   (a) $y = 9x^2 - 30x + 25$ (b) $y = x^2 - 6x + 13$
   (c) $y = 5 - x^2$ (d) $y = 36 + 48x - 9x^2$
8 Given that $3x^2 - kx + 12$ is positive for all values of x, find the range of possible values for k.
9 Given that α and β are the roots of the quadratic equation $x^2 - 7x + 3 = 0$, find α and β from the formula, and verify that $\alpha + \beta = 7$ and $\alpha\beta = 3$.
10 By completing the square, find the greatest values of:
   (a) $2 - 2x - x^2$ (b) $-7 + 12x - 3x^2$
   and the least values of:
   (c) $13 + 6x + 3x^2$ (d) $15 + 8x + \frac{1}{2}x^2$

11.5 Imaginary numbers

We have seen that the equation $x^2 + 1 = 0$, or $x^2 = -1$, has no real roots. For the moment, let us not worry too much about this; instead, we will write i for $\sqrt{(-1)}$. We could then say that $x^2 + 1 = 0$ has two roots, namely $x = \pm i$. Historically, this *is* how the subject developed. The sixteenth century mathematicians Cardano and Bombelli started to use symbols for square roots of negative numbers even though they knew they were not *real* numbers. Later Descartes started to call these numbers *imaginary numbers*. Then, in the eighteenth century, the Swiss mathematician Euler introduced the symbol i for $\sqrt{(-1)}$.

Having introduced i there is no need to invent further symbols for the square roots of other negative numbers. Consider, for example, $\sqrt{(-25)}$.

$$\begin{aligned}\sqrt{(-25)} &= \sqrt{(25 \times -1)} \\ &= \sqrt{25} \times \sqrt{(-1)} \\ &= 5i\end{aligned}$$

So an equation in the form

$$x^2 + n^2 = 0 \quad \text{or} \quad x^2 = -n^2 \quad \text{where} \quad n \in \mathbb{R},$$

has two roots, $x = \pm ni$.

[In some contexts, especially electricity where i is used to represent the current in an electrical circuit, the symbol j is used instead of i.]

Qu. 4 Solve the equations:
(a) $x^2 + 64 = 0$ (b) $x^2 + 7 = 0$ (c) $4x^2 + 9 = 0$ (d) $(x + 3)^2 = -25$

11.6 Complex numbers

We can now return to the problem of solving

$$ax^2 + bx + c = 0 \quad \text{when} \quad b^2 < 4ac$$

Previously (Section 11.2) we decided that no real roots exist in this case.

First, we consider a particular example; we shall try to solve

$$x^2 - 4x + 5 = 0$$

Completing the square gives

$$\begin{aligned}x^2 - 4x &= -5 \\ (x - 2)^2 - 4 &= -5 \\ (x - 2)^2 &= -1\end{aligned}$$

Previously, at this stage we were unable to proceed further because we could not find the square root of -1. Now, we can use our imaginary numbers. Hence

$$\begin{aligned}(x - 2) &= \pm i \\ \therefore \quad x &= 2 \pm i\end{aligned}$$

Qu. 5 Solve $x^2 - 6x + 34 = 0$.

The general solution of the equation $ax^2 + bx + c = 0$ is

$$x = \frac{-b \pm \sqrt{(b^2 - 4ac)}}{2a}$$

When $b^2 < 4ac$ this can be written

$$x = \frac{-b \pm \sqrt{[-1(4ac - b^2)]}}{2a}$$

$$= \frac{-b}{2a} \pm \frac{\sqrt{(4ac - b^2)}}{2a} \, i$$

Notice that both $-b/(2a)$ and $\sqrt{(4ac - b^2)}/(2a)$ are real numbers.

Numbers of the form $p + iq$, where p and q are real numbers, are called **complex numbers**. The standard symbol for the set of complex numbers is $\mathbb{C}$.

Example 6

Solve $x^2 - 6x + 13 = 0$, where $x \in \mathbb{C}$.

$$x^2 - 6x + 13 = 0$$

Using the formula

$$x = \frac{+6 \pm \sqrt{(36 - 4 \times 1 \times 13)}}{2}$$

$$= \frac{6 \pm \sqrt{(-16)}}{2}$$

$$= \frac{6 \pm 4i}{2}$$

$$\therefore \quad x = 3 \pm 2i$$

In the complex number $p + iq$, the number p is called the **real part** of the complex number and q is called its **imaginary part**. (Thus the real part of $5 + 4i$ is 5, and the imaginary part is 4.) It is frequently convenient to have a single letter to represent a complex number, and the normal choice for this is z, although w is also sometimes used. The real part of a complex number z can then be abbreviated to Re(z) and the imaginary part is written Im(z). Thus if $z = 2 + 7i$, then Re(z) = 2 and Im(z) = 7, or again, if $w = 4 - 3i$, then we can write Re(w) = 4 and Im(w) = -3.

It is important to notice that two complex numbers are equal if, and only if, their real parts are equal and their imaginary parts are equal, for if

$$a + ib = c + id$$

then

$$a - c = i(d - b)$$

and, squaring both sides,

$$(a - c)^2 = -(d - b)^2$$

Now, since, a, b, c and d are real numbers, $(a - c)^2$ and $(d - b)^2$ are either positive or they are zero. It is impossible for them to be positive, because we would then have a positive number on the left-hand side and a negative number on the right. Therefore $(a - c)^2$ and $(d - b)^2$ are both zero, i.e.

$$a = c \quad \text{and} \quad b = d$$

[The reader may feel that this is a rather trivial point, but, as we will see later, this is a very valuable feature of complex numbers. It may seem less trivial if it is compared with a similar situation in rational numbers. Here it *is* possible to have $a/b = c/d$, even though $a \neq c$ and $b \neq d$, for example, $2/3 = 10/15$.]

Since it was necessary to introduce complex numbers in order to include the roots of all quadratic equations, it might be thought that yet further types of number might be necessary in order to find the roots of equations of higher degree. However this is not so; it can be proved that a polynomial equation of degree n has exactly n roots (possibly repeated) in $\mathbb{C}$, but the proof is beyond the scope of this book.

Qu. 6 Solve the following equations with the quadratic formula or by completing the square:
(a) $z^2 - 4z + 13 = 0$ (b) $9z^2 + 25 = 0$
(c) $2z^2 = 2z - 13$ (d) $34z^2 - 6z + 1 = 0$

11.7 The algebra of complex numbers

In the course of learning elementary arithmetic, one has to learn how to add, subtract, multiply, and divide fractions: we are now faced with the problem of manipulating complex numbers. The operations addition, subtraction, multiplication, and division which we have used so far are concerned with real numbers, hence it is necessary to define what we mean by these operations with regard to complex numbers. It is easiest for us to define these operations by saying that we shall use the usual laws of algebra together with the relation $i^2 = -1$. Thus:

$$(a + ib) + (c + id) = (a + c) + i(b + d)$$
$$(a + ib) - (c + id) = (a - c) + i(b - d)$$
$$(a + ib) \times (c + id) = ac + aid + ibc + i^2 bd$$
$$= (ac - bd) + i(ad + bc)$$

At this stage it is worth comparing the corresponding operations with real numbers in the form $a + \sqrt{2}b$ (a, b rational):

$$(a + b\sqrt{2}) + (c + d\sqrt{2}) = (a + c) + \sqrt{2}(b + d)$$
$$(a + b\sqrt{2}) - (c + d\sqrt{2}) = (a - c) + \sqrt{2}(b - d)$$
$$(a + b\sqrt{2}) \times (c + d\sqrt{2}) = ac + ad\sqrt{2} + bc\sqrt{2} + 2bd$$
$$= (ac + 2bd) + \sqrt{2}(ad + bc)$$

This helps us to find a way of expressing $(a + ib)/(c + id)$ in the form $p + iq$. The reader may recall the corresponding process with $(a + b\sqrt{2})/(c + d\sqrt{2})$. The method is to multiply numerator and denominator in such a way that the new denominator involves a difference of two squares:

$$\frac{a + b\sqrt{2}}{c + d\sqrt{2}} \times \frac{c - d\sqrt{2}}{c - d\sqrt{2}} = \frac{(ac - 2bd) + \sqrt{2}(bc - ad)}{c^2 - 2d^2}$$

$$= \frac{ac - 2bd}{c^2 - 2d^2} + \sqrt{2}\frac{bc - ad}{c^2 - 2d^2}$$

Similarly, the expression $(a + ib)/(c + id)$ may be expressed in the form $p + iq$ by multiplying numerator and denominator by $c - id$ because

$$(c + id) \times (c - id) = c^2 - i^2 d^2 = c^2 + d^2$$

In other words,

$$\frac{a + ib}{c + id} = \frac{a + ib}{c + id} \times \frac{c - id}{c - id}$$

$$= \frac{(ac + bd) + i(bc - ad)}{c^2 + d^2}$$

Definition

Two complex numbers in the form $x + iy$, $x - iy$ are called **conjugate complex numbers**.

The symbol z^* is used to represent the complex conjugate of z, so if $z = x + iy$, then we write

$$z^* = x - iy$$

Qu. 7 Express $(2 + 3i)/(1 + i)$ in the form $p + iq$ ($p, q \in \mathbb{R}$). [Multiply numerator and denominator by $1 - i$.]

Do not attempt to memorise expressions for the sum, difference, product, and quotient of two complex numbers: simply use the usual laws of algebra, together with the relation $i^2 = -1$.

Exercise 11b

Simplify in nos. 1, 2 and 3:

1 (a) i^3 (b) i^4 (c) i^5 (d) i^6 (e) $\dfrac{1}{i^2}$ (f) $\dfrac{1}{i}$ (g) $\dfrac{1}{i^3}$

2 (a) $(3 + i) + (1 + 2i)$ (b) $(5 - 3i) + (4 + 3i)$
    (c) $(2 - 3i) - (1 + 2i)$ (d) $(1 + i) - (1 - i)$
3 (a) $(2 + 3i)(4 + 5i)$ (b) $(2 - i)(3 + 2i)$
    (c) $(1 + i)(1 - i)$ (d) $(3 + 4i)(3 - 4i)$
    (e) $(u + iv)(u - iv)$ (f) $(x + 2iy)(2x + iy)$
    (g) $i(2p + 3iq)$ (h) $(p + 2iq)(p - 2iq)$
4 Express with real denominators:

(a) $\dfrac{1 - i}{1 + i}$ (b) $\dfrac{1}{2 - 3i}$ (c) $\dfrac{3i - 2}{1 + 2i}$ (d) $\dfrac{5 + 4i}{5 - 4i}$

(e) $\dfrac{1}{x + iy}$ (f) $\dfrac{1}{x - iy}$ (g) $\dfrac{1}{2 + 3i} + \dfrac{1}{2 - 3i}$

Simplify the expressions in nos. 5 and 6:
5 (a) $(2 + 3i)^2$ (b) $(4 - 5i)^2$ (c) $(x + iy)^2$
6 (a) $(1 + i)^3$ (b) $(1 - i)^3$ (c) $1/(1 + i)^3$
7 Solve the quadratic equations:
    (a) $z^2 - 4z + 29 = 0$ (b) $4z^2 + 7 = 0$
    (c) $2z^2 + 3z + 5 = 0$ (d) $4z^2 + 4z + 5 = 0$
8 If α and β are the roots of $z^2 - 10z + 29 = 0$, find α and β by using the formula. Verify that $\alpha + \beta = 10$ and $\alpha\beta = 29$.
9 If α and β are the roots of $az^2 + bz + c = 0$, find, by using the formula, expressions for α and β, in terms of a, b and c. Verify that $\alpha + \beta = -b/a$ and that $\alpha\beta = c/a$.
10 Solve the cubic equation $2z^3 + 3z^2 + 8z - 5 = 0$.

11.8 Complex numbers as ordered pairs

To see how a satisfactory definition of complex numbers can be given, consider the problem of defining rational numbers in terms of the integers.

Note (a) A rational number is formed from a *pair* of integers, e.g. 2/3, 7/5, 4/1 (the last of which is commonly abbreviated to 4). (See Section 3.3.)

    (b) The position of the integers is important because in general $\dfrac{a}{b} \neq \dfrac{b}{a}$.

We therefore say that a rational number is an *ordered pair* of integers — but this, by itself, is not enough. To complete the definition, we must say how numbers of this type are to be added, subtracted, multiplied and divided.

We know that for rational numbers

$$\frac{a}{b} + \frac{c}{d} = \frac{ad + bc}{bd}$$

but this is by no means the only possible way of defining addition of the ordered pairs a/b, c/d. For instance, it would be much simpler to define addition by the rule

$$\frac{a}{b} + \frac{c}{d} = \frac{a + c}{b + d}$$

As to multiplication, with rational numbers,

$$\frac{a}{b} \times \frac{c}{d} = \frac{ac}{bd}$$

but multiplication of the ordered pairs a/b, c/d might have been defined by the rule

$$\frac{a}{b} \times \frac{c}{d} = \frac{ac - bd}{ad + bc}$$

We need not go through the process of defining subtraction and division: the point to note about defining the various operations on ordered pairs is that the properties of the numbers so defined will depend on the rules chosen.

Now consider complex numbers. We have seen that a complex number involves a *pair* of real numbers and that the *order* of the pair is important because in general $a + ib \neq b + ia$. We therefore define a complex number as an ordered pair of real numbers which we shall write as $[a, b]$. The fundamental operations of addition and multiplication are defined by the rules:

$$[a, b] + [c, d] = [a + c, b + d]$$
$$[a, b] \times [c, d] = [ac - bd, ad + bc]$$

Subtraction and division are defined in terms of addition and multiplication thus, for any type of number,

$p - q$ is the number x such that $q + x = p$ and
$p \div q$ is the number y such that $q \times y = p$

Now

$$[c, d] + [a - c, b - d] = [a, b]$$
$$\therefore \qquad [a, b] - [c, d] = [a - c, b - d].$$

Qu. 8 Use the definition of division above to show that

(a) for the rational numbers $\dfrac{a}{b}, \dfrac{c}{d}$,

$$\frac{a}{b} \div \frac{c}{d} = \frac{ad}{bc}$$

(b) for the complex numbers $[a, b]$, $[c, d]$,

$$[a, b] \div [c, d] = \left(\frac{ac + bd}{c^2 + d^2}, \frac{bc - ad}{c^2 + d^2} \right)$$

Qu. 9 Note that to every real number a there corresponds a unique complex number $[a, 0]$. Find, from the definitions of the four operations on complex numbers:

(a) $[a, 0] + [c, 0]$ (b) $[a, 0] \times [c, 0]$
(c) $[a, 0] - [c, 0]$ (d) $[a, 0] \div [c, 0]$

Compare these results with the corresponding operations on the real numbers a, c.

The next stage would be to show that these ordered pairs obey the laws of arithmetic. This would justify the use of the term *complex numbers*. However, we shall not pursue this argument.

The definition of a complex number as an ordered pair was first given by Hamilton in 1835.

11.9 The Argand diagram

The last section was written to show the reader that complex numbers can be put on a satisfactory logical basis. However, manipulation of complex numbers is most easily carried out as before: the ordered pair notation is simply a device for defining these numbers without reference to $\sqrt{(-1)}$. We could write $\sqrt{(-1)}$ as the ordered pair $[0, 1]$ but this would be rather clumsy and it is easier to write $\sqrt{(-1)} = i$.

Qu. 10 Prove from the definition of multiplication of complex numbers that

$$[0, 1] \times [0, 1] = [-1, 0]$$

Although the idea of an ordered pair may appear to some readers to have been a digression, it leads to the next step in our treatment of the subject. The Argand diagram is named after J R Argand, who published his work on the graphical representation of complex numbers in 1806.

Corresponding to every complex number $[x, y]$ or $x + iy$, there is a point (x, y) in the Cartesian plane; and corresponding to any point (x, y) in the plane, there is a complex number $x + iy$. (Here it is worth comparing the equivalent situation with real numbers. Corresponding to every real number x there is a point on the x-axis. What is less easy to prove is that corresponding to every point on the x-axis there is a real number.) At first this correspondence between complex numbers and points on the plane may appear to be rather obvious and not very useful, but in fact it proves to be of considerable importance to the theory of complex numbers.

The value of this correspondence is increased by the fact that with every point $P(x, y)$ in the plane there is associated a *radius vector* OP (see Figure 11.4). This means that corresponding to every complex number $x + iy$ there is a radius

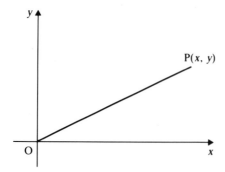

Figure 11.4

vector OP where P is (x, y). Further, corresponding to every radius vector OP in the plane there is a complex number $x + iy$.

Look at Figure 11.5. The points A, B, A', B' are respectively $(1, 0)$, $(0, 1)$, $(-1, 0)$, $(0, -1)$. Corresponding to

OA there is the complex number $1 + 0i$ or 1
OB there is the complex number $0 + 1i$ or i
OA' there is the complex number $-1 + 0i$ or -1
OB' there is the complex number $0 + (-1)i$ or $-i$

Looking down the right-hand side of the last four lines, each number is equal to the previous one multiplied by i. Meanwhile, the corresponding radius vector has rotated in the positive (anti-clockwise) sense through one right angle. Would the same thing happen if any complex number were multiplied by i?

Qu. 11 Find the complex numbers obtained by multiplying $x + iy$ once, twice and three times by i. Does the corresponding radius vector rotate through one right angle each time?

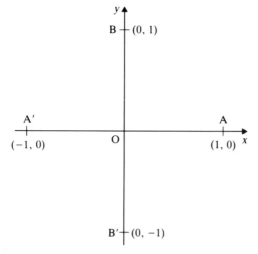

Figure 11.5

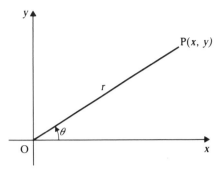

Figure 11.6

Two quantities are required to specify a vector through the origin: magnitude and direction. The magnitude r of OP (Figure 11.6) presents no difficulty

$$r = \sqrt{(x^2 + y^2)}$$

This quantity is called the **modulus** of the complex number $x + iy$. 'The modulus of $x + iy$' is abbreviated to $|x + iy|$ hence

$$|x + iy| = \sqrt{(x^2 + y^2)}$$

Qu. 12 Write down the moduli of:
(a) $3 + 4i$ (b) $-i$ (c) $\cos \theta + i \sin \theta$
(d) $\frac{1}{2} - \frac{1}{2}\sqrt{3}i$ (e) -3 (f) $1 + i$

The direction specifying the radius vector OP is not quite so easy to deal with because there are infinitely many positive and negative angles which would do.

The problem of which angle to choose is well illustrated by a radius vector in the third quadrant (Figure 11.7). It is simply a matter of convention whether we take the positive reflex angle or the negative obtuse angle. In fact the numerically smaller angle is used. The angle between the radius vector OP and the positive x-axis is called the **argument** of the complex number $x + iy$. This

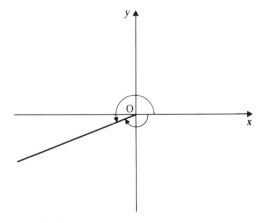

Figure 11.7

is abbreviated to arg $(x + iy)$ and has, as we have said before, infinitely many values. The value uniquely specified by the above convention is called the **principal value** of the argument and is written arg $(x + iy)$, so that

$$-180° < \arg (x + iy) \leqslant 180°$$

[In some textbooks, the argument is called the amplitude but this term is less acceptable because of possible confusion with the amplitude of a current, motion, or wave.]

Qu. 13 Find the principal values of the arguments of:
(a) $\cos 45° + i \sin 45°$ (b) $+1$
(c) $-i$ (d) $1 - i$
(e) $\frac{1}{2} + \frac{1}{2}\sqrt{3}i$ (f) $\cos 120° + i \sin 120°$
(g) $\cos 20° - i \sin 20°$ (h) $\sin 20° + i \cos 20°$

A complex number can be completely specified by its modulus and argument, because, as we can see from Figure 11.8, $x = r \cos \theta$ and $y = r \sin \theta$. Thus if $|z| = r$ and arg $z = \theta$, then

$$z = r \cos \theta + ir \sin \theta$$
$$= r(\cos \theta + i \sin \theta)$$

Notice, also, that if we are given a complex number $z = x + iy$, then its complex conjugate, $z^* = x - iy$. In other words z^* is the reflection of z in the real axis. Hence $|z^*| = |z|$ and arg $(z^*) = -\arg z$. ($\bar{z}$ may also be used to denote the complex conjugate of z.)

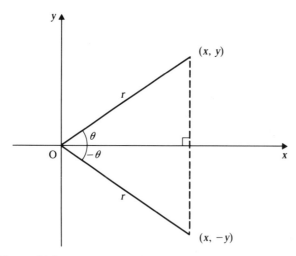

Figure 11.8

Example 7

▦   Given $|z| = 10$ and arg $z = 120°$, write down z.   ▩

$z = 10(\cos 120° + i \sin 120°)$

$$= 10\left(-\frac{1}{2} + i\frac{\sqrt{3}}{2}\right)$$

$$= -5 + 5\sqrt{3}i$$

Exercise 11c

1 Mark on the Argand diagram, the radius vectors corresponding to:
   (a) $1 + i$ (b) $-3 + 2i$ (c) $-3 - 2i$
   (d) $3 - 4i$ (e) $-4 + 3i$ (f) $\cos 60° + i \sin 60°$
   (g) $\cos 120° + i \sin 120°$ (h) $\cos 180° + i \sin 180°$
   Write down the moduli of these complex numbers and give the principal
   values of their arguments.
2 Write down, in the form $x + iy$, the complex numbers whose moduli are
   equal to one and whose arguments are:
   (a) $0°$ (b) $90°$ (c) $180°$ (d) $270°$ (e) $360°$
   (f) $30°$ (g) $-30°$ (h) $120°$ (i) $-120°$ (j) $150°$
3 If $z = 3 + 4i$ and $w = 12 + 5i$, write down the moduli and arguments of:
   (a) z (b) w (c) $1/z$ (d) $1/w$ (e) zw
   (f) $z*$ (g) $w*$ (h) $(zw)*$ (i) z^2 (j) w^2
4 Simplify: $(1 + i)^2$, $(1 + i)^3$, $(1 + i)^4$.
   Draw in the Argand diagram the radius vectors corresponding to $(1 + i)$,
   $(1 + i)^2$, $(1 + i)^3$, $(1 + i)^4$. Find the principal values of the arguments of these
   complex numbers.
5 Repeat no. 4
   (a) for the complex number $\frac{1}{2}\sqrt{3} + \frac{1}{2}i$ (b) for the complex number $\sqrt{3} + i$
6 Given the complex number $z = a + ib$, where a and $b \in \mathbb{R}$, find z^2 and $1/z$
   in terms of a and b. Verify that $|z^2| = |z|^2$ and $|1/z| = 1/|z|$.
7 Prove that if $|z| = r$, then $zz* = r^2$.
8 Given that $z = a + ib$ and $w = c + id$, where a, b, c and $d \in \mathbb{R}$, find zw in
   terms of a, b, c, and d, and verify that $|zw| = |z| \times |w|$.
9 By writing $z = a + bi$, where a and b are real, solve the equation $z^2 = 5 + 12i$.
10 Using the method of no. 9, find the square roots of $3 - 4i$.

11.10 Roots of quadratic equations

If an algebraic equation, in which the unknown quantity is x, is satisfied by
putting $x = c$, we say that c is a **root** of the equation; e.g. $x^2 - 5x + 6 = 0$ is
satisfied by putting $x = 2$, so one root of this equation is 2 (the other is 3).

It is often useful to be able to obtain information about the roots of an equation
without actually solving it. For instance, if α and β are the roots of the equation
$3x^2 + x - 1 = 0$, the value of $\alpha^2 + \beta^2$ can be found without first finding the
values of α and β. This is done by finding the values of $\alpha + \beta$ and $\alpha\beta$, and
expressing $\alpha^2 + \beta^2$ in terms of $\alpha + \beta$ and $\alpha\beta$.

The equation whose roots are α and β may be written

$$(x - \alpha)(x - \beta) = 0$$
$$\therefore \quad x^2 - \alpha x - \beta x + \alpha\beta = 0$$
$$\therefore \quad x^2 - (\alpha + \beta)x + \alpha\beta = 0 \qquad \qquad \qquad \ldots \ (1)$$

But suppose that α and β are also the roots of the equation

$$ax^2 + bx + c = 0$$

which may be written

$$x^2 + \frac{b}{a}x + \frac{c}{a} = 0 \qquad \qquad \qquad \ldots \ (2)$$

Now equations (1) and (2), having the same roots, must be precisely the same equation, written in two different ways, since the coefficients of x^2 are both 1. Therefore

(a) the coefficients of x must be equal,

$$\therefore \quad \alpha + \beta = -\frac{b}{a}$$

(b) the constant terms must be equal,

$$\therefore \quad \alpha\beta = \frac{c}{a}$$

Remember that either α and β are real, or they are a pair of complex conjugate numbers.

Note If it is required to write down an equation whose roots are known, equation (1) gives it in a convenient form. It may be written:

$$\boxed{x^2 - (\text{sum of the roots})x + (\text{product of the roots}) = 0}$$

Qu. 14 Write down the sums and products of the roots of the following equations:
(a) $3x^2 - 2x - 7 = 0$ (b) $5x^2 + 11x + 3 = 0$
(c) $2x^2 + 5x = 1$ (d) $2x(x + 1) = x + 7$
Qu. 15 Write down equations with integral coefficients, the sums and products of whose roots are respectively:
(a) $7, 12$ (b) $3, -2$ (c) $-\frac{1}{2}, -\frac{3}{8}$ (d) $\frac{2}{3}, 0$
Qu. 16 Write down the sum and product of the roots of the equation

$$3x^2 + 9x + 7 = 0$$

Example 8

The roots of the equation $3x^2 + 4x - 5 = 0$ are α, β. Find the values of
(a) $1/\alpha + 1/\beta$ (b) $\alpha^2 + \beta^2$.

Both $1/\alpha + 1/\beta$ and $\alpha^2 + \beta^2$ can be expressed in terms of $\alpha + \beta$ and $\alpha\beta$.

$$\alpha + \beta = -\tfrac{4}{3} \qquad \alpha\beta = -\tfrac{5}{3}$$

(a) $\dfrac{1}{\alpha} + \dfrac{1}{\beta} = \dfrac{\beta + \alpha}{\alpha\beta} = \dfrac{-\tfrac{4}{3}}{-\tfrac{5}{3}} = \dfrac{4}{5}$

(b) $\begin{aligned}[t] \alpha^2 + \beta^2 &= \alpha^2 + 2\alpha\beta + \beta^2 - 2\alpha\beta \\ &= (\alpha + \beta)^2 - 2\alpha\beta = (-\tfrac{4}{3})^2 - 2(-\tfrac{5}{3}) \end{aligned}$

$$\therefore \alpha^2 + \beta^2 = \frac{16}{9} + \frac{10}{3} = \frac{46}{9}$$

Alternatively, since α and β are roots of the equation $3x^2 + 4x - 5 = 0$,

$$3\alpha^2 + 4\alpha - 5 = 0$$
$$3\beta^2 + 4\beta - 5 = 0$$

Adding,

$$3(\alpha^2 + \beta^2) + 4(\alpha + \beta) - 10 = 0$$
$$\therefore \qquad 3(\alpha^2 + \beta^2) - \tfrac{16}{3} - 10 = 0$$
$$\therefore \qquad \alpha^2 + \beta^2 = \tfrac{16}{9} + \tfrac{10}{3} = \tfrac{46}{9}$$

Example 9

The roots of the equation $2x^2 - 7x + 4 = 0$ are α, β. Find an equation with integral coefficients whose roots are α/β, β/α.

Since α, β are the roots of the equation $2x^2 - 7x + 4 = 0$, we have

$$\alpha + \beta = \tfrac{7}{2} \quad \text{and} \quad \alpha\beta = 2$$

The sum of the new roots equals

$$\frac{\alpha}{\beta} + \frac{\beta}{\alpha} = \frac{\alpha^2 + \beta^2}{\alpha\beta} = \frac{(\alpha + \beta)^2 - 2\alpha\beta}{\alpha\beta}$$

$$= \frac{\tfrac{49}{4} - 4}{2} = \frac{33}{8}$$

The product of the new roots is

$$\frac{\alpha}{\beta} \times \frac{\beta}{\alpha} = 1$$

Hence the equation with roots α/β, β/α is

$$x^2 - \tfrac{33}{8}x + 1 = 0$$

Multiplying through by 8, in order to obtain integral coefficients, the required equation is

$$8x^2 - 33x + 8 = 0$$

11.11 Symmetrical functions

The functions of α and β that have been used in the previous section all show a certain symmetry. Consider, for example,

$$\alpha + \beta, \quad \alpha\beta, \quad \frac{1}{\alpha} + \frac{1}{\beta}, \quad \alpha^2 + \beta^2, \quad \frac{\alpha}{\beta} + \frac{\beta}{\alpha}$$

Notice that if α and β are interchanged:

$$\beta + \alpha, \quad \beta\alpha, \quad \frac{1}{\beta} + \frac{1}{\alpha}, \quad \beta^2 + \alpha^2, \quad \frac{\beta}{\alpha} + \frac{\alpha}{\beta}$$

the resulting functions are the same. When a function of α and β is unchanged when α and β are interchanged, it is called a **symmetrical** function of α and β. Such functions occurring in this chapter may be expressed in terms of $\alpha + \beta$ and $\alpha\beta$, as in the next example.

Example 10

Express in terms of $\alpha + \beta$ and $\alpha\beta$:   (a) $\alpha^3 + \beta^3$ (b) $(\alpha - \beta)^2$

(a) α^3 and β^3 occur in the expansion of $(\alpha + \beta)^3$.

$$(\alpha + \beta)^3 = \alpha^3 + 3\alpha^2\beta + 3\alpha\beta^2 + \beta^3$$
$$\therefore \quad \alpha^3 + \beta^3 = (\alpha + \beta)^3 - 3\alpha^2\beta - 3\alpha\beta^2$$
$$\therefore \quad \alpha^3 + \beta^3 = (\alpha + \beta)^3 - 3\alpha\beta(\alpha + \beta)$$

(b) $(\alpha - \beta)^2 = \alpha^2 - 2\alpha\beta + \beta^2$.
α^2 and β^2 occur in the expansion of $(\alpha + \beta)^2$.

$$(\alpha + \beta)^2 = \alpha^2 + 2\alpha\beta + \beta^2$$
$$\therefore \quad (\alpha - \beta)^2 = (\alpha + \beta)^2 - 4\alpha\beta$$

Exercise 11d

1 Find the sums and products of the roots of the following equations:
(a) $2x^2 - 11x + 3 = 0$ (b) $2x^2 + x - 1 = 0$ (c) $3x^2 = 7x + 6$
(d) $x^2 + x = 1$ (e) $t(t - 1) = 3$ (f) $y(y + 1) = 2y + 5$

(g) $x + \dfrac{1}{x} = 4$ (h) $\dfrac{1}{t} + \dfrac{1}{t+1} = \dfrac{1}{2}$

2 Find equations, with integral coefficients, the sums and products of whose roots are respectively:
(a) $3, 4$ (b) $-5, 6$ (c) $\frac{3}{2}, -\frac{5}{2}$ (d) $-\frac{7}{3}, 0$
(e) $0, -7$ (f) $1.2, 0.8$ (g) $-\frac{1}{3}, \frac{1}{36}$ (h) $-2.5, -1.6$

3 The roots of the equation $2x^2 + 3x - 4 = 0$ are α, β. Find the values of:
(a) $\alpha^2 + \beta^2$ (b) $1/\alpha + 1/\beta$ (c) $(\alpha + 1)(\beta + 1)$ (d) $\beta/\alpha + \alpha/\beta$

4 If the roots of the equation $3x^2 - 5x + 1 = 0$ are α, β, find the values of:
(a) $\alpha\beta^2 + \alpha^2\beta$ (b) $\alpha^2 - \alpha\beta + \beta^2$ (c) $\alpha^3 + \beta^3$ (d) $\alpha^2/\beta + \beta^2/\alpha$

5 The equation $4x^2 + 8x - 1 = 0$ has roots α, β. Find the values of:

(a) $1/\alpha^2 + 1/\beta^2$ (b) $(\alpha - \beta)^2$ (c) $\alpha^3\beta + \alpha\beta^3$ (d) $\dfrac{1}{\alpha^2\beta} + \dfrac{1}{\alpha\beta^2}$

6 If the roots of the equation $x^2 - 5x - 7 = 0$ are α, β, find the equations whose roots are:

(a) α^2, β^2 (b) $\alpha + 1, \beta + 1$ (c) $\alpha^2\beta, \alpha\beta^2$

7 The roots of the equation $2x^2 - 4x + 1 = 0$ are α, β. Find equations with integral coefficients whose roots are:

(a) $\alpha - 2, \beta - 2$ (b) $1/\alpha, 1/\beta$ (c) $\alpha/\beta, \beta/\alpha$

8 Find an equation, with integral coefficients, whose roots are the squares of the roots of the equation $2x^2 + 5x - 6 = 0$.

9 The roots of the equation $x^2 + 6x + q = 0$ are α and $\alpha - 1$. Find the value of q.

10 The roots of the equation $x^2 - px + 8 = 0$ are α and $\alpha + 2$. Find two possible values of p.

11 The roots of the equation $x^2 + 2px + q = 0$ differ by 2. Show that $p^2 = 1 + q$.

12 If the roots of the equation $ax^2 + bx + c = 0$ are α, β, find expressions in terms of a, b, c for:

(a) $\alpha^2\beta + \alpha\beta^2$ (b) $\alpha^2 + \beta^2$ (c) $\alpha^3 + \beta^3$ (d) $1/\alpha + 1/\beta$

13 The equation $ax^2 + bx + c = 0$ has roots α, β. Find equations whose roots are:

(a) $-\alpha, \quad -\beta$ (b) $\alpha + 1, \quad \beta + 1$
(c) $\alpha^2, \quad \beta^2$ (d) $-1/\alpha, \quad -1/\beta$

14 Prove that, if the difference between the roots of the equation

$$ax^2 + bx + c = 0$$

is 1, then $a^2 = b^2 - 4ac$.

15 Prove that, if one root of the equation $ax^2 + bx + c = 0$ is twice the other, then $2b^2 = 9ac$.

Exercise 11e (Miscellaneous)

1 Prove that $3x - 2$ is a factor of $3x^3 - 2x^2 + 3x - 2$.
Find the solution set of the equation $3x^3 - 2x^2 + 3x - 2 = 0$, when x belongs to the set of (a) integers, $\mathbb{Z}$; (b) rational numbers, $\mathbb{Q}$; (c) real numbers, $\mathbb{R}$; (d) complex numbers, $\mathbb{C}$.

2 Solve each of the equations:

    (i) $(x + 4)(5x - 7) = 0$ (ii) $(x^2 + 4)(5x^2 - 7) = 0$

when x belongs to the set of (a) integers, (b) rational numbers, (c) real numbers, (d) complex numbers.

3 Given that $z = 3 + i$ and $w = 1 + 3i$, express in the form $a + ib$, where $a, b \in \mathbb{R}$, the complex numbers (a) zw, (b) z/w, (c) $z^2 - w^2$ and find their moduli and arguments in degrees, correct to the nearest $1°$.

4 (a) Express the following complex numbers in a form having a real denominator: $1/(3 - 2i)$, $1/(1 - i)^2$.

(b) Find the modulus and principal argument of each of the complex numbers $z = 1 + 2i$ and $w = 2 - i$, and represent z and w clearly by points A and B in an Argand diagram. Find also the sum and product of z and w and mark the corresponding points C and D in your diagram. (C)

5 If the complex number $x + iy$ is denoted by z, then the complex conjugate number $x - iy$ is denoted by $z*$.

(a) Express $|z*|$ and $\arg(z*)$ in terms of $|z|$ and $\arg(z)$.

(b) If a, b, and c are real numbers, prove that if $az^2 + bz + c = 0$ then

$$a(z*)^2 + b(z*) + c = 0$$

(c) If p and q are complex numbers and $q \neq 0$, prove that $\left(\dfrac{p}{q}\right)^* = \dfrac{p*}{q*}$. (C)

6 Find the values of a and b such that $(a + ib)^2 = i$. Hence or otherwise, solve the equation $z^2 + 2z + 1 - i = 0$, giving your answers in the form $p + iq$, where p and q are real numbers. (O)

7 (a) The equation $x^4 - 4x^3 + 3x^2 + 2x - 6 = 0$ has a root $1 - i$. Find the other three roots.

(b) Given that $1, w_1, w_2$ are the roots of the equation $z^3 = 1$ express w_1 and w_2 in the form $x + iy$ and hence, or otherwise, show that

(i) $1 + w_1 + w_2 = 0$,

(ii) $1/w_1 = w_2$. (L)

8 (a) Given that the complex numbers w_1 and w_2 are the roots of the equation $z^2 - 5 - 12i = 0$, express w_1 and w_2 in the form $a + ib$, where a and b are real.

(b) Indicate the point sets in an Argand diagram corresponding to the sets of complex numbers

$$A = \{z : |z| = 3, z \in \mathbb{C}\}$$
$$B = \{z : |z| = 2, z \in \mathbb{C}\}$$

Shade the region corresponding to values of z for which the inequalities

$$2 < |z| < 3 \quad \text{and} \quad 30° < \arg z < 60°$$

are simultaneously satisfied. (L)

9 If $z = \frac{1}{2}(1 + i)$, write down the modulus and argument for each of the numbers z, z^2, z^3, z^4. Hence, or otherwise, show in an Argand diagram, the point representing the number $1 + z + z^2 + z^3 + z^4$.

(O & C: SMP I, part of question)

10 If α and β are the roots of the quadratic equation

$$(1 + j)z^2 - 2jz + (3 + j) = 0$$

where $j = \sqrt{(-1)}$, express each of $\alpha + \beta$ and $\alpha\beta$ in the form $a + jb$, where a and b are real, and show, on an Argand diagram, the points representing the complex numbers $\alpha + \beta$ and $\alpha\beta$.

Find, in a form not involving α and β, the quadratic equation whose roots are $\alpha + 2\beta$ and $2\alpha + \beta$. (O & C: MEI)

Chapter 12

Matrices

12.1 Introduction

Readers who are already familiar with this topic are advised to check through Sections 12.2–12.5 to ensure that their knowledge of the basic work is absolutely secure, while those to whom it is totally new may find it helpful to supplement the exercises in this book with further practice from a more elementary textbook.

A matrix is nothing more than a rectangular array of numbers. A matrix containing m rows and n columns is called an $m \times n$ **matrix**. Matrices are often used to store information; the matrix **P**, below, records the sales of three books, labelled A, B and C, each of which is published in hardback and paperback form, on one particular day. (This is a 2×3 matrix.)

	A	B	C
Hardback	5	2	1
Paperback	10	7	4

This matrix tells us, for example, that, on the day in question, 7 copies of the paperback edition of book B were sold.

There are conventions in mathematics about the way matrices are written. Firstly, if the layout of the matrix, in a particular context, has been standardised, the labels of the rows and columns may be discarded. Secondly, the array of numbers should be enclosed in large round brackets (some writers use square brackets), and the letter used as the name of the matrix (**P** in the example above) should be printed in bold type (in handwriting it should be a capital letter with a wavy line underneath, i.e. P̰). So the matrix described in the preceding paragraph is written

$$\mathbf{P} = \begin{pmatrix} 5 & 2 & 1 \\ 10 & 7 & 4 \end{pmatrix}$$

The matrix **Q**, below, represents the sales of the same books on the following day:

$$\mathbf{Q} = \begin{pmatrix} 3 & 0 & 1 \\ 8 & 7 & 4 \end{pmatrix}$$

On this day, for example, 3 copies of the hardback version of book *A* were sold.

One very common use for matrices in mathematics is to store the coordinates of points in coordinate geometry. In the example below, the first row of the 2×4 matrix **M** gives the *x*-coordinate and the second row gives the *y*-coordinate of four points, A, B, C and D, in order.

$$\mathbf{M} = \begin{pmatrix} 0 & -3 & \frac{1}{2} & 5 \\ 1 & 2 & -1 & 4 \end{pmatrix}$$

This matrix tell us that A is the point $(0, 1)$, B is $(-3, 2)$, C is $(\frac{1}{2}, -1)$ and D is $(5, 4)$. Unlike the previous example, the entries in this matrix do not have to be whole numbers. In general, the elements in a matrix can be any real numbers (in more advanced work, even complex numbers may be used).

12.2 Matrix addition

In the last section, we used **P** and **Q** to represent the sales of books on two consecutive days. If the book shop owner wishes to know the number of books sold on the two days taken together, all he has to do is to add the corresponding elements, i.e. the numbers which appear in the corresponding positions in the two matrices. If he is good at arithmetic, he should obtain

$$\begin{pmatrix} 8 & 2 & 2 \\ 18 & 14 & 8 \end{pmatrix}$$

It is natural to call the matrix obtained in this way the sum of **P** and **Q**, and so we write

$$\mathbf{P} + \mathbf{Q} = \begin{pmatrix} 8 & 2 & 2 \\ 18 & 14 & 8 \end{pmatrix}$$

The difference of **P** and **Q** is obtained in a similar fashion:

$$\mathbf{P} - \mathbf{Q} = \begin{pmatrix} 2 & 2 & 0 \\ 2 & 0 & 0 \end{pmatrix}$$

What meaning could the bookseller attach to this matrix?

In the preceding paragraphs we have described **P** and **Q** as '2×3 matrices' and **M** as 'a 2×4 matrix'. This was because **P** and **Q** each had two rows and three columns; **M**, on the other hand, had two rows and four columns. A matrix which has *m* rows and *n* columns is called an $m \times n$ matrix and we say that the **order** of the matrix is $m \times n$. It is only possible to add (or subtract) matrices which have the same order, i.e. they must each have the same number of rows and the same number of columns. If $m = n$, that is, the number of rows equals the number of columns, the matrix is called a **square** matrix.

Example 1

Find $\mathbf{A} + \mathbf{B}$ and $\mathbf{A} - \mathbf{B}$ when

(a) $\mathbf{A} = \begin{pmatrix} 3 & 5 & \frac{1}{2} & 4 \\ 4 & -1 & 2 & 0 \end{pmatrix}$ $\mathbf{B} = \begin{pmatrix} -1 & 4 & 0 & 3 \\ 0 & 2 & 1 & 5 \end{pmatrix}$

(b) $\mathbf{A} = \begin{pmatrix} 2 & 0 \\ 3 & -6 \\ 5 & 1 \end{pmatrix}$ $\mathbf{B} = \begin{pmatrix} 0 & -6 \\ 6 & 7 \\ 3 & 0 \end{pmatrix}$

(a) $\mathbf{A} + \mathbf{B} = \begin{pmatrix} 3-1 & 5+4 & \frac{1}{2}+0 & 4+3 \\ 4+0 & -1+2 & 2+1 & 0+5 \end{pmatrix}$

$\qquad = \begin{pmatrix} 2 & 9 & \frac{1}{2} & 7 \\ 4 & 1 & 3 & 5 \end{pmatrix}$

$\mathbf{A} - \mathbf{B} = \begin{pmatrix} 3+1 & 5-4 & \frac{1}{2}-0 & 4-3 \\ 4-0 & -1-2 & 2-1 & 0-5 \end{pmatrix}$

$\qquad = \begin{pmatrix} 4 & 1 & \frac{1}{2} & 1 \\ 4 & -3 & 1 & -5 \end{pmatrix}$

(b) $\mathbf{A} + \mathbf{B} = \begin{pmatrix} 2+0 & 0-6 \\ 3+6 & -6+7 \\ 5+3 & 1+0 \end{pmatrix}$

$\qquad = \begin{pmatrix} 2 & -6 \\ 9 & 1 \\ 8 & 1 \end{pmatrix}$

$\mathbf{A} - \mathbf{B} = \begin{pmatrix} 2-0 & 0+6 \\ 3-6 & -6-7 \\ 5-3 & 1-0 \end{pmatrix}$

$\qquad = \begin{pmatrix} 2 & 6 \\ -3 & -13 \\ 2 & 1 \end{pmatrix}$

A matrix in which every element is zero is called a **zero matrix**. When a zero matrix is added to another matrix with the same number of rows and columns, that matrix will be unchanged:

$$\begin{pmatrix} a & b & c \\ d & e & f \end{pmatrix} + \begin{pmatrix} 0 & 0 & 0 \\ 0 & 0 & 0 \end{pmatrix} = \begin{pmatrix} a & b & c \\ d & e & f \end{pmatrix}$$

The zero matrix, then, has the property $A + 0 = A$, which is very similar to the way the number zero behaves in ordinary algebra. (When you write **0** for the zero matrix, do not forget to put the wavy line under it to distinguish it from the number zero.)

12.3 Multiplication by a scalar

If **M** is the matrix $\begin{pmatrix} 1 & 2 \\ 3 & 4 \end{pmatrix}$ then, proceeding as in the last section,

$$\mathbf{M} + \mathbf{M} + \mathbf{M} + \mathbf{M} + \mathbf{M} = \begin{pmatrix} 5 & 10 \\ 15 & 20 \end{pmatrix}$$

In ordinary algebra we reduce $x + x + x + x + x$ to $5x$ and it is natural to do the same in matrix algebra, and so we write

$$5\mathbf{M} = \begin{pmatrix} 5 & 10 \\ 15 & 20 \end{pmatrix}$$

In general, to multiply a matrix **A** by a real number k (often called a **scalar** in this context), we multiply each number, or element, in the matrix **A** by k. Two examples are given below to illustrate this:

$$k\begin{pmatrix} a & b & c \\ d & e & f \end{pmatrix} = \begin{pmatrix} ka & kb & kc \\ kd & ke & kf \end{pmatrix}$$

and

$$x\begin{pmatrix} x+y & x-y \\ 2x & 3y \end{pmatrix} = \begin{pmatrix} x^2+xy & x^2-xy \\ 2x^2 & 3xy \end{pmatrix}$$

Qu. 1 Given that $A = \begin{pmatrix} 1 & 3 & 5 \\ 2 & 4 & 6 \end{pmatrix}$ and $B = \begin{pmatrix} 3 & 2 & 1 \\ 1 & 0 & 1 \end{pmatrix}$, find $5A + 4B$.

12.4 Matrix multiplication

Returning to the illustration of the book sales in Section 12.2, suppose the matrix **S**, below, represents the total sales of the hardback books in one week,

$$\mathbf{S} = (20 \quad 25 \quad 10)$$

and, let us suppose the prices of the three books are £5, £6 and £7, respectively, then the total value of the books sold is

$$£(20 \times 5 + 25 \times 6 + 10 \times 7) = £320$$

Now, in any logical game, whether it is mathematics or chess or any similar intellectual pastime, it is necessary to define the basic rules of the game and adhere to them rigidly. (If we change the rule for moving a knight on a chessboard, we might have invented an interesting new game, but it is no longer chess!) In matrix algebra, the rule for multiplying matrices is very complicated and it requires care and patience to learn it and apply it accurately. In its simplest form, the rule for multiplying a single row by a single column, each containing the same number of elements can be expressed as follows:

$$(a \quad b \quad c \quad d)\begin{pmatrix} p \\ q \\ r \\ s \end{pmatrix} = (ap + bq + cr + ds)$$

If there are more than four elements, just continue to multiply each element of the row by the corresponding element in the column and add the product to the total. Notice that the result of the operation is a 1×1 matrix, that is, it is a single number (but it is still a matrix, so do not leave out the brackets).

The illustration of the book sales, above, can be expressed in matrix algebra as follows.

The *sales* are represented by the 1×3 matrix **S**, above, the *prices* are shown in a 3×1 column matrix **P**, where $\mathbf{P} = \begin{pmatrix} 5 \\ 6 \\ 7 \end{pmatrix}$ and the total value of the books sold is found by evaluating the matrix product **SP**.

$$\mathbf{SP} = (20 \quad 25 \quad 10)\begin{pmatrix} 5 \\ 6 \\ 7 \end{pmatrix}$$

$$= (100 + 150 + 70)$$
$$= (320)$$

Now suppose the sales of the same books in the following week are represented by the matrix **R**, where $\mathbf{R} = (30 \quad 15 \quad 5)$, then the value of the total sales in the second week is given by the matrix product **RP**.

$$\mathbf{RP} = (30 \quad 15 \quad 5)\begin{pmatrix} 5 \\ 6 \\ 7 \end{pmatrix}$$

$$= (150 + 90 + 35)$$
$$= (275)$$

We can combine these two sets of figures into a single matrix product, namely,

$$\begin{pmatrix} 20 & 25 & 10 \\ 30 & 15 & 5 \end{pmatrix}\begin{pmatrix} 5 \\ 6 \\ 7 \end{pmatrix} = \begin{pmatrix} 320 \\ 275 \end{pmatrix}$$

When we read this, it must be clearly understood that the first row of the first matrix and the first row of the product represent the first week's figures and the second row in each case represents the second week's figures.

Let us now suppose that our bookseller discovered that the price list he had been using was out of date and the prices he should have been charging were £5.50, £6.50 and £7.50. He would, of course, want to know how much he should have got for his two weeks' sales. Proceeding as before, he would calculate the matrix product:

$$\begin{pmatrix} 20 & 25 & 10 \\ 30 & 15 & 5 \end{pmatrix}\begin{pmatrix} 5.50 \\ 6.50 \\ 7.50 \end{pmatrix} = \begin{pmatrix} 347.50 \\ 300.00 \end{pmatrix}$$

He could go a stage further and display both sets of figures side by side. Here, it must be understood, the second column of the price matrix corresponds to the second column of the product.

$$\begin{pmatrix} 20 & 25 & 10 \\ 30 & 15 & 5 \end{pmatrix}\begin{pmatrix} 5 & 5.50 \\ 6 & 6.50 \\ 7 & 7.50 \end{pmatrix} = \begin{pmatrix} 320 & 347.50 \\ 275 & 300.00 \end{pmatrix}$$

It is unlikely that there are many booksellers who bother to learn matrix algebra in order to do their accounts! Nevertheless this example will, it is hoped, serve to introduce the multiplication of matrices, which is absolutely fundamental in the study of matrix algebra. Matrix algebra was the brain-child of a Cambridge mathematician, Arthur Cayley (1821–1895). Cayley produced a paper on the subject in 1858; at the time he was working on the theory of transformations (see Section 12.6). The study of matrices has been one of the most significant factors in the development of mathematics in the twentieth century. Although it originated as a branch of pure mathematics it has turned out to be an extremely useful subject and today it is extensively used in applied mathematics and physics.

Let us now take another look at matrix multiplication. Here we multiply a 3×2 matrix **A** by a 2×1 matrix **B**. (Notice that, for multiplication to be possible, it is essential that the number of *columns* in the *first* matrix should be the same as the number of *rows* in the *second* matrix.) Remember to work across each row and down each column.

If $\quad \mathbf{A} = \begin{pmatrix} 1 & 2 \\ 3 & 4 \\ 5 & 6 \end{pmatrix} \quad$ and $\quad \mathbf{B} = \begin{pmatrix} 7 \\ 8 \end{pmatrix}$

$$\mathbf{AB} = \begin{pmatrix} 1 & 2 \\ 3 & 4 \\ 5 & 6 \end{pmatrix} \begin{pmatrix} 7 \\ 8 \end{pmatrix}$$

$$= \begin{pmatrix} 1 \times 7 & + & 2 \times 8 \\ 3 \times 7 & + & 4 \times 8 \\ 5 \times 7 & + & 6 \times 8 \end{pmatrix}$$

$$= \begin{pmatrix} 23 \\ 53 \\ 83 \end{pmatrix}$$

Now we examine the product of a 3×2 matrix **P** and a 2×2 matrix **Q**, bearing in mind that in picking out the pairs of corresponding elements for multiplying together, we work across each row of **P** and down each column of **Q**.

If $\quad \mathbf{P} = \begin{pmatrix} 1 & 2 \\ 3 & 4 \\ 5 & 6 \end{pmatrix} \quad$ and $\quad \mathbf{Q} = \begin{pmatrix} 7 & 8 \\ 9 & 0 \end{pmatrix}$

$$\mathbf{PQ} = \begin{pmatrix} 1 \times 7 & + & 2 \times 9 & \quad 1 \times 8 & + & 2 \times 0 \\ 3 \times 7 & + & 4 \times 9 & \quad 3 \times 8 & + & 4 \times 0 \\ 5 \times 7 & + & 6 \times 9 & \quad 5 \times 8 & + & 6 \times 0 \end{pmatrix}$$

$$= \begin{pmatrix} 25 & 8 \\ 57 & 24 \\ 89 & 40 \end{pmatrix}$$

It should be noted (a) that for each row of matrix **P** there is a row in the product **PQ**, and that for each column of matrix **Q** there is a column in the product **PQ**, and (b) that, for example, the element 89 in the third row and first column of **PQ** is the sum of the products of the corresponding elements of the third row of **P** and the first column of **Q**.

We can now set out the following general features of matrix multiplication:

(1) In any matrix product **CD**, if the first matrix **C** has m rows and n columns and the second matrix **D** has n rows and p columns, then the product **CD** has m rows and p columns.
(2) The element which lies in the ith row and jth column of **CD** is the sum of the products of the corresponding elements of the ith row of **C** and the jth column of **D**.

Example 2

Find, where possible, the products **PQ** and **MN**, given that:

(a) $\mathbf{P} = \begin{pmatrix} 2 & 3 & 4 \\ 1 & 5 & 2 \end{pmatrix} \quad \mathbf{Q} = \begin{pmatrix} 1 & -1 \\ 0 & 2 \\ 1 & 3 \end{pmatrix}$

(b) $\mathbf{M} = \begin{pmatrix} 2 & 1 & 0 \\ 3 & 4 & 7 \end{pmatrix} \quad \mathbf{N} = \begin{pmatrix} 3 & 1 \\ 4 & 5 \end{pmatrix}$

(a) $\mathbf{PQ} = \begin{pmatrix} 2 & 3 & 4 \\ 1 & 5 & 2 \end{pmatrix} \begin{pmatrix} 1 & -1 \\ 0 & 2 \\ 1 & 3 \end{pmatrix}$

$= \begin{pmatrix} 2 \times 1 + 3 \times 0 + 4 \times 1 & 2 \times (-1) + 3 \times 2 + 4 \times 3 \\ 1 \times 1 + 5 \times 0 + 2 \times 1 & 1 \times (-1) + 5 \times 2 + 2 \times 3 \end{pmatrix}$

$= \begin{pmatrix} 6 & 16 \\ 3 & 15 \end{pmatrix}$

(b) It is impossible to form the product **MN**, because **M** has three columns, while **N** has only two rows.

Qu. 2 Find the following matrix products:

(a) $\begin{pmatrix} 3 & 1 \\ 2 & 0 \\ 4 & 1 \end{pmatrix} \begin{pmatrix} 1 & 0 \\ 2 & 1 \end{pmatrix}$ (b) $\begin{pmatrix} 1 & 5 & 6 \\ 2 & 3 & 4 \end{pmatrix} \begin{pmatrix} 1 \\ 2 \\ 3 \end{pmatrix}$

(c) $(1 \quad 2 \quad 3)\begin{pmatrix} 2 & -1 \\ 3 & 1 \\ 4 & 2 \end{pmatrix}$ (d) $\begin{pmatrix} 1 & 0 & 3 \\ 2 & 1 & 1 \end{pmatrix}\begin{pmatrix} 3 & 2 \\ 1 & 0 \\ 1 & 1 \end{pmatrix}$

In the algebra of real numbers, the order of the terms in a product does not matter, for instance 3×5 and 5×3 both equal 15. We say that in the algebra of real numbers multiplication is *commutative*, that is, $ab = ba$ for any pair of real numbers. This is not the case in matrix algebra. For example,

if

$$A = \begin{pmatrix} 1 & 2 \\ 3 & 4 \end{pmatrix} \quad \text{and} \quad B = \begin{pmatrix} 5 & 6 \\ 7 & 8 \end{pmatrix}$$

then

$$AB = \begin{pmatrix} 1 & 2 \\ 3 & 4 \end{pmatrix}\begin{pmatrix} 5 & 6 \\ 7 & 8 \end{pmatrix} = \begin{pmatrix} 19 & 22 \\ 43 & 50 \end{pmatrix}$$

but

$$BA = \begin{pmatrix} 5 & 6 \\ 7 & 8 \end{pmatrix}\begin{pmatrix} 1 & 2 \\ 3 & 4 \end{pmatrix} = \begin{pmatrix} 23 & 34 \\ 31 & 46 \end{pmatrix}$$

So in matrix algebra, the order of the matrices in a product *does* matter. We say that in matrix algebra, multiplication is *not commutative*.

Exercise 12a

1 Given that $A = \begin{pmatrix} 3 & 1 & 2 \\ 5 & 1 & 7 \end{pmatrix}$ and $B = \begin{pmatrix} 4 & -1 & 2 \\ 3 & 1 & 3 \end{pmatrix}$ evaluate:

(a) $3A$ (b) $2B$ (c) $3A + 2B$ (d) $3A - 2B$

2 A newspaper agent records the number of papers sold on each day of one week, as follows:

	Mon	Tue	Wed	Thu	Fri	Sat
The Post	120	250	350	300	420	200
The News	120	300	420	200	300	500

Write this as a 2×6 matrix S.

The Post costs 24p and *The News* costs 30p. Write this information as a 1×2 row matrix P. It is only possible to form *one* of the products PS and SP. Evaluate the product which it is possible to form and explain the meaning of the first element in the product matrix.

3 Find, where possible, the following products. When it is not possible to form the product, state this clearly and give the reason for your conclusion.

(a) $(2 \quad 3 \quad 1) \begin{pmatrix} 3 & 2 \\ 4 & 7 \\ 1 & 6 \end{pmatrix}$ (b) $\begin{pmatrix} 2 & 3 \\ 1 & 4 \end{pmatrix} \begin{pmatrix} 1 & 2 & 3 \\ 4 & 5 & 6 \end{pmatrix}$

(c) $\begin{pmatrix} 1 & 2 \\ 3 & 4 \end{pmatrix} (5 \quad 6)$ (d) $\begin{pmatrix} 2 & 3 \\ 4 & 5 \end{pmatrix} \begin{pmatrix} 7 \\ 8 \end{pmatrix}$

4 Given that $\mathbf{A} = \begin{pmatrix} 3 & -1 \\ 4 & 5 \end{pmatrix}$ and $\mathbf{B} = \begin{pmatrix} \frac{1}{2} & 0 \\ 1 & 2 \end{pmatrix}$, find $\mathbf{AB}$ and $\mathbf{BA}$. State the property of matrix multiplication which is illustrated by the answer.

5 Given that $\mathbf{I} = \begin{pmatrix} 1 & 0 \\ 0 & 1 \end{pmatrix}$ and $\mathbf{A} = \begin{pmatrix} a & b \\ c & d \end{pmatrix}$, find $\mathbf{IA}$ and $\mathbf{AI}$. In the algebra of real numbers there is a number which has a property which is very similar to the property shown by $\mathbf{I}$ in this question. State the number and describe this property.

6 Given that $\mathbf{A} = \begin{pmatrix} 3 & 2 \\ 5 & 4 \end{pmatrix}$ and $\mathbf{B} = \begin{pmatrix} 4 & -2 \\ -5 & 3 \end{pmatrix}$, find $\mathbf{AB}$ and $\mathbf{BA}$.

7 Given that $\mathbf{A} = \begin{pmatrix} 3 & 2 \\ 5 & 4 \end{pmatrix}$, $\mathbf{X} = \begin{pmatrix} x \\ y \end{pmatrix}$ and $\mathbf{C} = \begin{pmatrix} 1 \\ -4 \end{pmatrix}$, use the result of no. 6 to solve the matrix equation $\mathbf{AX} = \mathbf{C}$.
[*Hint*: Multiply both sides of the equation by $\mathbf{B}$.]

8 Repeat no. 6, given that $\mathbf{A} = \begin{pmatrix} 5 & 2 \\ 8 & 4 \end{pmatrix}$ and $\mathbf{B} = \begin{pmatrix} 4 & -2 \\ -8 & 5 \end{pmatrix}$.

9 Repeat no. 7, given that $\mathbf{A} = \begin{pmatrix} 5 & 2 \\ 8 & 4 \end{pmatrix}$, $\mathbf{X} = \begin{pmatrix} x \\ y \end{pmatrix}$ and $\mathbf{C} = \begin{pmatrix} 1 \\ -4 \end{pmatrix}$.

10 Evaluate the matrix products:

(a) $\begin{pmatrix} 1 & 2 & 3 \\ 4 & 5 & 6 \\ 1 & 0 & -1 \end{pmatrix} \begin{pmatrix} 2 & 1 & 0 \\ 3 & -1 & 4 \\ 1 & 0 & 7 \end{pmatrix}$ (b) $\begin{pmatrix} 2 & \frac{1}{2} & \frac{3}{4} \\ 1 & 0 & \frac{1}{4} \\ 3 & 1 & 0 \end{pmatrix} \begin{pmatrix} 8 & -4 \\ 0 & 12 \\ 4 & 0 \end{pmatrix}$

11 Matrices $\mathbf{M}$ and $\mathbf{N}$ are members of a set S which is defined as follows:

$$S = \left\{ \begin{pmatrix} a & b \\ -b & a \end{pmatrix} : a, b \in \mathbb{R} \right\}$$

Prove that the product **MN** is also a member of set S.

$$\left[\text{Hint } \text{Let } \mathbf{M} = \begin{pmatrix} p & q \\ -q & p \end{pmatrix} \text{ and } \mathbf{N} = \begin{pmatrix} r & s \\ -s & r \end{pmatrix} . \right]$$

12 Matrices **P** and **Q** are members of a set R which is defined as follows:

$$R = \left\{ \begin{pmatrix} a & b \\ c & d \end{pmatrix} : a, b, c, d \in \mathbb{R}, ad - bc = 1 \right\}$$

Prove that the product **PQ** is also a member of set R.

13 S is the set of matrices of the form $\begin{pmatrix} a & -kb \\ b/k & a \end{pmatrix}$ where a and b can be *any*

real numbers, but k is the *same* real number for *all* members of S. If **A** and **B** are two distinct members of set S, show that the product **AB** also belongs to set S.

14 Given that $\mathbf{P} = \begin{pmatrix} a & b \\ c & d \end{pmatrix}$ and that $\mathbf{Q} = \begin{pmatrix} d & -b \\ -c & a \end{pmatrix}$, evaluate the products

PQ and **QP**. Comment on your answers.

12.5 Matrix algebra

The rules for adding and subtracting a pair of $m \times n$ matrices, which were introduced in Section 12.3, are very simple and unremarkable. The reader should have no difficulty verifying that, if **A** and **B** are a pair of such matrices,

$$\mathbf{A} + \mathbf{B} = \mathbf{B} + \mathbf{A}$$

so *matrix addition is commutative*. Also if **0** is the $m \times n$ zero matrix, then

$$\mathbf{A} + \mathbf{0} = \mathbf{A}$$

If **C** is another $m \times n$ matrix, then it follows from the associative property of real numbers under addition that

$$(\mathbf{A} + \mathbf{B}) + \mathbf{C} = \mathbf{A} + (\mathbf{B} + \mathbf{C})$$

The technical term for this is that *matrix addition is associative*. (This terminology may be new to some readers. All it means is that the position of the brackets does not matter; and if this remark seems trivial, contrast it with $(24 \div 12) \div 2$ which does *not* equal $24 \div (12 \div 2)$. Division is *not* an associative operation in real numbers.)

Multiplication of matrices, which was introduced in Section 12.4, is a more complicated operation and, as a result, the rules of matrix multiplication are more interesting. We have already seen that it is possible to have a pair of matrices **A** and **B**, for which $\mathbf{AB} \neq \mathbf{BA}$, so *matrix multiplication is not commutative*. However, it can be shown that *matrix multiplication is associative*.

We have also seen (Exercise 12a, no. 5) that if **A** is any 2×2 matrix and if

$$\mathbf{I} = \begin{pmatrix} 1 & 0 \\ 0 & 1 \end{pmatrix},$$ then $\mathbf{IA} = \mathbf{AI} = \mathbf{A}$. This is very similar to the way the real number

1 behaves in ordinary algebra, that is, $1 \times x = x \times 1 = x$, where x is any real number. This matrix **I** is plainly a very special matrix and so it is given a special name; it is usually called the **unit matrix** (in recognition of its similarity to the number 1) or the **identity matrix**. More generally, if **A** is any $n \times n$ matrix, then the corresponding unit matrix is an $n \times n$ matrix, with 1's along the **leading diagonal** (the one that goes from the top left-hand corner to the bottom right-hand corner), and 0's elsewhere.

So the 3×3 unit matrix is $\begin{pmatrix} 1 & 0 & 0 \\ 0 & 1 & 0 \\ 0 & 0 & 1 \end{pmatrix}$.

Qu. 3 If $\mathbf{A} = \begin{pmatrix} a & b & c \\ d & e & f \\ g & h & j \end{pmatrix}$ and **I** is the 3×3 unit matrix, verify that $\mathbf{AI} = \mathbf{IA} = \mathbf{A}$.

In ordinary algebra, if we have a pair of numbers p and q such that $pq = 1$ (for example $4 \times \frac{1}{4} = 1$) we say that q is the **inverse** of p, and conversely p is the inverse of q. (Similarly $\frac{1}{2}$ is the inverse of 2; 3/5 is the inverse of 5/3.) The same term is used in matrix algebra to describe a pair of matrices **A** and **B** such that $\mathbf{AB} = \mathbf{BA} = \mathbf{I}$. We say that **A** is the inverse of **B** and **B** is the inverse of **A**. For such a statement to be possible, both **A** and **B** must be square matrices which have the same number of rows and columns as each other. (If this is not obvious, write down a pair of matrices for which it is not true and try to evaluate both **AB** and **BA**.)

If we are given any square matrix **A**, the task of finding its inverse can be very difficult. In this section we shall tackle the simplest case, where **A** is a 2×2 matrix.

Suppose we are given a 2×2 matrix $\mathbf{A} = \begin{pmatrix} a & b \\ c & d \end{pmatrix}$. The problem is to find a

2×2 matrix **B**, such that $\mathbf{AB} = \mathbf{I}$. Let us write **B** as $\begin{pmatrix} p & q \\ r & s \end{pmatrix}$. (In the work that

follows, remember that a, b, c and d are known, but p, q, r and s are unknown; the task is to find p, q, r and s.)

$$\mathbf{AB} = \begin{pmatrix} a & b \\ c & d \end{pmatrix} \begin{pmatrix} p & q \\ r & s \end{pmatrix} = \begin{pmatrix} ap + br & aq + bs \\ cp + dr & cq + ds \end{pmatrix}$$

This product is to be equal to the identity matrix $\begin{pmatrix} 1 & 0 \\ 0 & 1 \end{pmatrix}$, so we can write

down four equations

$$ap + br = 1 \qquad\qquad \ldots \ \ (1)$$
$$cp + dr = 0 \qquad\qquad \ldots \ \ (2)$$
$$aq + bs = 0 \qquad\qquad \ldots \ \ (3)$$
$$cq + ds = 1 \qquad\qquad \ldots \ \ (4)$$

from which to find p, q, r and s.

Multiplying (1) by d and (2) by b, we have:

$$adp + bdr = d$$
$$bcp + bdr = 0$$

Subtracting:

$$(ad - bc)p = d$$

Provided $ad - bc$ is not zero we may divide by it, hence

$$p = \frac{d}{\Delta} \qquad \text{(where } \Delta = ad - bc\text{)}$$

Substituting this in equation (2) gives

$$\frac{cd}{\Delta} + dr = 0$$

$$\therefore \qquad\qquad r = -\frac{c}{\Delta}$$

The reader should now solve equations (3) and (4) to find q and s. The solutions are $q = -b/\Delta$ and $s = a/\Delta$.

Hence the inverse matrix **B** is given by

$$\mathbf{B} = \begin{pmatrix} d/\Delta & -b/\Delta \\ -c/\Delta & a/\Delta \end{pmatrix} = \frac{1}{\Delta} \begin{pmatrix} d & -b \\ -c & a \end{pmatrix}$$

This is the required inverse of the matrix **A** and the standard abbreviation of this is $\mathbf{A}^{-1}$. Consequently we write:

$$\boxed{\text{If} \quad \mathbf{A} = \begin{pmatrix} a & b \\ c & d \end{pmatrix} \quad \text{then} \quad \mathbf{A}^{-1} = \frac{1}{\Delta} \begin{pmatrix} d & -b \\ -c & a \end{pmatrix}.}$$

This is an important result and every effort should be made to memorise it.

The method for finding the inverse of a matrix $\begin{pmatrix} a & b \\ c & d \end{pmatrix}$ can be summarised as follows:

– the elements on the leading diagonal, a and d, are interchanged,
– the elements on the other diagonal, b and c, have their signs changed,
– the matrix is divided by $ad - bc$.

Qu. 4 Using the matrices **A** and $\mathbf{A}^{-1}$ above, verify that $\mathbf{A}^{-1}\mathbf{A} = \mathbf{I}$.

Notice that in finding the inverse of $\begin{pmatrix} a & b \\ c & d \end{pmatrix}$ the term $\Delta = ad - bc$ has a very important role to play. We shall be referring to this term quite frequently and so it is given a special name; it is called the **determinant** of the matrix $\begin{pmatrix} a & b \\ c & d \end{pmatrix}$.

It is convenient to reduce the phrase 'the determinant of matrix **M**' to det **M**, so if $\mathbf{M} = \begin{pmatrix} a & b \\ c & d \end{pmatrix}$ then we write det $\mathbf{M} = ad - bc$.

Matrices for which $\Delta = 0$ are often called **singular** matrices. A singular matrix has no inverse because we cannot divide by zero.

Example 3

Given that $\mathbf{M} = \begin{pmatrix} 7 & 9 \\ 5 & 7 \end{pmatrix}$, write the simultaneous equations

$$7x + 9y = 3$$
$$5x + 7y = 1$$

in the form $\mathbf{MX} = \mathbf{C}$, where **X** is the column matrix $\begin{pmatrix} x \\ y \end{pmatrix}$ and **C** is the column matrix $\begin{pmatrix} 3 \\ 1 \end{pmatrix}$. Hence solve the equations.

In matrix notation the equations can be expressed

$$\begin{pmatrix} 7 & 9 \\ 5 & 7 \end{pmatrix} \begin{pmatrix} x \\ y \end{pmatrix} = \begin{pmatrix} 3 \\ 1 \end{pmatrix}$$

This is the form

$$\mathbf{MX} = \mathbf{C}$$

as required. Multiply both sides of this matrix equation by $\mathbf{M}^{-1}$ and we have

$$\mathbf{M}^{-1}(\mathbf{MX}) = \mathbf{M}^{-1}\mathbf{C} \qquad \qquad \cdots \quad (1)$$

Now the left-hand side of this equation can be simplified, as follows:

$$\mathbf{M}^{-1}(\mathbf{MX}) = (\mathbf{M}^{-1}\mathbf{M})\mathbf{X}$$

using the associative property of matrix multiplication, and

$$(\mathbf{M}^{-1}\mathbf{M})\mathbf{X} = \mathbf{IX} = \mathbf{X}$$

using the properties of the inverse and identity matrices.

Equation (1) can now be reduced to

$$\mathbf{X} = \mathbf{M}^{-1}\mathbf{C}$$

$$= \frac{1}{4}\begin{pmatrix} 7 & -9 \\ -5 & 7 \end{pmatrix}\begin{pmatrix} 3 \\ 1 \end{pmatrix}$$

$$= \frac{1}{4}\begin{pmatrix} 12 \\ -8 \end{pmatrix}$$

$$= \begin{pmatrix} 3 \\ -2 \end{pmatrix}$$

Hence $x = 3$ and $y = -2$.

As a method for solving a pair of simultaneous equations, this is using a sledge-hammer to crack a nut. Nevertheless, it is a method which can be developed for tackling the more general problem of solving n simultaneous equations in n unknowns. It also gives an example of the way the basic properties of matrix algebra can be combined into a logical argument.

Exercise 12b (Oral)

Find the determinants of the following matrices:

1 (a) $\begin{pmatrix} 5 & 7 \\ 2 & 3 \end{pmatrix}$ (b) $\begin{pmatrix} 3 & 2 \\ 5 & 8 \end{pmatrix}$ (c) $\begin{pmatrix} 4 & -2 \\ 1 & 7 \end{pmatrix}$ (d) $\begin{pmatrix} 6 & \frac{1}{4} \\ 8 & \frac{1}{2} \end{pmatrix}$

2 (a) $\begin{pmatrix} 3 & 12 \\ 2 & 8 \end{pmatrix}$ (b) $\begin{pmatrix} \frac{1}{2} & \frac{1}{5} \\ \frac{1}{6} & \frac{1}{3} \end{pmatrix}$ (c) $\begin{pmatrix} a & b \\ -b & a \end{pmatrix}$ (d) $\begin{pmatrix} a & b/k \\ ck & d \end{pmatrix}$ $k \neq 0$

3 State which of these matrices are singular:

(a) $\begin{pmatrix} 3 & -2 \\ 9 & 6 \end{pmatrix}$ (b) $\begin{pmatrix} 3 & 2 \\ 9 & 6 \end{pmatrix}$ (c) $\begin{pmatrix} 34 & 119 \\ 26 & 91 \end{pmatrix}$ (d) $\begin{pmatrix} x & x^2 \\ x^2 & x^3 \end{pmatrix}$

4 Find the values of x for which the following matrices have no inverse:

(a) $\begin{pmatrix} x & 7 \\ 8 & 2 \end{pmatrix}$ (b) $\begin{pmatrix} x & 8 \\ 2 & x \end{pmatrix}$ (c) $\begin{pmatrix} x-2 & 1 \\ 2 & x-3 \end{pmatrix}$ (d) $\begin{pmatrix} x & 2 \\ -2 & x \end{pmatrix}$

5 State the inverse of each of these matrices (read each column in turn):

(a) $\begin{pmatrix} 3 & 4 \\ 5 & 7 \end{pmatrix}$ (b) $\begin{pmatrix} 2 & 3 \\ 3 & 5 \end{pmatrix}$ (c) $\begin{pmatrix} 6 & 11 \\ 2 & 7 \end{pmatrix}$ (d) $\begin{pmatrix} x & -1 \\ 1 & x \end{pmatrix}$

Exercise 12c

1 Find, where possible, the inverses of the following matrices:

(a) $\begin{pmatrix} 7 & 4 \\ 5 & 3 \end{pmatrix}$ (b) $\begin{pmatrix} 8 & 2 \\ 11 & 3 \end{pmatrix}$ (c) $\begin{pmatrix} \frac{1}{2} & \frac{1}{3} \\ \frac{1}{2} & 1 \end{pmatrix}$ (d) $\begin{pmatrix} 6 & 3 \\ 8 & 4 \end{pmatrix}$

2 Find the inverses of the following matrices:

(a) $\begin{pmatrix} 1/\sqrt{2} & 1/\sqrt{2} \\ -1/\sqrt{2} & 1/\sqrt{2} \end{pmatrix}$ (b) $\begin{pmatrix} 1/2 & \sqrt{3}/2 \\ -\sqrt{3}/2 & 1/2 \end{pmatrix}$

(c) $\begin{pmatrix} 3/5 & -4/5 \\ 4/5 & 3/5 \end{pmatrix}$ (d) $\begin{pmatrix} 1/2 & \sqrt{3}/2 \\ \sqrt{3}/2 & -1/2 \end{pmatrix}$

3 Find the inverse of the matrix $\mathbf{M}$, where $\mathbf{M} = \begin{pmatrix} 3 & 2 \\ 5 & 4 \end{pmatrix}$ and hence solve the

matrix equation $\mathbf{MX} = \mathbf{C}$, in which $\mathbf{X} = \begin{pmatrix} x \\ y \end{pmatrix}$ and $\mathbf{C} = \begin{pmatrix} 1 \\ 3 \end{pmatrix}$.

4 Repeat no. 3 for $\mathbf{M} = \begin{pmatrix} 9 & 2 \\ 8 & 4 \end{pmatrix}$.

5 Write the simultaneous equations

$$7x + 9y = 1$$
$$10x + 13y = 2$$

in matrix form, and, using the method employed in nos. 3 and 4, solve the equations.

6 Solve the matrix equation $\mathbf{AX} = \mathbf{B}$, where $\mathbf{A} = \begin{pmatrix} 7 & 5 \\ 4 & 3 \end{pmatrix}$ and

$\mathbf{B} = \begin{pmatrix} 1 & -1 \\ 1 & 1 \end{pmatrix}$, to find the (unknown) matrix $\mathbf{X}$.

7 Given that $\mathbf{P} = \begin{pmatrix} 3 & 4 \\ -4 & 3 \end{pmatrix}$ and $\mathbf{A} = \begin{pmatrix} 2 & 0 \\ 0 & 1 \end{pmatrix}$, find the matrix $\mathbf{M}$, where

$\mathbf{M} = \mathbf{P}^{-1}\mathbf{AP}$. Hence, or otherwise, find $\mathbf{M}^5$.

8 By writing $\mathbf{M} = \begin{pmatrix} a & b \\ c & d \end{pmatrix}$ and $\mathbf{N} = \begin{pmatrix} p & q \\ r & s \end{pmatrix}$, prove that, for any two 2×2

matrices $\mathbf{M}$ and $\mathbf{N}$, $\det \mathbf{MN} = \det \mathbf{M} \det \mathbf{N}$.

9 Verify that if $\mathbf{M} = \begin{pmatrix} -5 & 10 & 8 \\ 4 & -7 & -6 \\ -3 & 6 & 5 \end{pmatrix}$ and $\mathbf{N} = \begin{pmatrix} -1 & 2 & 4 \\ 2 & 1 & -2 \\ -3 & 0 & 5 \end{pmatrix}$, then

$\mathbf{MN} = \mathbf{NM} = \mathbf{I}$, where $\mathbf{I}$ is the 3×3 unit matrix. Use this to solve the matrix equation

$$\begin{pmatrix} -5 & 10 & 8 \\ 4 & -7 & -6 \\ -3 & 6 & 5 \end{pmatrix} \begin{pmatrix} x \\ y \\ z \end{pmatrix} = \begin{pmatrix} -3 \\ 3 \\ 2 \end{pmatrix}$$

10 Express the simultaneous equations:

$$\begin{aligned} -x + 2y + 4z &= 7 \\ 2x + y - 2z &= -2 \\ -3x + 5z &= 7 \end{aligned}$$

in the form of a matrix equation $\mathbf{NX} = \mathbf{C}$, where $\mathbf{N}$ is the 3×3 matrix in no. 9 and $\mathbf{X}$ and $\mathbf{C}$ are suitable column matrices. Hence, using the information from no. 9, solve these equations by the matrix method.

11 Given that $\mathbf{A} = \begin{pmatrix} 2 & 1 & 0 \\ 0 & 1 & 1 \\ 0 & 4 & -3 \end{pmatrix}$, verify that $\mathbf{A}^3 = 11\mathbf{A} - 14\mathbf{I}$, where $\mathbf{I}$ is the

3×3 unit matrix. Hence find $\mathbf{A}^{-1}$.

12 Solve, by elimination, the simultaneous equations:

$$\begin{aligned} 2x + y &= a \\ y + z &= b \\ 4y - 3z &= c \end{aligned}$$

in terms of a, b and c. Express the three simultaneous equations in the form

$\mathbf{AX} = \mathbf{C}$, where $\mathbf{A}$ and $\mathbf{C}$ are suitably chosen matrices and $\mathbf{X} = \begin{pmatrix} x \\ y \\ z \end{pmatrix}$, and

give your answer in the form $\mathbf{X} = \mathbf{BC}$. Hence write down the inverse of matrix $\mathbf{A}$.

12.6 Transformations and matrices

As mentioned earlier (Section 12.4), matrices were invented by Cayley in the course of his work on linear transformations. In this section we shall take a closer look at this topic. In two dimensions, a linear transformation is a transformation which moves any point P, with coordinates (x, y), to a new position P', whose coordinates (x', y') are given by a pair of linear equations, that is equations of the form

$$x' = ax + by$$
$$y' = cx + dy$$

In matrix notation this can be written

$$\begin{pmatrix} x' \\ y' \end{pmatrix} = \begin{pmatrix} a & b \\ c & d \end{pmatrix} \begin{pmatrix} x \\ y \end{pmatrix}$$

Example 4

A transformation is defined by the matrix equation

$$\begin{pmatrix} x' \\ y' \end{pmatrix} = \begin{pmatrix} 2 & 0 \\ 0 & -2 \end{pmatrix} \begin{pmatrix} x \\ y \end{pmatrix}$$

Draw a diagram showing the unit square OIRJ, whose vertices are at $(0, 0)$, $(1, 0)$, $(1, 1)$ and $(0, 1)$ respectively, and its image O'I'R'J' under the transformation. Describe in words the effect of the transformation on the unit square.

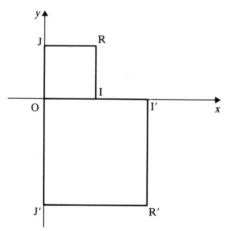

Figure 12.1

$$\begin{pmatrix} 2 & 0 \\ 0 & -2 \end{pmatrix} \begin{pmatrix} 0 \\ 0 \end{pmatrix} = \begin{pmatrix} 0 \\ 0 \end{pmatrix} \qquad \begin{pmatrix} 2 & 0 \\ 0 & -2 \end{pmatrix} \begin{pmatrix} 1 \\ 0 \end{pmatrix} = \begin{pmatrix} 2 \\ 0 \end{pmatrix}$$

$$\begin{pmatrix} 2 & 0 \\ 0 & -2 \end{pmatrix} \begin{pmatrix} 1 \\ 1 \end{pmatrix} = \begin{pmatrix} 2 \\ -2 \end{pmatrix} \qquad \begin{pmatrix} 2 & 0 \\ 0 & -2 \end{pmatrix} \begin{pmatrix} 0 \\ 1 \end{pmatrix} = \begin{pmatrix} 0 \\ -2 \end{pmatrix}$$

It is worth noting that these four operations can be combined into a

single one, in which the matrix $\begin{pmatrix} 2 & 0 \\ 0 & -2 \end{pmatrix}$ is applied to the 2 × 4 matrix $\begin{pmatrix} 0 & 1 & 1 & 0 \\ 0 & 0 & 1 & 1 \end{pmatrix}$, that is:

$$\begin{pmatrix} 2 & 0 \\ 0 & -2 \end{pmatrix}\begin{pmatrix} 0 & 1 & 1 & 0 \\ 0 & 0 & 1 & 1 \end{pmatrix} = \begin{pmatrix} 0 & 2 & 2 & 0 \\ 0 & 0 & -2 & -2 \end{pmatrix}$$

From the diagram (Figure 12.1) we can see that OIRJ has been enlarged by a scale-factor of 2 and it has been reflected in the x-axis.

If we are given a description, in words, of a certain transformation, it can be quite difficult to find the corresponding matrix, but in some simple cases the matrix can be found by considering the effect of the transformation on a triangle OPM, whose vertices are the points $(0, 0)$, (x, y) and $(x, 0)$ respectively. It should be noted, at this stage, that the image of $(0, 0)$ under this type of transformation is always $(0, 0)$.

(a) Rotation, about O, through 90° anticlockwise

From Figure 12.2, we can see that the new y-coordinate is OM′ and that this is equal in length to OM (since OM′ is OM rotated through 90°) and OM is the original x-coordinate, so $y' = x$. The new x-coordinate is equal to P′M′ in magnitude, but it is negative; however, P′M′ is equal in length to the original y-coordinate and so, $x' = -y$. Hence the new coordinates (x', y') are given by the pair of equations

$$\begin{aligned} x' &= -y \\ y' &= x \end{aligned}$$

and these can be written in matrix form as

$$\begin{pmatrix} x' \\ y' \end{pmatrix} = \begin{pmatrix} 0 & -1 \\ 1 & 0 \end{pmatrix}\begin{pmatrix} x \\ y \end{pmatrix}$$

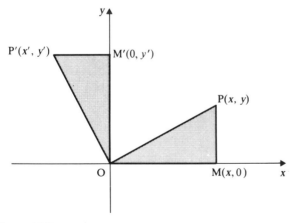

Figure 12.2

In the next two cases the detailed explanation is omitted; the reader should make sure that he or she understands how the matrix equations are obtained from the diagram.

(b) Reflection in the x-axis (see Figure 12.3)

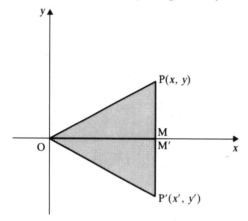

Figure 12.3

$$x' = x$$
$$y' = -y$$

$$\begin{pmatrix} x' \\ y' \end{pmatrix} = \begin{pmatrix} 1 & 0 \\ 0 & -1 \end{pmatrix} \begin{pmatrix} x \\ y \end{pmatrix}$$

(c) Reflection in the line y = x (see Figure 12.4)

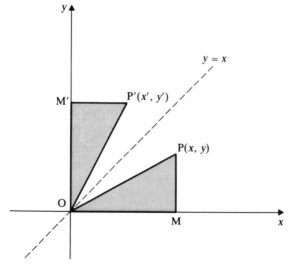

Figure 12.4

$$x' = y$$
$$y' = x$$

$$\begin{pmatrix} x' \\ y' \end{pmatrix} = \begin{pmatrix} 0 & 1 \\ 1 & 0 \end{pmatrix} \begin{pmatrix} x \\ y \end{pmatrix}$$

Qu. 5 Find the matrices which correspond to the following transformations:
(a) a rotation about the origin, through 90°, clockwise
(b) a reflection in the line $x + y = 0$
(c) an enlargement by a factor of 5, with the origin as the centre of the enlargement.

12.7 General properties of linear transformations

In the last section, we were able to look at some simple transformations and write down the corresponding matrices. Before we can tackle more complicated transformations, we must look more closely at the general properties of transformations which are defined by matrix equations of the form

$$\begin{pmatrix} x' \\ y' \end{pmatrix} = \begin{pmatrix} a & b \\ c & d \end{pmatrix} \begin{pmatrix} x \\ y \end{pmatrix}$$

Where appropriate, the notation $(x, y) \mapsto (x', y')$ will be used to indicate that, under the transformation, the point (x, y) moves to the point (x', y'). It is the normal practice to say '(x', y') is the image of (x, y) under the transformation' and that '(x, y) is mapped onto the point (x', y')'.

The following four properties of such transformations are very important; the reader should make sure that they are understood before proceeding further.

(1) The image of (0, 0) is (0, 0)

We can see from the matrix product $\begin{pmatrix} a & b \\ c & d \end{pmatrix} \begin{pmatrix} 0 \\ 0 \end{pmatrix} = \begin{pmatrix} 0 \\ 0 \end{pmatrix}$ that the image of

$(0, 0)$ is $(0, 0)$, for all values of a, b, c and d. We say that the origin is *invariant* under any linear transformation; $(0, 0) \mapsto (0, 0)$.

(2) The images of (1, 0) and (0, 1) are (a, c) and (b, d) respectively

[Throughout this chapter the points $(1, 0)$ and $(0, 1)$ will be labelled I and J respectively; a similar convention is used in Chapter 16.]

As before we need only look at the matrix products

$$\begin{pmatrix} a & b \\ c & d \end{pmatrix} \begin{pmatrix} 1 \\ 0 \end{pmatrix} = \begin{pmatrix} a \\ c \end{pmatrix} \quad \text{and} \quad \begin{pmatrix} a & b \\ c & d \end{pmatrix} \begin{pmatrix} 0 \\ 1 \end{pmatrix} = \begin{pmatrix} b \\ d \end{pmatrix}$$

to see that $(1, 0) \mapsto (a, c)$ and $(0, 1) \mapsto (b, d)$.

This property is especially valuable because it means that, if we are given the description of a transformation, we only have to look at its effect on the unit square OIRJ, and in particular, the images of I and J, to find the values of a, b, c and d. (At this stage the reader should look back at the transformations in Section 12.6 to confirm this.) Figure 12.5 shows the unit square OIRJ and its image, for a general transformation

$$\begin{pmatrix} x' \\ y' \end{pmatrix} = \begin{pmatrix} a & b \\ c & d \end{pmatrix} \begin{pmatrix} x \\ y \end{pmatrix}$$

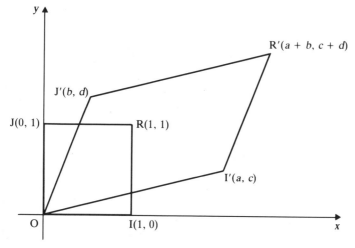

Figure 12.5

(3) The area of the parallelogram OI'R'J' is $(ad - bc)$

This is left as an exercise for the reader. It can be proved fairly easily if the parallelogram is 'framed' in a rectangle which has O and R' as a pair of diagonally opposite vertices. The region surrounding the parallelogram should then be dissected into suitable rectangles and right-angled triangles.

Notice that $(ad - bc)$ is Δ, the determinant of the matrix $\begin{pmatrix} a & b \\ c & d \end{pmatrix}$. Notice also

that it is possible for $(ad - bc)$ to be negative. This will happen when the unit square is 'turned inside-out', as in a reflection.

(4) Any set of parallel lines is transformed into a set of lines which are also parallel to one another

Let the original set of lines have equations of the form $y = mx + k$, where m is constant, thereby ensuring that the lines in the original set all have the same gradient, i.e. they are parallel to one another. We shall show that these are transformed into a set of lines whose gradient does not depend upon the value of k, i.e. the gradient is the same for any line from the original set of lines.

The new coordinates (x', y') are given by

$$\begin{pmatrix} x' \\ y' \end{pmatrix} = \begin{pmatrix} a & b \\ c & d \end{pmatrix}\begin{pmatrix} x \\ y \end{pmatrix}$$

Solving this equation, as in Section 12.5, Example 3, we obtain

$$\begin{pmatrix} x \\ y \end{pmatrix} = \frac{1}{\Delta}\begin{pmatrix} d & -b \\ -c & a \end{pmatrix}\begin{pmatrix} x' \\ y' \end{pmatrix}$$

where $\Delta = ad - bc$ and $\Delta \neq 0$. Hence,

$$x = \frac{dx' - by'}{\Delta} \qquad y = \frac{-cx' + ay'}{\Delta}$$

Now (x, y) is a point on the line $y = mx + k$, and consequently its coordinates satisfy this equation. Substituting for x and y we find

$$\frac{-cx' + ay'}{\Delta} = \frac{m(dx' - by')}{\Delta} + k$$

$$-cx' + ay' = mdx' - mby' + k\Delta$$
$$(a + bm)y' = (c + dm)x' + k\Delta$$

so the coordinates (x', y') of P′ satisfy the equation $(a + bm)y = (c + dm)x + k\Delta$

This is the equation of a straight line and its gradient, $(c + dm)/(a + bm)$, does not depend on k. Consequently all members of the original set of lines are transformed into another set of lines, all of which have the same gradient as each other, namely $(c + dm)/(a + bm)$.

Figure 12.6a shows the original plane with a set of equally spaced lines parallel to the x-axis and another set parallel to the y-axis. The second diagram shows these two sets of lines after the transformation. The unit square is labelled $OI_1 RJ_1$ in the first diagram and its image $OI'_1 R'J'_1$ appears in the second.

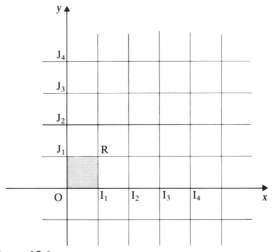

Figure 12.6a

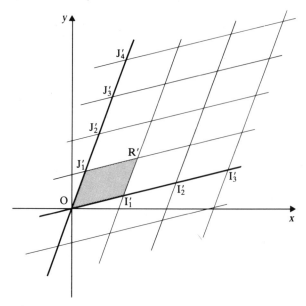

Figure 12.6b

Notice that each little square in the original diagram has an area of one square unit and that each of these is transformed into a parallelogram whose area is $(ad - bc)$. Consequently any region in the original diagram will be transformed into a region whose area is $(ad - bc)$ times greater than the area of the original region.

Example 5

A linear transformation is defined by

$$\begin{pmatrix} x' \\ y' \end{pmatrix} = \begin{pmatrix} 3 & 2 \\ 5 & 4 \end{pmatrix} \begin{pmatrix} x \\ y \end{pmatrix}$$

Find the images of (1, 0) and (0, 1) and find the factor by which areas are increased by the transformation. Find also the point whose image is (4, 6).

The image of (1, 0) is given by the first column of the matrix. Hence $(1, 0) \mapsto (3, 5)$. The image of (0, 1) is given by the second column. Hence $(0, 1) \mapsto (2, 4)$. The area is increased by a factor equal to the determinant, i.e. $(3 \times 4 - 2 \times 5) = 2$.

Let the point (4, 6) be the image of (x, y), then

$$\begin{pmatrix} 3 & 2 \\ 5 & 4 \end{pmatrix}\begin{pmatrix} x \\ y \end{pmatrix} = \begin{pmatrix} 4 \\ 6 \end{pmatrix}$$

Multiplying both sides of this equation by the inverse matrix, we obtain

$$\begin{pmatrix} x \\ y \end{pmatrix} = \frac{1}{\Delta}\begin{pmatrix} 4 & -2 \\ -5 & 3 \end{pmatrix}\begin{pmatrix} 4 \\ 6 \end{pmatrix} \qquad \text{where } \Delta = 12 - 10 = 2$$

$$\begin{pmatrix} x \\ y \end{pmatrix} = \frac{1}{2}\begin{pmatrix} 4 \\ -2 \end{pmatrix} = \begin{pmatrix} 2 \\ -1 \end{pmatrix}$$

Hence (4, 6) is the image of $(2, -1)$.

Property (2), (p 249), is especially useful because it enables us to write down, with very little working, the matrices which represent some common transformations, which we can add to our list (a), (b), (c) in Section 12.6.

(d) Rotation through an angle α about the origin

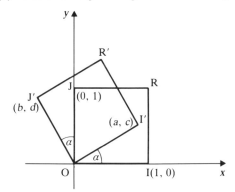

Figure 12.7

Since $OI' = 1$, we can see that $a = \cos \alpha$ and $c = \sin \alpha$. Also, since $OJ' = 1$, $b = -\sin \alpha$ and $d = \cos \alpha$. (See Figure 12.7.) Hence the required matrix is

$$\begin{pmatrix} \cos \alpha & -\sin \alpha \\ \sin \alpha & \cos \alpha \end{pmatrix}$$

(e) Reflection in the line $y = mx$, where $m = \tan \alpha$

The required matrix is

$$\begin{pmatrix} \cos 2\alpha & \sin 2\alpha \\ \sin 2\alpha & -\cos 2\alpha \end{pmatrix}$$

Proof of this is left to the reader; it is not difficult, provided a careful diagram is drawn.

(f) The transformation under which the unit square is mapped onto the parallelogram with vertices O, I' (1, 0), R' (3, 1) and J' (2, 1)

[See Figure 12.8; a transformation such as this is called a **shear**, parallel to the x-axis.]

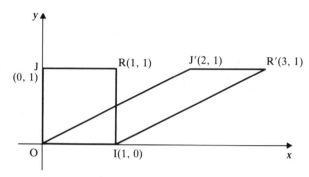

Figure 12.8

Using the same method as before, the required matrix is $\begin{pmatrix} 1 & 2 \\ 0 & 1 \end{pmatrix}$.

Qu. 6 Write down the matrix which represents the shear parallel to the y-axis, under which the unit square is mapped onto the parallelogram with vertices O, I' (1, 5), R' (1, 6) and J' (0, 1).

It should be noticed that the same letter may be used to represent both the transformation and its corresponding matrix – indeed this causes less confusion than using two different letters. Thus we can say 'the transformation **E** is an enlargement with a scale factor k' and we can also say that the matrix representing this transformation is **E**, where $\mathbf{E} = \begin{pmatrix} k & 0 \\ 0 & k \end{pmatrix}$.

12.8 Composite transformations

Suppose that we have two transformations **P** and **Q**, which are given by the matrix equations

$$\mathbf{P}: \begin{pmatrix} x' \\ y' \end{pmatrix} = \begin{pmatrix} a_1 & b_1 \\ c_1 & d_1 \end{pmatrix} \begin{pmatrix} x \\ y \end{pmatrix} \qquad \mathbf{Q}: \begin{pmatrix} x' \\ y' \end{pmatrix} = \begin{pmatrix} a_2 & b_2 \\ c_2 & d_2 \end{pmatrix} \begin{pmatrix} x \\ y \end{pmatrix}$$

and suppose that **P** is applied first, mapping (x, y) onto (x', y') and that **Q** is then applied, mapping (x', y') onto (x'', y'') i.e.

$$\begin{pmatrix} x'' \\ y'' \end{pmatrix} = \begin{pmatrix} a_2 & b_2 \\ c_2 & d_2 \end{pmatrix} \begin{pmatrix} x' \\ y' \end{pmatrix}$$

Then, substituting for $\begin{pmatrix} x' \\ y' \end{pmatrix}$ we obtain

$$\begin{pmatrix} x'' \\ y'' \end{pmatrix} = \begin{pmatrix} a_2 & b_2 \\ c_2 & d_2 \end{pmatrix} \begin{pmatrix} a_1 & b_1 \\ c_1 & d_1 \end{pmatrix} \begin{pmatrix} x \\ y \end{pmatrix}$$

So the matrix which represents the composite transformation 'do **P**, then do **Q**' is the matrix product

$$\begin{pmatrix} a_2 & b_2 \\ c_2 & d_2 \end{pmatrix} \begin{pmatrix} a_1 & b_1 \\ c_1 & d_1 \end{pmatrix}$$

Notice that the matrix which represents the *first* transformation is the matrix on the *right* in this product. This composite matrix is always written **QP**. Remember that **P** is applied first and **Q** second. This may seem strange, but it is logical if we look at the way the matrix product, above, was formed. Notice also that it is the same convention as that used in forming composite functions (see Section 3.10).

Example 6

Write down the matrices **R** and **S**, which represent a reflection in the line $y = x$, and a rotation through 90°, anticlockwise about the origin, respectively. Find the matrix which represents the composite transformation **SR** and draw a diagram showing the unit square and its image under the transformation **SR**. Describe **SR** in words.

$$\mathbf{R} = \begin{pmatrix} 0 & 1 \\ 1 & 0 \end{pmatrix} \quad \text{and} \quad \mathbf{S} = \begin{pmatrix} 0 & -1 \\ 1 & 0 \end{pmatrix} \quad \text{(see Section 12.6)}$$

$$\mathbf{SR} = \begin{pmatrix} 0 & -1 \\ 1 & 0 \end{pmatrix} \begin{pmatrix} 0 & 1 \\ 1 & 0 \end{pmatrix} = \begin{pmatrix} -1 & 0 \\ 0 & 1 \end{pmatrix}$$

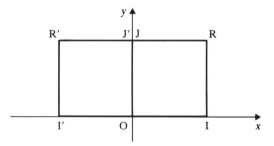

Figure 12.9

The transformation **SR** is a reflection in the line $x = 0$ (see Figure 12.9).

Example 7

Write down the matrices **A** and **B** which represent rotations about the origin, through angles α and β, respectively. Find the matrix which represents the transformation **AB** and describe this transformation in words. Write down another matrix which represents this transformation and hence find expressions, in terms of $\sin \alpha$, $\cos \alpha$, $\sin \beta$ and $\cos \beta$, for $\sin (\alpha + \beta)$ and $\cos (\alpha + \beta)$.

$$\mathbf{A} = \begin{pmatrix} \cos \alpha & -\sin \alpha \\ \sin \alpha & \cos \alpha \end{pmatrix} \quad \text{and} \quad \mathbf{B} = \begin{pmatrix} \cos \beta & -\sin \beta \\ \sin \beta & \cos \beta \end{pmatrix}$$

(see Section 12.7).

The composite transformation is given by the product

$$\mathbf{AB} = \begin{pmatrix} \cos \alpha & -\sin \alpha \\ \sin \alpha & \cos \alpha \end{pmatrix} \begin{pmatrix} \cos \beta & -\sin \beta \\ \sin \beta & \cos \beta \end{pmatrix}$$

$$= \begin{pmatrix} \cos \alpha \cos \beta - \sin \alpha \sin \beta & -\cos \alpha \sin \beta - \sin \alpha \cos \beta \\ \sin \alpha \cos \beta + \cos \alpha \sin \beta & \cos \alpha \cos \beta - \sin \alpha \sin \beta \end{pmatrix}$$

The composite transformation is a rotation through an angle β followed by a rotation through an angle α: this can be simplified by replacing it by a single rotation through an angle $(\alpha + \beta)$. (In this particular case the order of the transformations is immaterial; in other words the transformations are commutative.) The single rotation through an angle $(\alpha + \beta)$ can be represented by the matrix

$$\begin{pmatrix} \cos (\alpha + \beta) & -\sin (\alpha + \beta) \\ \sin (\alpha + \beta) & \cos (\alpha + \beta) \end{pmatrix}$$

Comparing this with the matrix **AB**, above, we see that

$$\cos (\alpha + \beta) = \cos \alpha \cos \beta - \sin \alpha \sin \beta$$
$$\sin (\alpha + \beta) = \sin \alpha \cos \beta + \cos \alpha \sin \beta$$

[See also Chapter 18.]

Example 8

Write down the matrix **R** which represents a reflection in the line $y = mx$, where $m = \tan \alpha$. Prove that $\mathbf{R}^2 = \mathbf{I}$, and hence write down the inverse of the matrix **R**. Verify that this agrees with the result obtained by using the normal method for finding $\mathbf{R}^{-1}$ (see Section 12.5).

$$\mathbf{R} = \begin{pmatrix} \cos 2\alpha & \sin 2\alpha \\ \sin 2\alpha & -\cos 2\alpha \end{pmatrix}$$

$$\therefore \quad \mathbf{R}^2 = \begin{pmatrix} \cos 2\alpha & \sin 2\alpha \\ \sin 2\alpha & -\cos 2\alpha \end{pmatrix} \begin{pmatrix} \cos 2\alpha & \sin 2\alpha \\ \sin 2\alpha & -\cos 2\alpha \end{pmatrix}$$

$$= \begin{pmatrix} \cos^2 2\alpha + \sin^2 2\alpha & \cos 2\alpha \sin 2\alpha - \sin 2\alpha \cos 2\alpha \\ \cos 2\alpha \sin 2\alpha - \sin 2\alpha \cos 2\alpha & \cos^2 2\alpha + \sin^2 2\alpha \end{pmatrix}$$

$$= \begin{pmatrix} 1 & 0 \\ 0 & 1 \end{pmatrix}$$

$$= \mathbf{I}$$

Since $\mathbf{R}^2 = \mathbf{I}$, the inverse of $\mathbf{R}$ is $\mathbf{R}$ itself, so

$$\mathbf{R}^{-1} = \begin{pmatrix} \cos 2\alpha & \sin 2\alpha \\ \sin 2\alpha & -\cos 2\alpha \end{pmatrix}$$

[This is not very surprising because we have reflected an object in a given line, and then reflected it again in the same line; this would return the object to its original position. In other words $\mathbf{R}^2$ leaves the object unchanged. Any matrix $\mathbf{M}$ with the property $\mathbf{M}^{-1} = \mathbf{M}$ is called a **self-inverse matrix**.]

The determinant of $\mathbf{R}$ is given by

$$\det \mathbf{R} = -\cos^2 2\alpha - \sin^2 2\alpha$$
$$= -(\cos^2 2\alpha + \sin^2 2\alpha)$$
$$= -1$$

Hence, applying the method in Section 12.5 for inverting a matrix, we obtain

$$\mathbf{R}^{-1} = \frac{1}{-1} \begin{pmatrix} -\cos 2\alpha & -\sin 2\alpha \\ -\sin 2\alpha & +\cos 2\alpha \end{pmatrix}$$

$$= \begin{pmatrix} \cos 2\alpha & \sin 2\alpha \\ \sin 2\alpha & -\cos 2\alpha \end{pmatrix}$$

$$= \mathbf{R}$$

Exercise 12d

1 Describe the transformations represented by:

(a) $\begin{pmatrix} 1 & 0 \\ 0 & -1 \end{pmatrix}$ (b) $\begin{pmatrix} -1 & 0 \\ 0 & 1 \end{pmatrix}$ (c) $\begin{pmatrix} 0 & -1 \\ 1 & 0 \end{pmatrix}$

(d) $\begin{pmatrix} 0 & -1 \\ -1 & 0 \end{pmatrix}$ (e) $\begin{pmatrix} 1 & 4 \\ 0 & 1 \end{pmatrix}$

2 A certain transformation is represented by

$$\begin{pmatrix} x' \\ y' \end{pmatrix} = \begin{pmatrix} 4 & -3 \\ 3 & 4 \end{pmatrix} \begin{pmatrix} x \\ y \end{pmatrix}$$

Draw a diagram showing the unit square and its image under this transformation. The triangle whose vertices are A(3, 2), B(7, 2) and C(6, 5) is mapped onto A'B'C', by this transformation. Find the coordinates of A', B' and C'. Find also the areas of the triangles ABC and A'B'C'.

3 Two matrices **P** and **Q** are given below:

$$\mathbf{P} = \begin{pmatrix} 1 & 0 \\ -1 & 1 \end{pmatrix} \qquad \mathbf{Q} = \begin{pmatrix} 1 & 1 \\ 0 & 1 \end{pmatrix}$$

Find the product **QPQ** and describe the transformation it represents.

4 A circle, centre O, radius a, is subject to a transformation whose matrix is

$\begin{pmatrix} 1 & 0 \\ 0 & b/a \end{pmatrix}$. Draw a diagram showing the circle and its image and write down

the area inside each of the curves.

5 Write down the matrices which represent:
   (a) an anticlockwise rotation, about the origin, through an acute angle whose sine is 3/5
   (b) an enlargement by a factor of 5, followed by a reflection in the line $y = x$.

6 Describe the transformation which is given by

$$\begin{pmatrix} x' \\ y' \end{pmatrix} = \begin{pmatrix} a & -b \\ b & a \end{pmatrix} \begin{pmatrix} x \\ y \end{pmatrix}$$

where a and b are real numbers. State the condition required if this matrix represents a pure rotation.

7 By considering the effect on the unit square, describe the transformation

which is represented by the matrix $\mathbf{A} = \begin{pmatrix} 1 & 1 \\ 1 & -1 \end{pmatrix}$. Hence, or otherwise, find

λ and m such that

$$\begin{pmatrix} 1 & 1 \\ 1 & -1 \end{pmatrix} \begin{pmatrix} 1 \\ m \end{pmatrix} = \lambda \begin{pmatrix} 1 \\ m \end{pmatrix}$$

expressing m in the form $\tan \alpha$. Hence prove that $\tan 22\frac{1}{2}° = \sqrt{2} - 1$.

8 Show that $\mathbf{A} = \begin{pmatrix} 3/5 & 4/5 \\ 4/5 & -3/5 \end{pmatrix}$ is 'self-inverse', that is, $\mathbf{A}^2 = \mathbf{I}$, the unit matrix.

Hence describe the transformation which **A** represents.

9 Write down the matrix which represents a reflection in the line $y = (\tan \alpha)x$. Hence show that a reflection in a line which is inclined at an angle α to the x-axis, followed by a reflection in a line which is inclined at an angle β to the x-axis, is equivalent to a rotation about the origin through $(2\beta - 2\alpha)$. [You will need the formulae:

$$\sin (P - Q) = \sin P \cos Q - \cos P \sin Q$$
$$\cos (P - Q) = \cos P \cos Q + \sin P \sin Q$$

See Chapter 18.]

10 State the transformation which is represented by the matrix **A**, where

$$\mathbf{A} = \begin{pmatrix} \cos \theta & -\sin \theta \\ \sin \theta & \cos \theta \end{pmatrix}$$

and find the matrix $\mathbf{A}^2$. Describe the transformation represented by $\mathbf{A}^2$ and hence write down expressions for $\cos 2\theta$ and $\sin 2\theta$, in terms of $\cos \theta$ and $\sin \theta$.

Exercise 12e (Miscellaneous)

1 Find, where possible, the following products:

(a) $\begin{pmatrix} 2 & 3 \\ 1 & 5 \end{pmatrix} \begin{pmatrix} 4 \\ -7 \end{pmatrix}$ (b) $(3 \quad 1 \quad 2) \begin{pmatrix} 5 & 2 \\ 1 & 1 \\ 3 & 4 \end{pmatrix}$

(c) $\begin{pmatrix} 3 & 4 \\ 7 & 2 \end{pmatrix} (1 \quad 5)$ (d) $\begin{pmatrix} 1 & 2 \\ 3 & 4 \end{pmatrix} \begin{pmatrix} 0 & 1 & 1 & 0 \\ 0 & 1 & 0 & 1 \end{pmatrix}$

2 Find, where possible, the inverses of the following matrices:

(a) $\begin{pmatrix} 3 & 7 \\ 2 & 5 \end{pmatrix}$ (b) $\begin{pmatrix} 5 & 3 \\ 6 & 4 \end{pmatrix}$ (c) $\begin{pmatrix} 2 & 3 \\ 4 & 5 \end{pmatrix}$ (d) $\begin{pmatrix} 39 & 91 \\ 51 & 119 \end{pmatrix}$

3 Find, where possible, the inverses of the following matrices:

(a) $\begin{pmatrix} a & b \\ -b & a \end{pmatrix}$ (b) $\begin{pmatrix} \cos \theta & \sin \theta \\ -\sin \theta & \cos \theta \end{pmatrix}$ (c) $\begin{pmatrix} 0 & a \\ 1/a & 0 \end{pmatrix}$ (d) $\begin{pmatrix} b & b \\ b & b \end{pmatrix}$

4 Solve the following matrix equations:

(a) $\begin{pmatrix} 7 & 6 \\ 5 & 4 \end{pmatrix} \begin{pmatrix} x \\ y \end{pmatrix} = \begin{pmatrix} 1 \\ -3 \end{pmatrix}$ (b) $\begin{pmatrix} 5 & 3 \\ 8 & 5 \end{pmatrix} \begin{pmatrix} u & x \\ v & y \end{pmatrix} = \begin{pmatrix} 2 & 3 \\ 3 & 4 \end{pmatrix}$

5 Find the equation of the line onto which the line $x + y = 0$ is mapped by the transformation $\begin{pmatrix} x' \\ y' \end{pmatrix} = \begin{pmatrix} 5 & 12 \\ 3 & 5 \end{pmatrix} \begin{pmatrix} x \\ y \end{pmatrix}$.

6 The transformation $\begin{pmatrix} x' \\ y' \end{pmatrix} = \begin{pmatrix} 5 & 2 \\ 1 & 4 \end{pmatrix} \begin{pmatrix} x \\ y \end{pmatrix}$ maps the triangle A(3, 2), B(7, 2), C(3, 8) onto the triangle A′B′C′. Find the coordinates of A′, B′, and C′ and calculate the area of the triangle A′B′C′.

7 Under a certain transformation, the image of the point (x, y) is (X, Y), where $\begin{pmatrix} X \\ Y \end{pmatrix} = \begin{pmatrix} 1 & 4 \\ 2 & 3 \end{pmatrix} \begin{pmatrix} x \\ y \end{pmatrix}$. This transformation maps any point on the line $y = mx$ onto another point on the line $y = mx$. Find the (two) possible values of m.

8 Under a certain transformation, the images of the points $(1, 0)$ and $(0, 1)$ are $(3, 5)$ and $(5, 9)$ respectively. Find the image of the point $(2, -5)$ under the same transformation. Find also the point whose image is $(8, 6)$ under this transformation.

9 Given that **A** is the matrix $\begin{pmatrix} 1 & 1 & 0 \\ 1 & 0 & -1 \\ 1 & 1 & 2 \end{pmatrix}$ and **B** is the matrix $\begin{pmatrix} 1 & -2 & -1 \\ -3 & 2 & 1 \\ 1 & 0 & -1 \end{pmatrix}$, find the product **AB**. Hence write down $\mathbf{A}^{-1}$, the inverse of **A**.

10 As a result of market research, it is known that a per cent of the population buys *Soft* shampoo and b per cent does not, and that if the product is advertised on television for a week, these percentages change from **C** to **AC**, where $\mathbf{C} = \begin{pmatrix} a \\ b \end{pmatrix}$ and $\mathbf{A} = \begin{pmatrix} \frac{3}{4} & \frac{4}{5} \\ \frac{1}{4} & \frac{1}{5} \end{pmatrix}$. However, if it is not advertised for a week, **C** changes to **BC**, where $\mathbf{B} = \begin{pmatrix} \frac{1}{2} & \frac{3}{10} \\ \frac{1}{2} & \frac{7}{10} \end{pmatrix}$.

At the start of week 1, $a = 20$ and $b = 80$. Find the values of a and b two weeks later, if *Soft* shampoo is advertised:
(a) in both weeks
(b) in week 1, but not in week 2
(c) in week 2, but not in week 1

11 Given that z is the complex number $x + iy$ and that the matrix $\mathbf{A}(z)$ is defined as $\mathbf{A}(z) = \begin{pmatrix} x & -y \\ y & x \end{pmatrix}$, prove that

$$\mathbf{A}(z_1 z_2) = \mathbf{A}(z_1)\mathbf{A}(z_2)$$

12 By considering the effect on the unit square, or otherwise, write down the matrices **M** and **R** which represent a reflection in the line $x = y$, and a rotation about the origin through an angle θ, respectively. Find the matrix $\mathbf{M}^{-1}\mathbf{RM}$ and describe it in words.

Find also the matrix product $\mathbf{R}^{-1}\mathbf{MR}$ and, by considering the effect of $\mathbf{R}^{-1}\mathbf{MR}$ on the unit square, show that

$$\mathbf{R}^{-1}\mathbf{MR} = \begin{pmatrix} \sin 2\theta & \cos 2\theta \\ \cos 2\theta & -\sin 2\theta \end{pmatrix}$$

Hence write down expressions, in terms of $\cos \theta$ and $\sin \theta$, for $\cos 2\theta$ and $\sin 2\theta$.

13 The matrix **A** is $\begin{pmatrix} 3 & 0 & 0 \\ 0 & -1 & 2 \\ 0 & 3 & -2 \end{pmatrix}$. Show that **A** satisfies the matrix equation

$\mathbf{A}^3 = 13\mathbf{A} - 12\mathbf{I}$. Assuming that $\mathbf{A}^{-1}$ exists, show that this equation can be written $\mathbf{A}^{-1} = \frac{1}{12}(13\mathbf{I} - \mathbf{A}^2)$, and hence find $\mathbf{A}^{-1}$.

14 The matrix **M** is given by $\mathbf{M} = \begin{pmatrix} a & b \\ c & d \end{pmatrix}$, where $a, b, c, d \in \mathbb{R}$. Find $\mathbf{M}^2$.

Given that $\mathbf{M}^2 = \mathbf{M}$ and that b and c are non-zero, prove that **M** is singular. Prove also that, in this case, the transformation **T**, defined by

$$\mathbf{T}: \begin{pmatrix} x \\ y \end{pmatrix} \mapsto \mathbf{M}\begin{pmatrix} x \\ y \end{pmatrix}$$

maps all points of the plane to points of the line $(1 - a)x = by$.   (C)

15 Given the matrix $\mathbf{M} = \dfrac{1}{13}\begin{pmatrix} 5 & 12 \\ 12 & -5 \end{pmatrix}$, evaluate $\mathbf{M}^2$ and the determinant

of **M**. Find a set of matrices $\begin{pmatrix} x \\ y \end{pmatrix}$ such that $\mathbf{M}\begin{pmatrix} x \\ y \end{pmatrix} = \begin{pmatrix} x \\ y \end{pmatrix}$ and also a set

of matrices $\begin{pmatrix} u \\ v \end{pmatrix}$ such that $\mathbf{M}\begin{pmatrix} u \\ v \end{pmatrix} = \begin{pmatrix} -u \\ -v \end{pmatrix}$.

Describe, in geometrical terms, the transformation represented by the matrix **M**.   (JMB)

16 The transpose of a matrix $\mathbf{M} = \begin{pmatrix} a & b \\ c & d \end{pmatrix}$ is the matrix $\mathbf{M}^T = \begin{pmatrix} a & c \\ b & d \end{pmatrix}$, and **M**

is said to be orthogonal when $\mathbf{M}^T\mathbf{M} = \mathbf{I}$, where **I** is the unit matrix. Given

that the matrix $\mathbf{N} = \begin{pmatrix} 2/\sqrt{5} & 1/\sqrt{5} \\ -1/\sqrt{5} & k \end{pmatrix}$ is orthogonal, find the value of k.

Describe geometrically the transformation of the x–y plane which is represented by **N**.

Under a transformation **S** of the real plane into itself, a point $P = (x, y)$ is mapped onto the point $S(P) = (ax + by, cx + dy)$. Show that, when **M** is orthogonal, the distance between any two points P and Q is the same as the distance between their images S(P) and S(Q).   (L)

17 A transformation **T** is represented by

$$\begin{pmatrix} x' \\ y' \end{pmatrix} = \begin{pmatrix} b & 0 \\ 0 & 1/b \end{pmatrix} \begin{pmatrix} x \\ y \end{pmatrix}, \quad \text{where} \quad b \in \mathbb{R}^+.$$

(a) Draw a diagram showing the unit square and its image under **T**.
(b) Show that area is invariant under **T**.
(c) Show that **T** maps the curve $y = 1/x$ onto itself.
(d) Show that **T** maps the region bounded by the curve $y = 1/x$, the lines $x = 1$ and $x = a$, and the x-axis, onto the region bounded by the same curve, the lines $x = b$ and $x = ab$, and the x-axis.

(e) Hence show that $\displaystyle \int_1^a \frac{1}{x}\,\mathrm{d}x = \int_b^{ab} \frac{1}{x}\,\mathrm{d}x.$

(f) Given that $\displaystyle F(t) = \int_1^t \frac{1}{x}\,\mathrm{d}x$, show that

$$F(ab) = F(a) + F(b)$$

[The reader should note several interesting and significant points about this question. The integral in (e) cannot be evaluated by methods which have been introduced so far, and the result of (f) looks very much like a standard property of logarithms. We shall return to these points in Chapter 26.]

Revision Exercise 2

1 The roots of the equation

$$2x^2 + 5x + 7 = 0$$

are α and β. Without solving this equation, find the value of $\alpha^2 + \beta^2$. What can you deduce about the roots α and β?

Show that $8(\alpha^3 + \beta^3) = 85$ and find a quadratic equation with roots α^2/β and β^2/α. (O)

2 Sketch the graph of $y = |3x + 4|$ showing clearly the intercepts with the coordinate axes.

Using your graph, or otherwise, solve the inequality

$$|3x + 4| < x + 2 \tag{O}$$

3 (a) Solve the equation $2^x = 5$.

(b) Solve the equation $\lg x + \lg (3x + 1) = 1$.

(c) By using the substitution $y = e^x$, find the value of x such that $8e^{-x} - e^x = 2$.

(d) Given that $y = ax^b$, that $y = 2$ when $x = 3$ and that $y = 2/9$ when $x = 9$, find the values of a and b. (C)

4 Given that

$$y + z = a$$
$$x - y + z = b$$
$$2x - y + 2z = c$$

express x, y and z in terms of a, b and c.

Hence write down the inverse of the matrix $\mathbf{A}$, where

$$\mathbf{A} = \begin{pmatrix} 0 & 1 & 1 \\ 1 & -1 & 1 \\ 2 & -1 & 2 \end{pmatrix}$$

(JMB)

5 A curve is given parametrically by the equations

$$x = 1 + t^2 \qquad y = 2t - 1$$

Show that the equation of the tangent to the curve at the point with parameter t is

$$ty = x + t^2 - t - 1$$

Verify that the tangent at A(2, 1) passes through the point C(6, 5).

Show that the line $5y = x + 19$ passes through C and is also a tangent to the curve.

Find also the coordinates of the point of contact of this line with the given curve. (L)

6 (a) Evaluate $\displaystyle\int_1^4 \sqrt{x}\, dx$.

(b) Sketch the graph of $y = \sqrt{x}$, and indicate on your sketch the region whose area is given by the integral in part (a). (SUJB)

263

7 An object is placed a distance x metres in front of a lens which has a focal length f metres. The image is focused a distance d metres beyond the lens. The quantities x, f and d are related as follows:

$$\frac{1}{x} + \frac{1}{f+d} = \frac{1}{f}$$

In a particular optical system, it is required that $x = 1$ when $d = 1$. Find, correct to two significant figures, the necessary value of f. (C)

8 Given that $(x-2)$ and $(x+2)$ are factors of

$$x^3 + ax^2 + bx + 4$$

find the value of a and the value of b. (C)

9 Find the values of the constants p and q so that the polynomial

$$px^3 - 11x^2 + qx + 4$$

is divisible by $(x-1)$, and has a remainder of 70 when divided by $(x-3)$. Express the polynomial as a product of three linear factors. (L)

10 Given that $f(x) = x^2 + 4x + 5$, find the least value of $f(x)$. With the same axes, sketch the curves of $y = f(x)$ and $y = 1/f(x)$. (L)

11 By means of the substitution $y = 4^x$, or otherwise, find two values of x such that

$$2(4^x) + 4^{-x} = 3$$ (C)

12 A rectangular field has area A m^2 and perimeter P m. Show that its sides are of length

$$\frac{P \pm \sqrt{(P^2 - 16A)}}{4}$$ (W)

13 The sum of £1000 is invested in an account in which the interest of $\frac{1}{2}$% is added at the end of each month, so that after n complete months the amount of money in the account is £1000 × $(1.005)^n$. Calculate after how many complete months the sum of money first exceeds £1400. (C)

14 Mark in an Argand diagram the points P_1 and P_2 which represent the complex numbers z_1 and z_2, where $z_1 = 1 - i$ and $z_2 = 1 + i\sqrt{3}$. On the same diagram, mark the points P_3 and P_4 which represent $(z_1 + z_2)$ and $(z_1 - z_2)$ respectively. Find the modulus and argument of:
(a) z_1 (b) z_2 (c) $z_1 z_2$ (d) z_1/z_2 (L)

15 Find the roots z_1 and z_2, of the equation

$$z^2 - 5 + 12i = 0$$

in the form $a + bi$, where a and b are real, and give the value of $z_1 z_2$. Draw, on graph paper, an Argand diagram to illustrate the points representing

(a) $z_1 z_2$ (b) $\dfrac{1}{z_1 z_2}$ (c) $z_1^* z_2^*$ (L)

16 The roots of the quadratic equation

$$x^2 + 5x + 3 = 0$$

are α and β. Find a quadratic equation with roots α^2 and β^2. (L)

17 The roots of the equation $ax^2 + bx + c = 0$, where $a \neq 0$, are α and $n\alpha$. Show that

$$nb^2 = (1 + n)^2 ac. \qquad \text{(L)}$$

18 (a) By completing the square find the least value of the expression $2x^2 - x - 1$.

   (b) Solve completely the inequalities
   (i) $2x^2 - x - 1 < 0$,
   (ii) $2e^{2x} - e^x - 1 < 0$.   (AEB)

19 If $A = \begin{pmatrix} 1 & 1 \\ 0 & 1 \end{pmatrix}$ and $I = \begin{pmatrix} 1 & 0 \\ 0 & 1 \end{pmatrix}$, find a matrix X such that $AX = I - X$.

Prove that it is impossible to find a matrix Y such that $AY = I + Y$.
          (O & C)

20 Given that $A = \begin{pmatrix} 1 & 2 \\ 1 & 3 \end{pmatrix}$ and $B = \begin{pmatrix} 2 & 5 \\ 1 & 2 \end{pmatrix}$, find matrices X and Y such that

(a) $AXB = I$ (b) $AY = Y + B$ (O & C)

Chapter 13

Permutations and combinations

13.1 Arrangements

This chapter aims at teaching a method of approach to certain problems involving arrangements and selections. In the course of the work, a notation is introduced, and a formula is obtained for use in the proof of the binomial theorem (Chapter 15).

Example 1

From a pack of playing cards, the Ace, King, Queen, Jack, and Ten of Spades are taken. In how many ways can three of these five cards be placed in a row from left to right?

The first card can be any one of the five, namely:

A   K   Q   J   10

When the first card has been placed, there are four cards left to choose from, and so the possible ways of placing the first two cards are:

A K,	A Q,	A J,	A 10,
K A,	K Q,	K J,	K 10,
Q A,	Q K,	Q J,	Q 10,
J A,	J K,	J Q,	J 10,
10 A,	10 K,	10 Q,	10 J.

Thus, for *each* of the 5 ways of choosing the first, there are 4 ways in which the second card may be chosen; therefore there are 5×4 (i.e. 20) ways of choosing the first two cards.

Now for each of the 20 ways of placing the first two cards, there are three cards left to choose from (e.g. if the first two cards were A K, the third could be Q, J, or 10); therefore there are 20×3 ways of placing the third card.

Thus, three cards chosen from the Ace, King, Queen, Jack, and Ten of Spades may be placed in a row from left to right in 60 different ways.

Example 2

Three schools have teams of six or more runners in a cross-country race. In how many ways can the first six places be taken by the three schools, if there are no dead heats?

First it should be made clear that there is no question of the individuality of the runners, but only which school each of the first six runners belongs to.

The first place can be taken by any of the three schools.

When the first runner has come in, the second place can be taken by any of the three schools, so the first two places can be taken in 3×3, or 3^2, ways.

Similarly, the third place can be taken by any of the three schools, so the first three places can be taken in $3^2 \times 3$, or 3^3, ways.

Continuing the argument for the fourth, fifth and sixth places, it follows that the first six places may be taken in 3^6, or 729, ways by the three schools.

Example 3

How many even numbers, greater than 2000, can be formed with the digits 1, 2, 4, 8, if each digit may be used only once in each number?

If the number is greater than 2000, the first digit can be chosen in 3 ways (viz.: 2, 4, or 8).

Then, whichever has been chosen to be the first digit, there are 2 ways in which the last digit may be chosen, in order to make the number even. Thus there are 3×2 ways of choosing the first and last digits.

When the first and last digits have been chosen, there are 2 digits, either of which may be the second digit of the number. Thus there are $3 \times 2 \times 2$ ways of choosing the first, last, and second digit.

Now, when three digits have been chosen, there is only 1 left to fill the remaining place, and so there are $3 \times 2 \times 2 \times 1$, i.e. 12, even numbers greater than 2000 which may be formed from the digits 1, 2, 4, 8, without repetitions.

The following table is useful for showing the argument briefly:

Position of digit	First	Last	Second	Third
Number of possibilities	3	2	2	1

It is to be understood, in this and later tables, that the choice is made in the order of the first line.

Exercise 13a

1 There are ten runners in a race. In how many ways can the first three places be filled, if there are no dead heats?

2 In how many ways can four letters of the word BRIDGE be arranged in a row, if no letter is repeated?

3 A man, who works a five-day week, can travel to work on foot, by cycle or by bus. In how many ways can he arrange a week's travelling to work?

4 How many five-figure odd numbers can be made from the digits 1, 2, 3, 4, 5, if no digit is repeated?

5 A girl has two coats, four scarves and three pairs of gloves. How many different outfits, consisting of coat, scarf, and a pair of gloves, can she make out of these?

6 In a class of thirty pupils, one prize is awarded for English, another for French, and a third for mathematics. In how many ways can the recipients be chosen?

7 The computer department in a large company assigns a personal code number to each employee in the form of a three-digit number, using the digits 0 to 9 inclusive. Code numbers starting with 0 are reserved for members of the management. How many code numbers are available for non-management employees?

8 There are sixteen books on a shelf. In how many ways can these be arranged if twelve of them are volumes of a history, and must be kept together, in order?

9 A typist has six envelopes and six letters. In how many ways can one letter be placed in each envelope without getting every letter in the right envelope?

10 How many postal codes of the form AB1 2CD (i.e. two letters, followed by a single digit, a space, another digit and two more letters) can be formed from the symbols A, B, C, D, 1 and 2, if each symbol is used once only?

11 In how many ways can the letters of the word NOTATION be arranged?

12 How many odd numbers, greater than 500 000, can be made from the digits 2, 3, 4, 5, 6, 7, without repetitions?

13 Three letters from the word RELATION are arranged in a row. In how many ways can this be done? How many of these contain exactly one vowel?

14 Seven men and six women are to be seated in a row on a platform. In how many ways can they be arranged if no two men sit next to each other? In how many ways can the arrangement be made if there are six men and six women, subject to the same restriction?

15 I have fifteen books of three different sizes, five of each. In how many ways can I arrange them on my shelf if I keep books of the same size together?

13.2 The factorial notation

There are times when a problem on arrangements leads to an answer involving a product of more factors than it is convenient to write down. The next example shows how this may arise.

Example 4

In how many ways can the cards of one suit, from a pack of playing cards, be placed in a row?

Position of card in row	1st	2nd	. . .	12th	13th
Number of possibilities	13	12	. . .	2	1

The table abbreviates the type of argument used in the last three examples, and it leads to the conclusion that the cards of one suit can be placed in a row in

$$13 \times 12 \times 11 \times 10 \times 9 \times 8 \times 7 \times 6 \times 5 \times 4 \times 3 \times 2 \times 1 \text{ ways}$$

To shorten the answer, the product could be evaluated, giving 6 227 020 800; but it is easier to write

$$13!$$

(which is read, 'thirteen factorial').

Thus:

$$7! = 7 \times 6 \times 5 \times 4 \times 3 \times 2 \times 1 = 5040$$

and similarly for any other positive integer.

The factorial notation will be used freely in this chapter and Chapter 15, and the reader should become thoroughly used to it before going on to the next section.

Example 5

(a) Evaluate $\dfrac{9!}{2! \, 7!}$.

(b) Write $40 \times 39 \times 38 \times 37$ in factorial notation.

(a) Written in full,

$$\frac{9!}{2! \, 7!} = \frac{9 \times 8 \times 7 \times 6 \times 5 \times 4 \times 3 \times 2 \times 1}{2 \times 1 \times 7 \times 6 \times 5 \times 4 \times 3 \times 2 \times 1}$$

$$= \frac{9 \times 8}{2 \times 1}$$

$$= 36$$

(b) $40 \times 39 \times 38 \times 37 = 40 \times 39 \times 38 \times 37 \times \dfrac{36 \times 35 \times \ldots \times 2 \times 1}{36 \times 35 \times \ldots \times 2 \times 1}$

$$= \frac{40!}{36!}$$

Exercise 13b

1 Evaluate:

(a) 3!   (b) 4!   (c) 5!   (d) $\dfrac{10!}{8!}$ (e) $\dfrac{7!}{4!}$ (f) $\dfrac{12!}{9!}$

(g) $\dfrac{11!}{7!\,4!}$ (h) $\dfrac{6!\,2!}{8!}$ (i) $(2!)^2$ (j) $\dfrac{6!}{(3!)^2}$ (k) $\dfrac{10!}{3!\,7!}$ (l) $\dfrac{10!}{2!\,3!\,5!}$

2 Express in factorial notation:

(a) $6 \times 5 \times 4$ (b) 10×9 (c) $12 \times 11 \times 10 \times 9$

(d) $n(n-1)(n-2)$ (e) $(n+2)(n+1)n$ (f) $\dfrac{10 \times 9}{2 \times 1}$

(g) $\dfrac{7 \times 6 \times 5}{3 \times 2 \times 1}$ (h) $\dfrac{52 \times 51 \times 50}{3 \times 2 \times 1}$ (i) $\dfrac{n(n-1)}{2 \times 1}$

(j) $\dfrac{(n+1)n(n-1)}{3 \times 2 \times 1}$ (k) $\dfrac{2n(2n-1)}{2 \times 1}$ (l) $n(n-1)\ldots(n-r+1)$

3 Express in factors:

(a) $20! + 21!$ (b) $26! - 25!$ (c) $14! - 2(13!)$

(d) $15! + 4(14!)$ (e) $(n+1)! + n!$ (f) $(n-1)! - (n-2)!$

(g) $n! + 2(n-1)!$ (h) $(n+2)! + (n+1)! + n!$

4 Simplify:

(a) $\dfrac{15!}{11!\,4!} + \dfrac{15!}{12!\,3!}$ (b) $\dfrac{21!}{7!\,14!} + \dfrac{21!}{8!\,13!}$

(c) $\dfrac{16!}{9!\,7!} + \dfrac{2 \times 16!}{10!\,6!} + \dfrac{16!}{11!\,5!}$ (d) $\dfrac{35!}{16!\,19!} + \dfrac{3 \times 35!}{17!\,18!}$

(e) $\dfrac{n!}{(n-r)!\,r!} + \dfrac{n!}{(n-r+1)!\,(r-1)!}$

(f) $\dfrac{n!}{(n-r)!\,r!} + \dfrac{2 \times n!}{(n-r+1)!\,(r-1)!} + \dfrac{n!}{(n-r+2)!\,(r-2)!}$

13.3 Permutations

In Example 4, it was found that 13 playing cards could be placed in a row in 13! ways. If we consider n unlike objects placed in a row, using the same method,

Position of object in row	1st	2nd	. . .	$(n-1)$th	nth
Number of possibilities	n	$n-1$	. . .	2	1

we find they may be arranged in $n!$ ways.

The arrangements of the *n* objects are called **permutations**. Thus

ABC,   ACB,   BCA,   BAC,   CAB,   CBA,

are the 3! permutations of the three letters A, B, C.

Again, in Example 1, it was found that 3 cards chosen from 5 unlike cards could be arranged in 60 ways. This might be expressed by saying that there are 60 permutations of 3 cards chosen from 5 unlike cards.

A permutation is an arrangement of a number of objects in a particular order. In practice, the order may be in space, such as from left to right in a row; or it may be in time, such as reaching the winning post in a race, or dialling on a telephone.

How many permutations are there of *r* objects chosen from *n* unlike objects?

The method is indicated in the table below.

Order of choice of object	1st	2nd	3rd	. . .	$(r-1)$th	*r*th
Number of possibilities	n	$(n-1)$	$(n-2)$	. . .	$(n-r+2)$	$(n-r+1)$

Thus there are

$$n(n-1)(n-2)\ldots(n-r+2)(n-r+1)$$

permutations of the objects. But

$$n(n-1)(n-2)\ldots(n-r+2)(n-r+1)$$

$$= \frac{n(n-1)(n-2)\ldots(n-r+2)(n-r+1)\times(n-r)\ldots2\times1}{(n-r)\ldots2\times1}$$

$$= \frac{n!}{(n-r)!}$$

> Therefore there are $n!/(n-r)!$ permutations of *r* objects chosen from *n* unlike objects, if *r* is less than *n*.

[We have already found that there are *n*! permutations of *n* unlike objects.]

Example 6

There are 20 books on a shelf, but the red covers of two of them clash, and they must not be put together. In how many ways can the books be arranged?

This is best tackled by finding out the number of ways in which the two books *are* together, and subtracting this from the number of ways in which the 20 books can be arranged if there is no restriction.

Suppose the two red books are tied together, then there are 19 objects, which can be arranged in 19! ways. Now if the order of the two red books is reversed, there will again be 19! arrangements; so that there are $2 \times 19!$ ways of arranging the books with the red ones next to each other.

With *no* restriction, 20 books can be arranged in 20! ways; therefore the number of arrangements in which the red books are not together is

$$20! - 2 \times 19! = 18 \times 19!$$

Example 7

In how many ways can 8 people sit at a round table?

Since the table is round, the position of people relative to the *table* is of no consequence. Thus, supposing they sit down, and then all move one place to the left, the arrangement is still the same.

Therefore one person may be considered to be fixed, and the other 7 can then be arranged about him or her in 7! ways.

Thus there are 5040 ways in which 8 people can sit at a round table.

Example 8

In how many ways can the letters of the word BESIEGE be arranged?

First, give the three E's suffixes: $BE_1SIE_2GE_3$. Then, treating the E's as different, the 7 letters may be arranged in 7! ways.

Now, in every distinct arrangement, the 3 E's may be rearranged amongst themselves in 3! ways, without altering the positions of the B, S, I, or G; for instance, SEIBEEG would have been counted 3! times in the 7! arrangements as

$$SE_1IBE_2E_3G, \qquad SE_2IBE_3E_1G, \qquad SE_3IBE_1E_2G,$$
$$SE_1IBE_3E_2G, \qquad SE_2IBE_1E_3G, \qquad SE_3IBE_2E_1G.$$

Therefore the number of distinct arrangements of the letters in BESIEGE is $7!/3! = 840$.

Notice that 3 letter A's and 5 letter B's can be arranged in

$$\frac{8!}{3! \times 5!} \text{ ways}$$

and more generally:

> p letter A's and q letter B's can be arranged in
>
> $$\frac{(p + q)!}{p! \times q!} \text{ ways}$$

Exercise 13c

1 Seven boys and two girls are to sit together on a bench. In how many ways can they arrange themselves so that the girls do not sit next to each other?

2 Eight women and two men are to sit at a round table. In how many ways can they be arranged? If, however, the two men sit directly opposite each other, in how many ways can the ten people be arranged?

3 How many arrangements can be made of the letters in the word TROTTING? In how many of these are the N and the G next to each other?

4 On a bookshelf, four books are bound in leather and sixteen in cloth. If the books are to be arranged so that the leather-bound ones are together, in how many ways can this be done? If, in addition, the cloth-bound books are to be kept together, in how many ways can the shelf be arranged?

5 There is room for ten books on a bedside table, but there are fifteen to choose from. Of these, however, a Bible and a book of ghost stories must go at the ends. In how many ways can the books be arranged?

6 At a conference of five powers, each delegation consists of three members. If each delegation sits together, with their leader in the middle, in how many ways can the members be arranged at a round table?

7 How many numbers, divisible by 5, can be made with the digits 2, 3, 4, 5, no digit being used more than once in each number?

8 In a cricket team, the captain has settled the first four places in the batting order, and has decided that the four bowlers will occupy the last four places. In how many ways can the batting order be made out?

9 How many arrangements can be made of the letters in the word TERRITORY?

10 How many odd numbers, greater than 60 000, can be made from the digits 5, 6, 7, 8, 9, 0, if no number contains any digit more than once?

13.4 Combinations

In the last section, attention was given to permutations, where the order of a set of objects was of importance; but in other circumstances, the order of selection is irrelevant. If, for instance, eight tourists find there is only room for five of them at a hotel, they will be chiefly interested in which five of them stay there, rather than in any order of arrangement.

When a selection of objects is made with no regard being paid to order, it is referred to as a **combination**. Thus, ABC, ACB, CBA, are different permutations, but they are the same combination of letters.

Example 9

In how many ways can 13 cards be selected from a pack of 52 playing cards?

First of all, suppose that 13 cards from the pack are laid on a table in an order from left to right. From the last section, it follows that this can be done in $52!/39!$ ways.

Now each combination of cards can be arranged in 13! ways, therefore

the number of permutations $= 13! \times$ (the number of combinations)

$\therefore \qquad \dfrac{52!}{39!} = 13! \times$ (the number of combinations)

Therefore the number of combinations of 13 cards chosen from a pack of playing cards is $52!/(39!\,13!)$.

In how many ways can r objects be chosen from n unlike objects?

In Section 13.3 it was shown that there are $n!/(n-r)!$ permutations of r objects chosen from n unlike objects.

Now each combination of r objects can be arranged in $r!$ ways, therefore

the number of permutations $= r! \times$ (the number of combinations)

$\therefore \qquad \dfrac{n!}{(n-r)!} = r! \times$ (the number of combinations)

Hence the number of combinations of r objects chosen from n unlike objects is

$$\frac{n!}{(n-r)!\,r!}$$

For brevity, the number of combinations of r objects chosen from n unlike objects is written $^{n}C_{r}$, thus

$$\boxed{^{n}C_{r} = \frac{n!}{(n-r)!\,r!}}$$

$^{n}C_{r}$ is also sometimes written as $_{n}C_{r}$ and $\dbinom{n}{r}$ (see Section 15.5).

Qu. 1 Find the values of:
(a) $^{8}C_{3}, \,^{8}C_{5}$ (b) $^{10}C_{6}, \,^{10}C_{4}$

Qu. 2 In how many ways can $n - r$ objects be chosen from n unlike objects?

Qu. 3 Show that $^nC_r = {}^nC_{n-r}$.

Example 10

A mixed hockey team containing 5 men and 6 women is to be chosen from 7 men and 9 women. In how many ways can this be done?

Five men can be selected from 7 men in $^7C_5$ ways, and 6 women can be selected from 9 women in $^9C_6$ ways.

Now for each of the $^7C_5$ ways of selecting the men, there are $^9C_6$ ways of selecting the women, therefore there are $^7C_5 \times {}^9C_6$ ways of selecting the team.

$$^7C_5 \times {}^9C_6 = \frac{7!}{2!\,5!} \times \frac{9!}{3!\,6!}$$

$$= 21 \times 84$$

Therefore the team can be chosen in 1764 ways.

Exercise 13d

1 Evaluate:
   (a) $^{10}C_2$ (b) $^6C_4$ (c) $^7C_3$ (d) $^9C_5$ (e) $^8C_4$
   Express in factors:
   (f) $^nC_2$ (g) $^nC_3$ (h) $^nC_{n-2}$ (i) $^{n+1}C_2$ (j) $^{n+1}C_{n-1}$

2 In how many ways can a cricket team be selected from thirteen players?

3 There are ten possible players for the VI to represent a tennis club, and of these the captain and the secretary must be in the team. In how many ways can the team be selected?

4 Ten boxes each hold one white ball and one coloured ball, every colour being different. Find the number of ways in which one ball may be taken from each box if half those taken are white.

5 Nine people are going to travel in two taxis. The larger has five seats, and the smaller has four. In how many ways can the party be split up?

6 A girl wants to ask eight friends to tea, but there is only room for four of them. In how many ways can she choose whom to invite if two of them are sisters and must not be separated? (Consider two cases, (a) when both sisters are invited, (b) when neither sister is invited.)

7 In a game of mixed hockey there are ten married couples and two spinsters playing. In how many ways can the two teams be made up, if no husband may play against his wife?

8 A ferry which holds ten people carries a party of thirteen men and seven women across a river. Find the number of ways in which the party may be taken across if all the women go on the first trip.

9 Twelve people each spin a coin. Find the number of ways in which exactly five heads may be obtained.

10 Two punts each hold six people. In how many ways can a party of six boys and six girls divide themselves so that there are equal numbers of boys and girls in each punt?

Exercise 13e (Miscellaneous)

1 In how many ways can a committee of four men and three women be formed from seven men and eight women?

2 Show that the number of ways of choosing six objects from fourteen unlike objects is equal to the number of ways of choosing five objects from fifteen unlike objects.

3 How many arrangements can be made of the letters in THIRTIETH?

4 In how many ways can a boy arrange in a row six balls from seven cricket balls, six tennis balls and five squash balls?

5 Find the number of diagonals of a polygon of n sides.

6 How many five-figure numbers can be made from the digits of 10 242?

7 In how many ways can ten books be arranged on a shelf if four of them are kept together?

8 How many odd numbers, greater than 600 000, can be made from the digits 5, 6, 7, 8, 9, 0:
   (a) if repetitions are not allowed
   (b) if repetitions are allowed?

9 How many arrangements can be made with the letters of LEATHERETTE?

10 In how many ways can four mince-pies, three jam tarts, and three cakes be given to ten children if each receives one?

Chapter 14

Series

14.1 Sequences

The reader should examine the following lists of numbers. Each list is written down in a definite order, and there is a simple rule by which the terms are obtained. Such a list of terms is called a **sequence**.

Qu. 1 Write down the next two terms in each of the following sequences:

(a) 1, 3, 5, 7, ...   (b) 2, 5, 8, 11, ...   (c) 1, 2, 4, 8, ...

(d) $\frac{1}{3}, \frac{1}{6}, \frac{1}{12}, \frac{1}{24}$, ...   (e) $1^3, 2^3, 3^3, 4^3$, ...   (f) $\frac{1}{2}, \frac{2}{3}, \frac{3}{4}, \frac{4}{5}$, ...

(g) 1, 4, 9, 16, ...   (h) 1, 2, 6, 24, 120, ...   (i) $1, \frac{2}{3}, \frac{3}{9}, \frac{4}{27}$, ...

(j) 4, 2, 0, -2, ...   (k) 1, -1, 1, -1, ...   (l) $1, -\frac{1}{2}, \frac{1}{4}, -\frac{1}{8}$, ...

Suppose one is asked to add up the integers from 1 to 100. This could be done by elementary arithmetic, but it would be very tedious: fortunately there is a short-cut.

First write the numbers down in their natural order:

$$1 + 2 + 3 + \ldots + 98 + 99 + 100$$

Now write the numbers down again in the opposite order, so that we have:

$$
\begin{array}{cccccccc}
1 + & 2 + & 3 + & \ldots + & 98 + & 99 + 100 \\
100 + & 99 + & 98 + & \ldots + & 3 + & 2 + & 1 \\
\hline
101 + & 101 + & 101 + & \ldots + & 101 + & 101 + 101
\end{array}
$$

The numbers in each column have been added together, and, since there are 100 terms in the top line, the total is $100 \times 101 = 10\,100$. But this is twice the sum required, therefore the sum of the integers from 1 to 100 is 5050.

If the terms of a sequence are considered as a sum, for instance

$$1 + 2 + 3 + \ldots + 98 + 99 + 100$$

or

$$1 + \tfrac{1}{2} + \tfrac{1}{4} + \tfrac{1}{8} + \ldots$$

the expression is called a **series**. A series may end after a finite number of terms, in which case it is called a **finite series**; or it may be considered not to end, and it is then called an **infinite series**.

14.2 Arithmetical progressions

The method of Section 14.1, for finding the sum of a series, may only be applied to a certain type, which is usually called an arithmetical progression (often abbreviated to A.P.). For example,

$$1 + 3 + 5 + \ldots + 99$$
$$7 + 11 + 15 + \ldots + 79$$
$$3 - 2 - 7 - \ldots - 42$$
$$1\tfrac{1}{8} + 1\tfrac{1}{4} + 1\tfrac{3}{8} + \ldots + 3\tfrac{1}{2}$$
$$-2 - 4 - 6 - \ldots - 16$$

are arithmetical progressions. In such a series, any term may be obtained from the previous term by adding a certain number, called the **common difference**. Thus the common differences in the above progressions are 2, 4, -5, $\tfrac{1}{8}$, -2.

Example 1

Find the third, tenth, twenty-first and nth terms of the A.P. with first term 6 and common difference 5.

Position of term	1st	2nd	3rd	4th	10th	21st	nth
Value	6	$6+5$	$6+2\times5$	$6+3\times5$	$6+9\times5$	$6+20\times5$	$6+(n-1)\times5$

Note that to find the nth term $n-1$ common differences are added to the first term. (Throughout this chapter it should be assumed that n represents a positive integer.)

The third, tenth, twenty-fifth, and nth terms are 16, 51, 106, and $5n+1$.

Example 2

Find the sum of the first twenty terms of the A.P. $-4 - 1 + 2 + \ldots$.

To find the twentieth term, add 19 times the common difference to the first term: $-4 + 19 \times 3 = 53$.

Write S_{20} for the sum of the first twenty terms, then using the method of Section 14.1,

$$S_{20} = -4 - 1 + 2 + \ldots + 53$$

Again,

$$S_{20} = 53 + 50 + 47 + \ldots - 4$$

Adding,

$$2S_{20} = 49 + 49 + 49 + \ldots + 49 = 20 \times 49$$
$$\therefore \quad S_{20} = 490$$

Therefore the sum of the first twenty terms of the A.P. is 490.

Exercise 14a

1 Which of the following series are arithmetical progressions? Write down the common differences of those that are:
   (a) $7 + 8\frac{1}{2} + 10 + 11\frac{1}{2}$ (b) $-2 - 5 - 8 - 11$
   (c) $1 + 1.1 + 1.2 + 1.3$ (d) $1 + 1.1 + 1.11 + 1.111$
   (e) $\frac{1}{2} + \frac{5}{6} + \frac{7}{6} + \frac{3}{2}$ (f) $1^2 + 2^2 + 3^2 + 4^2$
   (g) $n + 2n + 3n + 4n$ (h) $1 + \frac{1}{2} + \frac{1}{3} + \frac{1}{4}$
   (i) $1\frac{1}{8} + 2\frac{1}{4} + 3\frac{3}{8} + 4\frac{1}{2}$ (j) $19 + 12 + 5 - 2 - 9$
   (k) $1 - 2 + 3 - 4 + 5$ (l) $1 + 0.8 + 0.6 + 0.4$

2 Write down the terms indicated in each of the following A.P.s:
   (a) $3 + 11 + \ldots$, 10th, 19th   (b) $8 + 5 + \ldots$, 15th, 31st
   (c) $\frac{1}{4} + \frac{7}{8} + \ldots$, 12th, nth   (d) $50 + 48 + \ldots$, 100th, nth
   (e) $7 + 6\frac{1}{2} + \ldots$, 42nd, nth   (f) $3 + 7 + \ldots$, 200th, $(n+1)$th

3 Find the number of terms in the following A.P.s:
   (a) $2 + 4 + 6 + \ldots + 46$ (b) $50 + 47 + 44 + \ldots + 14$
   (c) $2.7 + 3.2 + \ldots + 17.7$ (d) $6\frac{1}{4} + 7\frac{1}{2} + \ldots + 31\frac{1}{4}$
   (e) $407 + 401 + \ldots - 133$ (f) $2 - 9 - \ldots - 130$
   (g) $2 + 4 + \ldots + 4n$ (h) $x + 2x + \ldots + nx$
   (i) $a + (a+d) + \ldots + \{a + (n-1)d\}$ (j) $a + (a+d) + \ldots + l$

4 Find the sums of the following A.P.s:
   (a) $1 + 3 + 5 + \ldots + 101$ (b) $2 + 7 + 12 + \ldots + 77$
   (c) $-10 - 7 - 4 - \ldots + 50$ (d) $71 + 67 + 63 + \ldots - 53$
   (e) $2.01 + 2.02 + 2.03 + \ldots + 3.00$ (f) $1 + 1\frac{1}{6} + 1\frac{1}{3} + \ldots + 4\frac{1}{2}$
   (g) $x + 3x + 5x + \ldots + 21x$ (h) $a + (a+1) + \ldots + (a+n-1)$
   (i) $a + (a+d) + \ldots + \{a + (n-1)d\}$

5 Find the sums of the following arithmetical progressions as far as the terms indicated:
   (a) $4 + 10 + \ldots$ 12th term   (b) $15 + 13 + \ldots$ 20th term
   (c) $1 + 2 + \ldots$ 200th term   (d) $20 + 13 + \ldots$ 16th term
   (e) $6 + 10 + \ldots$ nth term   (f) $1\frac{1}{4} + 1 + \ldots$ nth term

6 The second term of an A.P. is 15, and the fifth is 21. Find the common difference, the first term and the sum of the first ten terms.

7 The fourth term of an A.P. is 18, and the common difference is -5. Find the first term and the sum of the first sixteen terms.

8 Find the difference between the sums of the first ten terms of the A.P.s whose first terms are 12 and 8, and whose common differences are respectively 2 and 3.

9 The first term of an A.P. is -12, and the last term is 40. If the sum of the progression is 196, find the number of terms and the common difference.

10 Find the sum of the odd numbers between 100 and 200.

11 Find the sum of the even numbers, divisible by three, lying between 400 and 500.

12 The twenty-first term of an A.P. is $5\frac{1}{2}$, and the sum of the first twenty-one terms is $94\frac{1}{2}$. Find the first term, the common difference and the sum of the first thirty terms.

13 Show that the sum of the integers from 1 to n is $\frac{1}{2}n(n+1)$.

14 The twenty-first term of an A.P. is 37 and the sum of the first twenty terms is 320. What is the sum of the first ten terms?

15 Show that the sum of the first n terms of the A.P. with first term a and common difference d is $\frac{1}{2}n\{2a+(n-1)d\}$.

14.3 Geometrical progressions

Another series of common occurrence is the geometrical progression, for example:

$$1+\tfrac{1}{2}+\tfrac{1}{4}+\tfrac{1}{8}+ \ldots +\tfrac{1}{512}$$
$$3+6+12+ \ldots +192$$
$$\tfrac{16}{27}-\tfrac{8}{9}+\tfrac{4}{3}- \ldots +\tfrac{27}{4}$$

In such a progression, the ratio of a term to the previous one is a constant, called the **common ratio**. Thus, the common ratios of the above progressions are respectively $\frac{1}{2}$, 2 and $-\frac{3}{2}$.

Qu. 2 Write down the third and fourth terms of the progressions which begin
(i) $2+4+ \ldots$ (ii) $12+6+ \ldots$:
(a) if they are A.P.s   (b) if they are G.P.s

Example 3

Find the third, tenth, twenty-first and nth terms of the G.P. which begins $3+6+ \ldots$.

Position of term	1st	2nd	3rd	4th	10th	21st	nth
Value	3	3×2	3×2^2	3×2^3	3×2^9	3×2^{20}	$3 \times 2^{n-1}$

Note that to find the nth term, the first term is multiplied by the $(n-1)$th power of the common ratio.

The third, tenth, twenty-first, and nth terms are 12, 1536, 3 145 728, and $3 \times 2^{n-1}$.

Example 4

Find the sum of the first eight terms of the geometrical progression $2 + 6 + 18 + \dots$.

To find the eighth term, multiply the first term by the seventh power of the common ratio: 2×3^7.

Let S_8 be the sum of the first eight terms of the expression.

$$\therefore \quad S_8 = 2 + 2 \times 3 + 2 \times 3^2 + \dots + 2 \times 3^7$$

Now multiply both sides by the common ratio and write the terms obtained one place to the right, so that we have

$$S_8 = 2 + 2 \times 3 + 2 \times 3^2 + \dots + 2 \times 3^7$$
$$3S_8 = \quad\quad 2 \times 3 + 2 \times 3^2 + \dots + 2 \times 3^7 + 2 \times 3^8$$

Subtracting the top line from the lower,

$$2S_8 = -2 + 2 \times 3^8$$
$$\therefore \quad S_8 = 3^8 - 1$$

Therefore the sum of the first eight terms is 6560.

Exercise 14b

1 Which of the following series are geometrical progressions? Write down the common ratios of those that are:
   (a) $3 + 9 + 27 + 81$
   (b) $1 + \frac{1}{4} + \frac{1}{16} + \frac{1}{64}$
   (c) $-1 + 2 - 4 + 8$
   (d) $1 - 1 + 1 - 1$
   (e) $1 + 1\frac{1}{2} + 1\frac{1}{4} + 1\frac{1}{8}$
   (f) $a + a^2 + a^3 + a^4$
   (g) $1 + 1.1 + 1.21 + 1.331$
   (h) $\frac{1}{2} + \frac{1}{6} + \frac{1}{12} + \frac{1}{36}$
   (i) $2 + 4 - 8 - 16$
   (j) $\frac{3}{4} + \frac{9}{2} + 27 + 162$

2 Write down the terms indicated in each of the following geometrical progressions. Do not simplify your answers.
   (a) $5 + 10 + \dots$, 11th, 20th
   (b) $10 + 25 + \dots$, 7th, 19th
   (c) $\frac{2}{3} + \frac{3}{4} + \dots$, 12th, nth
   (d) $3 - 2 + \dots$, 8th, nth
   (e) $\frac{2}{7} - \frac{3}{7} + \dots$, 9th, nth
   (f) $3 + 1\frac{1}{2} + \dots$, 19th, $2n$th

3 Find the number of terms in the following geometrical progressions:
   (a) $2 + 4 + 8 + \dots + 512$
   (b) $81 + 27 + 9 + \dots + \frac{1}{27}$
   (c) $0.03 + 0.06 + 0.12 + \dots + 1.92$
   (d) $\frac{8}{81} - \frac{4}{27} + \frac{2}{9} - \dots - 1\frac{11}{16}$
   (e) $5 + 10 + 20 + \dots + 5 \times 2^n$
   (f) $a + ar + ar^2 + \dots + ar^{n-1}$

4 Find the sums of the geometrical progressions in no. 3. Simplify, but do not evaluate, your answers.

5 Find the sums of the following geometrical progressions as far as the terms indicated. Simplify, but do not evaluate, your answers.
   (a) $4 + 12 + 36 + \dots$, 12th term
   (b) $15 + 5 + 1\frac{2}{3} + \dots$, 20th term
   (c) $1 - 2 + 4 - \dots$, 50th term
   (d) $24 - 12 + 6 - \dots$, 17th term
   (e) $1.1 + 1.21 + 1.331 + \dots$, 23rd term
   (f) $\frac{1}{2} + \frac{1}{4} + \frac{1}{8} + \dots$, 13th term
   (g) $3 + 6 + 12 + \dots$, nth term
   (h) $1 - \frac{1}{3} + \frac{1}{9} - \dots$, nth term

6 The third term of a geometrical progression is 10, and the sixth is 80. Find the common ratio, the first term and the sum of the first six terms.

7 The third term of a geometrical progression is 2, and the fifth is 18. Find two possible values of the common ratio, and the second term in each case.

8 The three numbers, $n-2$, n, $n+3$, are consecutive terms of a geometrical progression. Find n, and the term after $n+3$.

9 A man starts saving on 1st April. He saves 1p the first day, 2p the second, 4p the third, and so on, doubling the amount every day. If he managed to keep on saving under this system until the end of the month (30 days), how much would he have saved? Give your answer in pounds, correct to three significant figures.

10 The first term of a G.P. is 16 and the fifth term is 9. What is the value of the seventh term?

14.4 Formulae for the sums of A.P.s and G.P.s

The methods of Examples 2 and 4 will now be applied to general A.P.s and G.P.s to obtain formulae for their sums.

(a) If the first term of an A.P. is a, and the nth term is l, we may find the sum S_n of the first n terms.

We have

$$S_n = a + (a+d) + \ldots + (l-d) + l$$

(where there are n terms), and again,

$$S_n = l + (l-d) + \ldots + (a+d) + a$$

Adding,

$$2S_n = (a+l) + (a+l) + \ldots + (a+l) + (a+l)$$

Now there are n terms on the right-hand side,

$$\therefore \quad 2S_n = n(a+l)$$

$$\therefore \quad S_n = \frac{n(a+l)}{2}$$

(b) If the first term of an A.P. is a, and the common difference is d, the nth term is $a+(n-1)d$. Substituting $l = a+(n-1)d$ in the formula above,

$$S_n = \frac{n}{2}\{a + a + (n-1)d\}$$

$$\therefore \quad S_n = \frac{n}{2}\{2a + (n-1)d\}$$

(c) If the first term of a G.P. is a and the common ratio is r, we may find the sum S_n of the first n terms.

The nth term is ar^{n-1}, therefore

$$S_n = a + ar + ar^2 + \ldots + ar^{n-1}$$
$$\therefore \quad rS_n = \quad ar + ar^2 + \ldots + ar^{n-1} + ar^n$$

Subtracting,

$$S_n - rS_n = a - ar^n$$
$$\therefore \quad S_n(1-r) = a(1-r^n)$$

$$\boxed{\therefore \quad S_n = a\left(\frac{1-r^n}{1-r}\right)}$$

An alternative formula for the sum of a G.P. is obtained by multiplying numerator and denominator by -1:

$$S_n = a\left(\frac{r^n - 1}{r - 1}\right)$$

This is more convenient if r is greater than 1.

Example 5

In an arithmetical progression, the thirteenth term is 27, and the seventh term is three times the second term. Find the first term, the common difference and the sum of the first ten terms.

[We have two unknowns (the first term and the common difference). We have two pieces of information:
(a) the thirteenth term is 27
(b) the seventh term is three times the second term.
Thus we can form two equations which will enable us to find the two unknowns.]

Let the first term be a, and let the common difference be d.

Then the thirteenth term is $a + 12d$, therefore

$$a + 12d = 27$$

The seventh term is $a + 6d$, and the second term is $a + d$, therefore

$$a + 6d = 3(a + d)$$
$$\therefore \qquad 3d = 2a$$

Substituting in the first equation,

$$a + 8a = 27$$
$$\therefore \qquad a = 3$$

and so

$$d = 2$$

Therefore the first term is 3, and the common difference is 2.

To find the sum of the first ten terms, we know that

$$S_n = \frac{n}{2}\{2a + (n-1)d\}$$

$$\therefore \quad S_{10} = \tfrac{10}{2}(6 + 9 \times 2)$$
$$= 5 \times 24$$

Therefore the sum of the first ten terms is 120.

Example 6

In a geometrical progression, the sum of the second and third terms is 6, and the sum of the third and fourth terms is -12. Find the first term and the common ratio.

[As in the last example, we have two unknowns (the first term and the common ratio). We have two pieces of information:
(a) the sum of the second and third terms is 6
(b) the sum of the third and fourth terms is -12.
We may therefore write down two equations and these will enable us to find the two unknowns.]

Let the first term be a, and let the common ratio be r. Then the second term is ar, and the third term is ar^2, therefore

$$ar + ar^2 = 6$$

The third term is ar^2, and the fourth term is ar^3, therefore

$$ar^2 + ar^3 = -12$$

Factorising the left-hand sides of the equations,

$$ar(1 + r) = 6$$
$$ar^2(1 + r) = -12$$

We may eliminate a by dividing:

$$\frac{ar(1 + r)}{ar^2(1 + r)} = -\frac{6}{12}$$

$$\therefore \quad \frac{1}{r} = -\frac{1}{2}$$

$$\therefore \quad r = -2$$

Substituting $r = -2$ in $ar(1 + r) = 6$,

$$a(-2)(-1) = 6$$
$$\therefore \qquad a = 3$$

Therefore the first term is 3, and the common ratio is -2.

Example 7

The sum of a number of consecutive terms of an arithmetical progression is $-19\frac{1}{2}$, the first term is $16\frac{1}{2}$, and the common difference is -3. Find the number of terms.

The sum of n terms is given by,

$$S_n = \frac{n}{2}\{2a + (n-1)d\}$$

Substituting $S_n = -19\frac{1}{2}$, $\quad a = 16\frac{1}{2}$, $\quad d = -3$:

$$-\frac{39}{2} = \frac{n}{2}\{33 - 3(n-1)\}$$

$$\therefore \qquad -39 = n(36 - 3n)$$
$$\therefore \quad 3n^2 - 36n - 39 = 0$$

Dividing through by 3,

$$n^2 - 12n - 13 = 0$$
$$\therefore \quad (n - 13)(n + 1) = 0$$
$$\therefore \qquad n = 13 \quad \text{or} \quad -1$$

Therefore the number of terms is 13.

Example 8

What is the smallest number of terms of the geometrical progression, $8 + 24 + 72 + \dots$, that will give a total greater than 6 000 000?

The sum of n terms is given by,

$$S_n = a\left(\frac{r^n - 1}{r - 1}\right)$$

Substituting $a = 8$ and $r = 3$,

$$S_n = 8\left(\frac{3^n - 1}{3 - 1}\right) = 4(3^n - 1)$$

Now if we solve the equation

$$4(3^n - 1) = 6\,000\,000$$

the first integer greater than the value of n found from this will be the number of terms required.

To solve the equation:

$$3^n - 1 = 1\,500\,000$$
$$\therefore \quad 3^n = 1\,500\,001$$

Taking logarithms (base 10) of both sides,

$$n \lg 3 = \lg 1\,500\,001$$

$$\therefore \quad n = \frac{\lg 1\,500\,001}{\lg 3}$$

$$\approx \frac{6.1761\dagger}{0.4771}$$

$$= 12.94, \quad \text{correct to four significant figures.}$$

Therefore the number of terms required to make a total exceeding 6 000 000 is 13.

14.5 Arithmetic and geometric means

If three numbers a, b, c are in arithmetical progression, b is called the **arithmetic mean** of a and c. The common difference of the progression is given by $b - a$ or $c - b$. Therefore:

$$b - a = c - b$$
$$\therefore \quad 2b = a + c$$

Therefore, the arithmetic mean of a and c is $(a + c)/2$. This is the ordinary 'average' of a and c.

If three numbers a, b, c are in geometrical progression, b is called the **geometric mean** of a and c. The common ratio is given by b/a or c/b. Therefore:

$$\frac{b}{a} = \frac{c}{b}$$

$$\therefore \quad b^2 = ac$$

Therefore, the geometric mean of a and c is $\sqrt{(ac)}$. If a rectangle is drawn with sides a and c, then b is the side of a square whose area is equal to that of the rectangle.

Qu. 3 Find:
(a) the arithmetic mean and (b) the geometric mean of 4 and 64

† If a calculator is used it is not necessary, or desirable, to write these figures down.

Qu. 4 The reciprocal of the harmonic mean of two numbers is the arithmetic mean of their reciprocals. Find the harmonic mean of 5 and 20. Also find the arithmetic and geometric means of 5 and 20.

Qu. 5 Find an expression for the harmonic mean of a and c.

Exercise 14c

1 Find the sum of the even numbers up to and including 100.

2 How many terms of the series $2 - 6 + 18 - 54 + \dots$ are needed to make a total of $\frac{1}{2}(1 - 3^8)$?

3 The fifth term of an A.P. is 17 and the third term is 11. Find the sum of the first seven terms.

4 The fourth term of a G.P. is -6 and the seventh term is 48. Write down the first three terms of the progression.

5 Find the sum of the first eight terms of the G.P. $5 + 15 + \dots$.

6 What is the difference between the sums to ten terms of the A.P. and G.P. whose first terms are $-2 + 4 \dots$?

7 The sum of the second and fourth terms of an arithmetical progression is 15, and the sum of the fifth and sixth terms is 25. Find the first term and the common difference.

8 The second term of an arithmetical progression is three times the seventh, and the ninth term is 1. Find the first term, the common difference, and which is the first term less than 0.

9 In a geometrical progression, the sum of the second and third terms is 9, and the seventh term is eight times the fourth. Find the first term, the common ratio, and the fifth term.

10 The fourth term of an arithmetical progression is 15, and the sum of the first five terms is 55. Find the first term and the common difference, and write down the first five terms.

11 The sum of the first three terms of an arithmetic progression is 3, and the sum of the first five terms is 20. Find the first five terms of the progression.

12 The sum of the first two terms of a geometrical progression is 3, and the sum of the second and third terms is -6. Find the first term and the common ratio.

13 How many terms of the A.P. $15 + 13 + 11 + \dots$ are required to make a total of -36?

14 Which is the first term of the geometrical progression $5 + 10 + 20 + \dots$ to exceed 400 000?

15 Find how many terms of the G.P. $1 + 3 + 9 + \dots$ are required to make a total of more than a million.

16 The sum of the first six terms of an arithmetical progression is 21, and the seventh term is three times the sum of the third and fourth. Find the first term and the common difference.

17 In an arithmetical progression, the sum of the first five terms is 30, and the third term is equal to the sum of the first two. Write down the first five terms of the progression.

18 Find the difference between the sums of the first ten terms of the geometrical and arithmetical progressions which begin, $6 + 12 + \dots$.

19 The sum of the first n terms of a certain series is $n^2 + 5n$, for all integral values of n. Find the first three terms and prove that the series is an arithmetical progression.

20 The second, fourth, and eighth terms of an A.P. are in geometrical progression, and the sum of the third and fifth terms is 20. Find the first four terms of the progression.

14.6 Infinite geometrical progressions

Consider the geometrical progression:

$$1 + \frac{1}{2} + \frac{1}{4} + \frac{1}{8} + \dots + \frac{1}{2^{n-1}}$$

The sum of these n terms, obtained by the formula of Section 14.4, is given by

$$S_n = \frac{1 - (\frac{1}{2})^n}{1 - \frac{1}{2}} = 2\left(1 - \left(\frac{1}{2}\right)^n\right)$$

Now as n increases, $(\frac{1}{2})^n$ approaches zero; and $(\frac{1}{2})^n$ can be made as close to zero as we like, if n is large enough. Therefore the sum of n terms approaches 2, as closely as we please, as n increases.

This is what is meant by writing that the infinite series

$$1 + \frac{1}{2} + \frac{1}{4} + \dots + \frac{1}{2^{m-1}} + \dots = 2$$

The limit 2 is called its **sum to infinity**.

In general, the sum of the geometrical progression

$$a + ar + ar^2 + \dots + ar^{n-1} = a\left(\frac{1 - r^n}{1 - r}\right)$$

If r lies between -1 and $+1$, i.e. $|r| < 1$, then r^n approaches zero as n increases, and the sum to infinity of the series

$$a + ar + ar^2 + \dots ar^{m-1} + \dots = \frac{a}{1 - r}$$

Example 9

Express as fractions in their lowest terms: (a) $0.0\dot{7}$ (b) $0.\dot{4}\dot{5}$.

(a) $0.0\dot{7}$ means $0.0777\dots$, which may be written

$$\frac{7}{100} + \frac{7}{1000} + \frac{7}{10\,000} + \dots$$

This is a geometrical progression, and in the notation of Section 14.4, $a = \frac{7}{100}$ and $r = \frac{1}{10}$. Therefore

$$S_n = \frac{7}{100}\left(\frac{1 - (\frac{1}{10})^n}{1 - \frac{1}{10}}\right)$$

Therefore, the sum to infinity, S_∞, is given by

$$S_\infty = \frac{7}{100}\left(\frac{1}{\frac{9}{10}}\right) = \frac{7}{100} \times \frac{10}{9} = \frac{7}{90}$$

$$\therefore \quad 0.0\dot{7} = \frac{7}{90}$$

(b) $0.\dot{4}\dot{5}$ means $0.454\ 545\ ...$, which may be written

$$\frac{45}{100} + \frac{45}{10\ 000} + \frac{45}{1\ 000\ 000} + \ ...$$

In this geometrical progression, $a = \frac{45}{100}$, and $r = \frac{1}{100}$.

$$\therefore \quad S_n = \frac{45}{100}\left(\frac{1 - (\frac{1}{100})^n}{1 - \frac{1}{100}}\right)$$

$$\therefore \quad S_\infty = \frac{45}{100}\left(\frac{1}{\frac{99}{110}}\right) = \frac{45}{100} \times \frac{100}{99} = \frac{5}{11}$$

$$\therefore \quad 0.\dot{4}\dot{5} = \frac{5}{11}$$

Using this method, any recurring decimal can be expressed as a rational number. (See Section 3.3.)

Exercise 14d

1 Write down the sums of the first n terms of the following series, and deduce their sums to infinity:

(a) $1 + \frac{1}{3} + \frac{1}{9} + \frac{1}{27} + \ ...$

(b) $12 + 6 + 3 + 1\frac{1}{2} + \ ...$

(c) $\frac{3}{10} + \frac{3}{100} + \frac{3}{1000} + \frac{3}{10\ 000} + \ ...$

(d) $\frac{13}{100} + \frac{13}{10\ 000} + \frac{13}{1\ 000\ 000} + \ ...$

(e) $0.5 + 0.05 + 0.005 + \ ...$

(f) $0.54 + 0.0054 + 0.000\ 054 + \ ...$

(g) $1 - \frac{1}{2} + \frac{1}{4} - \frac{1}{8} + \ ...$

(h) $54 - 18 + 6 - 2 + \ ...$

2 Express the following recurring decimals as rational numbers:

(a) $0.\dot{8}$ (b) $0.\dot{1}\dot{2}$ (c) $3.\dot{2}$ (d) $2.6\dot{9}$ (e) $1.00\dot{4}$ (f) $2.9\dot{6}\dot{0}$

3 If the sum to infinity of a G.P. is three times the first term, what is the common ratio?

4 The sum to infinity of a G.P. is 4 and the second term is 1. Find the first, third, and fourth terms.

5 The second term of a G.P. is 24 and its sum to infinity is 100. Find the two possible values of the common ratio and the corresponding first terms.

14.7 Proof by induction

It sometimes happens that a result is found by some means which does not provide a proof. For example, consider the following table:

n	1	2	3	4	5
Sum of the integers up to n	1	3	6	10	15
n^3	1	8	27	64	125
Sum of the cubes of the integers up to n	1	9	36	100	225

Here the terms in the fourth row are the squares of the corresponding terms in the second row. Thus it is natural to suppose that

$$1^3 + 2^3 + \ ... \ + n^3 = (1 + 2 + \ ... \ + n)^2$$

Now $1 + 2 + \ ... \ + n$ is an arithmetical progression whose sum is $\frac{1}{2}n(n+1)$.

Therefore we might guess that

$$1^3 + 2^3 + \ ... \ + n^3 = \tfrac{1}{4}n^2(n+1)^2$$

Proof by induction, is a very useful method for proving that a given proposition is true for all positive integers. It is not a means of discovering a result, but when we have a result which seems to be true, like the sum of the cubes, above, the method of induction provides us with a rigorous proof.

The first step is to prove that the proposition is true when $n = 1$.†

The second step is to assume the proposition is true when $n = k$ and, from this assumption, we deduce that the proposition is true when $n = k + 1$. If we combine this with step one, we can be sure that the proposition is true for $n = 2$. If it is true for $n = 2$, then step two ensures that it is true for $n = 3$, and so on, quite literally, *ad infinitum*.

Example 10

Prove by induction that

$$1^3 + 2^3 + 3^3 + \ ... \ + n^3 = \tfrac{1}{4}n^2(n+1)^2$$

Step 1 When $n = 1$:

L.H.S. $= 1^3 = 1$,
R.H.S. $= \tfrac{1}{4} \times 1^2 \times 2^2 = 1$

The proposition is true when $n = 1$.

---

† On some occasions it may be impossible to start with $n = 1$. If we start at some higher number, say 7, then step two will ensure that the proposition is true for all integers from 7 onwards.

Step 2 Assume the proposition is true when $n = k$, that is:

$$1^3 + 2^3 + \ldots + k^3 = \tfrac{1}{4}k^2(k+1)^2$$

Then, adding the next term of the series, $(k+1)^3$, to both sides, we obtain

$$1^3 + 2^3 + \ldots + k^3 + (k+1)^3 = \tfrac{1}{4}k^2(k+1)^2 + (k+1)^3$$

$$= (k+1)^2\left(\frac{k^2}{4} + k + 1\right)$$

$$= (k+1)^2\left(\frac{k^2 + 4k + 4}{4}\right)$$

$$\therefore \qquad 1^3 + 2^3 + \ldots + (k+1)^3 = \tfrac{1}{4}(k+1)^2(k+2)^2$$

Now this is the formula with $n = k + 1$. Therefore if the result holds for $n = k$, then it also holds for $n = k + 1$.

Since the result is true for $n = 1$, it follows, by what has been shown above, that it must also be true for $n = 2$. From this it follows that the result is true for $n = 3$, and so on, for all positive integral values of n.

Example 11

Prove by mathematical induction that

$$3^{2n} - 1$$

is a multiple of 8, for all positive integers n.

Step 1 We must prove that the proposition is true when $n = 1$.

When $n = 1$, $3^{2n} - 1$ becomes $3^2 - 1$, which equals 8. So the proposition is true for $n = 1$.

Step 2 Now we assume that the proposition is true for $n = k$, i.e.

$$3^{2k} - 1 = 8M \qquad\qquad \ldots \ (1)$$

where M is a positive integer.

(Using this assumption, we must now endeavour to show that the proposition is true for $n = k + 1$.)

$$3^{2(k+1)} - 1 = 3^{2k} \times 3^2 - 1$$
$$= 9 \times 3^{2k} - 1$$

Using (1), we may write $3^{2k} = 8M + 1$, so:

$$3^{2(k+1)} - 1 = 9 \times (8M + 1) - 1$$
$$= 72M + 8$$
$$= 8(9M + 1)$$

But $(9M + 1)$ is a positive integer, so we have shown that $3^{2(k+1)} - 1$ is a multiple of 8, i.e. the proposition is true for $n = k + 1$.

Hence by the principle of mathematical induction it is true for all positive integers.

Exercise 14e

Prove the following results by induction:

1 $1 + 2 + \ldots + n = \frac{1}{2}n(n+1)$

2 $1^2 + 2^2 + \ldots + n^2 = \frac{1}{6}n(n+1)(2n+1)$

3 $1 \times 2 + 2 \times 3 + \ldots + n(n+1) = \frac{1}{3}n(n+1)(n+2)$

4 $1 \times 3 + 2 \times 4 + \ldots + n(n+2) = \frac{1}{6}n(n+1)(2n+7)$

5 $3 + 8 + \ldots + (n^2 - 1) = \frac{1}{6}n(n-1)(2n+5)$

6 $a + ar + \ldots + ar^{n-1} = a\left(\dfrac{1 - r^n}{1 - r}\right)$

7 $\dfrac{1}{1 \times 2} + \dfrac{1}{2 \times 3} + \ldots + \dfrac{1}{n(n+1)} = \dfrac{n}{n+1}$

8 $\dfrac{1}{1 \times 3} + \dfrac{1}{2 \times 4} + \ldots + \dfrac{1}{n(n+2)} = \dfrac{3}{4} - \dfrac{2n+3}{2(n+1)(n+2)}$

9 $\dfrac{3}{4} + \dfrac{5}{36} + \ldots + \dfrac{2n+1}{n^2(n+1)^2} = 1 - \dfrac{1}{(n+1)^2}$

10 $\dfrac{1}{1 \times 2 \times 3} + \dfrac{1}{2 \times 3 \times 4} + \ldots + \dfrac{1}{n(n+1)(n+2)} = \dfrac{1}{4} - \dfrac{1}{2(n+1)(n+2)}$

11 $\dfrac{d}{dx}(x^n) = nx^{n-1}$ [Use the formula for differentiating a product.]

12 $1^2 + 3^2 + 5^2 + \ldots + (2n-1)^2 = \frac{1}{3}n(4n^2 - 1)$

13 $1^3 + 3^3 + 5^3 + \ldots + (2n-1)^3 = n^2(2n^2 - 1)$

14 $4^2 + 7^2 + 10^2 + \ldots + (3n+1)^2 = \frac{1}{2}n(6n^2 + 15n + 11)$

15 Show that $\dbinom{n}{r} + \dbinom{n}{r-1} = \dbinom{n+1}{r}$, and prove by induction that

$$(1 + x)^n = 1 + nx + \ldots + \binom{n}{r}x^r + \ldots + x^n$$

where $\dbinom{n}{r} = \dfrac{n!}{(n-r)!\,r!}$ and r is a positive integer, less than or equal to n.

14.8 Further series

Certain series can be summed by means of the results:

$$
\begin{array}{l}
1 + 2 + \ldots + n = \frac{1}{2}n(n+1) \\
1^2 + 2^2 + \ldots + n^2 = \frac{1}{6}n(n+1)(2n+1) \\
1^3 + 2^3 + \ldots + n^3 = \frac{1}{4}n^2(n+1)^2
\end{array}
$$

which appear in the last section and exercise.

It should be noted that they may be used to sum the series to more or less than n terms. For instance,

$$1^3 + 2^3 + \ldots + (2n+1)^3 = \tfrac{1}{4}(2n+1)^2\{(2n+1)+1\}^2$$
$$= \tfrac{1}{4}(2n+1)^2(2n+2)^2$$
$$= \tfrac{1}{4}(2n+1)^2\,4(n+1)^2$$
$$= (2n+1)^2(n+1)^2$$

Qu. 6 Find the sums of the following series:

(a) $1 + 2 + \ldots + 2n$

(b) $1^2 + 2^2 + \ldots + (n+1)^2$

(c) $1^3 + 2^3 + \ldots + (n-1)^3$

(d) $1 + 2 + \ldots + (2n-1)$

(e) $1^2 + 2^2 + \ldots + (2n)^2$

(f) $1^3 + 2^3 + \ldots + (2n-1)^3$

Example 12

Find the sum of the series $1^3 + 3^3 + 5^3 + \ldots + (2n+1)^3$.

This series can be thought of as $1^3 + 2^3 + 3^3 + 4^3 + 5^3 + \ldots + (2n+1)^3$ with the even terms missing.

We found above that

$$1^3 + 2^3 + 3^3 + 4^3 + 5^3 + \ldots + (2n+1)^3 = (2n+1)^2(n+1)^2$$

and so it remains to find the sum of the series

$$2^3 + 4^3 + 6^3 + \ldots + (2n)^3 = 2^3 \times 1^3 + 2^3 \times 2^3 + 2^3 \times 3^3 +$$
$$\ldots + 2^3 \times n^3$$
$$= 8(1^3 + 2^3 + 3^3 + \ldots + n^3)$$
$$= 8 \times \tfrac{1}{4}n^2(n+1)^2 = 2n^2(n+1)^2$$

Therefore

$$1^3 + 3^3 + 5^3 + \ldots + (2n+1)^3 = (2n+1)^2(n+1)^2 - 2n^2(n+1)^2$$
$$= (n+1)^2\{(2n+1)^2 - 2n^2\}$$
$$= (n+1)^2(4n^2 + 4n + 1 - 2n^2)$$

Therefore the sum is $(n+1)^2(2n^2 + 4n + 1)$.

Example 13

Find the sum of n terms of the series $2 \times 3 + 3 \times 4 + 4 \times 5 + \ldots.$

The mth term of this series is $(m+1)(m+2)$, or $m^2 + 3m + 2$. Therefore we require the sum of:

$$1^2 + 3 \times 1 + 2$$
$$+ 2^2 + 3 \times 2 + 2$$
$$+ 3^2 + 3 \times 3 + 2$$
$$+ \ldots\ldots\ldots\ldots\ldots$$
$$+ n^2 + 3 \times n + 2$$

Now the sums of the three columns are respectively:

$$1^2 + 2^2 + 3^2 + \ldots + n^2 = \tfrac{1}{6}n(n+1)(2n+1)$$
$$3(1+2+3+ \ldots +n) = \tfrac{3}{2}n(n+1)$$
$$(2+2+2+ \ldots +2) = 2n$$

Therefore the sum of the series is:

$$\frac{1}{6}n(n+1)(2n+1) + \frac{3}{2}n(n+1) + 2n = \frac{n}{6}\{(n+1)(2n+1) + 9(n+1) + 12\}$$

$$= \frac{n}{6}(2n^2 + 3n + 1 + 9n + 9 + 12)$$

$$= \frac{n}{6}(2n^2 + 12n + 22)$$

$$= \frac{n}{3}(n^2 + 6n + 11)$$

Therefore the sum of the first n terms of the series

$$2 \times 3 + 3 \times 4 + 4 \times 5 + \ldots$$

is $\tfrac{1}{3}n(n^2 + 6n + 11)$.

14.9 The Σ notation

It is useful to have a short way of writing expressions like

$$1^2 + 2^2 + \ldots + n^2$$

This is done by writing

$$\sum m^2$$

which means, 'the sum of all the terms like m^2'. The symbol Σ is the Greek capital letter sigma. For extra precision, however, numbers are placed below and above the Σ, to show where the series begins and ends. Thus:

$$\sum_1^n m^2 = 1^2 + 2^2 + \ldots + n^2$$

and

$$\sum_2^5 m(m+2) = 2 \times 4 + 3 \times 5 + 4 \times 6 + 5 \times 7$$

Exercise 14f

1 Write in full:

(a) $\displaystyle\sum_1^4 m^3$ (b) $\displaystyle\sum_2^n m^2$ (c) $\displaystyle\sum_1^n (m^2 + m)$

(d) $\displaystyle\sum_{1}^{3} \frac{1}{m(m+1)}$ (e) $\displaystyle\sum_{2}^{5} 2^m$ (f) $\displaystyle\sum_{1}^{4} (-1)^m m^2$

(g) $\displaystyle\sum_{1}^{n} m^m$ (h) $\displaystyle\sum_{3}^{6} \frac{(-1)^m}{m}$ (i) $\displaystyle\sum_{n}^{n+2} m(m-1)$

(j) $\displaystyle\sum_{n-2}^{n} \frac{m}{m+1}$

2 Write in the Σ notation:
   (a) $1 + 2 + 3 + \dots + n$
   (b) $1^4 + 2^4 + \dots + n^4 + (n+1)^4$
   (c) $1 + \frac{1}{2} + \frac{1}{3} + \frac{1}{4} + \frac{1}{5}$
   (d) $3^2 + 3^3 + 3^4 + 3^5$
   (e) $2 \times 7 + 3 \times 8 + 4 \times 9 + 5 \times 10 + 6 \times 11$
   (f) $1 + \frac{2}{3} + \frac{3}{9} + \frac{4}{27} + \frac{5}{81}$
   (g) $\dfrac{1 \times 3}{4} + \dfrac{2 \times 5}{6} + \dfrac{3 \times 7}{8} + \dfrac{4 \times 9}{10} + \dfrac{5 \times 11}{12}$
   (h) $-1 + 2 - 3 + 4 - 5 + 6$
   (i) $1 - 2 + 4 - 8 + 16 - 32$
   (j) $1 \times 3 - 2 \times 5 + 3 \times 7 - 4 \times 9 + 5 \times 11$

3 Use the results quoted at the beginning of Section 14.8 to find the sums of the following series:
   (a) $1 + 2 + 3 + \dots + (2n+1)$
   (b) $1^2 + 2^2 + 3^2 + \dots + (n-1)^2$
   (c) $1^3 + 2^3 + 3^3 + \dots + (2n)^3$
   (d) $3 + 5 + 7 + \dots + (2n+1)$
   (e) $2 + 5 + 8 + 11 + \dots$, to n terms
   (f) $5 + 9 + 13 + 17 + \dots$, to n terms
   (g) $2 + 5 + 10 + \dots + (n^2 + 1)$
   (h) $1 \times 2 + 2 \times 3 + 3 \times 4 + 4 \times 5 + \dots$, to n terms
   (i) $1 \times 3 + 2 \times 4 + 3 \times 5 + 4 \times 6 + \dots$, to n terms
   (j) $2^2 + 4^2 + 6^2 + \dots + (2n)^2$
   (k) $1^2 + 3^2 + 5^2 + \dots + (2n-1)^2$
   (l) $2 + 10 + 30 + \dots + (n^3 + n)$
   (m) $2 + 12 + 36 + \dots + (n^3 + n^2)$

Exercise 14g (Miscellaneous)

1 Find the sum of the integers between 1 and 100 which are divisible by 3.
2 How many terms of the geometrical progression $\frac{1}{16} + \frac{1}{8} + \frac{1}{4} + \dots$ are needed to make a total of $2^{16} - \frac{1}{16}$?
3 Prove by induction that $1 \times 4 + 2 \times 5 + \dots + n(n+3) = \frac{1}{3}n(n+1)(n+5)$.
4 Show that the sums to infinity of the geometrical progressions

$$3 + \tfrac{9}{4} + \tfrac{27}{16} + \dots \quad \text{and} \quad 4 + \tfrac{8}{3} + \tfrac{16}{9} + \dots$$

are equal.

5 How many terms of the arithmetical progression $2 + 3\frac{1}{4} + 4\frac{1}{2} + \ldots$ are needed to make a total of 204?

6 An arithmetical progression has thirteen terms whose sum is 143. The third term is 5. Find the first term.

7 The sum of n terms of a certain series is $3n^2 + 10n$ for all values of n. Find the nth term and show that the series is an arithmetical progression.

8 Find the sum of the series $2 + 6 + \ldots + (n^2 - n)$.

9 Show that the sum of the first n odd numbers is a perfect square. Show also, that $57^2 - 13^2$ is the sum of certain consecutive odd numbers, and find them.

10 What is the sum of the integers from 1 to 100, inclusive, which are not divisible by 6?

11 Find the sum of the first n terms of the geometrical progression

$$5 + 15 + 45 + \ldots$$

What is the smallest number of terms whose total is more than 10^8?

12 The sum to infinity of a geometrical progression with a positive common ratio is 9 and the sum of the first two terms is 5. Find the first four terms of the progression.

13 Show that, if $\log a$, $\log b$, $\log c$ are consecutive terms of an arithmetical progression, then a, b, c are in geometrical progression.

14 The eighth term of an arithmetical progression is twice the third term, and the sum of the first eight terms is 39. Find the first three terms of the progression, and show that its sum to n terms is $\frac{3}{8}n(n + 5)$.

15 Find the number n such that the sum of the integers from 1 to $n - 1$ is equal to the sum of the integers from $n + 1$ to 49.

16 Show that there are two possible geometrical progressions in each of which the first term is 8, and the sum of the first three terms is 14. Find the second term and the sum of the first seven terms in each progression.

17 Prove by induction that

$$\frac{1}{2} + \frac{1}{6} + \ldots + \frac{1}{n(n-1)} = 1 - \frac{1}{n}$$

18 Find the sum of the series $3 + 6 + 11 + \ldots + (n^2 + 2)$.

19 If a and b are the first and last terms of an arithmetical progression of $r + 2$ terms, find the second and the $(r + 1)$th terms.

20 The sum of n terms of a certain series is $4^n - 1$ for all values of n. Find the first three terms and the nth term, and show that the series is a geometrical progression.

Chapter 15

The binomial theorem

15.1 Pascal's triangle

It is well known that

$$(a+b)^2 = a^2 + 2ab + b^2$$

and it is the object of this chapter to show how higher powers of $a+b$ can be expanded with little difficulty.

Most readers will not be able to write down similar expressions for $(a+b)^3$ and $(a+b)^4$ without doing some work on paper, and so the long multiplication is given below. The reason for printing the coefficients in heavy type will appear later.

$$1a^2 + 2ab + 1b^2$$
$$\underline{\quad a+b \quad}$$
$$1a^3 + 2a^2b + 1ab^2$$
$$\underline{\quad 1a^2b + 2ab^2 + 1b^3}$$
$$1a^3 + 3a^2b + 3ab^2 + 1b^3$$

$$1a^3 + 3a^2b + 3ab^2 + 1b^3$$
$$\underline{\quad a+b \quad}$$
$$1a^4 + 3a^3b + 3a^2b^2 + 1ab^3$$
$$\underline{\quad 1a^3b + 3a^2b^2 + 3ab^3 + 1b^4}$$
$$1a^4 + 4a^3b + 6a^2b^2 + 4ab^3 + 1b^4$$

The results so far obtained are summarised below.

$$(a+b)^2 = 1a^2 + 2ab + 1b^2$$
$$(a+b)^3 = 1a^3 + 3a^2b + 3ab^2 + 1b^3$$
$$(a+b)^4 = 1a^4 + 4a^3b + 6a^2b^2 + 4ab^3 + 1b^4$$

It is clearer, however, if the coefficients are written alone.

```
        1   2   1
      1   3   3   1
    1   4   6   4   1
```

The reader may be able to guess the next line and, more important, may be able to see how the table can be continued, obtaining each line from the previous one.

To show the construction of the table of coefficients, the last three lines of the long multiplications are written overleaf, leaving out the letters.

$$
\begin{array}{llll}
1 & 2 & 1 \\
 & 1 & 2 & 1 \\
\hline
1 & 3 & 3 & 1
\end{array}
\qquad
\begin{array}{lllll}
1 & 3 & 3 & 1 \\
 & 1 & 3 & 3 & 1 \\
\hline
1 & 4 & 6 & 4 & 1
\end{array}
$$

Thus it may be seen that every coefficient in the table is obtained from the two on either side of it in the row above. In this way the next line can be obtained:

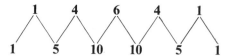

For completeness, it may be observed that

$$(a+b)^0 = 1 \quad \text{and} \quad (a+b)^1 = 1a + 1b$$

Therefore the table of coefficients may be written in a triangle (known as Pascal's triangle, after the French mathematician and philosopher Blaise Pascal, 1623–1662) as follows:

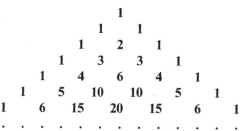

When an expression is written as a series of terms, it is said to be **expanded**, and the series is called its **expansion**. Thus the expansion of $(a+b)^3$ is

$$a^3 + 3a^2b + 3ab^2 + b^3$$

Certain points should be noted about the expansion of $(a+b)^n$. They should be verified for the cases $n = 2, 3, 4$, in the expansions obtained so far.
(a) Reading from either end of each row, the *coefficients* are the same.
(b) There are $(n+1)$ terms.
(c) Each term is of degree n.
(d) The coefficients are obtained from the row in Pascal's triangle beginning 1, n.

Example 1

Expand $(a+b)^6$ in descending powers of a.

There will be 7 terms, involving

$$a^6, \quad a^5b, \quad a^4b^2, \quad a^3b^3, \quad a^2b^4, \quad ab^5, \quad b^6$$

each of which is of degree 6. Their coefficients, obtained from Pascal's triangle, are respectively

$$1, \quad 6, \quad 15, \quad 20, \quad 15, \quad 6, \quad 1$$

Therefore the expansion of $(a + b)^6$ in descending powers of a is:

$$a^6 + 6a^5b + 15a^4b^2 + 20a^3b^3 + 15a^2b^4 + 6ab^5 + b^6$$

Example 2

Expand $(2x + 3y)^3$ in descending powers of x.

Here $a = 2x$, $b = 3y$, and so there will be four terms involving

$$(2x)^3, \quad (2x)^2(3y), \quad (2x)(3y)^2, \quad (3y)^3$$

Their coefficients, obtained from Pascal's triangle are respectively

$$1, \qquad 3, \qquad 3, \qquad 1$$

Therefore the expansion of $(2x + 3y)^3$, in descending powers of x is

$$(2x)^3 + 3(2x)^2(3y) + 3(2x)(3y)^2 + (3y)^3$$

which simplifies to

$$8x^3 + 36x^2y + 54xy^2 + 27y^3$$

Example 3

Obtain the expansion of $(2x - \frac{1}{2})^4$, in descending powers of x.

Here $a = 2x$ and $b = -\frac{1}{2}$, therefore the five terms of the expansion will involve

$$(2x)^4, \quad (2x)^3(-\tfrac{1}{2}), \quad (2x)^2(-\tfrac{1}{2})^2, \quad (2x)(-\tfrac{1}{2})^3, \quad (-\tfrac{1}{2})^4$$

and their coefficients will be respectively

$$1, \qquad 4, \qquad 6, \qquad 4, \qquad 1$$

$$\therefore \quad (2x - \tfrac{1}{2})^4 = (2x)^4 + 4(2x)^3(-\tfrac{1}{2}) + 6(2x)^2(-\tfrac{1}{2})^2 + 4(2x)(-\tfrac{1}{2})^3 + (-\tfrac{1}{2})^4$$
$$= 16x^4 + 4(8x^3)(-\tfrac{1}{2}) + 6(4x^2)(\tfrac{1}{4}) + 4(2x)(-\tfrac{1}{8}) + \tfrac{1}{16}$$

Therefore the expansion of $(2x - \frac{1}{2})^4$, in descending powers of x, is

$$16x^4 - 16x^3 + 6x^2 - x + \tfrac{1}{16}$$

Note that terms are alternately $+$ and $-$, according to the even or odd degree of $(-\frac{1}{2})$.

Example 4

Use Pascal's triangle to obtain the value of $(1.002)^5$, correct to six places of decimals.

1.002 may be written $(1 + 0.002)$, so that the expansion of $(a + b)^5$ may be used, with $a = 1$ and $b = 0.002$.

The terms in the expansion will involve

$$1, \quad (0.002), \quad (0.002)^2, \quad (0.002)^3, \quad (0.002)^4, \quad (0.002)^5$$

and their coefficients will be

$$1, \quad 5, \quad 10, \quad 10, \quad 5, \quad 1$$

respectively. Now the last three terms will make no difference to the answer, correct to six places of decimals. Therefore

$$(1.002)^5 \approx 1 + 5(0.002) + 10(0.002)^2$$
$$= 1 + 0.010 + 0.000\,040$$

and so $(1.002)^5 = 1.010\,040$, correct to six places of decimals.

Exercise 15a

This exercise is intended to give the reader some practice in using Pascal's triangle; calculators should not be used in the numerical questions.

1 Expand:

(a) $(a+b)^5$ (b) $(x+y)^3$ (c) $(x+2y)^4$
(d) $(1-z)^4$ (e) $(2x+3y)^4$ (f) $(4z+1)^3$
(g) $(a-b)^6$ (h) $(a-2b)^3$ (i) $(3x-y)^4$

(j) $(2x+\frac{1}{3})^3$ (k) $\left(x-\dfrac{1}{x}\right)^5$ (l) $\left(\dfrac{x}{2}+\dfrac{2}{x}\right)^4$

(m) $(a+b)^7$ (n) $(a^2-b^2)^5$ (o) $(a-b)^3(a+b)^3$

2 Simplify, leaving surds in the answers, where appropriate:

(a) $(1+\sqrt{2})^3 + (1-\sqrt{2})^3$ (b) $(2+\sqrt{3})^4 + (2-\sqrt{3})^4$
(c) $(1+\sqrt{2})^3 - (1-\sqrt{2})^3$ (d) $(2+\sqrt{6})^4 - (2-\sqrt{6})^4$
(e) $(\sqrt{2}+\sqrt{3})^4 + (\sqrt{2}-\sqrt{3})^4$ (f) $(\sqrt{6}+\sqrt{2})^3 - (\sqrt{6}-\sqrt{2})^3$

3 Write down the expansion of $(2+x)^5$ in ascending powers of x. Taking the first three terms of the expansion, put $x = 0.001$, and find the value of $(2.001)^5$ correct to five places of decimals.

4 Write down the expansion of $(1+\frac{1}{4}x)^4$. Taking the first three terms of the expansion, put $x = 0.1$, and find the value of $(1.025)^4$, corrrect to three places of decimals.

5 Expand $(2-x)^6$ in ascending powers of x. Taking $x = 0.002$, and using the first three terms of the expansion, find the value of $(1.998)^6$ as accurately as you can. Examine the fourth term of the expansion to find to how many places of decimals your answer is correct.

15.2 Introduction to the binomial theorem

In the last section it was shown how $(a+b)^n$ could be expanded, for a known value of n, by using Pascal's triangle. If n is large, this may involve a considerable amount of addition, and when (as is often the case) only the first few terms are required, it is much quicker to use a formula that will be obtained in the next section.

The last section began with the expansions of $(a+b)^2$ and $(a+b)^3$. Now, consider the expansions of $(a+b)(c+d)$ and $(a+b)(c+d)(e+f)$.

It is easily seen that

$$(a+b)(c+d) = ac + ad + bc + bd$$

To obtain the expansion of $(a+b)(c+d)(e+f)$, each term of $ac + ad + bc + bd$ is multiplied by e and f, giving

$$ace + ade + bce + bde + acf + adf + bcf + bdf$$

Note that each term contains one factor from each bracket, and that the expansion consists of the sum of all such combinations.

Now the expansion of $(a+b)(c+d)(e+f)(g+h)$ would be obtained by multiplying each term of the expansion by g and by h. So, continuing this method of expansion, it follows that, if the product of n factors is expanded, each term contains one factor from each bracket, and that the expansion consists of the sum of all such combinations.

The expansion of $(a+b)^5$ will be obtained by an argument making use of this fact.

$$(a+b)^5 = (a+b)(a+b)(a+b)(a+b)(a+b)$$

(a) Choosing an a from each bracket we obtain a^5.
(b) The term in a^4 is obtained by choosing a b from one bracket, and a's from the other four. This can be done in $^5C_1$ ways, giving $^5C_1 a^4 b$.
(c) The term in a^3 is obtained by choosing b's from two brackets, and a's from the other three. This can be done in $^5C_2$ ways, giving $^5C_2 a^3 b^2$.
(d) Similarly, the terms in a^2 and a are $^5C_3 a^2 b^3$ and $^5C_4 ab^4$.
(e) Choosing a b from each bracket we obtain b^5.

$$\therefore \quad (a+b)^5 = a^5 + {}^5C_1 a^4 b + {}^5C_2 a^3 b^2 + {}^5C_3 a^2 b^3 + {}^5C_4 ab^4 + b^5$$

15.3 The binomial theorem

If n is a positive integer,

$$(a+b)^n = a^n + {}^nC_1 a^{n-1} b + \ldots + {}^nC_r a^{n-r} b^r + \ldots + b^n$$

where $\displaystyle {}^nC_r = \frac{n!}{(n-r)!\,r!}$.

The expansion of $(a+b)^n$ is obtained as follows.

$$(a+b)^n = (a+b)(a+b) \ldots (a+b), \quad \text{to } n \text{ factors.}$$

(a) Choosing an a from each bracket we obtain a^n.
(b) The term in a^{n-1} is obtained by choosing a b from one bracket, and a's from the other $n-1$. This can be done in $^nC_1$ ways, giving $^nC_1 a^{n-1} b$.

(c) The term in a^{n-2} is obtained by choosing a b from two brackets, and a's from the other $n-2$. This can be done in $^nC_2$ ways, giving $^nC_2a^{n-2}b^2$.

(d) The term in a^{n-r} is obtained by choosing a b from r brackets, and a's from the other $n-r$. This can be done in ^nC_r ways, giving $^nC_ra^{n-r}b^r$.

(e) Choosing a b from each bracket we obtain b^n.

This proves the theorem.

When only the first few terms of an expansion are required, the theorem is used in the form

$$(a+b)^n = a^n + na^{n-1}b + \frac{n(n-1)}{2!}a^{n-2}b^2 + \frac{n(n-1)(n-2)}{3!}a^{n-3}b^3 + \ldots + b^n$$

This follows immediately, since

$$^nC_1 = n, \qquad ^nC_2 = \frac{n!}{(n-2)!\,2!} = \frac{n(n-1)}{2!} \quad \text{and}$$

$$^nC_3 = \frac{n!}{(n-3)!\,3!} = \frac{n(n-1)(n-2)}{3!}$$

In case the name of the theorem is not understood, it may be helpful to remark that an expression with one term is called a mononomial, one which has two terms is a binomial, and one with three terms is a trinomial. Thus the theorem about the expansion of a power of two terms is called the binomial theorem.

Example 5

Find the coefficient of x^{10} in the expansion of $(2x-3)^{14}$.

The term in $(2x)^{10}(-3)^4$ is the only one needed, and by the binomial theorem it is

$$^{14}C_4(2x)^{10}(-3)^4$$

Therefore the coefficient of x^{10} is $\dfrac{14!}{10!\,4!}\,2^{10} \times 3^4$.

It is important to note that we could equally well have written the term as

$$^{14}C_{10}(2x)^{10}(-3)^4$$

because $^{14}C_{10} = {}^{14}C_4$. This is clear if they are written in factorial notation:

$$^{14}C_{10} = \frac{14!}{4!\,10!} \quad \text{and} \quad ^{14}C_4 = \frac{14!}{10!\,4!}$$

Alternatively, $^{14}C_{10}$ is the number of ways of choosing ten objects from fourteen unlike objects; but if ten are chosen, four are left, and so it must also be the number of ways of choosing four objects from fourteen unlike objects, which is $^{14}C_4$.

Qu. 1 Show that $^nC_{n-r} = {}^nC_r$.

It is useful to note in Example 5 that the numbers whose factorials appear in the coefficient

$$\frac{14!}{10!\,4!}$$

are all indices. 14 is the index of $2x - 3$, 10 is the index of $2x$ and 4 is the index of -3. That this is always the case should be clear if the term in $a^{n-r}b^r$ in the expansion of $(a + b)^n$ is written with factorial notation:

$$\frac{n!}{(n-r)!\,r!}\,a^{n-r}b^r$$

Example 6

Obtain the first four terms of the expansion of $(1 + \frac{1}{2}x)^{10}$ in ascending powers of x. Hence find the value of $(1.005)^{10}$, correct to four decimal places.

Using the second form of the binomial theorem,

$$\left(1 + \frac{1}{2}x\right)^{10} = 1 + 10\left(\frac{x}{2}\right) + \frac{10 \times 9}{2 \times 1}\left(\frac{x}{2}\right)^2 + \frac{10 \times 9 \times 8}{3 \times 2 \times 1}\left(\frac{x}{2}\right)^3 + \dots$$

$$= 1 + 5x + \frac{45}{4}x^2 + 15x^3 + \dots$$

Now $\frac{1}{2}x = 0.005$, if $x = 0.01$; so substituting this value of x,

$$(1.005)^{10} \approx 1 + 5(0.01) + 11.25(0.01)^2 + 15(0.01)^3$$
$$= 1 + 0.05 + 0.001\,125 + 0.000\,015$$

Therefore $(1.005)^{10} = 1.0511$, correct to four places of decimals.

Exercise 15b

Calculators should not be used in this exercise.

1 Write down the terms indicated, in the expansions of the following, and simplify your answers:
   (a) $(x + 2)^8$, term in x^5 (b) $(3u - 2)^5$, term in u^3
   (c) $(2t - \frac{1}{2})^{12}$, term in t^7 (d) $(2x + y)^{11}$, term in x^3
2 Write down, and simplify, the terms indicated, in the expansions of the following in ascending powers of x:
   (a) $(1 + x)^9$, 4th term   (b) $(2 - x/2)^{12}$, 4th term
   (c) $(3 + x)^7$, 5th term   (d) $(x + 1)^{20}$, 3rd term

3 Write down, and simplify, the coefficients of the terms indicated, in the expansions of the following:

(a) $(\frac{1}{2}t + \frac{1}{2})^{10}$, term in t^4 (b) $(4 + \frac{3}{4}x)^6$, term in x^3

(c) $(2x - 3)^7$, term in x^5 (d) $(3 + \frac{1}{3}y)^{11}$, term in y^5

4 Write down the coefficients of the terms indicated, in the expansions of the following in ascending powers of x:

(a) $(1 + x)^{16}$, 3rd term   (b) $(2 - x)^{20}$, 18th term

(c) $(3 + 2x)^6$, 4th term   (d) $(2 + \frac{3}{2}x)^8$, 5th term

5 Write down the terms in the expansion of $\left(x + \dfrac{1}{x}\right)^6$ involving:

(a) $x^4 \left(\dfrac{1}{x}\right)^2$ (b) $x^3 \left(\dfrac{1}{x}\right)^3$

6 Write down the constant terms in the expansions of:

(a) $\left(x - \dfrac{1}{x}\right)^8$ (b) $\left(2x^2 - \dfrac{1}{2x}\right)^6$

7 Find the coefficients of the terms indicated in the expansions of the following:

(a) $\left(x + \dfrac{1}{x}\right)^6$, term in x^4 (b) $\left(2x + \dfrac{1}{x}\right)^7$, term in $\dfrac{1}{x^5}$

(c) $\left(x - \dfrac{2}{x}\right)^8$, term in x^6

8 Find the ratio of the term in x^5 to the term in x^6, in the expansion of $(2x + 3)^{20}$

9 Write down the first four terms of the expansions of the following, in ascending powers of x:

(a) $(1 + x)^{10}$ (b) $(1 + \frac{1}{2}x)^9$ (c) $(1 - x)^{11}$

(d) $(x + 1)^{12}$ (e) $(2 + \frac{1}{2}x)^8$ (f) $(2 - \frac{1}{2}x)^7$

10 Use the binomial theorem to find the values of:

(a) $(1.01)^{10}$, correct to three places of decimals

(b) $(2.001)^{10}$, correct to six significant figures

(c) $(0.997)^{12}$, correct to three places of decimals

(d) $(1.998)^8$, correct to two places of decimals

15.4 Convergent series

The series

$$1 + x + x^2 + \ldots + x^{n-1}$$

is a geometrical progression, with common ratio x, and may be summed by the method of Section 14.4. In this way

$$1 + x + x^2 + \ldots + x^{n-1} = \frac{1 - x^n}{1 - x}$$

If x lies between -1 and $+1$, we will assume that x^n approaches zero as n increases, which makes the right-hand side of the identity approach $1/(1-x)$.

Thus when we write

$$1 + x + x^2 + \ldots + x^r + \ldots = \frac{1}{1-x}$$

we mean that the left-hand side can be made to differ as little as we please from the right-hand side, provided enough terms are taken. It must not be forgotten, however, that we have taken x to lie between -1 and $+1$.

A series of terms, whose sum approaches a finite value as the number of terms is increased indefinitely is called a **convergent** series, and the finite value is called its **sum to infinity**.

Thus $1 + x + x^2 + \ldots + x^r + \ldots$ is a convergent series, provided x lies between -1 and $+1$, and its sum to infinity is $1/(1-x)$.

To emphasise the necessity for the condition

$$-1 < x < +1 \qquad (\text{i.e. } |x| < 1)$$

the behaviour of the series for the other values of x is examined below.

(a) If $x = 1$, $1 + x + x^2 + \ldots + n^{n-1} = n$.   Therefore as n increases, the value of the series increases indefinitely.
(b) If $x = -1$,

$$1 + x + x^2 + \ldots + x^{n-1} = 1 - 1 + 1 - \ldots + (-1)^{n-1}$$

which is equal to 1 or 0, according to whether n is odd or even.
(c) If x is greater than 1, x^n is greater than 1, and can be made as large as we like, if n is sufficiently large. Therefore the sum of the series, $(1 - x^n)/(1 - x)$, can be made as large as we like.
(d) When x is less than -1, $1 - x$ is positive and x^n is numerically greater than 1. If n is even, x^n is positive, therefore $1 - x^n$ is negative and so the sum $(1 - x^n)/(1 - x)$ is negative. If n is odd, x^n is negative, therefore $1 - x^n$ is positive and so the sum is positive. Hence the sum is alternately positive and negative.

It is beyond the scope of this book to give tests to discover whether any particular series is convergent, but this section has been written to draw the reader's attention to the fact that series are not always convergent.

15.5 The binomial theorem for any index

It has been shown that

$$(a + b)^n = a^n + na^{n-1}b + \frac{n(n-1)}{2!}a^{n-2}b^2 + \ldots + b^n$$

where n is a positive integer.

Now it will be *assumed* that

$$(1 + x)^n = 1 + nx + \frac{n(n-1)}{2!}x^2 + \frac{n(n-1)(n-2)}{3!}x^3 + \ldots$$

(the series being continued indefinitely), for *any* rational value of n *provided* $-1 < x < +1$, i.e. $|x| < 1$. The proof is beyond the scope of this book.

It should be remembered that, if n is a positive integer, there will only be a finite number of terms (see Section 15.3).

For the sake of those who go on to read other books, it should be added that the index, n, is often called the **exponent**.

The coefficient of x^r in the expansion of $(1 + x)^n$ is usually written $\binom{n}{r}$, that is,

$$\binom{n}{r} = \frac{n(n-1)(n-2) \ldots (n-r+1)}{1 \times 2 \ \times \ 3 \times \ \ldots \ \times \ r}$$

(It should be noticed that for each factor in the top line, there is a corresponding factor in the bottom line.)

Unlike ^nC_r, the symbol $\binom{n}{r}$ may be used when n is *not* a positive integer.

Historical note Pascal's triangle was given by a Chinese author of the early fourteenth century, but Pascal made considerable use of it in connection with problems on probability, and it became associated with his name. From it he obtained the theorem for positive integral indices. The series for fractional and negative indices was given by Newton in 1676.

Example 7

Use the binomial theorem to expand $1/(1 - x)$ in ascending powers of x, as far as the term in x^3.

(This example has been chosen because the result has already been established in Section 15.4.)

Since $1/(1 - x)$ may be written $(1 - x)^{-1}$, the binomial theorem may be used. Thus

$$(1 - x)^{-1} = 1 + (-1)(-x) + \frac{(-1)(-2)}{2!}(-x)^2 +$$

$$+ \frac{(-1)(-2)(-3)}{3!}(-x)^3 + \ldots$$

$$\therefore \quad \frac{1}{1 - x} = 1 + x + x^2 + x^3 + \ldots \quad \text{provided } |x| < 1.$$

Example 8

Obtain the first five terms of the expansion of $\sqrt{(1 + 2x)}$ in ascending powers of x. State the values of x for which the expansion is valid.

Since $\sqrt{(1 + 2x)} = (1 + 2x)^{1/2}$, the binomial theorem may be used.

$$(1 + 2x)^{1/2} = 1 + \frac{1}{2}(2x) + \frac{(\frac{1}{2})(-\frac{1}{2})}{2!}(2x)^2 + \frac{(\frac{1}{2})(-\frac{1}{2})(-\frac{3}{2})}{3!}(2x)^3 +$$

$$+ \frac{(\frac{1}{2})(-\frac{1}{2})(-\frac{3}{2})(-\frac{5}{2})}{4!}(2x)^4 + \ldots$$

$$\therefore \quad \sqrt{(1 + 2x)} = 1 + x - \tfrac{1}{2}x^2 + \tfrac{1}{2}x^3 - \tfrac{5}{8}x^4 + \ldots$$

For the expansion to be valid, $-1 < 2x < +1$, i.e. $|x| < \tfrac{1}{2}$.

Example 9

Expand $1/(2 + x)^2$ in ascending powers of x, as far as the term in x^3 and state for what values of x the expansion is valid.

First it may be observed that $1/(2 + x)^2 = (2 + x)^{-2}$. However, the binomial theorem has been stated for $(1 + x)^n$. Therefore a factor must be taken out, in order to leave the bracket in this form.

$$(2 + x)^{-2} = \{2(1 + \tfrac{1}{2}x)\}^{-2} = 2^{-2}(1 + \tfrac{1}{2}x)^{-2}$$
$$= \tfrac{1}{4}(1 + \tfrac{1}{2}x)^{-2}$$

and this may now be expanded.

$$\left[\text{Alternatively:} \quad \frac{1}{(2 + x)^2} = \frac{1}{2^2(1 + \tfrac{1}{2}x)^2} = \tfrac{1}{4}(1 + \tfrac{1}{2}x)^{-2} \right]$$

$$\tfrac{1}{4}\left(1 + \tfrac{1}{2}x\right)^{-2} = \tfrac{1}{4}\left\{1 + (-2)\left(\frac{x}{2}\right) + \frac{(-2)(-3)}{2!}\left(\frac{x}{2}\right)^2 +\right.$$

$$\left. + \frac{(-2)(-3)(-4)}{3!}\left(\frac{x}{2}\right)^3 + \ldots\right\}$$

$$\therefore \quad \frac{1}{(2 + x)^2} = \tfrac{1}{4}\left(1 - x + \frac{3}{4}x^2 - \frac{1}{2}x^3 + \ldots\right)$$

For the expansion to be valid, $-1 < \tfrac{1}{2}x < +1$, i.e. $|x| < 2$.

Exercise 15c

Calculators should not be used in this exercise.

1 Evaluate the following binomial coefficients:

(a) $\dbinom{5}{3}$ (b) $\dbinom{-2}{4}$ (c) $\dbinom{\frac{1}{2}}{2}$ (d) $\dbinom{-\frac{1}{4}}{3}$

2 Expand the following in ascending powers of x, as far as the terms in x^3, and state the values of x for which the expansions are valid:

(a) $(1 + x)^{-2}$ (b) $(1 + x)^{1/3}$ (c) $(1 + x)^{3/2}$

(d) $(1 - 2x)^{1/2}$ (e) $\left(1 + \dfrac{x}{2}\right)^{-3}$ (f) $(1 - 3x)^{-1/2}$

(g) $\dfrac{1}{1 + 3x}$ (h) $\sqrt{(1 - x^2)}$ (i) $\sqrt[3]{(1 - x)}$

(j) $\dfrac{1}{\sqrt{(1 + 2x)}}$ (k) $\dfrac{1}{(1 + x/2)^2}$ (l) $\sqrt{(1 - 2x)^3}$

3 Use the binomial theorem to find the values of the following:

(a) $\sqrt{(1.001)}$, correct to six places of decimals

(b) $\dfrac{1}{(1.02)^2}$, correct to four places of decimals

(c) $\sqrt{(0.998)}$, correct to six places of decimals

(d) $\sqrt[3]{(1.03)}$, correct to four places of decimals

(e) $\dfrac{1}{\sqrt{(0.98)}}$, correct to four places of decimals

4 Find the first four terms of the expansions of the following in ascending powers of x:

(a) $\dfrac{1 + x}{1 - x}$ (b) $\dfrac{x + 2}{(1 + x)^2}$ (c) $\dfrac{1 - x}{\sqrt{(1 + x)}}$

5 Find the first four terms of the expansion of $(1 - 8x)^{1/2}$ in ascending powers of x. Substitute $x = \frac{1}{100}$ and obtain the value of $\sqrt{23}$ correct to five significant figures.

Exercise 15d (Miscellaneous)

Calculators should not be used in this exercise.

1 Write down the sixth term of the expansion of $(3x + 2y)^{10}$ in ascending powers of x, and evaluate the term when $x = \frac{1}{2}$ and $y = \frac{1}{3}$.

2 (a) Expand $\left(2x + \dfrac{1}{2x}\right)^5$ in descending powers of x.

(b) Simplify $(\sqrt{2} + \sqrt{3})^4 - (\sqrt{2} - \sqrt{3})^4$.

3 Write down the expansion of $(a - b)^5$ and use the result to find the value of $(9\frac{1}{2})^5$ correct to the nearest 100.

4 (a) Expand $(a + b)^{11}$ in descending powers of a as far as the fourth term.

(b) Find the middle term in the expansion of $(6x + \frac{1}{3}y)^{10}$.

(c) Find the constant term in the expansion of $(x^2 + 2/x)^9$.

5 Expand $(x + 2)^5$ and $(x - 2)^4$. Obtain the coefficient of x^5 in the product of the expansions.

6 Obtain the expansion of $(x-2)^2(1-x)^6$ in ascending powers of x as far as the term in x^4.

7 Find the first four terms in the expansions of
   (a) $(1-x+2x^2)^5$ (b) $(1+x)^{-4}$
   in ascending powers of x.

8 (a) Write down the expansion of $(1+x)^{-3}$ as far as the term in x^4, simplifying each term.
   (b) Write down the first four terms of the expansion of $(2+\frac{1}{4}x)^{10}$ in ascending powers of x. Hence find the value of 2.025^{10}, correct to the nearest whole number.

9 (a) Find the middle term of the expansion of $(2x+3)^8$, and the value of this term when $x=\frac{1}{12}$.
   (b) Find the first four terms in the expansion of $(1-2x)^{-2}$.

10 (a) Find the value of the fifth term in the expansion of $(\sqrt{2}+\sqrt{3})^8$.
   (b) Give the expansion of $(1+x)^{1/3}$ up to and including the term in x^2. Hence, by putting $x=\frac{1}{8}$, calculate the cube root of 9, giving your answer correct to three decimal places.

Chapter 16

Vectors

16.1 Introduction

Consider the following sentences:
(a) The temperature is 15 °C.
(b) The journey lasted 2 hours.
(c) The plane is flying due east at 800 km h^{-1}.
(d) A horizontal force of 2 N was applied to the ruler at right-angles to its length.
(e) Shift the piano 10 m to the right.

One does not have to be a scientist to see that the first two sentences differ from the others in one very important respect: the first two are complete when the magnitude of the quantity is given, but in the others it is necessary to define both the magnitude and the direction. A quantity which is completely specified by its magnitude alone is called a **scalar** quantity and one which requires both the magnitude and the direction to be given is called a **vector** quantity. (Strictly speaking, a vector quantity must obey the triangle law of addition; see Section 16.6.)

Let us consider sentences (d) and (e) in more detail. The effect of the force applied to the ruler will be determined by the point at which the force is applied; if it is applied to the end of the ruler, the ruler will start to rotate, but if it is applied to the mid-point of the ruler, the ruler will start to slide without rotating. So when we describe a force we shall have to give not only its magnitude and direction, but we shall also have to state its line of action. (This is usually done by describing a point through which the force passes.) Vectors which have a definite line of action are called **localised vectors**.

On the other hand, when the piano in sentence (e) is shifted, then, as we can see in Figure 16.1, every point in the piano is shifted 10 m to the right. All the line segments AA', BB', CC', DD', and PP' are equal in length and they are parallel to one another. Any one of them can be used to describe the shift which has been applied to the piano.

Vectors which do not have a particular line of action are called **free vectors**; all free vectors which have the same magnitude and direction are equivalent

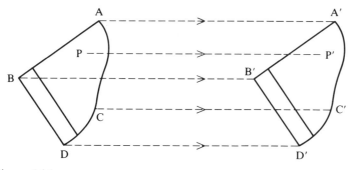

Figure 16.1

to one another and, in the example above, we write

$$\overrightarrow{AA'} = \overrightarrow{BB'} = \overrightarrow{CC'} = \overrightarrow{DD'} = \overrightarrow{PP'}$$

In this chapter all the vectors described, with one important exception, will usually be free vectors. The main exception is the position vector (see Section 16.7), which must always start from the origin.

16.2 Displacement vectors

Looking at a map of England, we see that Cambridge is about eighty miles from Oxford, and it is approximately north east of Oxford. This is an example of a very common type of vector quantity, namely a **displacement**. The displacement of one point from another can be defined, as in the example above, by giving the distance and the direction. Alternatively, when using Cartesian coordinates, the displacement can be defined by giving the increase in the x-coordinate and the increase in the y-coordinate.

In Figure 16.2, A is the point (1, 2) and B is the point (8, 6), so the displacement from A to B is '7 across and 4 up'. Obviously it is desirable to have a concise

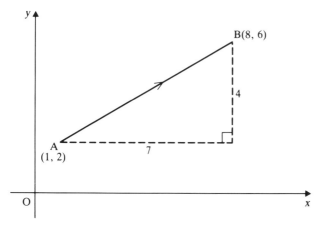

Figure 16.2

way of making statements like this; the normal notation is $\begin{pmatrix} 7 \\ 4 \end{pmatrix}$. The upper

number is the increase in the x-coordinate, and the lower one is the increase in the y-coordinate. It is also necessary to make it clear that the displacement goes *from* A *to* B, and so we write:

$$\overrightarrow{AB} = \begin{pmatrix} 7 \\ 4 \end{pmatrix}$$

The displacement *from* B *to* A is written $\overrightarrow{BA}$, and, in the case we are considering,

this is equal to $\begin{pmatrix} -7 \\ -4 \end{pmatrix}$.

Qu. 1 Write down the displacement vector $\overrightarrow{AB}$ for each of the following pairs of points:
(a) A(3, 5), B(5, 9)   (b) A(9, 7), B(12, 4)   (c) A(12, 5), B(5, 4)
(d) A(2, 3), B(2, 5)   (e) A(5, 1), B(8, 1)

Figure 16.3 illustrates the fact that the displacement from $A(x_1, y_1)$ to $B(x_2, y_2)$ is

$$\overrightarrow{AB} = \begin{pmatrix} x_2 - x_1 \\ y_2 - y_1 \end{pmatrix}.$$

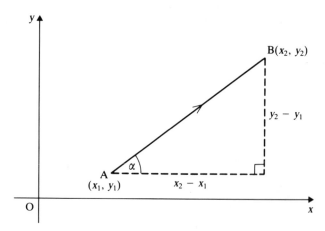

Figure 16.3

Notice that the magnitude of the vector (i.e. its length) is given by

$$\boxed{AB = \sqrt{\{(x_2 - x_1)^2 + (y_2 - y_1)^2\}}}$$

and that its direction is defined by the angle α which it makes with the x-axis, where

$$\tan \alpha = \frac{y_2 - y_1}{x_2 - x_1}$$

(note that this is the gradient of the line AB). The magnitude is never negative and the angle is usually given in the range $-180° < \alpha \leqslant +180°$; however, angles outside this range may be used, provided the meaning is clear. In the special case when $x_2 = x_1$, $\tan \alpha$ is not defined, because the denominator is zero. However if a diagram is consulted, it is clear that in this case the vector is parallel to the y-axis.

Example 1

Find the magnitude and direction of the displacement vector $\overrightarrow{AB}$, where A and B are the points (2, 1) and (8, 9) respectively. Find also the magnitude and direction of $\overrightarrow{BA}$, giving the angle correct to the nearest tenth of a degree.

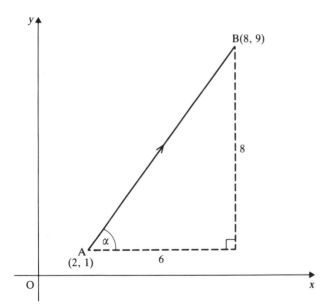

Figure 16.4

From Figure 16.4, we can see that

$$\overrightarrow{AB} = \binom{8-2}{9-1} = \binom{6}{8}$$

$$\therefore \quad AB^2 = 6^2 + 8^2 = 36 + 64 = 100$$
$$AB = 10$$

We can also see that the direction is given by

$$\tan \alpha = \frac{8}{6}$$

∴ $\alpha = 53.1°$ correct to the nearest tenth of a degree

Similarly,

$$\overrightarrow{BA} = \begin{pmatrix} 2 - 8 \\ 1 - 9 \end{pmatrix} = \begin{pmatrix} -6 \\ -8 \end{pmatrix}$$

$\overrightarrow{BA}$ is inclined at $-126.9°$ to the x-axis.

Qu. 2 Find the magnitude and direction of each of the vectors in Qu. 1.

16.3 Unit vectors

Any vector whose magnitude is 1, for example $\begin{pmatrix} 0.6 \\ 0.8 \end{pmatrix}$, is called a **unit vector**.

The unit vectors $\begin{pmatrix} 1 \\ 0 \end{pmatrix}$ and $\begin{pmatrix} 0 \\ 1 \end{pmatrix}$ are especially important because they are parallel to the x-axis and y-axis respectively; they are called **base vectors**, and the letters **i** and **j** are reserved for them (**i** and **j** are always printed in bold type; in manuscript they should be underlined).

The unit vector $\begin{pmatrix} \cos \theta \\ \sin \theta \end{pmatrix}$ is very useful as it is inclined at an angle θ to the x-axis (see Figure 16.5).

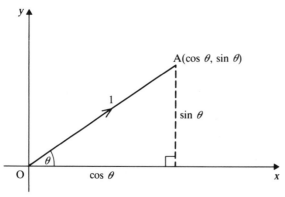

Figure 16.5

16.4 Multiplication by a scalar

In Figure 16.6, the displacement $\overrightarrow{AB}$ has been enlarged by a factor k, that is

$\overrightarrow{AB'} = k\overrightarrow{AB}$. If $\overrightarrow{AB} = \begin{pmatrix} a \\ b \end{pmatrix}$, then $AP = a$ and $PB = b$. Also, since the triangles

APB and AP'B' are similar, $AB' = kAB$, $AP' = ka$ and $P'B' = kb$, and so

$$\overrightarrow{AB'} = \begin{pmatrix} ka \\ kb \end{pmatrix}$$

Thus we can write $\begin{pmatrix} 20 \\ 30 \end{pmatrix} = 10\begin{pmatrix} 2 \\ 3 \end{pmatrix}$, $\begin{pmatrix} 5 \\ 0 \end{pmatrix} = 5\begin{pmatrix} 1 \\ 0 \end{pmatrix} = 5\mathbf{i}$, etc.

In general

$$\boxed{k\begin{pmatrix} a \\ b \end{pmatrix} = \begin{pmatrix} ka \\ kb \end{pmatrix}}$$

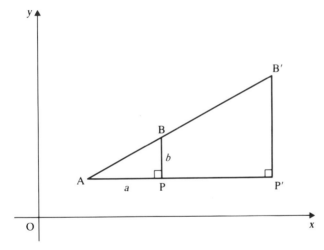

Figure 16.6

16.5 Equal vectors

In Figure 16.7, $\overrightarrow{AB} = \begin{pmatrix} 5 \\ 2 \end{pmatrix}$ and $\overrightarrow{DC} = \begin{pmatrix} 5 \\ 2 \end{pmatrix}$, that is the displacement from A to

B is the same as that from D to C. In this sense we can say that the vectors $\overrightarrow{AB}$ and $\overrightarrow{DC}$ are equal. Vectors are equal when they have the same magnitude and direction. Notice that $\overrightarrow{AD}$ and $\overrightarrow{BC}$ are also equal; the figure ABCD is of course a parallelogram.

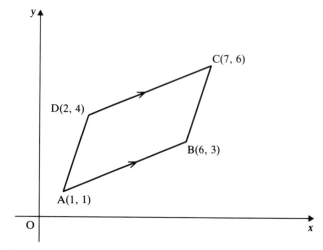

Figure 16.7

Example 2

Given that A is the point (1, 3) and that $\overrightarrow{AB}$ and $\overrightarrow{AD}$ are $\begin{pmatrix} 4 \\ -1 \end{pmatrix}$ and $\begin{pmatrix} 2 \\ 3 \end{pmatrix}$ respectively, find the coordinates of the vertices B, C and D of the parallelogram ABCD (Figure 16.8).

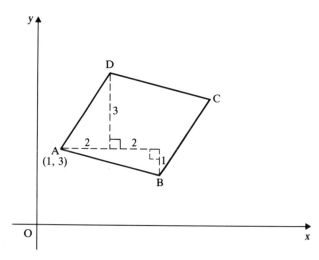

Figure 16.8

B is the point $(1 + 4, 3 - 1) = (5, 2)$

D is the point $(1 + 2, 3 + 3) = (3, 6)$

$$\overrightarrow{DC} = \overrightarrow{AB} = \begin{pmatrix} 4 \\ -1 \end{pmatrix}$$

hence

C is the point $(3 + 4, 6 - 1) = (7, 5)$

Example 3

Given the points A(1, 1), B(5, 4), C(8, 9) and D(0, 3), show that ABCD is a trapezium (Figure 16.9).

$$\overrightarrow{AB} = \begin{pmatrix} 4 \\ 3 \end{pmatrix} \quad \text{and} \quad \overrightarrow{DC} = \begin{pmatrix} 8 \\ 6 \end{pmatrix}$$

$$\therefore \quad 2\,\overrightarrow{AB} = \overrightarrow{DC}$$

Hence $\overrightarrow{DC}$ is parallel to $\overrightarrow{AB}$ (and twice as long). So ABCD is a trapezium.

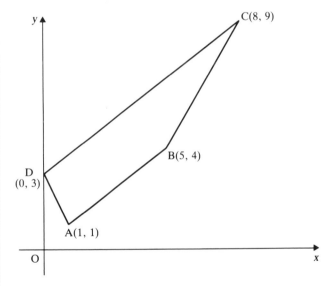

Figure 16.9

16.6 Addition and subtraction of vectors

If we make the displacement $\begin{pmatrix} 2 \\ 3 \end{pmatrix}$ and follow this with the displacement $\begin{pmatrix} 5 \\ 1 \end{pmatrix}$, then overall we shall have moved 7 units to the right and 4 units up. We could also achieve the same result by making the displacement $\begin{pmatrix} 5 \\ 1 \end{pmatrix}$ *first* and the

displacement $\begin{pmatrix} 2 \\ 3 \end{pmatrix}$ *second.* We write

$$\begin{pmatrix} 2 \\ 3 \end{pmatrix} + \begin{pmatrix} 5 \\ 1 \end{pmatrix} = \begin{pmatrix} 5 \\ 1 \end{pmatrix} + \begin{pmatrix} 2 \\ 3 \end{pmatrix} = \begin{pmatrix} 7 \\ 4 \end{pmatrix}$$

and we say that we have 'added' the vectors. In Figure 16.10, $\overrightarrow{PQ} = \begin{pmatrix} 2 \\ 3 \end{pmatrix}$,

$\overrightarrow{QR} = \begin{pmatrix} 5 \\ 1 \end{pmatrix}$ and $\overrightarrow{PR} = \begin{pmatrix} 7 \\ 4 \end{pmatrix}$. Notice that $\overrightarrow{PQ} + \overrightarrow{QR} = \overrightarrow{PR}$ (this is the 'triangle law

of addition', which some readers may have met in physics). We could also say

that $\overrightarrow{PQ'} = \begin{pmatrix} 5 \\ 1 \end{pmatrix}$, $\overrightarrow{Q'R} = \begin{pmatrix} 2 \\ 3 \end{pmatrix}$ and that $\overrightarrow{PQ'} + \overrightarrow{Q'R} = \overrightarrow{PR}$.

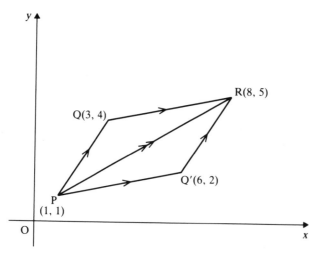

Figure 16.10

In general

$$\boxed{\begin{pmatrix} a_1 \\ b_1 \end{pmatrix} + \begin{pmatrix} a_2 \\ b_2 \end{pmatrix} = \begin{pmatrix} a_1 + a_2 \\ b_1 + b_2 \end{pmatrix}}$$

If $\overrightarrow{AB} = \begin{pmatrix} h \\ k \end{pmatrix}$, then $\overrightarrow{BA} = \begin{pmatrix} -h \\ -k \end{pmatrix}$. Notice that $\overrightarrow{BA} = -\overrightarrow{AB}$, and also that

$\overrightarrow{AB} + \overrightarrow{BA} = \begin{pmatrix} 0 \\ 0 \end{pmatrix}$; the vector $\begin{pmatrix} 0 \\ 0 \end{pmatrix}$ is called the **zero vector** and is denoted by **0**.

Any vector $\begin{pmatrix} x \\ y \end{pmatrix}$ can be expressed as $\begin{pmatrix} x \\ 0 \end{pmatrix} + \begin{pmatrix} 0 \\ y \end{pmatrix}$, and this in turn can be written

$$x \begin{pmatrix} 1 \\ 0 \end{pmatrix} + y \begin{pmatrix} 0 \\ 1 \end{pmatrix} = x\mathbf{i} + y\mathbf{j}.$$

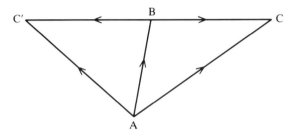

Figure 16.11

To subtract vectors, see Figure 16.11, where C′ is the point on CB produced, such that BC′ = CB.

$$\overrightarrow{AB} - \overrightarrow{BC} = \overrightarrow{AB} + (-\overrightarrow{BC})$$
$$= \overrightarrow{AB} + \overrightarrow{BC'}$$
$$= \overrightarrow{AC'}$$

Thus

$$\boxed{\begin{pmatrix} a_1 \\ b_1 \end{pmatrix} - \begin{pmatrix} a_2 \\ b_2 \end{pmatrix} = \begin{pmatrix} a_1 - a_2 \\ b_1 - b_2 \end{pmatrix}}$$

It is frequently convenient to use a single letter to represent a vector. When this is done, a lower case letter (i.e. not a capital letter) is always used and it is always printed in bold type (in handwriting it must be underlined with a wavy line, i.e. a͌). For example we may write

$$\mathbf{x} = \begin{pmatrix} 2 \\ 1 \end{pmatrix} \qquad \mathbf{y} = \begin{pmatrix} 1 \\ 5 \end{pmatrix}$$

$$\mathbf{x} + \mathbf{y} = \begin{pmatrix} 3 \\ 6 \end{pmatrix} \quad \text{and} \quad \mathbf{x} - \mathbf{y} = \begin{pmatrix} 1 \\ -4 \end{pmatrix}$$

In **i**, **j** notation, the statement above could be written

$$\mathbf{x} = 2\mathbf{i} + \mathbf{j} \qquad \mathbf{y} = \mathbf{i} + 5\mathbf{j}$$
$$\mathbf{x} + \mathbf{y} = 3\mathbf{i} + 6\mathbf{j} \quad \text{and} \quad \mathbf{x} - \mathbf{y} = \mathbf{i} - 4\mathbf{j}$$

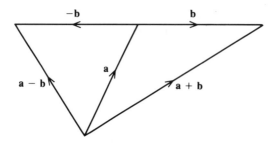

Figure 16.12

This is especially useful for labelling diagrams. For example, Figure 16.12 illustrates the sum, $\mathbf{a} + \mathbf{b}$, and the difference, $\mathbf{a} - \mathbf{b}$, of the vectors $\mathbf{a}$ and $\mathbf{b}$.

When using the single letter notation, an *italic* letter is always used to denote the *magnitude* of the vector which is represented by the same letter in **bold** type, e.g. if $\mathbf{a} = 3\mathbf{i} + 4\mathbf{j}$, then $a = 5$. (In handwriting, the magnitude of vector $\mathbf{a}$ can be written $|\underset{\sim}{a}|$.)

Example 4

In Figure 16.13 each set of parallel lines is equally spaced and it is given that $\overrightarrow{OP} = \mathbf{p}$ and $\overrightarrow{OU} = \mathbf{u}$. Express the following vectors in terms of $\mathbf{p}$ and $\mathbf{u}$:

(a) $\overrightarrow{OQ}$ (b) $\overrightarrow{QW}$ (c) $\overrightarrow{OW}$ (d) $\overrightarrow{OM}$ (e) $\overrightarrow{OS}$ (f) $\overrightarrow{OA}$

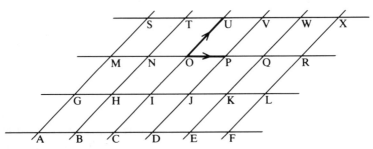

Figure 16.13

(a) $\overrightarrow{OQ} = 2\mathbf{p}$ (b) $\overrightarrow{QW} = \mathbf{u}$
(c) $\overrightarrow{OW} = 2\mathbf{p} + \mathbf{u}$ (d) $\overrightarrow{OM} = -2\mathbf{p}$
(e) $\overrightarrow{OS} = \overrightarrow{OM} + \overrightarrow{MS} = -2\mathbf{p} + \mathbf{u}$ (f) $\overrightarrow{OA} = -2\mathbf{p} - 2\mathbf{u}$

Example 5

In triangle OAB (Figure 16.14), $\overrightarrow{OA} = \mathbf{a}$ and $\overrightarrow{OB} = \mathbf{b}$. Given that P and Q are the mid-points of OA and OB, express $\overrightarrow{PQ}$ and $\overrightarrow{AB}$ in terms of $\mathbf{a}$ and $\mathbf{b}$. State the geometrical relationship between $\overrightarrow{PQ}$ and $\overrightarrow{AB}$.

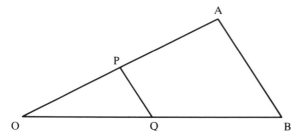

Figure 16.14

Since P and Q are the mid-points of $\overrightarrow{OA}$ and $\overrightarrow{OB}$, we can write

$$\overrightarrow{OP} = \tfrac{1}{2}\mathbf{a} \quad \text{and} \quad \overrightarrow{OQ} = \tfrac{1}{2}\mathbf{b}$$

Now

$$\begin{aligned}
\overrightarrow{PQ} &= \overrightarrow{PO} + \overrightarrow{OQ} \\
&= -\tfrac{1}{2}\mathbf{a} + \tfrac{1}{2}\mathbf{b} \\
&= \tfrac{1}{2}(\mathbf{b} - \mathbf{a}) \\
\overrightarrow{AB} &= \overrightarrow{AO} + \overrightarrow{OB} \\
&= -\mathbf{a} + \mathbf{b} \\
\therefore \quad \overrightarrow{AB} &= 2\overrightarrow{PQ}
\end{aligned}$$

In other words, $\overrightarrow{AB}$ is parallel to $\overrightarrow{PQ}$ and twice its length.

From a mathematical point of view, the beauty of this kind of argument is that it does not depend upon the actual dimensions of the triangle.

Exercise 16a

1 Given that $\mathbf{x} = \begin{pmatrix} 3 \\ 5 \end{pmatrix}$ and $\mathbf{y} = \begin{pmatrix} 4 \\ -6 \end{pmatrix}$ write down as column vectors:

(a) $2\mathbf{x}$ (b) $3\mathbf{y}$ (c) $-\mathbf{y}$ (d) $\tfrac{1}{2}\mathbf{y}$
(e) $\mathbf{x} + \mathbf{y}$ (f) $2\mathbf{x} + 3\mathbf{y}$ (g) $\mathbf{x} - \mathbf{y}$ (h) $3\mathbf{x} - 2\mathbf{y}$

2 Find the magnitude and direction of the vectors:
(a) $3\mathbf{i} + 4\mathbf{j}$ (b) $-5\mathbf{i} + 12\mathbf{j}$ (c) $-10\mathbf{j}$ (d) $\mathbf{i} - \mathbf{j}$

3 The vector $\overrightarrow{XY}$ has magnitude 10 units and it is inclined at $30°$ to the x-axis. Express $\overrightarrow{XY}$ as a column vector.

4 The vector $\overrightarrow{PQ}$ has magnitude 5 units and is inclined at $150°$ to the x-axis. Express $\overrightarrow{PQ}$ in the form $a\mathbf{i} + b\mathbf{j}$, where $a, b \in \mathbb{R}$.

5 A and B are the points $(3, 7)$ and $(15, 13)$ respectively. P is a point on AB such that $\overrightarrow{AP} = s\overrightarrow{AB}$. Write down the vector $\overrightarrow{OP}$ in terms of s. Find the coordinates of P, when:
(a) $s = \tfrac{3}{4}$ (b) $s = \tfrac{3}{2}$ (c) $s = -2$

6 In Figure 16.15, OABC is a quadrilateral and P, Q, R and S are the mid-points of the sides OA, AB, BC and CO, respectively. Given that

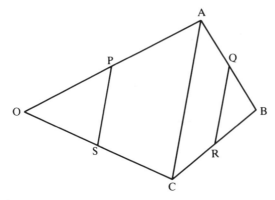

Figure 16.15

$\overrightarrow{OA} = \mathbf{a}$, $\overrightarrow{OB} = \mathbf{b}$ and $\overrightarrow{OC} = \mathbf{c}$, express the following vectors in terms of $\mathbf{a}$, $\mathbf{b}$ and $\mathbf{c}$:

(a) $\overrightarrow{PS}$ (b) $\overrightarrow{AC}$ (c) $\overrightarrow{QR}$

What can you deduce about the lines PS, AC and QR?

7 In no. 6 above, X is the mid-point of PR, and Y is the mid-point of QS. Express $\overrightarrow{OX}$ and $\overrightarrow{OY}$ in terms of $\mathbf{a}$, $\mathbf{b}$ and $\mathbf{c}$. State clearly in words the deduction which can be made from these expressions.

16.7 Position vectors

In the preceding exercise, the reader will have noticed that the vector from the origin O to a point P is frequently required. This vector $\overrightarrow{OP}$ is called the **position vector** of the point P; it is always denoted by the single letter $\mathbf{p}$ (similarly, the position vectors of points A, B, C, ... would be written $\mathbf{a}$, $\mathbf{b}$, $\mathbf{c}$, ...). It is important to notice that position vectors are localised; they *must* start from the origin.

If the coordinates of P are (x, y) then $\mathbf{p}$ is the column vector $\begin{pmatrix} x \\ y \end{pmatrix}$. Notice that the displacement vector $\overrightarrow{PQ}$ is related to the position vectors of P and Q, as follows:

$$\overrightarrow{PQ} = \overrightarrow{PO} + \overrightarrow{OQ} = -\mathbf{p} + \mathbf{q} = \mathbf{q} - \mathbf{p}$$

Similarly:

$$\boxed{\overrightarrow{AB} = \mathbf{b} - \mathbf{a}, \quad \overrightarrow{XY} = \mathbf{y} - \mathbf{x}}$$

and so on. Expressions like these are very common in vector geometry and the reader is advised to commit the form of them to memory.

In Figure 16.16, R is a point on the line PQ, such that $\overrightarrow{PR} = t\overrightarrow{PQ}$.

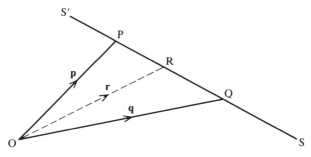

Figure 16.16

Applying the results above to $\overrightarrow{PR}$ and $\overrightarrow{PQ}$, we have

$$\overrightarrow{PR} = t\overrightarrow{PQ}$$

hence

$$\mathbf{r} - \mathbf{p} = t(\mathbf{q} - \mathbf{p})$$
$$\therefore \qquad \mathbf{r} = \mathbf{p} + t(\mathbf{q} - \mathbf{p})$$
$$= (1 - t)\mathbf{p} + t\mathbf{q}$$

Since R lies *between* P and Q, $0 < t < 1$. But if $t = 1$, then R will coincide with Q, and if $t = 0$, then R will coincide with P. The position vector of a point such as S, is given by a similar expression, e.g.

$$\mathbf{s} = (1 - t)\mathbf{p} + t\mathbf{q}$$

but here the number t is greater than 1. A point such as S′ can be obtained by using a negative value for t.

Example 6

In Figure 16.17, $\overrightarrow{OS} = 2\mathbf{r}$ and $\overrightarrow{OQ} = \frac{3}{2}\mathbf{p}$. Given that $\overrightarrow{QK} = m\overrightarrow{QR}$ and $\overrightarrow{PK} = n\overrightarrow{PS}$, find two distinct expressions, in terms of $\mathbf{p}$, $\mathbf{r}$, m and n, for $\overrightarrow{OK}$. By equating these expressions, find the values of m and n and hence calculate the ratios $QK:KR$ and $PK:KS$.

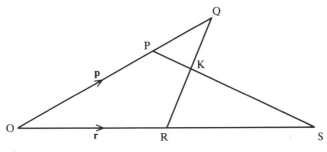

Figure 16.17

$$\overrightarrow{QR} = \overrightarrow{QO} + \overrightarrow{OR}$$
$$= -\tfrac{3}{2}\mathbf{p} + \mathbf{r}$$

One expression for $\overrightarrow{OK}$ is given by

$$\overrightarrow{OK} = \overrightarrow{OQ} + \overrightarrow{QK} = \overrightarrow{OQ} + m\overrightarrow{QR}$$
$$= \tfrac{3}{2}\mathbf{p} + m(\mathbf{r} - \tfrac{3}{2}\mathbf{p})$$

Similarly, $\overrightarrow{OK} = \overrightarrow{OP} + \overrightarrow{PK}$, hence

$$\overrightarrow{OK} = \mathbf{p} + n(-\mathbf{p} + 2\mathbf{r})$$

Equating the two expressions for $\overrightarrow{OK}$, we have

$$\tfrac{3}{2}\mathbf{p} + m(\mathbf{r} - \tfrac{3}{2}\mathbf{p}) = \mathbf{p} + n(-\mathbf{p} + 2\mathbf{r})$$

and rearranging this gives

$$(\tfrac{1}{2} - \tfrac{3}{2}m + n)\mathbf{p} = (2n - m)\mathbf{r}$$

but since $\mathbf{p}$ and $\mathbf{r}$ are not parallel, the two sides of this equation cannot be equal unless they are both zero. (The reader should think carefully about this statement, and make sure he or she fully understands it. This argument is very common when vectors are used in geometrical problems.) Hence

$$\tfrac{1}{2} - \tfrac{3}{2}m + n = 0 \qquad\qquad \text{. . . (1)}$$
$$\text{and} \qquad 2n - m = 0 \qquad\qquad \text{. . . (2)}$$

Substituting $m = 2n$ in equation (1), we have:

$$\tfrac{1}{2} - \tfrac{3}{2} \times 2n + n = 0$$
$$\tfrac{1}{2} - \quad 3n + n = 0$$
$$2n = \tfrac{1}{2}$$
$$n = \tfrac{1}{4}$$
$$\text{and hence} \qquad m = \tfrac{1}{2}$$

But $\overrightarrow{QK} = m\overrightarrow{QR}$ (given) so $\overrightarrow{QK} = \tfrac{1}{2}\overrightarrow{QR}$ and hence $\overrightarrow{QK} = \overrightarrow{KR}$. Therefore

$$QK : KR = 1 : 1$$

Also $\overrightarrow{PK} = n\overrightarrow{PS}$, so $\overrightarrow{PK} = \tfrac{1}{4}\overrightarrow{PS}$ and hence

$$PK : KS = 1 : 3$$

Example 7

At noon, two boats P and Q are at points whose position vectors are $4\mathbf{i} + 8\mathbf{j}$ and $4\mathbf{i} + 3\mathbf{j}$ respectively. Both boats are moving with constant velocity; the velocity of P is $4\mathbf{i} + \mathbf{j}$ and the velocity of Q is $2\mathbf{i} + 5\mathbf{j}$ (all distances are in kilometres and the time is measured in hours). Find the position vectors of P and Q, and $\overrightarrow{PQ}$ after t hours, and hence express the distance PQ between the boats in terms of t. Show that the least distance between the boats is $\sqrt{5}$ km.

After t hours the displacement of P from its starting point is $t(4\mathbf{i} + \mathbf{j})$, hence

$$\begin{aligned}\mathbf{p} &= (4\mathbf{i} + 8\mathbf{j}) + t(4\mathbf{i} + \mathbf{j}) \\ &= (4 + 4t)\mathbf{i} + (8 + t)\mathbf{j}\end{aligned}$$

Similarly

$$\mathbf{q} = (4 + 2t)\mathbf{i} + (3 + 5t)\mathbf{j}$$

Hence

$$\begin{aligned}\overrightarrow{PQ} = \mathbf{q} - \mathbf{p} &= -2t\mathbf{i} + (-5 + 4t)\mathbf{j} \\ \therefore \quad PQ^2 = (-2t)^2 &+ (-5 + 4t)^2 \\ &= 20t^2 - 40t + 25\end{aligned}$$

Hence the distance between the boats is given by

$$PQ = \sqrt{(20t^2 - 40t + 25)} \text{ km}$$

To find the least distance, consider

$$\begin{aligned}PQ^2 &= 20(t^2 - 2t + 1) + 5 \\ &= 20(t - 1)^2 + 5\end{aligned}$$

Since $(t - 1)^2$ cannot be negative, its least value is zero and this is obtained by putting $t = 1$. Hence the least value of PQ^2 is 5. (See Section 11.3.)

$\therefore$ The shortest possible distance between the boats is $\sqrt{5}$ km.

Exercise 16b

1 Given that A is the point $(2, 5)$ and that B is the point $(10, -1)$, find the position vector of a point P on AB, such that:
   (a) $\overrightarrow{AP} = \overrightarrow{PB}$ (b) $2\overrightarrow{AP} = \overrightarrow{PB}$ (c) $\overrightarrow{AP} = 4\overrightarrow{AB}$
   (d) $AP:PB = 2:3$ (e) $AP:PB = 4:1$ (f) $AP:PB = m:n$
2 Repeat no. 1 for $A(-7, 3)$ and $B(-1, -15)$.
3 A, B, C are three collinear points whose position vectors are $\mathbf{a}$, $\mathbf{b}$ and $\mathbf{c}$ respectively and $\overrightarrow{AC} = 3\overrightarrow{AB}$. Express $\mathbf{c}$ in the form $\mathbf{c} = m\mathbf{a} + n\mathbf{b}$; find the scalars m and n and verify that $m + n = 1$. Show also that if $\mathbf{a} = p\mathbf{b} + q\mathbf{c}$ then $p + q = 1$.
4 Repeat no. 3 given that $\overrightarrow{AC} = -2\overrightarrow{AB}$.
5 A stationary observer O observes a ship S at noon, at a point whose coordinates relative to O are $(20, 15)$; the units are kilometres. The ship is moving at a steady 10 km h^{-1} on a bearing $150°$ (a bearing is measured clockwise from north). Express its velocity as a column vector. Write down, in terms of t, its position after t hours. Hence find the values of t when it is due east of O. How far is it from O at this instant?

6 Find numbers m and n such that $m\begin{pmatrix} 3 \\ 5 \end{pmatrix} + n\begin{pmatrix} 2 \\ 1 \end{pmatrix} = \begin{pmatrix} 4 \\ 9 \end{pmatrix}$.

7 In Figure 16.18, $\overrightarrow{OP} = \mathbf{p}$ and $\overrightarrow{OR} = \mathbf{r}$.
P is the mid-point of OQ and $PX:XR = 1:3$. Express $\mathbf{x}$ in terms of $\mathbf{p}$ and $\mathbf{r}$. Taking $\overrightarrow{OY}$ to be $h\overrightarrow{OX}$, find $\overrightarrow{QY}$ in terms of $\mathbf{p}$, $\mathbf{r}$ and h and hence find the ratio QY:YR.

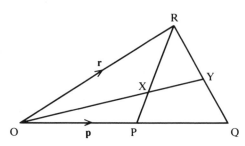

Figure 16.18

8 In Figure 16.19, OBC is a triangle and the line NL produced meets the line OC produced at M.

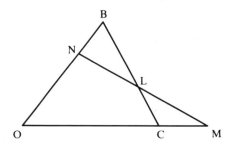

Figure 16.19

Given that $\overrightarrow{ON} = \frac{3}{4}\overrightarrow{OB}$ and $\overrightarrow{BL} = \frac{2}{3}\overrightarrow{BC}$, express the vector $\overrightarrow{NL}$ in terms of $\mathbf{b}$ and $\mathbf{c}$, the position vectors of the points B and C with respect to the origin O. Find an expression for the position vector of any point R on the line NL. Hence express $\overrightarrow{OM}$ as a multiple of $\overrightarrow{OC}$. Find the ratio CM/MO and verify that

$$\frac{ON}{NB} \times \frac{BL}{LC} \times \frac{CM}{MO} = -1$$

9 In a triangle OAB, X is a point on OB such that $\overrightarrow{OX} = 2\overrightarrow{XB}$ and Y is a point on AB such that $2\overrightarrow{BY} = 3\overrightarrow{YA}$. Express $\mathbf{x}$ and $\mathbf{y}$ in terms of $\mathbf{a}$ and $\mathbf{b}$. Find the position vector of any point on XY and hence find the position vector of the point Z, where XY produced meets OA produced. Calculate the value of AZ/OZ.

10 Prove that if **a** and **b** are the position vectors of points A and B, then the position vector of a point P on AB, where $AP:PB = m:n$ is given by $(m + n)\mathbf{p} = n\mathbf{a} + m\mathbf{b}$.

11 Prove that if $\mathbf{p} = h\mathbf{a} + k\mathbf{b}$ represents the point P on the line AB, then $h + k = 1$.

12 Given that A, B and C are three collinear points whose position vectors satisfy the equation $\alpha\mathbf{a} + \beta\mathbf{b} + \gamma\mathbf{c} = \mathbf{0}$, prove that $\alpha + \beta + \gamma = 0$.

16.8 The ratio theorem

In Figure 16.20, $\overrightarrow{OA'} = h\mathbf{a}$, $\overrightarrow{OB'} = k\mathbf{b}$ and $\overrightarrow{OC} = h\mathbf{a} + k\mathbf{b}$. We say that $\overrightarrow{OC}$ is a **linear combination** of **a** and **b**. Any point C, whose position vector is a linear combination of **a** and **b**, will be a point in the plane of O, A and B. (So far we have only considered vectors in two dimensions; this last statement becomes very important when we start to consider three dimensions.)

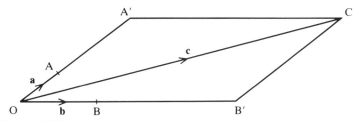

Figure 16.20

However, if $\overrightarrow{OC} = h\mathbf{a} + k\mathbf{b}$ and $h + k = 1$, it can be shown that C lies on the line AB, as follows:

$$\begin{aligned} \mathbf{c} &= h\mathbf{a} + k\mathbf{b} \\ &= (1 - k)\mathbf{a} + k\mathbf{b} \\ &= \mathbf{a} + k(\mathbf{b} - \mathbf{a}) \end{aligned}$$

Using the double letter notation this last equation becomes

$$\overrightarrow{OC} = \overrightarrow{OA} + k\overrightarrow{AB}$$

hence

$$\overrightarrow{AC} = k\overrightarrow{AB}$$

so C is the point on AB such that $\overrightarrow{AC} = k\overrightarrow{AB}$ (see Figure 16.21).

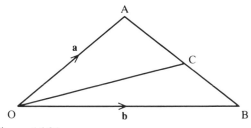

Figure 16.21

Similarly $\overrightarrow{BC} = h\overrightarrow{BA}$. Hence $AC:CB = k:h$.

Conversely if we are given that C is a point on the line AB such that $AC:CB = m:n$, then we can write

$$\frac{AC}{CB} = \frac{m}{n}$$

so $n\overrightarrow{AC} = m\overrightarrow{CB}$
∴ $n(\mathbf{c} - \mathbf{a}) = m(\mathbf{b} - \mathbf{c})$
            $n\mathbf{c} - n\mathbf{a} = m\mathbf{b} - m\mathbf{c}$
            $m\mathbf{c} + n\mathbf{c} = n\mathbf{a} + m\mathbf{b}$
            $(m + n)\mathbf{c} = n\mathbf{a} + m\mathbf{b}$

$$\boxed{\therefore \quad \mathbf{c} = \left(\frac{n}{m+n}\right)\mathbf{a} + \left(\frac{m}{m+n}\right)\mathbf{b}}$$

This is usually called the **ratio theorem**. Notice that the sum of the coefficients $n/(m + n)$ and $m/(m + n)$ is 1.

If M is the mid-point of AB, then $AM:MB = 1:1$ and $\mathbf{m} = \tfrac{1}{2}\mathbf{a} + \tfrac{1}{2}\mathbf{b}$.

Example 8

If $\mathbf{c} = \tfrac{2}{5}\mathbf{a} + \tfrac{3}{5}\mathbf{b}$, show that C is a point on AB and that $AC:CB = 3:2$.

Since $\tfrac{2}{5} + \tfrac{3}{5}$ is equal to 1, C lies on the line AB. Also,

$$AC:CB = \tfrac{3}{5}:\tfrac{2}{5} = 3:2$$

16.9 The centroid of a triangle

In Figure 16.22, ABC is any triangle and P is the mid-point of BC. G is the point on AP such that $AG:GP = 2:1$. The origin is not shown in the diagram.

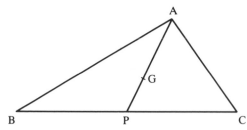

Figure 16.22

Since $BP:PC = 1:1$,

$$\mathbf{p} = \tfrac{1}{2}\mathbf{b} + \tfrac{1}{2}\mathbf{c}$$

and since $AG:GP = 2:1$,

$$g = \tfrac{1}{3}a + \tfrac{2}{3}p$$
$$= \tfrac{1}{3}a + \tfrac{2}{3}(\tfrac{1}{2}b + \tfrac{1}{2}c)$$
$$= \tfrac{1}{3}(a + b + c)$$

This last expression is symmetrical in a, b and c (that is, the letters a, b and c can be interchanged without altering g), so the same result could be obtained by dividing the median from B to AC (or that from C to AB) in the ratio $2:1$. Hence the point G, whose position vector is given by

$$\boxed{g = \tfrac{1}{3}(a + b + c)}$$

is the point of intersection of the three medians. G is called the **centroid** of the triangle.

Qu. 3 Find the centroid of the triangle whose vertices are $A(1, 2)$, $B(3, 7)$ and $C(2, 3)$.

16.10 Menelaus' theorem

In Figure 16.23, OAB is any triangle and PQR is a straight line intersecting the sides of the triangle as shown.

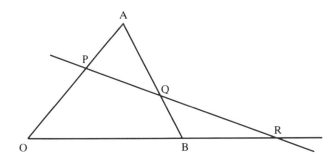

Figure 16.23

Menelaus' theorem can be stated as follows: if $\overrightarrow{OP} = \alpha\overrightarrow{PA}$, $\overrightarrow{AQ} = \beta\overrightarrow{QB}$ and $\overrightarrow{BR} = \gamma\overrightarrow{RO}$, then $\alpha\beta\gamma = -1$. (Notice that since R is on OB produced, γ is a negative number.)

This famous theorem appeared in a treatise published by Menelaus in AD 100, although it was probably known to Euclid almost 400 years earlier. These great mathematicians would not, of course, have expressed the proof in vector notation.

Menelaus' theorem can be proved by vector methods, as follows:

$\overrightarrow{OP} = \alpha\overrightarrow{PA}$, hence $p = \alpha(a - p)$.

$\therefore \quad (1 + \alpha)p = \alpha a$ $\qquad\qquad\qquad\qquad\qquad\qquad$ . . . (1)

$\overrightarrow{AQ} = \beta\overrightarrow{QB}$, hence $\mathbf{q} - \mathbf{a} = \beta(\mathbf{b} - \mathbf{q})$.

$\therefore \quad (1 + \beta)\mathbf{q} = \mathbf{a} + \beta\mathbf{b}$ . . . (2)

$\overrightarrow{BR} = \gamma\overrightarrow{RO}$, hence $\mathbf{r} - \mathbf{b} = -\gamma\mathbf{r}$.

$\therefore \quad (1 + \gamma)\mathbf{r} = \mathbf{b}$ . . . (3)

From equation (1) we have

$$\mathbf{a} = \left(\frac{1 + \alpha}{\alpha}\right)\mathbf{p}$$

and from equation (3),

$$\mathbf{b} = (1 + \gamma)\mathbf{r}$$

Substituting these expressions for $\mathbf{a}$ and $\mathbf{b}$ in equation (2) gives

$$(1 + \beta)\mathbf{q} = \left(\frac{1 + \alpha}{\alpha}\right)\mathbf{p} + \beta(1 + \gamma)\mathbf{r}$$

$$\therefore \qquad \mathbf{q} = \frac{(1 + \alpha)}{\alpha(1 + \beta)}\mathbf{p} + \frac{\beta(1 + \gamma)}{(1 + \beta)}\mathbf{r}$$

However, Q is a point on PR, so, using the ratio theorem (see Section 16.8),

$$\frac{(1 + \alpha)}{\alpha(1 + \beta)} + \frac{\beta(1 + \gamma)}{(1 + \beta)} = 1$$

$$(1 + \alpha) + \alpha\beta(1 + \gamma) = \alpha(1 + \beta)$$
$$1 + \alpha + \alpha\beta + \alpha\beta\gamma = \alpha + \alpha\beta$$
$$\therefore \qquad\qquad\qquad \alpha\beta\gamma = -1$$

The result looks slightly more elegant, and it is perhaps easier to remember, if the diagram is re-lettered as in Figure 16.24.

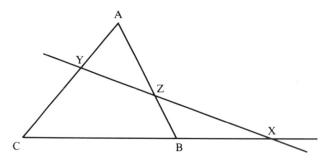

Figure 16.24

Menelaus' theorem can then be expressed:

$$\frac{AZ}{ZB} \times \frac{BX}{XC} \times \frac{CY}{YA} = -1$$

16.11 Vectors in three dimensions

So far in this chapter, we have only considered vectors in two dimensions, but the real world is three dimensional, so we must now consider the problems which arise when vectors are used in three dimensions. One of the great attractions of vectors is that the transition from two dimensions to three is very easy. First we will look at Cartesian coordinates in three dimensions. For convenience, the three axes Ox, Oy and Oz will be mutually perpendicular. They cannot be drawn mutually perpendicular on a flat page, so Figure 16.25 should be viewed with the page held in a vertical plane so that the z-axis is vertical and in the plane of the page, the y-axis is horizontal and in the plane of the page, and the x-axis is imagined to be horizontal, but coming out of the page at right angles to the plane of the page. By convention, the three axes must form a 'right-handed set'. If the thumb, index finger and middle finger of the right hand are stretched out so that they are mutually perpendicular, it should be possible to make the thumb correspond to the x-axis, the index finger to the y-axis and the middle finger to the z-axis. (In a 'left-handed set' the x-axis would go into, instead of come out of, the page.)

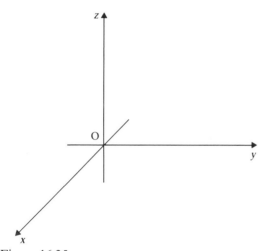

Figure 16.25

A point A(2, 3, 5) is located in the usual way, namely by starting from the origin and moving 2 units along Ox, 3 units parallel to Oy and 5 units parallel to Oz (see Figure 16.26).

The position vector of this point A is written $\overrightarrow{OA} = \begin{pmatrix} 2 \\ 3 \\ 5 \end{pmatrix}$. Similarly the displace-

ment vector from A(2, 3, 5) to B(3, 6, 4) is written $\overrightarrow{AB} = \begin{pmatrix} 1 \\ 3 \\ -1 \end{pmatrix}$.

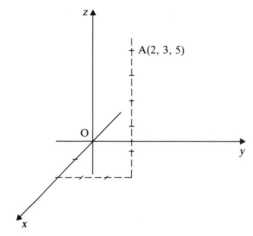

Figure 16.26

In general, if A is the point (x_1, y_1, z_1) and B is the point (x_2, y_2, z_2) then we write

$$\mathbf{a} = \begin{pmatrix} x_1 \\ y_1 \\ z_1 \end{pmatrix} \qquad \mathbf{b} = \begin{pmatrix} x_2 \\ y_2 \\ z_2 \end{pmatrix} \quad \text{and} \quad \overrightarrow{AB} = \begin{pmatrix} x_2 - x_1 \\ y_2 - y_1 \\ z_2 - z_1 \end{pmatrix}$$

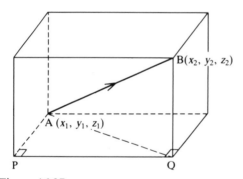

Figure 16.27

Figure 16.27 represents a cuboid, in which AP is parallel to the x-axis, PQ is parallel to the y-axis and QB is parallel to the z-axis. Hence

$$AP = x_2 - x_1, \quad PQ = y_2 - y_1 \quad \text{and} \quad QB = z_2 - z_1$$

The length of vector $\overrightarrow{AB}$ can be found, using Pythagoras' theorem, as follows. In the right-angled triangle ABQ,

$$AB^2 = AQ^2 + QB^2$$

and, in the right-angled triangle APQ,

$$AQ^2 = AP^2 + PQ^2$$

hence

$$AB^2 = AP^2 + PQ^2 + QB^2$$
$$= (x_2 - x_1)^2 + (y_2 - y_1)^2 + (z_2 - z_1)^2$$

Multiplication of a vector by a scalar in three dimensions is defined by a simple extension of the method used in two dimensions (see Section 16.4), that is,

$$k\begin{pmatrix} x \\ y \\ z \end{pmatrix} = \begin{pmatrix} kx \\ ky \\ kz \end{pmatrix}$$

Addition and subtraction are also defined by a similar method to that used before, i.e.

$$\begin{pmatrix} x_1 \\ y_1 \\ z_1 \end{pmatrix} + \begin{pmatrix} x_2 \\ y_2 \\ z_2 \end{pmatrix} = \begin{pmatrix} x_1 + x_2 \\ y_1 + y_2 \\ z_1 + z_2 \end{pmatrix}$$

and

$$\begin{pmatrix} x_1 \\ y_1 \\ z_1 \end{pmatrix} - \begin{pmatrix} x_2 \\ y_2 \\ z_2 \end{pmatrix} = \begin{pmatrix} x_1 - x_2 \\ y_1 - y_2 \\ z_1 - z_2 \end{pmatrix}$$

All the results described so far in this chapter [e.g. the centroid of a triangle ABC is given by $\mathbf{g} = \frac{1}{3}(\mathbf{a} + \mathbf{b} + \mathbf{c})$] are equally valid in three dimensions.

The letter $\mathbf{k}$ is always used to represent the unit vector parallel to the z-axis.

Consequently in $\mathbf{i}, \mathbf{j}, \mathbf{k}$ notation the vector $\begin{pmatrix} x \\ y \\ z \end{pmatrix}$ becomes $x\mathbf{i} + y\mathbf{j} + z\mathbf{k}$.

Example 9

If A and B are the points $(1, 1, 1)$ and $(13, 4, 5)$ respectively, find, in terms of $\mathbf{i}, \mathbf{j}$ and $\mathbf{k}$, the displacement vector $\overrightarrow{AB}$. Find also the unit vector parallel to $\overrightarrow{AB}$.

$$\mathbf{a} = \mathbf{i} + \mathbf{j} + \mathbf{k} \quad \text{and} \quad \mathbf{b} = 13\mathbf{i} + 4\mathbf{j} + 5\mathbf{k}$$
$$\overrightarrow{AB} = \mathbf{b} - \mathbf{a} = 12\mathbf{i} + 3\mathbf{j} + 4\mathbf{k}$$
$$\therefore \quad AB^2 = 12^2 + 3^2 + 4^2 = 169$$
$$\therefore \quad AB = 13$$

The magnitude of $\overrightarrow{AB}$ is 13 and so the vector $\frac{1}{13}\overrightarrow{AB}$ is a parallel vector of magnitude 1. Hence the required unit vector is $\frac{12}{13}\mathbf{i} + \frac{3}{13}\mathbf{j} + \frac{4}{13}\mathbf{k}$.

Example 10

Using the points A and B in Example 9, find the point P on $\overrightarrow{AB}$ such that $AP:PB = 1:3$.

We are given that $AP:PB = 1:3$, so $\overrightarrow{AP} = \frac{1}{4}\overrightarrow{AB}$, hence

$$4(\mathbf{p} - \mathbf{a}) = (\mathbf{b} - \mathbf{a})$$
$$\therefore \quad 4\mathbf{p} = 4\mathbf{a} + \mathbf{b} - \mathbf{a}$$
$$= 3\mathbf{a} + \mathbf{b}$$
$$= 3(\mathbf{i} + \mathbf{j} + \mathbf{k}) + (13\mathbf{i} + 4\mathbf{j} + 5\mathbf{k})$$
$$= 16\mathbf{i} + 7\mathbf{j} + 8\mathbf{k}$$
$$\therefore \qquad \mathbf{p} = 4\mathbf{i} + \tfrac{7}{4}\mathbf{j} + 2\mathbf{k}$$

Hence P is the point $(4, \tfrac{7}{4}, 2)$.

Example 11

Show that the points A(1, 2, 3), B(3, 8, 1), C(7, 20, −3) are collinear.

$$\overrightarrow{AB} = (3\mathbf{i} + 8\mathbf{j} + \mathbf{k}) - (\mathbf{i} + 2\mathbf{j} + 3\mathbf{k})$$
$$= 2\mathbf{i} + 6\mathbf{j} - 2\mathbf{k}$$

Similarly

$$\overrightarrow{BC} = 4\mathbf{i} + 12\mathbf{j} - 4\mathbf{k}$$

hence

$$\overrightarrow{BC} = 2\overrightarrow{AB}$$

consequently $\overrightarrow{AB}$ and $\overrightarrow{BC}$ are in the same direction and so ABC is a straight line.

Qu. 4 Find the centroid of the triangle whose vertices are A(1, 2, 3), B(3, 7, 4), C(2, 0, 5).

Qu. 5 Prove that A(1, 2, 1), B(4, 7, 8), C(6, 4, 12) and D(3, −1, 5) are the vertices of a parallelogram.

16.12 The vector equation of a line

Given any two points A and B, with position vectors **a** and **b**, the position vector of any point R on $\overrightarrow{AB}$ can be expressed as follows:

$$\overrightarrow{OR} = \overrightarrow{OA} + \overrightarrow{AR}$$
Let $\quad \overrightarrow{AR} = t\overrightarrow{AB}$, where $t \in \mathbb{R}$, hence
$$\overrightarrow{OR} = \overrightarrow{OA} + t\overrightarrow{AB}$$
$$\therefore \qquad \mathbf{r} = \mathbf{a} + t(\mathbf{b} - \mathbf{a})$$
$$= (1 - t)\mathbf{a} + t\mathbf{b}$$

The letter t in this equation represents any real number and, for all values of t, $\mathbf{r}$ is the position vector of a point on $\overrightarrow{AB}$. The equation

$$\boxed{\mathbf{r} = (1 - t)\mathbf{a} + t\mathbf{b}}$$

is called the **vector equation** of the line AB. The number t is called the **parameter**; for any value of the parameter, R is a point on AB.

Example 12

Find the equation of the line through the points A(1, 2, 3) and B(4, 4, 4) and find the coordinates of the point where this line meets the plane $z = 0$.

$$\overrightarrow{AB} = 3\mathbf{i} + 2\mathbf{j} + \mathbf{k}$$

Let R be any point on AB, so that

$$\overrightarrow{OR} = \overrightarrow{OA} + t\overrightarrow{AB}, \quad \text{where } t \in \mathbb{R}$$
$$\therefore \quad \mathbf{r} = (\mathbf{i} + 2\mathbf{j} + 3\mathbf{k}) + t(3\mathbf{i} + 2\mathbf{j} + \mathbf{k})$$
$$= (1 + 3t)\mathbf{i} + (2 + 2t)\mathbf{j} + (3 + t)\mathbf{k}$$

This is the equation of the line.

The line meets the plane $z = 0$, where $(3 + t) = 0$. Thus the parameter at this point is $t = -3$. Substituting this in the equation of the line, we have

$$\mathbf{r} = -8\mathbf{i} - 4\mathbf{j} + 0\mathbf{k}$$

so the line meets the plane at the point $(-8, -4, 0)$.

Any vector equation of the form

$$\boxed{\mathbf{r} = \mathbf{a} + t\mathbf{u}}$$

where $\mathbf{a}$ and $\mathbf{u}$ are given vectors, represents the equation of a line passing through the point whose position vector is $\mathbf{a}$. The direction of the line is parallel to the vector $\mathbf{u}$.

If $\mathbf{a} = \begin{pmatrix} x_1 \\ y_1 \\ z_1 \end{pmatrix}$ and $\mathbf{u} = \begin{pmatrix} l \\ m \\ n \end{pmatrix}$

then $\mathbf{r} = \begin{pmatrix} x_1 \\ y_1 \\ z_1 \end{pmatrix} + t\begin{pmatrix} l \\ m \\ n \end{pmatrix}$

If the point R has coordinates (x, y, z) then **r** can be written $\begin{pmatrix} x \\ y \\ z \end{pmatrix}$ and hence the

last equation becomes

$$\begin{pmatrix} x \\ y \\ z \end{pmatrix} = \begin{pmatrix} x_1 + tl \\ y_1 + tm \\ z_1 + tn \end{pmatrix}$$

Thus the coordinates of R are $x = x_1 + tl$, $y = y_1 + tm$, $z = z_1 + tn$. These three equations are frequently arranged in the form

$$\boxed{\dfrac{x - x_1}{l} = \dfrac{y - y_1}{m} = \dfrac{z - z_1}{n} = t}$$

Example 13

Given the equation of the line in the form

$$\frac{x - 2}{3} = \frac{y - 4}{5} = \frac{z - 7}{2}$$

express the equation in the form $\mathbf{r} = \mathbf{a} + t\mathbf{u}$ and show that the line passes through the point $(8, 14, 11)$.

Let $\dfrac{x - 2}{3} = \dfrac{y - 4}{5} = \dfrac{z - 7}{2} = t$

then $x - 2 = 3t \qquad y - 4 = 5t \qquad z - 7 = 2t$

hence

$$x = 2 + 3t$$
$$y = 4 + 5t$$
$$z = 7 + 2t$$

that is, in vector form:

$$\begin{pmatrix} x \\ y \\ z \end{pmatrix} = \begin{pmatrix} 2 + 3t \\ 4 + 5t \\ 7 + 2t \end{pmatrix}$$

which can be written in the form $\mathbf{r} = \mathbf{a} + t\mathbf{u}$ as follows:

$$\begin{pmatrix} x \\ y \\ z \end{pmatrix} = \begin{pmatrix} 2 \\ 4 \\ 7 \end{pmatrix} + t \begin{pmatrix} 3 \\ 5 \\ 2 \end{pmatrix}$$

Compare this with the coordinates (8, 14, 11); when $2 + 3t = 8$, $t = 2$.
[Now try this value of the parameter on the y- and z-coordinates.]
When $t = 2$, $4 + 5t = 14$ and $7 + 2t = 11$. Hence the line passes through
the point (8, 14, 11).

Qu. 6 Find the unit vector which is parallel to the line $\dfrac{x-1}{3} = \dfrac{y-2}{4} = \dfrac{z-7}{12}$.

Qu. 7 Show that the equations

$$\begin{pmatrix} x \\ y \\ z \end{pmatrix} = \begin{pmatrix} 2 \\ 3 \\ 1 \end{pmatrix} + m \begin{pmatrix} 4 \\ 6 \\ -2 \end{pmatrix} \quad \text{and} \quad \begin{pmatrix} x \\ y \\ z \end{pmatrix} = \begin{pmatrix} 10 \\ 15 \\ -3 \end{pmatrix} + n \begin{pmatrix} -2 \\ -3 \\ 1 \end{pmatrix}$$

represent the same line.

16.13 Planes

If A, B and C are three given points it is always possible to find a plane which
contains all three of them. (Imagine the tips of the thumb and first two fingers
of the right hand as the three given points. A flat surface, say a book, can then
be placed on these points to represent the plane passing through them.) A
fourth point, P, may or may not lie in the same plane. If it does, then, as was
shown in Section 16.8, the vector $\overrightarrow{AP}$ can be expressed as a linear combination
of $\overrightarrow{AB}$ and $\overrightarrow{AC}$, that is scalars m and n can be found so that

$$\overrightarrow{AP} = m\overrightarrow{AB} + n\overrightarrow{AC}$$

hence

$$\mathbf{p} - \mathbf{a} = m(\mathbf{b} - \mathbf{a}) + n(\mathbf{c} - \mathbf{a})$$
$$\therefore \qquad \mathbf{p} = (1 - m - n)\mathbf{a} + m\mathbf{b} + n\mathbf{c}$$

In other words, $\mathbf{p}$ can be expressed as a linear combination of $\mathbf{a}$, $\mathbf{b}$ and $\mathbf{c}$:

$$\mathbf{p} = \alpha\mathbf{a} + \beta\mathbf{b} + \gamma\mathbf{c}$$

where $\alpha + \beta + \gamma = 1$ [since $(1 - m - n) + m + n = 1$].

(It is interesting to compare this with the statement 'if R is a point on the line
AB then $\mathbf{r}$ can be expressed as a linear combination of $\mathbf{a}$ and $\mathbf{b}$, in other words
$\mathbf{r} = \lambda\mathbf{a} + \mu\mathbf{b}$ where $\lambda + \mu = 1$'.)

Example 14

Given that A, B, C are the points (1, 1, 1), (5, 0, 0) and (3, 2, 1)
respectively, find the equation which must be satisfied by the
coordinates (x, y, z) of any point, P, in the plane ABC.

As P lies in the plane ABC, we may write $\overrightarrow{AP} = m\overrightarrow{AB} + n\overrightarrow{AC}$. Then, since

$$\overrightarrow{AB} = \begin{pmatrix} 4 \\ -1 \\ -1 \end{pmatrix} \quad \overrightarrow{AC} = \begin{pmatrix} 2 \\ 1 \\ 0 \end{pmatrix} \quad \text{and} \quad \overrightarrow{AP} = \begin{pmatrix} x-1 \\ y-1 \\ z-1 \end{pmatrix}$$

$$\begin{pmatrix} x-1 \\ y-1 \\ z-1 \end{pmatrix} = m\begin{pmatrix} 4 \\ -1 \\ -1 \end{pmatrix} + n\begin{pmatrix} 2 \\ 1 \\ 0 \end{pmatrix}$$

Thus

$$\left.\begin{aligned} x &= 1 + 4m + 2n \\ y &= 1 - m + n \\ z &= 1 - m \end{aligned}\right\} \qquad \ldots \quad (1)$$

Eliminating n,

$$x - 2y = -1 + 6m$$

and eliminating m,

$$x - 2y + 6z = 5$$

This is the equation of the plane ABC.

In the equations (1), the scalars m and n are usually called 'the parameters of the plane'. For any values of m and n the coordinates (x, y, z) resulting from these equations are the coordinates of a point in the plane ABC. In the two-dimensional world of the plane ABC, we have two degrees of freedom; we can choose a value for m and we can choose a value for n. (Compare this with the one-dimensional world of the line, in Section 16.12, in which there is only one degree of freedom; that is we can choose a value for the parameter t.)

Qu. 8 Find the equation of the plane containing the points (1, 1, 0), (0, 1, 2), (2, 3, −8).

Qu. 9 Find the equation of the plane which passes through the point (1, 2, 3) and which is parallel to the vectors $\begin{pmatrix} 2 \\ 4 \\ -10 \end{pmatrix}$ and $\begin{pmatrix} 6 \\ -4 \\ 2 \end{pmatrix}$.

16.14 The intersection of two planes

Two nonparallel planes will always meet in a straight line. If we are given the equations of two such planes, say, $3x - 5y + z = 8$ and $2x - 3y + z = 3$, then the equation of the line of intersection can be found as follows.

For any point (x, y, z) which lies in *both* planes, the values of x, y and z fit both equations simultaneously. Hence eliminating z from both equations (in this case by subtracting the second equation from the first) we obtain

$$x - 2y = 5$$

There are infinitely many pairs of values of x and y which satisfy this equation, but if we choose a value for x then the value of y is fixed and *vice versa*. (For example, if $x = 7$ then $y = 1$.)

Let $y = t$, then x must be $5 + 2t$ and substituting these expressions for x and y into the first of the original equations, we obtain

$$3(5 + 2t) - 5t + z = 8$$
$$15 + 6t - 5t + z = 8$$
$$\therefore \qquad\qquad z = -7 - t$$

Thus

$$\begin{pmatrix} x \\ y \\ z \end{pmatrix} = \begin{pmatrix} 5 + 2t \\ t \\ -7 - t \end{pmatrix} \qquad \text{i.e.} \qquad \begin{pmatrix} x \\ y \\ z \end{pmatrix} = \begin{pmatrix} 5 \\ 0 \\ -7 \end{pmatrix} + t \begin{pmatrix} 2 \\ 1 \\ -1 \end{pmatrix}$$

The latter is the equation of the line. It is parallel to the vector $\begin{pmatrix} 2 \\ 1 \\ -1 \end{pmatrix}$ and it

passes through the point $(5, 0, -7)$. A typical point on the line can be written $(5 + 2t, t, -7 - t)$ and it can easily be verified that, for all values of t, this point lies in both of the planes. It we substitute its coordinates into the first equation, we obtain

$$3x - 5y + z = 3(5 + 2t) - 5t + (-7 - t)$$
$$= 15 + 6t - 5t - 7 - t$$
$$= 8$$

and substituting in the second equation gives

$$2x - 3y + z = 2(5 + 2t) - 3t + (-7 - t)$$
$$= 10 + 4t - 3t - 7 - t$$
$$= 3$$

Exercise 16c

1 Given the points A and B below, write down the displacement vector, $\overrightarrow{AB}$, in each case:
   (a) A(1, 0, 2), B(3, 6, 4)   (b) A(5, 0, 4), B(3, 0, 4)
   (c) A(2, 1, 3), B(6, 4, 3)   (d) A(5, 4, 7), B(2, 8, 1)
   (e) A(k, $2k$, $3k$), B($3k$, $2k$, k)
2 For each part of no. 1, write down the position vector of the mid-point of AB.

3 For each part of no. 1, write down the position vector of the point P, such that $\vec{AP} = 5\vec{AB}$.

4 Find the equation of the plane through the points $(1, 2, 0)$, $(1, 1, 1)$ and $(0, 3, 0)$.

5 Find the equation of the plane through the point $(1, 1, 1)$ parallel to the vectors $\mathbf{i} + 2\mathbf{j} + 3\mathbf{k}$ and $\mathbf{i} + \mathbf{j}$.

6 Find the coordinates of the point where the line

$$\begin{pmatrix} x \\ y \\ z \end{pmatrix} = \begin{pmatrix} 1 \\ 2 \\ 1 \end{pmatrix} + t \begin{pmatrix} 3 \\ 1 \\ 4 \end{pmatrix}$$

meets the plane $x - 2y + 3z = 26$.

7 Show that the line $\begin{pmatrix} x \\ y \\ z \end{pmatrix} = \begin{pmatrix} 1 \\ 2 \\ 3 \end{pmatrix} + t \begin{pmatrix} 1 \\ 1 \\ 1 \end{pmatrix}$ lies in the plane

$$2x + 3y - 5z = -7$$

8 Find the point of intersection of the lines

$$\mathbf{r} = (1 + m)\mathbf{i} + (2 + m)\mathbf{j} + (4 + 2m)\mathbf{k}$$

and

$$\mathbf{r} = (1 + 3n)\mathbf{i} + 5n\mathbf{j} + (3 + 7n)\mathbf{k}$$

9 Show that the lines $\mathbf{r} = \begin{pmatrix} 3 \\ 5 \\ 7 \end{pmatrix} + m \begin{pmatrix} 1 \\ 2 \\ 1 \end{pmatrix}$ and $\mathbf{r} = \begin{pmatrix} 1 \\ 2 \\ 3 \end{pmatrix} + n \begin{pmatrix} 2 \\ 3 \\ 5 \end{pmatrix}$ do not meet.

(Nonparallel lines which do not meet are called *skew* lines.)

10 Given four points A, B, C and D, the point G, whose position vector $\mathbf{g}$ is defined by $\mathbf{g} = \frac{1}{4}(\mathbf{a} + \mathbf{b} + \mathbf{c} + \mathbf{d})$, is called the centroid of A, B, C and D. Prove that G lies on the line joining D to M, the centroid of triangle ABC. Find the ratio DG : GM.

11 Find the equation of the line of intersection of the planes

$$4x + 3y + z = 10$$
$$x + y + z = 6$$

12 Show that the three planes whose equations are

$$2x + 3y + z = 8$$
$$x + y + z = 10$$
$$3x + 5y + z = 6$$

contain a common line.

16.15 The scalar product of two vectors

So far we have added and subtracted vectors, and vectors have been multiplied by scalars, but we have not 'multiplied' one vector by another vector. In vector work there are two kinds of 'multiplication'; in one of them, the result is a scalar quantity, so this is called scalar multiplication, while in the other the result is a vector quantity. The latter kind, 'vector multiplication', is beyond the scope of this book.

Definition

> Given two vectors **a** and **b** (see Figure 16.28), whose magnitudes are a and b respectively, the scalar product **a.b** is $ab \cos \theta$, where θ is the angle between the vectors.

[The scalar product is always written with a very distinct dot between the **a** and the **b**. It is quite common to call this the 'dot product' of **a** and **b**.]

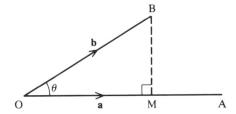

Figure 16.28

At first sight **a.b** $= ab \cos \theta$ might seem a rather odd definition to choose, and one might reasonably ask why it should be this and not, say $ab \tan \theta$, or $ab \sin \theta$. This particular definition, $ab \cos \theta$, is useful because it has many interesting mathematical properties, some of which will appear in the next few sections. Also, applied mathematicians and physicists find it a useful concept; in particular the 'work done' when the point of application of a force **F** (a vector) undergoes a displacement **x** (a vector) is given by **F.x** (a scalar).

Notice that **b.a** $= ba \cos \theta$, which of course is the same as $ab \cos \theta$, so the order of **a** and **b** in the scalar product does not matter; in other words scalar multiplication is *commutative*. (This may seem to be a rather trivial remark, nevertheless it is very important; in contrast vector multiplication is not commutative.) We shall frequently require the scalar products of the base vectors **i** and **j**, so the following results should be memorised (bearing in mind that $\cos 0° = 1$ and $\cos 90° = 0$):

> **i.i** $=$ **j.j** $=$ **k.k** $= 1$
> **i.j** $=$ **j.k** $=$ **k.i** $= 0$

For any vector **a**, the scalar product **a.a** is equal to a^2, and for any pair of perpendicular vectors **a** and **b** the scalar product **a.b** is zero (because cos 90° is zero). Conversely if we know that the scalar product of a pair of vectors is zero, then we can deduce that the vectors are perpendicular (or one of the vectors is zero).

Example 15

Given that OA = 6, OB = 4 and $\angle$ AOB = 60°, calculate the value of $\overrightarrow{OA}.\overrightarrow{OB}$.

$$\overrightarrow{OA}.\overrightarrow{OB} = 6 \times 4 \times \cos 60°$$
$$= 6 \times 4 \times 0.5$$
$$= 12$$

There is an alternative form of this definition. Note that in Figure 16.28 $b \cos \theta = $ OM; the length OM is often called the projection of $\overrightarrow{OB}$ onto $\overrightarrow{OA}$. Consequently we can say that the scalar product, **a.b**, is the product of OA and the projection of $\overrightarrow{OB}$ onto $\overrightarrow{OA}$. The A and B in this statement can, of course, be interchanged.

Although **a.b** has been called a 'product' and the process has been called scalar 'multiplication', it is necessary to establish that this 'multiplication' obeys the same rules that we are familiar with, from working with real numbers.

We have already seen that the order of **a** and **b** in the scalar product does not matter, so the *commutative* law, **a.b = b.a**, is obeyed.

Since **a.b** is scalar, it is impossible to attach any meaning to a triple product **(a.b).c**; consequently there is no question of scalar products obeying the *associative* law. However **(a.b)c** could be taken to mean the scalar **a.b** multiplied by the vector **c**, as in Section 16.4, so great care is needed.

It is, however, very important that we should be able to remove brackets from **a.(b + c)** and obtain **a.b + a.c**. The law

$$\mathbf{a.(b + c) = a.b + a.c}$$

is called the *distributive* law and this is proved in the next section.

16.16 The proof of the distributive law

In Figure 16.29, $\overrightarrow{OA}$ = **a**, $\overrightarrow{OB}$ = **b**, $\overrightarrow{OC}$ = **c** and $\overrightarrow{OR}$ = **b + c**.

$$\mathbf{a.b} = OA \times OL \text{ (the product of OA and the projection of } \overrightarrow{OB} \text{ onto } \overrightarrow{OA})$$

and similarly

$$\mathbf{a.c} = OA \times OM$$

Adding,

$$\mathbf{a.b + a.c} = OA \times (OL + OM)$$

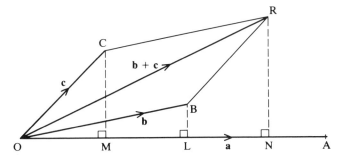

Figure 16.29

but since OC and BR are opposite sides of a parallelogram, the projection of $\overrightarrow{OC}$ onto $\overrightarrow{OA}$ is equal to the projection of $\overrightarrow{BR}$ onto $\overrightarrow{OA}$. Hence OM = LN. Thus

$$\mathbf{a}.\mathbf{b} + \mathbf{a}.\mathbf{c} = OA \times (OL + LN) = OA \times ON$$
$$= \overrightarrow{OA}.\overrightarrow{OR}$$
$$= \mathbf{a}.(\mathbf{b} + \mathbf{c})$$

With this law proved, we may now proceed to remove brackets according to the normal rules of algebra, e.g.

$$(\mathbf{a} + \mathbf{b}).(\mathbf{c} + \mathbf{d}) = \mathbf{a}.(\mathbf{c} + \mathbf{d}) + \mathbf{b}.(\mathbf{c} + \mathbf{d}) = \mathbf{a}.\mathbf{c} + \mathbf{a}.\mathbf{d} + \mathbf{b}.\mathbf{c} + \mathbf{b}.\mathbf{d}$$

In particular, if we wish to form the scalar product of $\mathbf{a}$ and $\mathbf{b}$, where

$$\mathbf{a} = 2\mathbf{i} + 3\mathbf{j} + 4\mathbf{k} \quad \text{and} \quad \mathbf{b} = 5\mathbf{i} + 6\mathbf{j} + 7\mathbf{k}$$

then, bearing in mind that $\mathbf{i}.\mathbf{i} = \mathbf{j}.\mathbf{j} = \mathbf{k}.\mathbf{k} = 1$ and $\mathbf{i}.\mathbf{j} = \mathbf{j}.\mathbf{k} = \mathbf{k}.\mathbf{i} = 0$, we have

$$\mathbf{a}.\mathbf{b} = (2\mathbf{i} + 3\mathbf{j} + 4\mathbf{k}).(5\mathbf{i} + 6\mathbf{j} + 7\mathbf{k}) = 2 \times 5 + 3 \times 6 + 4 \times 7 = 56$$

In general,

$$\begin{pmatrix} x_1 \\ y_1 \\ z_1 \end{pmatrix} . \begin{pmatrix} x_2 \\ y_2 \\ z_2 \end{pmatrix} = (x_1\mathbf{i} + y_1\mathbf{j} + z_1\mathbf{k}).(x_2\mathbf{i} + y_2\mathbf{j} + z_2\mathbf{k}) = x_1 x_2 + y_1 y_2 + z_1 z_2$$

Example 16

Given that $\mathbf{a} = 4\mathbf{i} + 3\mathbf{j} + 12\mathbf{k}$ and $\mathbf{b} = 8\mathbf{i} - 6\mathbf{j}$, find a^2, b^2 and $\mathbf{a}.\mathbf{b}$. Hence find the angle between the vectors $\mathbf{a}$ and $\mathbf{b}$.

By Pythagoras' theorem $a^2 = 16 + 9 + 144 = 169$

Similarly, $b^2 = 100$.

Hence $a = 13$ and $b = 10$.

$$\mathbf{a.b} = (4\mathbf{i} + 3\mathbf{j} + 12\mathbf{k}).(8\mathbf{i} - 6\mathbf{j})$$
$$= 32 - 18$$
$$= 14$$

However, by definition, $\mathbf{a.b} = ab \cos \theta$, where θ is the angle between $\mathbf{a}$ and $\mathbf{b}$. Consequently

$$14 = 13 \times 10 \cos \theta$$

$$\therefore \quad \cos \theta = \frac{14}{130}$$

$$\therefore \qquad \theta = 83.8°$$

The angle between $\mathbf{a}$ and $\mathbf{b}$ is $83.8°$, correct to the nearest tenth of a degree.

Example 17

Prove that $\mathbf{p} = 2\mathbf{i} + 3\mathbf{j} + 4\mathbf{k}$ is perpendicular to $\mathbf{q} = 5\mathbf{i} + 2\mathbf{j} - 4\mathbf{k}$.

$$\mathbf{p.q} = (2\mathbf{i} + 3\mathbf{j} + 4\mathbf{k}).(5\mathbf{i} + 2\mathbf{j} - 4\mathbf{k})$$
$$= 10 + 6 - 16$$
$$= 0$$

Since neither $\mathbf{p}$ nor $\mathbf{q}$ is zero, we can deduce that

$$\cos \theta = 0$$

where θ is the angle between $\mathbf{p}$ and $\mathbf{q}$, so $\theta = 90°$. Hence $\mathbf{p}$ is perpendicular to $\mathbf{q}$.

Qu. 10 Given that $a = 10$ and $b = 15$ and that the angle between $\mathbf{a}$ and $\mathbf{b}$ is $120°$, calculate the value of $\mathbf{a.b}$.

Qu. 11 Write down the condition for the vectors

$$\mathbf{a} = x_1\mathbf{i} + y_1\mathbf{j} + z_1\mathbf{k} \quad \text{and} \quad \mathbf{b} = x_2\mathbf{i} + y_2\mathbf{j} + z_2\mathbf{k}$$

to be perpendicular.

Qu. 12 Find the angle between the vectors

$$\mathbf{p} = \mathbf{i} + 2\mathbf{j} + 2\mathbf{k} \quad \text{and} \quad \mathbf{q} = 2\mathbf{i} + 3\mathbf{j} - 6\mathbf{k}$$

Qu. 13 The unit vector $\mathbf{u}$ makes angles α, β and γ with the x-, y- and z-axes respectively. By considering $\mathbf{u.i}$, or otherwise, show that

$$\mathbf{u} = \cos \alpha\mathbf{i} + \cos \beta\mathbf{j} + \cos \gamma\mathbf{k}$$

and prove that

$$\cos^2 \alpha + \cos^2 \beta + \cos^2 \gamma = 1$$

($\cos \alpha$, $\cos \beta$ and $\cos \gamma$ are called the **direction-cosines** of $\mathbf{u}$).

Qu. 14 Find the direction-cosines of the unit vector parallel to $3\mathbf{i} + 4\mathbf{j} + 12\mathbf{k}$ and calculate the angles this vector makes with the axes.

It is frequently convenient to have a symbol for the *unit* vector in the direction of a given vector $\mathbf{r}$; the normal symbol for this is $\hat{\mathbf{r}}$. So if we use r to represent the magnitude of $\mathbf{r}$, the unit vector $\hat{\mathbf{r}}$ is given by

$$\hat{\mathbf{r}} = \frac{1}{r}\mathbf{r}$$

e.g. if we are given that $\mathbf{r} = 3\mathbf{i} + 4\mathbf{j}$, then $r = 5$ and

$$\hat{\mathbf{r}} = \frac{1}{5}\mathbf{r} = \frac{3}{5}\mathbf{i} + \frac{4}{5}\mathbf{j}$$

16.17 The equation of a plane

Earlier we found the equation of a plane through three given points. In this section we shall find the equation of a plane through a given point *and perpendicular to a given vector*, using the concept of the scalar product.

Suppose the plane is perpendicular to a given vector $\mathbf{n}$, where $\mathbf{n} = \begin{pmatrix} a \\ b \\ c \end{pmatrix}$; that is, every line in the plane is perpendicular to $\mathbf{n}$. Let the given point through which the plane passes be $A(x_1, y_1, z_1)$ and let $P(x, y, z)$ be any point in the plane (Figure 16.30), then AP is perpendicular to $\mathbf{n}$. This fact can be expressed in

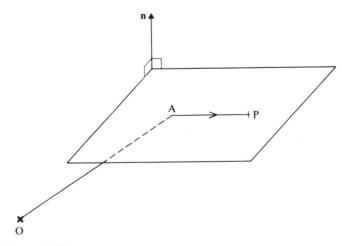

Figure 16.30

terms of a scalar product, namely

$$\mathbf{n}.\overrightarrow{AP} = 0$$

$$\therefore \quad \begin{pmatrix} a \\ b \\ c \end{pmatrix} . \begin{pmatrix} x - x_1 \\ y - y_1 \\ z - z_1 \end{pmatrix} = 0$$

Hence $a(x - x_1) + b(y - y_1) + c(z - z_1) = 0$.

$$\therefore \quad ax + by + cz = d$$

where $d = ax_1 + by_1 + cz_1$. Notice that the coefficients a, b, c of x, y and z form the vector $\mathbf{n}$; consequently if we are given the equation of a plane, we can immediately write down the vector which is perpendicular to it.

Example 18

Write down the unit vector which is perpendicular to the plane $2x + 3y + 6z = 10$.

The vector $\begin{pmatrix} 2 \\ 3 \\ 6 \end{pmatrix}$ is normal to the plane and the magnitude of this is

$\sqrt{(4 + 9 + 36)} = \sqrt{49} = 7$, so the unit vector required is $\dfrac{1}{7} \begin{pmatrix} 2 \\ 3 \\ 6 \end{pmatrix}$.

Example 19

Find the equation of the plane through the point (1, 2, 3) and perpendicular to the vector $4\mathbf{i} + 5\mathbf{j} + 6\mathbf{k}$.

Any plane which is perpendicular to the given vector will have an equation of the form

$$4x + 5y + 6z = d$$

where d is a constant. To find the equation of the plane which passes through (1, 2, 3), we must choose the value of d, so that the equation is satisfied when $x = 1$, $y = 2$ and $z = 3$, i.e.

$$4 \times 1 + 5 \times 2 + 6 \times 3 = d$$

i.e.
$$d = 32$$

Hence the equation we require is $4x + 5y + 6z = 32$.

Example 20

Find the angle between the planes $4x + 3y + 12z = 10$ and $8x - 6y = 14$.

The angle required is the angle between the normal vectors and these are $\mathbf{m} = 4\mathbf{i} + 3\mathbf{j} + 12\mathbf{k}$ and $\mathbf{n} = 8\mathbf{i} - 6\mathbf{j}$. We shall find the angle between $\mathbf{m}$ and $\mathbf{n}$ by finding the scalar product $\mathbf{m.n}$ in two forms and equating them. Firstly,

$$\begin{aligned}\mathbf{m.n} &= (4\mathbf{i} + 3\mathbf{j} + 12\mathbf{k}).(8\mathbf{i} - 6\mathbf{j})\\ &= 32 - 18\\ &= 14\end{aligned}$$

Alternatively, using $\mathbf{m.n} = mn \cos \theta$, where m and n are the magnitudes of the vectors $\mathbf{m}$ and $\mathbf{n}$, and θ is the angle between them, we obtain

$$\begin{aligned}\mathbf{m.n} &= \sqrt{(16 + 9 + 144)} \times \sqrt{(64 + 36)} \times \cos \theta\\ &= \sqrt{169} \times \sqrt{100} \times \cos \theta\\ &= 130 \cos \theta\end{aligned}$$

Equating these two expressions for $\mathbf{m.n}$ gives

$$130 \cos \theta = 14$$

$$\therefore \quad \cos \theta = \frac{14}{130}$$

$$\therefore \quad \theta = 83.8°$$

The angle between the planes is $83.8°$, correct to one decimal place.

Example 21

Find the distance of the point A(25, 5, 7) from the plane $12x + 4y + 3z = 3$.

Let P be the point in the plane such that $\overrightarrow{AP}$ is perpendicular to the plane. Then the distance required is the length of the vector $\overrightarrow{AP}$.

We know that $12\mathbf{i} + 4\mathbf{j} + 3\mathbf{k}$ is perpendicular to the plane, so let $\overrightarrow{AP} = t(12\mathbf{i} + 4\mathbf{j} + 3\mathbf{k})$. Then, since $\overrightarrow{OP} = \overrightarrow{OA} + \overrightarrow{AP}$,

$$\begin{aligned}\overrightarrow{OP} &= (25\mathbf{i} + 5\mathbf{j} + 7\mathbf{k}) + t(12\mathbf{i} + 4\mathbf{j} + 3\mathbf{k})\\ &= (25 + 12t)\mathbf{i} + (5 + 4t)\mathbf{j} + (7 + 3t)\mathbf{k}\end{aligned}$$

Hence P is the point $(25 + 12t, 5 + 4t, 7 + 3t)$ and, since this point lies in the plane, its coordinates satisfy the equation of the plane, consequently,

$$12(25 + 12t) + 4(5 + 4t) + 3(7 + 3t) = 3$$
$$\therefore \quad 169t + 341 = 3$$
$$\therefore \quad t = -2$$

Hence $\overrightarrow{\text{AP}} = -2(12\mathbf{i} + 4\mathbf{j} + 3\mathbf{k}) = -24\mathbf{i} - 8\mathbf{j} - 6\mathbf{k}$, and so

$$\text{AP}^2 = 24^2 + 8^2 + 6^2$$
$$= 576 + 64 + 36$$
$$= 676$$
$$\therefore \quad \text{AP} = 26$$

The distance from the point A to the plane is 26 units.

The standard equation of the plane

$$ax + by + cz = d$$

is often written in the form

$$\mathbf{r.n} = d$$

where

$$\mathbf{r} = x\mathbf{i} + y\mathbf{j} + z\mathbf{k}$$

is the position vector of the general point P(x, y, z), and

$$\mathbf{n} = a\mathbf{i} + b\mathbf{j} + c\mathbf{k}$$

is the vector normal to the plane.

Example 22

Show that the planes

$$\mathbf{r.m} = 5 \quad \text{and } \mathbf{r.n} = 3$$

where $\mathbf{m} = 2\mathbf{i} + 3\mathbf{j} + 5\mathbf{k}$ and $\mathbf{n} = 4\mathbf{i} - \mathbf{j} - \mathbf{k}$

are perpendicular.

The scalar product of the normal vectors is

$$\mathbf{m.n} = (2\mathbf{i} + 3\mathbf{j} + 5\mathbf{k}).(4\mathbf{i} - \mathbf{j} - \mathbf{k})$$
$$= 8 - 3 - 5$$
$$= 0$$

Therefore the normal vectors, and hence the planes themselves, are perpendicular.

Exercise 16d

1 Find the equation of the plane through the point A(2, 1, 3) perpendicular to the vector $2\mathbf{i} - \mathbf{j} + \mathbf{k}$.
2 Find the equation of the plane through the point A(2, 7, −1) perpendicular to the vector $\mathbf{i} + \mathbf{j} + \mathbf{k}$.
3 Verify that the points A(1, 1, 1), B(2, 2, 0) and C(3, 3, −1) lie in the plane

$$2x + 3y + 5z = 10$$

Verify also that the vectors, $\overrightarrow{AB}$, $\overrightarrow{BC}$, and $\overrightarrow{CA}$ are perpendicular to $2\mathbf{i} + 3\mathbf{j} + 5\mathbf{k}$

4 A and B are the points $(3, 1, -1)$ and $(0, 1, 5)$ respectively. Verify that the vectors $\overrightarrow{OA}$ and $\overrightarrow{OB}$ are each perpendicular to $2\mathbf{i} - 5\mathbf{j} + \mathbf{k}$. Hence, or otherwise, find the equation of the plane OAB, where O is the origin.

Find also the equation of the plane through the point $(2, 3, 4)$ and parallel to the plane OAB.

5 Given the points $A(1, 1, 0)$, $B(2, -1, 1)$ and $C(-1, 5, -2)$, verify that the vector $3\mathbf{i} + \mathbf{j} - \mathbf{k}$ is perpendicular to the vectors $\overrightarrow{AB}$ and $\overrightarrow{AC}$.

Hence, or otherwise, find the equation of the plane through the points A, B and C.

6 Find the equation of the line through the point $P(2, 1, 1)$ perpendicular to the plane

$$4x + y + z = 5$$

7 Verify that the planes

$$2x + 3y - 4z = 5 \quad \text{and} \quad 5x - 2y + z = 7$$

are perpendicular.

8 Find the acute angle between the normal vectors to the two planes

$$2x + 3y + z = 4 \quad \text{and} \quad 5x + 2y + 4z = 1$$

9 Find the coordinates of the point where the perpendicular from the point $(37, 9, 10)$ meets the plane

$$12x + 4y + 3z = 3$$

10 The points $A(x_1, y_1, z_1)$ and $B(x_2, y_2, z_2)$ lie in the plane

$$ax + by + cz = d$$

Show that:

$$a(x_2 - x_1) + b(y_2 - y_1) + c(z_2 - z_1) = 0$$

Hence, prove that $\overrightarrow{AB}$ is perpendicular to the vector $a\mathbf{i} + b\mathbf{j} + c\mathbf{k}$.

11 Find the equation of the line through the point $A(9, 9, 23)$ and perpendicular to the plane

$$\mathbf{r}.\mathbf{n} = 1$$

where $\quad \mathbf{r} = x\mathbf{i} + y\mathbf{j} + z\mathbf{k}$

and $\quad \mathbf{n} = 3\mathbf{i} + 4\mathbf{j} + 12\mathbf{k}$

Find the coordinates of the point B where this line meets the plane, and find the length of AB.

12 Show that the lines

$$\mathbf{r} = \begin{pmatrix} 7 \\ 10 \\ 1 \end{pmatrix} + \lambda \begin{pmatrix} 3 \\ 4 \\ 0 \end{pmatrix} \qquad \mathbf{r} = \begin{pmatrix} 5 \\ 14 \\ 4 \end{pmatrix} + \mu \begin{pmatrix} 4 \\ 12 \\ 3 \end{pmatrix}$$

are concurrent, and find their point of intersection.

Find also the acute angle between these lines. Show that the vector $\begin{pmatrix} 12 \\ -9 \\ 20 \end{pmatrix}$ is perpendicular to both lines. Hence, or otherwise, find, in the form $\mathbf{r.n} = d$, the equation of the plane containing the two lines.

Exercise 16e (Miscellaneous)

1 In Figure 16.31, OABC and OPQR are parallelograms:

$$\overrightarrow{OA} = \mathbf{a} \quad \overrightarrow{OC} = \mathbf{c} \quad \overrightarrow{OP} = \tfrac{2}{3}\mathbf{a} \quad \overrightarrow{OR} = \tfrac{1}{2}\mathbf{c}$$

Express the following vectors in terms of $\mathbf{a}$ and $\mathbf{c}$:
(a) $\overrightarrow{OB}$ (b) $\overrightarrow{AC}$ (c) $\overrightarrow{OQ}$ (d) $\overrightarrow{PR}$ (e) $\overrightarrow{RC}$
(f) $\overrightarrow{AQ}$ (g) $\overrightarrow{QC}$ (h) $\overrightarrow{PB}$ (i) $\overrightarrow{PC}$ (j) $\overrightarrow{BQ}$

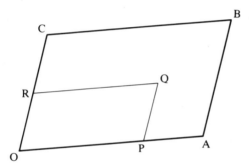

Figure 16.31

2 Find the scalars h and k, such that $h\begin{pmatrix} 3 \\ 5 \end{pmatrix} + k\begin{pmatrix} 4 \\ 7 \end{pmatrix} = \begin{pmatrix} 6 \\ 3 \end{pmatrix}$.

3 Given two points A and B, with position vectors $\mathbf{a}$ and $\mathbf{b}$, find, in terms of $\mathbf{a}$ and $\mathbf{b}$, the position vector of the point P, such that:
(a) P is the mid-point of AB   (b) B is the mid-point of AP
(c) $\overrightarrow{AP} : \overrightarrow{PB} = 3:7$ (d) $\overrightarrow{AP} = \tfrac{3}{8}\overrightarrow{AB}$
(e) $\overrightarrow{PA} = 2\overrightarrow{AB}$

4 (a) Find the scalar product of $\mathbf{a} = \begin{pmatrix} 7.2 \\ 9.6 \end{pmatrix}$ and $\mathbf{b} = \begin{pmatrix} 12 \\ -9 \end{pmatrix}$.

(b) Find the magnitudes of $\mathbf{a}$ and $\mathbf{b}$.
(c) Calculate the angle between $\mathbf{a}$ and $\mathbf{b}$.

5 Given that P, Q and R are the points (8, 10), (6, 20) and (16, 16) respectively, calculate the value of the scalar product $\overrightarrow{PQ}.\overrightarrow{PR}$. Hence calculate the size of the angle QPR.

6 The points A, B and C have coordinates $(4, -1, 5)$, $(8, 0, 6)$ and $(5, -3, 3)$ respectively. Prove that the angle BAC is a right angle.

7 In Figure 16.32, $\overrightarrow{OB} = \mathbf{b}$, $\overrightarrow{OC} = \frac{4}{3}\mathbf{b}$ and $\overrightarrow{AP} = \frac{2}{3}\overrightarrow{AB}$.

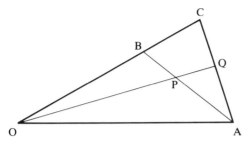

Figure 16.32

Given that $\overrightarrow{AQ} = m\overrightarrow{AC}$ and that $\overrightarrow{OQ} = n\overrightarrow{OP}$, calculate the values of m and n, and the ratio AQ:QC.

8 Find the coordinates of the point P where the line

$$\begin{pmatrix} x \\ y \\ z \end{pmatrix} = \begin{pmatrix} 2 \\ 1 \\ 3 \end{pmatrix} + t \begin{pmatrix} 1 \\ 2 \\ 5 \end{pmatrix}$$

meets the plane $3x + 2y - 2z + 7 = 0$.

9 Find the equation of the line through the points $(2, 3, 7)$ and $(3, 1, 4)$. Find also the equation of the plane perpendicular to this line which passes through the origin.

10 Find the equation of the plane containing the line

$$\begin{pmatrix} x \\ y \\ z \end{pmatrix} = \begin{pmatrix} 2 \\ 0 \\ 1 \end{pmatrix} + t \begin{pmatrix} -1 \\ 1 \\ 0 \end{pmatrix}$$

and passing through the point $(1, 0, 3)$.

11 Given the vectors $\mathbf{a}$ and $\mathbf{b}$, where

$$\mathbf{a} = x_1\mathbf{i} + y_1\mathbf{j} + z_1\mathbf{k}$$

and

$$\mathbf{b} = x_2\mathbf{i} + y_2\mathbf{j} + z_2\mathbf{k}$$

prove that the vector

$$\mathbf{c} = (y_1 z_2 - y_2 z_1)\mathbf{i} + (z_1 x_2 - z_2 x_1)\mathbf{j} + (x_1 y_2 - x_2 y_1)\mathbf{k}$$

is perpendicular to both $\mathbf{a}$ and $\mathbf{b}$.

12 Prove that the planes

$$x - 2y + z = 5$$
$$3x - 3y + z = 3$$
$$5x - 4y + z = 1$$

meet in a common line and find the coordinates of the point where this line meets the plane $z = 0$.

13 A destroyer sights a ship travelling with constant velocity $5\mathbf{j}$, whose position vector at the time of sighting is $2000(3\mathbf{i} + \mathbf{j})$ relative to the destroyer, distances being in m and velocity in m s^{-1}. The destroyer immediately begins to move with velocity $k(4\mathbf{i} + 3\mathbf{j})$, where k is a constant, in order to intercept the ship. Find k and the time to interception.

Find also the distance between the vessels when half the time to interception has elapsed. (O & C)

14 The position vectors, relative to the origin O, of points A and B are respectively $\mathbf{a}$ and $\mathbf{b}$. State, in terms of $\mathbf{a}$ and $\mathbf{b}$, the position vector of the point T which lies on AB and is such that $\overrightarrow{AT} = 2\overrightarrow{TB}$. (Give reasons.)

Find the position vector of the point M on OT produced such that BM and OA are parallel.

If AM is produced to meet OB produced in K, determine the ratio OB : BK. (O & C)

15 The point A has coordinates $(2, 0, -1)$ and the plane π has the equation $x + 2y - 2z = 8$. The line through A parallel to the line $\dfrac{x}{-2} = y = \dfrac{z+1}{2}$ meets π in the point B and the perpendicular from A to π meets π in the point C.

(a) Find the coordinates of B and C.

(b) Show that the length of AC is $4/3$.

(c) Find $\sin \angle ABC$. (O & C: MEI)

16 Of the following equations, which represent lines and which represent planes?

(a) $\dfrac{x-2}{1} = \dfrac{y-1}{2} = \dfrac{z-3}{-1}$

(b) $x + 2y - z = 1$

(c) $\begin{pmatrix} x \\ y \\ z \end{pmatrix} = \begin{pmatrix} 2 \\ 1 \\ 3 \end{pmatrix} + t \begin{pmatrix} 1 \\ -1 \\ -1 \end{pmatrix}$

Describe or show in a clear diagram, how these lines and planes are related to each other. (O & C: SMP)

17 Points P, Q and R have position vectors $\mathbf{p}$, $\mathbf{q}$ and $\mathbf{r}$. If $\mathbf{p} = (1 - \alpha)\mathbf{q} + \alpha\mathbf{r}$, for some number α, describe the position of P relative to Q and R.

OABC are four non-coplanar points in space. A, B, C have position vectors $\mathbf{a}, \mathbf{b}, \mathbf{c}$ relative to O. The position vector of V is $2\mathbf{a} - \mathbf{c}$, and of W is $-2\mathbf{a} + 3\mathbf{b}$. If VW meets the plane OBC in U, find the position vector of U and show that U is on BC.

Use scalar products to show that if V is in the plane through O perpendicular to OB, and W is in the plane through O perpendicular to OC, then U is in the plane through O perpendicular to OA. (O & C: SMP)

18 The vertices A, B, and C of a triangle have position vectors **a**, **b** and **c** respectively relative to an origin O. The point P is on BC such that BP:PC = 3:1; the point Q is on CA such that CQ:QA = 2:3; the point R is on BA produced such that BR:AR = 2:1. The position vectors of P, Q and R are **p**, **q** and **r**, respectively. Show that **q** can be expressed in terms of **p** and **r** and hence show that P, Q and R are collinear. State the ratio of the lengths of the line segments PQ and QR. (JMB)

19 The position vectors of the points A, B and C are given by $\mathbf{a} = 2\mathbf{i} + 3\mathbf{j} - 4\mathbf{k}$, $\mathbf{b} = 5\mathbf{i} - \mathbf{j} + 2\mathbf{k}$, $\mathbf{c} = 11\mathbf{i} + \lambda\mathbf{j} + 14\mathbf{k}$. Find
(a) the unit vector parallel to AB,
(b) the position vector of the point D such that ABCD is a parallelogram,
(c) the value of λ if A, B and C are collinear,
(d) the position vector of the point P on AB if AP:PB = 2:1. (C)

20 A tetrahedron OABC with vertex O at the origin is such that $\overrightarrow{OA} = \mathbf{a}$, $\overrightarrow{OB} = \mathbf{b}$ and $\overrightarrow{OC} = \mathbf{c}$. Show that the line segments joining the mid-points of opposite edges bisect one another. Given that two pairs of opposite edges are perpendicular prove that

$$\mathbf{a}.\mathbf{b} = \mathbf{b}.\mathbf{c} = \mathbf{c}.\mathbf{a}$$

and show that the third pair of opposite edges is also perpendicular. Prove also that, in this case,

$$OA^2 + BC^2 = OB^2 + AC^2 \tag{L}$$

Chapter 17

The general angle and Pythagoras' theorem

17.1 The general angle

Consider a wheel which is free to rotate about a fixed axis, and suppose that one spoke is marked with a thin line of paint. If the wheel starts from rest and makes one revolution, the marked spoke turns through 360°, and if the wheel makes another revolution the spoke turns through 360° again. Thus we may say that the wheel has turned through a total of 720°, and by using angles greater than 360° the number of revolutions may be specified, as well as the position of the marked spoke.

Now on the x-axis of a graph the positive direction is usually taken to the right and the negative direction is opposite to this. Similarly, if the wheel mentioned above was rotating anticlockwise, we could take that sense to be positive, and then a clockwise rotation would be considered negative. Angles measured from the x-axis in an anticlockwise sense are positive, and those measured in a clockwise sense are negative (see Figure 17.1).

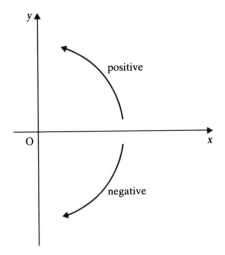

Figure 17.1

Trigonometrical ratios of angles of any magnitude are required in connection with oscillating bodies and rotation about an axis, and in physics they arise in connection with such topics as alternating currents. But as the reader may only have had the six ratios defined for a limited range of angles, we will now give a general definition.

The axes divide the plane into four quadrants, and, as angles are measured in an anticlockwise direction from the x-axis, the quadrants are numbered as in Figure 17.2. For the present, a point $P(x, y)$ and its coordinates will be given a suffix corresponding to the quadrant it lies in.

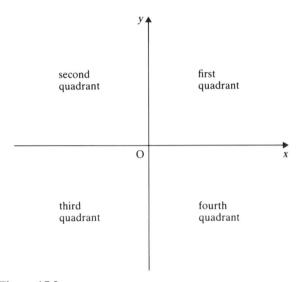

Figure 17.2

For an acute angle θ_1 (see Figure 17.3 overleaf),

$$\sin \theta_1 = \frac{y_1}{r} \qquad \cos \theta_1 = \frac{x_1}{r} \qquad \tan \theta_1 = \frac{y_1}{x_1}$$

In each case, r is the length of the vector $\overrightarrow{OP}$ and, as in the previous chapter, it should always be taken to be positive. Now

$$\frac{\sin \theta_1}{\cos \theta_1} = \frac{y_1/r}{x_1/r} = \frac{y_1}{x_1} = \tan \theta_1$$

so for an angle θ of *any* magnitude we shall define the six trigonometrical ratios as follows:

$$\sin \theta = \frac{y}{r} \qquad \cos \theta = \frac{x}{r} \qquad \tan \theta = \frac{\sin \theta}{\cos \theta}$$

$$\operatorname{cosec} \theta = \frac{1}{\sin \theta} \qquad \sec \theta = \frac{1}{\cos \theta} \qquad \cot \theta = \frac{1}{\tan \theta} = \frac{\cos \theta}{\sin \theta}$$

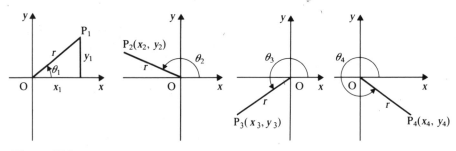

Figure 17.3

For an angle θ_2 in the second quadrant (see Figure 17.3), y_2 is positive (abbreviated +ve) but x_2 is negative (abbreviated −ve), therefore

$\sin \theta_2$ is +ve, $\cos \theta_2$ is −ve, $\tan \theta_2$ is −ve

In the third quadrant, x_3 and y_3 are both negative, hence

$\sin \theta_3$ is −ve, $\cos \theta_3$ is −ve, $\tan \theta_3$ is +ve

For an angle θ_4 in the fourth quadrant, x_4 is positive, and y_4 is negative, hence

$\sin \theta_4$ is −ve, $\cos \theta_4$ is +ve, $\tan \theta_4$ is −ve

These results can be summarised by writing which ratios are positive in each quadrant:

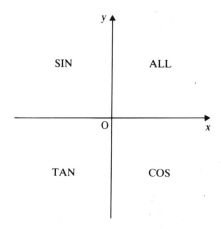

Figure 17.4

The signs of the ratios can be worked out as above quite easily, but for those who like them, there are mnemonics for the first letters in the four quadrants of Figure 17.4. One such is **All Silly Tom Cats**. The signs of cosec θ, sec θ, cot θ are, of course, the same as their reciprocals.

A useful point to note is that the angles for which OP is equally inclined to the positive or negative x-axis have trigonometrical ratios of the same magnitude, their signs being determined as above. Thus the ratios of 150°, 210°,

330° are *numerically* the same as the ratios of 30°, since in each case the acute angle between OP and the x-axis is 30°, as shown in the following list:

sin 150° = +sin 30°
cos 150° = −cos 30°
tan 150° = −tan 30°

sin 210° = −sin 30°
cos 210° = −cos 30°
tan 210° = +tan 30°

sin 330° = −sin 30°
cos 330° = +cos 30°
tan 330° = −tan 30°

Qu. 1 Express in terms of the trigonometrical ratios of acute angles:

(a) sin 170°   (b) tan 300°   (c) cos 200°
(d) sin (−50°)   (e) cos (−20°)   (f) sin 325°
(g) tan (−140°)   (h) cos 164°   (i) cosec 230°
(j) tan 143°   (k) cos (−130°)   (l) sin 250°
(m) tan (−50°)   (n) cot 200°   (o) cos 293°
(p) sin (−230°)   (q) sec 142°   (r) cot 156°
(s) cosec (−53°)   (t) sec (−172°)

17.2 Graphs of sin θ, cos θ, tan θ

It is instructive to draw the graphs of sin θ, cos θ, and tan θ. Figure 17.5 shows how the graph of sin θ may be drawn from the definition. Construct a circle of unit radius, then sin θ = y. Dotted lines show this for θ = 30°, 60°, 90°, and the rest of the figure is drawn similarly.

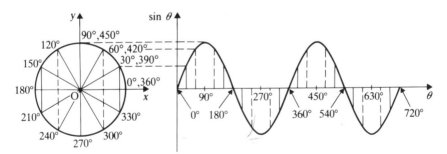

Figure 17.5

It will be seen that the graph of sin θ repeats itself at intervals of 360°. (That this is so should be clear from the way it was drawn, because points on the graph separated by 360° correspond to the same point on the circle.) If a function repeats itself at regular intervals, like sin θ, it is called a **periodic** function, and the interval is called its **period** (see Section 3.15).

The graph of cos θ may be drawn in a similar way to that of sin θ. In this case, since cos θ = x/r, the values of x are used instead of y.

The graph of tan θ may also be drawn from a unit circle, but in this case a tangent is drawn at the point $(1, 0)$ (see Figure 17.6). If P is any point on the circle and OP meets the tangent at Q, then the y-coordinate of Q is equal to tan θ.

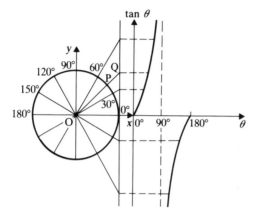

Figure 17.6

Qu. 2 Complete the graph of tan θ up to $\theta = 720°$.
Qu. 3 What are the periods of cos θ and tan θ?

17.3 Trigonometrical ratios of 30°, 45°, 60°

The trigonometrical ratios of 30°, 45°, and 60° are frequently needed, and they may be obtained from two figures. Figure 17.7 represents an equilateral triangle with an altitude constructed. The sides of the triangle are 2 units, and so, by Pythagoras' theorem, the altitude is $\sqrt{3}$ units. The ratios of 30° and 60° may now be read off. Figure 17.8 represents a right-angled isosceles triangle with two sides of unit length. By Pythagoras' theorem, the hypotenuse is $\sqrt{2}$ units, and so the ratios of 45° may be read off.

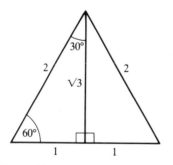

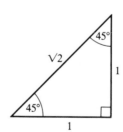

Figure 17.7   Figure 17.8

Qu. 4 Write down the values of:
(a) sin 30°   (b) cos 30°   (c) cos 45°   (d) tan 30°
(e) sec 60°   (f) cosec 60°   (g) tan 45°   (h) cosec 45°

17.4 Trigonometrical equations

Most equations in algebra have a finite number of roots, but in many cases trigonometrical equations have an unlimited number. For instance, the equation $\sin \theta = 0$ is satisfied by $\theta = 0°$, $\pm 180°$, $\pm 360°$, $\pm 540°$ and so on, indefinitely. In this book it will be specified for what range of values the roots are required.

Example 1

Solve the equation $\sin \theta = -\frac{1}{2}$ for values of θ from $0°$ to $360°$ inclusive.

The acute angle whose sine is $\frac{1}{2}$ is $30°$ and Figure 17.9 indicates the angles between $0°$ and $360°$ whose sines are $\pm \frac{1}{2}$. But $\sin \theta$ is negative only in the third and fourth quadrants. Therefore the roots of the equation in the required range are $210°$ and $330°$.

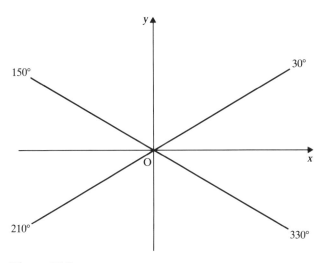

Figure 17.9

Example 2

Solve the equation $\cos 2\theta = 0.6428$, for values of θ between $-180°$ and $+180°$.

[Note that since θ must lie between $-180°$ and $+180°$, 2θ may lie between $-360°$ and $+360°$.]

From a calculator, it can be seen that the acute angle whose cosine is 0.6428 is $50°$ (see 'Note on degree of accuracy of answers' on page xiii), and since $\cos 2\theta$ is positive only in the first and fourth quadrants

$$2\theta = -310°, \quad -50°, \quad 50°, \quad 310°$$
$$\therefore \quad \theta = -155°, \quad -25°, \quad 25°, \quad 155°$$

Example 3

Solve the equation† $2 \sin^2 \theta = \sin \theta$, for values of θ from $0°$ to $360°$ inclusive.

[This equation is a quadratic equation for $\sin \theta$, and may be solved by factorisation.]

$$2 \sin^2 \theta - \sin \theta = 0$$
$$\therefore \quad \sin \theta \, (2 \sin \theta - 1) = 0$$
$$\therefore \quad \sin \theta = 0 \quad \text{or} \quad \sin \theta = \tfrac{1}{2}$$

If $\sin \theta = 0$, $\theta = 0°$, $180°$, $360°$. If $\sin \theta = \tfrac{1}{2}$, $\theta = 30°$, $150°$.

Therefore the roots of the equation, from $0°$ to $360°$ inclusive are $0°$, $30°$, $150°$, $180°$, and $360°$.

(Note that if we had divided both sides of the equation by $\sin \theta$, giving $2 \sin \theta = 1$, we should have lost some of the roots, namely those for which $\sin \theta = 0$.)

Example 4

Solve the equation $\tan \theta = 2 \sin \theta$, for values of θ from $0°$ to $360°$ inclusive.

[Equations are often solved by factorisation, so look for a common factor.] Remembering that $\tan \theta = \sin \theta / \cos \theta$ we may write

$$\frac{\sin \theta}{\cos \theta} = 2 \sin \theta$$

$$\therefore \qquad 2 \sin \theta \cos \theta = \sin \theta$$

$$\therefore \qquad 2 \sin \theta \cos \theta - \sin \theta = 0$$

$$\therefore \qquad \sin \theta \, (2 \cos \theta - 1) = 0$$

$$\therefore \quad \sin \theta = 0 \quad \text{or} \quad \cos \theta = \tfrac{1}{2}$$

If $\sin \theta = 0$, $\theta = 0°$, $180°$, $360°$. If $\cos \theta = \tfrac{1}{2}$, $\theta = 60°$, $300°$.
Therefore the required values of θ are $0°$, $60°$, $180°$, $300°$, and $360°$.

Exercise 17a

1 Write down the values of the following, leaving surds in your answers (calculators should not be used in this question):

(a) $\cos 270°$ (b) $\sin 540°$ (c) $\cos (-180°)$
(d) $\tan 135°$ (e) $\sin 150°$ (f) $\cos 210°$
(g) $\tan 120°$ (h) $\cos (-30°)$ (i) $\sin (-120°)$

---

† In order to avoid brackets $(\sin \theta)^2$ is written $\sin^2 \theta$.

(j) $\sin 405°$ (k) $\cos(-135°)$ (l) $\sin 225°$
(m) $\tan(-60°)$ (n) $\sin(-270°)$ (o) $\tan 210°$

2 Sketch the graph of $\sin\theta$, for values of θ from $-360°$ to $360°$.

3 Sketch the graph of $\cos\theta$, for values of θ from $0°$ to $720°$, and state its period.

4 Draw the graph of $\tan\theta$, for values of θ from $0°$ to $720°$. (This has been started in Figure 17.6.) What is the period of $\tan\theta$?

5 Sketch the graphs of:
  (a) $\cos 2\theta$ (b) $\sin\frac{1}{2}\theta$ (c) $\sin\frac{3}{2}\theta$ (d) $\cos(\theta+60°)$ (e) $\sin(\theta-45°)$
  for values of θ from $0°$ to $360°$, stating the period of each.

6 Find the values of θ from $180°$ to $360°$, inclusive, which satisfy the following equations:
  (a) $\cos\theta = -\frac{1}{2}$ (b) $\tan\theta = 1$
  (c) $\operatorname{cosec}\theta = 2$ (d) $\sin\theta = -0.7660$
  (e) $\cos\theta = 0.6$ (f) $\tan\theta = -\sqrt{3}$
  (g) $\cos(\theta+60°) = 0.5$ (h) $\sin(\theta-30°) = -\sqrt{3}/2$

7 Solve the following equations for values of θ from $0°$ to $360°$, inclusive:
  (a) $\sin^2\theta = \frac{1}{4}$ (b) $\tan^2\theta = \frac{1}{3}$
  (c) $\sin 2\theta = \frac{1}{2}$ (d) $\tan 2\theta = -1$
  (e) $\cos 3\theta = \sqrt{3}/2$ (f) $\sin 3\theta = -1$
  (g) $\sin^2 2\theta = 1$ (h) $\sec 2\theta = 3$
  (i) $\tan^2 3\theta = 1$ (j) $4\cos 2\theta = 1$
  (k) $\sin(2\theta+30°) = 0.8$ (l) $\tan(3\theta-45°) = \frac{1}{2}$

8 Solve the following equations for values of θ from $-180°$ to $+180°$, inclusive:
  (a) $\tan^2\theta + \tan\theta = 0$ (b) $2\cos^2\theta = \cos\theta$
  (c) $3\sin^2\theta + \sin\theta = 0$ (d) $2\sin^2\theta - \sin\theta - 1 = 0$
  (e) $2\cos^2\theta + 3\cos\theta + 1 = 0$ (f) $4\cos^3\theta = \cos\theta$
  (g) $\tan\theta = \sin\theta$ (h) $\sec\theta = 2\cos\theta$
  (i) $\cot\theta = 5\cos\theta$ (j) $4\sin^2\theta = 3\cos^2\theta$
  (k) $3\cos\theta = 2\cot\theta$ (l) $\tan\theta = 4\cot\theta + 3$
  (m) $5\sin\theta + 6\operatorname{cosec}\theta = 17$ (n) $3\cos\theta + 2\sec\theta + 7 = 0$

9 Write down the maximum and minimum values of the following expressions, giving the smallest positive or zero value of θ for which they occur:
  (a) $\sin\theta$ (b) $3\cos\theta$ (c) $2\cos\frac{1}{2}\theta$
  (d) $-\frac{1}{2}\sin 2\theta$ (e) $1 - 2\sin\theta$ (f) $3 + 2\cos 3\theta$
  (g) $\dfrac{1}{2+\sin\theta}$ (h) $\dfrac{1}{4-3\cos\theta}$

10 State, with reasons, which of the following equations have no roots:
  (a) $2\sin\theta = 3$ (b) $\sin\theta + \cos\theta = 0$
  (c) $\sin\theta + \cos\theta = 2$ (d) $3\sin\theta + \operatorname{cosec}\theta = 0$
  (e) $4\operatorname{cosec}^2\theta - 1 = 0$ (f) $\operatorname{cosec}\theta = \sin\theta$
  (g) $\sec\theta = \sin\theta$

11 Sketch on the same axes, for values of θ from $-360°$ to $360°$, the graphs of:
  (a) $\sin\theta$, $\operatorname{cosec}\theta$ (b) $\cos\theta$, $\sec\theta$
  (c) $\tan\theta$, $\cot\theta$

12 Sketch the graphs of the following functions and state the period in each case:

   (a) $y = \sin 2x$ (b) $y = \cos (x/3)$ (c) $y = \tan 3x$

   (d) $y = \tan (x/2)$ (e) $y = \sin (2x/3)$

17.5 Trigonometrical ratios of $-\theta$, $180° \pm \theta$, $90° \pm \theta$

The reader who has drawn the graphs of $y = \sin \theta$ and $y = \cos \theta$ may have noticed that they are the same, except for the positions of the y-axes relative to the curves.

Figure 17.10 suggests that, for any angle α,

   $\cos \alpha = \sin (90° + \alpha)$

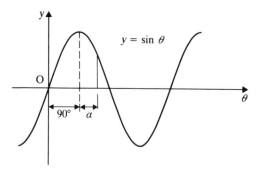

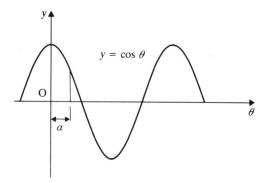

Figure 17.10

and other relationships of this sort may be found from the graphs. Some people find the graphs help them to remember such relationships, but now it will be shown how they may be obtained from first principles.

For any value of θ, in the notation of Section 17.1, we have by definition

   $\sin \theta = \dfrac{y}{r}$ $\cos \theta = \dfrac{x}{r}$

Consider the following ratios.

(a) Ratios of $-\theta$

In Figure 17.3, the angle $-\theta$ is obtained by replacing (x, y) by $(x, -y)$,

$$\therefore \quad \sin(-\theta) = -\frac{y}{r} = -\sin\theta$$

$$\cos(-\theta) = \frac{x}{r} = \cos\theta$$

i.e. $\sin\theta$ is an odd function and $\cos\theta$ is even function (see Section 3.14).

(b) Ratios of $(180° - \theta)$

Replace (x, y) by $(-x, y)$, hence:

$$\sin(180° - \theta) = \frac{y}{r} = \sin\theta$$

$$\cos(180° - \theta) = -\frac{x}{r} = -\cos\theta$$

(c) Ratios of $(180° + \theta)$

Replace (x, y) by $(-x, -y)$, hence:

$$\sin(180° + \theta) = -\frac{y}{r} = -\sin\theta$$

$$\cos(180° + \theta) = -\frac{x}{r} = -\cos\theta$$

[Note that in all these cases above, OP is inclined at an angle θ to the positive or negative x-axis, the ratios of these angles have the same magnitude as those of θ, and their signs are determined as on page 356 if θ is acute.]

(d) Ratios of $(90° - \theta)$

Replace (x, y) by (y, x), hence:

$$\sin(90° - \theta) = \frac{x}{r} = \cos\theta$$

$$\cos(90° - \theta) = \frac{y}{r} = \sin\theta$$

(e) Ratios of $(90° + \theta)$

Replace (x, y) by $(-y, x)$, hence:

$$\sin(90° + \theta) = \frac{x}{r} = \cos\theta$$

$$\cos(90° + \theta) = -\frac{y}{r} = -\sin\theta$$

Qu. 5 Express the following in terms of the trigonometrical ratios of θ:
(a) $\tan(90° - \theta)$ (b) $\operatorname{cosec}(180° - \theta)$ (c) $\sec(90° + \theta)$
(d) $\cot(90° + \theta)$ (e) $\sec(-\theta)$ (f) $\operatorname{cosec}(180° + \theta)$
(g) $\cos(270° - \theta)$ (h) $\sin(360° + \theta)$ (i) $\tan(-\theta)$
(j) $\sin(\theta - 90°)$ (k) $\cos(\theta - 180°)$ (l) $\sec(270° + \theta)$

17.6 Pythagoras' theorem

The reader will be familiar with Pythagoras' theorem, and will have found that it is a very useful one. In trigonometry, it retains its importance and provides relations between trigonometrical ratios.

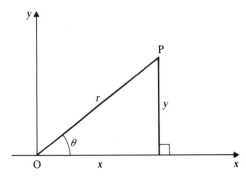

Figure 17.11

In Figure 17.11, the triangle is right-angled and so, by Pythagoras' thoerem,

$$x^2 + y^2 = r^2$$

But $\cos\theta = x/r$ and $\sin\theta = y/r$, so we divide by r^2 obtaining

$$\frac{x^2}{r^2} + \frac{y^2}{r^2} = 1$$

$$\boxed{\therefore \quad \cos^2\theta + \sin^2\theta \equiv 1}$$

[If P is not in the first quadrant, OP^2 is still $x^2 + y^2$ by the distance formula of Section 2.8 and the proof continues as before.]

The $\equiv$ symbol is used to stress that the relationship is an identity, i.e. it holds for *all* values of θ.

Two similar identities can be deduced from this. Dividing through by $\cos^2\theta$,

$$1 + \frac{\sin^2\theta}{\cos^2\theta} \equiv \frac{1}{\cos^2\theta}$$

but $\tan\theta = \sin\theta/\cos\theta$ and $\sec\theta = 1/\cos\theta$, therefore

$$\boxed{1 + \tan^2\theta \equiv \sec^2\theta}$$

Dividing the original identity by $\sin^2 \theta$,

$$\frac{\cos^2 \theta}{\sin^2 \theta} + 1 \equiv \frac{1}{\sin^2 \theta}$$

but $\cos \theta / \sin \theta = \cot \theta$ and $1/\sin \theta = \operatorname{cosec} \theta$, therefore

$$\boxed{\cot^2 \theta + 1 \equiv \operatorname{cosec}^2 \theta}$$

Historical note The equivalent of the identity

$$\cos^2 \theta + \sin^2 \theta \equiv 1$$

is found in the *Syntaxis* written during the first century AD by Claudius Ptolemy. Instead of sines and cosines, he used chords. (If a chord subtends an angle 2θ at the centre of a circle, the ratio of the chord to the diameter of the circle is $\sin \theta$.)

Example 5

Solve the equation $1 + \cos \theta = 2 \sin^2 \theta$, for values of θ between $0°$ and $360°$.

[The square on the right-hand side indicates that the equation is a quadratic, and to solve it, we must write it in terms of either $\cos \theta$ or $\sin \theta$.] We know that

$$\cos^2 \theta + \sin^2 \theta = 1$$
hence $\qquad \sin^2 \theta = 1 - \cos^2 \theta$

so substituting $2 - 2 \cos^2 \theta$ for $2 \sin^2 \theta$, we obtain

$$1 + \cos \theta = 2 - 2 \cos^2 \theta$$

This quadratic for $\cos \theta$ is solved by factorisation:

$$2 \cos^2 \theta + \cos \theta - 1 = 0$$
$$\therefore \quad (2 \cos \theta - 1)(\cos \theta + 1) = 0$$
$$\therefore \qquad\qquad\qquad \cos \theta = \tfrac{1}{2} \quad \text{or} \quad -1$$

If $\cos \theta = \tfrac{1}{2}$, $\theta = 60°, 300°$. If $\cos \theta = -1$, $\theta = 180°$.

Therefore the roots of the equation between $0°$ and $360°$ are $60°$, $180°$, and $300°$.

Example 6

Simplify $1/\sqrt{(x^2 - a^2)}$ when $x = a \operatorname{cosec} \theta$.

Substituting $x = a \operatorname{cosec} \theta$, we obtain

$$\frac{1}{\sqrt{(a^2 \operatorname{cosec}^2 \theta - a^2)}}$$

But the $\operatorname{cosec}^2 \theta$ in the denominator suggests the use of the identity

$$\cot^2 \theta + 1 = \operatorname{cosec}^2 \theta$$

With this the expression $(a^2 \operatorname{cosec}^2 \theta - a^2)$ may be simplified, giving

$$a^2 \operatorname{cosec}^2 \theta - a^2 = a^2(\cot^2 \theta + 1) - a^2 = a^2 \cot^2 \theta$$

Thus the original expression becomes

$$\frac{1}{\sqrt{(a^2 \cot^2 \theta)}} = \frac{1}{a \cot \theta} = \frac{1}{a} \tan \theta$$

Example 7

Eliminate θ from the equations $x = a \sin \theta$, $y = b \tan \theta$.

[Since $\sin \theta$ and $\tan \theta$ are the reciprocals of $\operatorname{cosec} \theta$ and $\cot \theta$ we use the identity $\operatorname{cosec}^2 \theta = \cot^2 \theta + 1$.]

$$\operatorname{cosec} \theta = \frac{a}{x} \quad \text{and} \quad \cot \theta = \frac{b}{y}$$

Substituting into the identity $\operatorname{cosec}^2 \theta = \cot^2 \theta + 1$,

$$\frac{a^2}{x^2} = \frac{b^2}{y^2} + 1$$

Exercise 17b

1 If $s = \sin \theta$, simplify:

(a) $\sqrt{(1 - s^2)}$ (b) $\dfrac{s}{\sqrt{(1 - s^2)}}$ (c) $\dfrac{1 - s^2}{s}$

2 If $c = \cos \theta$, simplify:

(a) $\sqrt{(1 - c^2)}$ (b) $\dfrac{\sqrt{(1 - c^2)}}{c}$ (c) $\dfrac{c}{1 - c^2}$

3 If $t = \tan \theta$, simplify:

(a) $\sqrt{(1 + t^2)}$ (b) $t(1 + t^2)$ (c) $\dfrac{t}{\sqrt{(1 + t^2)}}$

4 If $c = \operatorname{cosec} \theta$, simplify:

(a) $\sqrt{(c^2 - 1)}$ (b) $\dfrac{\sqrt{(c^2 - 1)}}{c}$ (c) $\dfrac{c}{c^2 - 1}$

5 If $x = a \sin \theta$, simplify:

(a) $a^2 - x^2$ (b) $\dfrac{1}{\sqrt{(a^2 - x^2)}}$ (c) $\dfrac{a^2 - x^2}{x}$

6 If $y = b \cot \theta$, simplify:

(a) $b^2 + y^2$ (b) $y\sqrt{(b^2 + y^2)}$ (c) $\dfrac{y}{b^2 + y^2}$

7 If $z = a \sec \theta$, simplify:

(a) $z^2 - a^2$ (b) $\dfrac{1}{\sqrt{(z^2 - a^2)}}$ (c) $\dfrac{\sqrt{(z^2 - a^2)}}{z}$

In nos. 8–13, solve the equations, giving the values of θ from $0°$ to $360°$ inclusive.

8 $3 - 3 \cos \theta = 2 \sin^2 \theta$
9 $\cos^2 \theta + \sin \theta + 1 = 0$
10 $\sec^2 \theta = 3 \tan \theta - 1$
11 $\operatorname{cosec}^2 \theta = 3 + \cot \theta$
12 $3 \tan^2 \theta + 5 = 7 \sec \theta$
13 $2 \cot^2 \theta + 8 = 7 \operatorname{cosec} \theta$

Do not use a calculator in nos. 14–16.

14 If $\sin \theta = \frac{3}{5}$, find the values of:
(a) $\cos \theta$ (b) $\tan \theta$
15 If $\cos \theta = -\frac{8}{17}$, and θ is obtuse, find the values of:
(a) $\sin \theta$ (b) $\cot \theta$
16 If $\tan \theta = \frac{7}{24}$ and θ is reflex, find the values of:
(a) $\sec \theta$ (b) $\sin \theta$

Prove the following identities:

17 $\tan \theta + \cot \theta = 1/(\sin \theta \cos \theta)$
18 $\operatorname{cosec} \theta + \tan \theta \sec \theta = \operatorname{cosec} \theta \sec^2 \theta$
19 $\sec^2 \theta - \operatorname{cosec}^2 \theta = \tan^2 \theta - \cot^2 \theta$
20 $\cos^4 \theta - \sin^4 \theta = \cos^2 \theta - \sin^2 \theta$
21 $(\sec \theta + \tan \theta)(\sec \theta - \tan \theta) = 1$

Eliminate θ from the following equations:

22 $x = a \cos \theta, \; y = b \sin \theta$
23 $x = a \cot \theta, \; y = b \operatorname{cosec} \theta$
24 $x = a \tan \theta, \; y = b \cos \theta$
25 $x = 1 - \sin \theta, \; y = 1 + \cos \theta$

Exercise 17c (Miscellaneous)

1 Express in terms of the ratios of acute angles:
(a) $\cos 205°$ (b) $\tan 153°$ (c) $\sec 309°$
(d) $\sin(-215°)$ (e) $\cot 406°$ (f) $\operatorname{cosec} 684°$
2 Find the values of the following, leaving surds in your answers:
(a) $\sin 270°$ (b) $\cos 150°$ (c) $\cot 210°$
(d) $\cos 315°$ (e) $\operatorname{cosec} 240°$ (f) $\sec 585°$
(g) $\tan(-225°)$ (h) $\sin(-690°)$ (i) $\cos(-300°)$

3 Solve the following equations for values of θ from $0°$ to $360°$ inclusive:
 (a) $2 \sin \theta = 1$ (b) $\tan \theta + 1 = 0$ (c) $\cos \theta = 0.8$
 (d) $\tan 2\theta = 1$ (e) $\sec 2\theta = 4$ (f) $\sin \frac{1}{2}\theta = \frac{1}{2}$
 (g) $3 \cos (\theta - 10°) = 1$ (h) $\sin (\theta + 30°) = 0.7$ (i) $\cot \frac{1}{2}\theta = 0.9$

4 Solve the following equations for values of θ from $-180°$ to $+180°$ inclusive:
 (a) $2 \sin^2 \theta + \sin \theta = 0$ (b) $3 \cos^2 \theta = 2 \sin \theta \cos \theta$
 (c) $2 \sin^2 \theta + 1 = 3 \sin \theta$ (d) $3 \cos^2 \theta = 7 \cos \theta + 6$
 (e) $4 \sin \theta + \operatorname{cosec} \theta = 4$ (f) $10 \cos \theta + 1 = 2 \sec \theta$
 (g) $\tan \theta + 2 \cot \theta = 3$ (h) $10 \sin \theta \cos \theta - 5 \sin \theta + 4 \cos \theta = 2$

5 Find the maximum and minimum values of the following functions of θ.
 Give the smallest non-negative values of θ for which they occur.

 (a) $3 + 2 \sin \theta$ (b) $1 - 3 \cos \theta$ (c) $4 \sin \frac{3}{2}\theta$

 (d) $3 \sin^2 \frac{1}{2}\theta$ (e) $\dfrac{1}{7 + 3 \cos \theta}$ (f) $\dfrac{1}{3 - 2 \sin 2\theta}$

6 Express in terms of the trigonometrical ratios of θ:
 (a) $\cot (90° - \theta)$ (b) $\sin (90° + \theta)$ (c) $\cos (270° + \theta)$
 (d) $\tan (90° + \theta)$ (e) $\operatorname{cosec} (360° - \theta)$ (f) $\sec (180° - \theta)$
 (g) $\sin (\theta - 180°)$ (h) $\tan (-\theta)$ (i) $\cos (450° - \theta)$

7 If $s = \sin \theta$ and $c = \cos \theta$, simplify:

 (a) $\dfrac{1 - s^2}{1 - c^2}$ (b) $\dfrac{sc}{\sqrt{(1 - s^2)}}$ (c) $\dfrac{s}{c^2 - 1}$

 (d) $\dfrac{c^4 - s^4}{c^2 - s^2}$ (e) $\dfrac{s\sqrt{(1 - s^2)}}{c\sqrt{(1 - c^2)}}$ (f) $\dfrac{c}{s} + \dfrac{s}{c}$

8 Solve the following equations for values of θ from $0°$ to $360°$ inclusive:
 (a) $2 \cos^2 \theta + \sin \theta = 1$
 (b) $5 \cos \theta = 2(1 + 2 \sin^2 \theta)$
 (c) $2 \tan^2 \theta + \sec \theta = 1$
 (d) $4 \cot^2 \theta + 39 = 24 \operatorname{cosec} \theta$
 (e) $5 \sec \theta - 2 \sec^2 \theta = \tan^2 \theta - 1$
 (f) $\sec \theta + 3 = \cos \theta + \tan \theta (2 + \sin \theta)$
 (g) $3 \sin^2 \theta - \sin \theta \cos \theta - 4 \cos^2 \theta = 0$

9 Find, without using a calculator, the values of:
 (a) $\sin \theta, \tan \theta$, if $\cos \theta = \frac{4}{5}$ and θ is acute
 (b) $\sec \theta, \sin \theta$, if $\tan \theta = -\frac{5}{12}$ and θ is obtuse
 (c) $\cos \theta, \cot \theta$, if $\sin \theta = \frac{15}{17}$ and θ is acute
 (d) $\sin \theta, \sec \theta$, if $\cot \theta = \frac{20}{21}$ and θ is reflex

Prove the following identities:

10 $\sec \theta + \operatorname{cosec} \theta \cot \theta = \sec \theta \operatorname{cosec}^2 \theta$
11 $\sin^2 \theta (1 + \sec^2 \theta) = \sec^2 \theta - \cos^2 \theta$

12 $\dfrac{1 - \cos \theta}{\sin \theta} = \dfrac{1}{\operatorname{cosec} \theta + \cot \theta}$

13 $\dfrac{\tan\theta + \cot\theta}{\sec\theta + \operatorname{cosec}\theta} = \dfrac{1}{\sin\theta + \cos\theta}$

Eliminate θ from the following pairs of equations:

14 $x = a\sec\theta,\ y = b\tan\theta$

15 $x = 1 - \cos\theta,\ y = 1 + \sin\theta$

16 $x = a\cot\theta,\ y = b\sin\theta$

17 $x = a\sec\theta,\ y = b\cot\theta$

18 Plot the graph of $y = \sin x + \cos x$ for values of x from $-180°$ to $180°$ at intervals of $30°$. Find from your graph the maximum and minimum values of $\sin x + \cos x$, and the values of x for which they occur.

19 Plot the graph of $y = \sin x + 2\cos x$ for values of x from $-180°$ to $180°$ at intervals of $30°$. Find from your graph the roots of the equation $\sin x + 2\cos x = 1$ which lie between $-180°$ and $+180°$.

20 State whether the following functions are odd, even or neither, and state the range of each function. Sketch the graph of each function.

   (a) $y = 1 + \sin x$ (b) $y = 2 + 3\cos x$

   (c) $y = 5\sin x + 10$ (d) $y = 1 - \cos x$

Chapter 18

Trigonometrical identities

18.1 The formulae for sin $(A \pm B)$, cos $(A \pm B)$

Place a rectangular piece of cardboard PQRS in a vertical plane with two edges horizontal, and then turn it through an angle B (see Figure 18.1). Take the diagonal PR as the unit of length and let angle RPQ be A.

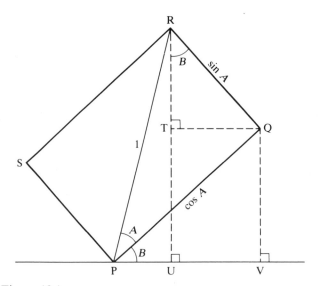

Figure 18.1

What is the height of R above P?
One way to find this out is to drop a perpendicular RU from R to the horizontal through P, then from the triangle RPU, RU = sin $(A + B)$.

Alternatively, since RQ = sin A, PQ = cos A and angle QRU = B, the height of R above P can be found in two parts. First, the height of R above Q, RT = sin A cos B (from triangle RTQ). Secondly, the height of Q above P, QV = cos A sin B (from triangle PQV). Thus, equating the height of R

370

above P obtained in the two ways,

$$\sin (A + B) = \sin A \cos B + \cos A \sin B$$

How far to the right of P is R?
In triangle RPU, PU = cos (A + B).

Alternatively, the distance of Q to the right of P, PV = cos A cos B (from triangle PQV), and the distance of R to the left of Q, QT = sin A sin B (from triangle RTQ). So, equating the distance of R to the right of P obtained in these two ways.

$$\cos (A + B) = \cos A \cos B - \sin A \sin B$$

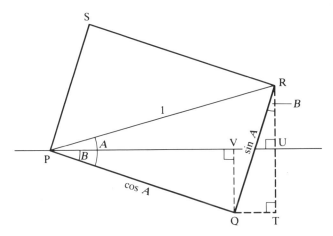

Figure 18.2

Consider now what happens if PQ is tilted through an angle B below the horizontal, as in Figure 18.2. The height of R above P is now sin (A − B). R is a distance sin A cos B above Q, but Q is a distance cos A sin B below P, therefore

$$\sin (A - B) = \sin A \cos B - \cos A \sin B$$

Further, R is a distance cos (A − B) to the right of P. Q is a distance cos A cos B to the right of P, but R is now a distance sin A sin B to the right of Q, therefore

$$\cos (A - B) = \cos A \cos B + \sin A \sin B$$

The four identities just obtained have many applications apart from their use in trigonometry. They, or identities which will be derived from them, are needed in calculus, coordinate geometry and mechanics. Some applications are found in Chapters 20 and 22.

Other proofs of these identities can be found in Section 12.8 and Section 18.6.

Historical note The equivalents of the identities for cos (A + B) and sin (A − B) were known to Ptolemy of Alexandria, almost 2000 years ago.

18.2 The formulae for tan $(A \pm B)$

Two more identities will be deduced from the four just obtained. They give $\tan(A + B)$ and $\tan(A - B)$ in terms of $\tan A$ and $\tan B$.

$$\tan(A + B) = \frac{\sin(A + B)}{\cos(A + B)}$$

Therefore, using the formulae for $\sin(A + B)$ and $\cos(A + B)$,

$$\tan(A + B) = \frac{\sin A \cos B + \cos A \sin B}{\cos A \cos B - \sin A \sin B}$$

Dividing numerator and denominator of the right-hand side by $\cos A \cos B$,

$$\tan(A + B) = \frac{\dfrac{\sin A \cos B}{\cos A \cos B} + \dfrac{\cos A \sin B}{\cos A \cos B}}{\dfrac{\cos A \cos B}{\cos A \cos B} - \dfrac{\sin A \sin B}{\cos A \cos B}}$$

$$= \frac{\dfrac{\sin A}{\cos A} + \dfrac{\sin B}{\cos B}}{1 - \dfrac{\sin A}{\cos A} \times \dfrac{\sin B}{\cos B}}$$

$$\therefore \quad \tan(A + B) = \frac{\tan A + \tan B}{1 - \tan A \tan B}$$

Similarly,

$$\tan(A - B) = \frac{\tan A - \tan B}{1 + \tan A \tan B}$$

For convenience, the six identities are printed together:

$$\cos(A + B) = \cos A \cos B - \sin A \sin B$$
$$\cos(A - B) = \cos A \cos B + \sin A \sin B$$
$$\sin(A + B) = \sin A \cos B + \cos A \sin B$$
$$\sin(A - B) = \sin A \cos B - \cos A \sin B$$

$$\tan(A + B) = \frac{\tan A + \tan B}{1 - \tan A \tan B}$$

$$\tan(A - B) = \frac{\tan A - \tan B}{1 + \tan A \tan B}$$

These are usually called the **addition formulae**; when memorising these, note the following:
(a) The formulae for the ratios of $(A - B)$ are the same as those for $(A + B)$, except for the changes in signs.
(b) The signs on the two sides of each of the sine formulae are the same, but in the cosine formulae they are different.

(c) In the tangent formulae, the signs in the numerators are the same as in the corresponding sine formulae, and those in the denominators are the same as in the cosine formulae.

Example 1

Find, without using calculators, the value of

$$\sin (120° + 45°)$$

leaving surds in the answer.

Using the formula for $\sin (A + B)$,

$$\sin (120° + 45°) = \sin 120° \cos 45° + \cos 120° \sin 45°$$

Reference to Figures 17.7 and 17.8 on page 358 should remind the reader how to obtain the ratios of 30°, 45°, and 60°. Thus we have

$$\sin 120° = \sin 60° = \frac{\sqrt{3}}{2}$$

$$\cos 120° = -\cos 60° = -\tfrac{1}{2}$$

$$\cos 45° = \sin 45° = \frac{1}{\sqrt{2}} = \frac{\sqrt{2}}{2}$$

$$\therefore \quad \sin (120° + 45°) = \frac{\sqrt{3}}{2} \times \frac{\sqrt{2}}{2} + \left(-\frac{1}{2}\right) \times \frac{\sqrt{2}}{2}$$

$$\therefore \quad \sin (120° + 45°) = \frac{\sqrt{2}}{4}(\sqrt{3} - 1)$$

Example 2

If $\sin A = \tfrac{3}{5}$ and $\cos B = \tfrac{15}{17}$, where A is obtuse and B is acute, find the exact value of $\sin (A + B)$.

$$\sin (A + B) = \sin A \cos B + \cos A \sin B$$

So it is necessary to find the values of $\cos A$ and $\sin B$, and Figures 18.3 and 18.4 (page 374) indicate the method. In Figure 18.3, the third side of the right-angled triangle is 4 (by Pythagoras' theorem), hence the x-coordinate of P is -4, therefore $\cos A = -\tfrac{4}{5}$. Similarly, in Figure 18.4, the y-coordinate of P is 8, and therefore $\sin B = \tfrac{8}{17}$.

$$\therefore \quad \sin (A + B) = \frac{3}{5} \times \frac{15}{17} + \left(-\frac{4}{5}\right) \times \frac{8}{17}$$

$$= \frac{45}{85} - \frac{32}{85}$$

$$\therefore \quad \sin (A + B) = \frac{13}{85}$$

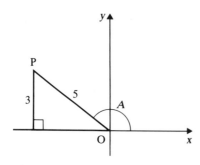

Figure 18.3

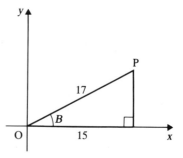

Figure 18.4

Example 3

If $\sin(x + \alpha) = \cos(x - \beta)$, find $\tan x$ in terms of α and β.

Since $\sin(x + \alpha) = \cos(x - \beta)$, we have

$$\sin x \cos \alpha + \cos x \sin \alpha = \cos x \cos \beta + \sin x \sin \beta$$

[Now $\tan x = \sin x / \cos x$, so collect terms in $\sin x$ on one side of the equation and terms in $\cos x$ on the other.]

Thus

$$\sin x \cos \alpha - \sin x \sin \beta = \cos x \cos \beta - \cos x \sin \alpha$$
$$\therefore \qquad \sin x (\cos \alpha - \sin \beta) = \cos x (\cos \beta - \sin \alpha)$$

$$\therefore \qquad \frac{\sin x}{\cos x} = \frac{\cos \beta - \sin \alpha}{\cos \alpha - \sin \beta}$$

$$\therefore \qquad \tan x = \frac{\cos \beta - \sin \alpha}{\cos \alpha - \sin \beta}$$

Exercise 18a

The questions in this exercise are intended to give the reader practice in using the trigonometrical identities introduced in the preceding section. Do not use a calculator in this exercise; to every question it is possible to give an exact answer. Leave surds in the answers where appropriate.

1 Find the values of the following:
(a) $\cos(45° - 30°)$ (b) $\sin(30° + 45°)$ (c) $\sin(60° + 45°)$
(d) $\cos 105°$ (e) $\cos(120° + 45°)$ (f) $\sin 165°$
(g) $\sin 15°$ (h) $\cos 75°$

2 If $\sin A = \frac{3}{5}$ and $\sin B = \frac{5}{13}$, where A and B are acute angles, find the values of:
(a) $\sin(A + B)$ (b) $\cos(A + B)$ (c) $\cot(A + B)$

3 If $\sin A = \frac{4}{5}$ and $\cos B = \frac{12}{13}$, where A is *obtuse* and B is acute, find the values of:
(a) $\sin(A - B)$ (b) $\tan(A - B)$ (c) $\tan(A + B)$

4 If $\cos A = \frac{3}{5}$ and $\tan B = \frac{12}{5}$, where A and B are both reflex angles, find the values of:
   (a) $\sin(A - B)$ (b) $\tan(A - B)$ (c) $\cos(A + B)$

5 If $\tan(x + 45°) = 2$, find the value of $\tan x$.

6 If $\tan(A + B) = \frac{1}{7}$ and $\tan A = 3$, find the value of $\tan B$.

7 If A and B are acute, $\tan A = \frac{1}{2}$ and $\tan B = \frac{1}{3}$, find the value of $A + B$.

8 If $\tan A = -\frac{1}{7}$ and $\tan B = \frac{3}{4}$, where A is obtuse and B is acute, find the value of $A - B$.

9 Express as single trigonometrical ratios:

  (a) $\dfrac{1}{2}\cos x - \dfrac{\sqrt{3}}{2}\sin x$

  (b) $\dfrac{1}{\sqrt{2}}\sin x + \dfrac{1}{\sqrt{2}}\cos x$

  (c) $\dfrac{\sqrt{3} + \tan x}{1 - \sqrt{3}\tan x}$

  (d) $\cos 16° \sin 42° - \sin 16° \cos 42°$

  (e) $\dfrac{1}{\cos 24° \cos 15° - \sin 24° \sin 15°}$

  (f) $\dfrac{1}{2}\cos 75° + \dfrac{\sqrt{3}}{2}\sin 75°$

10 Find the values of:
  (a) $\cos 75° \cos 15° + \sin 75° \sin 15°$

  (b) $\sin 50° \cos 20° - \cos 50° \sin 20°$

  (c) $\dfrac{\tan 10° + \tan 20°}{1 - \tan 10° \tan 20°}$

  (d) $\cos 70° \cos 20° - \sin 70° \sin 20°$

  (e) $\dfrac{1}{\sqrt{2}}\cos 15° - \dfrac{1}{\sqrt{2}}\sin 15°$

  (f) $\dfrac{\sqrt{3}}{2}\cos 15° - \dfrac{1}{2}\sin 15°$

  (g) $\dfrac{1 - \tan 15°}{1 + \tan 15°}$

  (h) $\cos 15° + \sin 15°$

11 Find the value of $\tan A$, when $\tan(A - 45°) = \frac{1}{3}$.

12 Find the value of $\cot B$, when $\cot A = \frac{1}{4}$ and $\cot(A - B) = 8$.

13 From the following equations, find the values of $\tan x$:
  (a) $\sin(x + 45°) = 2\cos(x + 45°)$
  (b) $2\sin(x - 45°) = \cos(x + 45°)$
  (c) $\tan(x - A) = \frac{3}{2}$, where $\tan A = 2$
  (d) $\sin(x + 30°) = \cos(x + 30°)$

14 If $\sin(x + \alpha) = 2\cos(x - \alpha)$, prove that:

$$\tan x = \dfrac{2 - \tan \alpha}{1 - 2\tan \alpha}$$

15 If $\sin(x - \alpha) = \cos(x + \alpha)$, prove that $\tan x = 1$.

16 Solve, for values of x between $0°$ and $360°$, the equations:
  (a) $2\sin x = \cos(x + 60°)$
  (b) $\cos(x + 45°) = \cos x$
  (c) $\sin(x - 30°) = \frac{1}{2}\cos x$
  (d) $3\sin(x + 10°) = 4\cos(x - 10°)$

Prove the following identities:

17 $\sin (A + B) + \sin (A - B) = 2 \sin A \cos B$

18 $\cos (A + B) - \cos (A - B) = -2 \sin A \sin B$

19 $\tan A + \tan B = \dfrac{\sin (A + B)}{\cos A \cos B}$

20 $\tan (A + B + C) = \dfrac{\tan A + \tan B + \tan C - \tan A \ \tan B \tan C}{1 - \tan B \tan C - \tan C \tan A - \tan A \tan B}$

Hence prove that if A, B, C are angles of a triangle, then

$$\tan A + \tan B + \tan C = \tan A \tan B \tan C$$

18.3 The double angle formulae

The special cases of the identities on page 372, when $A = B$, are even more useful than the identities themselves. For convenience of reference, they are given together below.

$$
\begin{aligned}
\cos 2A &= \cos^2 A - \sin^2 A \\
&= 2 \cos^2 A - 1 \\
&= 1 - 2 \sin^2 A \\[4pt]
\sin 2A &= 2 \sin A \cos A \\[4pt]
\tan 2A &= \frac{2 \tan A}{1 - \tan^2 A}
\end{aligned}
$$

Further, it is useful to remember that:

$$
\begin{aligned}
\cos^2 A &= \tfrac{1}{2}(1 + \cos 2A) \\
\sin^2 A &= \tfrac{1}{2}(1 - \cos 2A)
\end{aligned}
$$

To prove the identities concerning $\cos 2A$, we put $B = A$ in the identity

$$\cos (A + B) = \cos A \cos B - \sin A \sin B$$

which gives

$$\cos 2A = \cos^2 A - \sin^2 A$$

Now $\cos^2 A + \sin^2 A = 1$, so substituting $\sin^2 A = 1 - \cos^2 A$, we obtain

$$\cos 2A = \cos^2 A - 1 + \cos^2 A$$
$$\therefore \quad \cos 2A = 2 \cos^2 A - 1$$

If we had substituted $\cos^2 A = 1 - \sin^2 A$ in the identity

$$\cos 2A = \cos^2 A - \sin^2 A$$

we should have obtained

$$\cos 2A = 1 - \sin^2 A - \sin^2 A$$
$$\therefore \quad \cos 2A = 1 - 2 \sin^2 A$$

The expressions for $\cos^2 A$ and $\sin^2 A$ are obtained by changing the subjects in the formulae

$$\cos 2A = 2\cos^2 A - 1 \quad \text{and} \quad \cos 2A = 1 - 2\sin^2 A$$

The identities for $\sin 2A$ and $\tan 2A$ are obtained immediately, when the substitution $B = A$ is made in the formulae for $\sin (A + B)$ and $\tan (A + B)$.

Exercise 18b (Oral)

Express more simply:

1 $2 \sin 17° \cos 17°$

2 $\dfrac{2 \tan 30°}{1 - \tan^2 30°}$

3 $2 \cos^2 42° - 1$

4 $2 \sin \frac{1}{2}\theta \cos \frac{1}{2}\theta$

5 $1 - 2 \sin^2 22\frac{1}{2}°$

6 $\dfrac{2 \tan \frac{1}{2}\theta}{1 - \tan^2 \frac{1}{2}\theta}$

7 $\cos^2 15° - \sin^2 15°$

8 $2 \sin 2A \cos 2A$

9 $2 \cos^2 \frac{1}{2}\theta - 1$

10 $1 - 2 \sin^2 3\theta$

11 $\dfrac{\tan 2\theta}{1 - \tan^2 2\theta}$

12 $\sin x \cos x$

13 $\dfrac{1 - \tan^2 20°}{\tan 20°}$

14 $\sec \theta \operatorname{cosec} \theta$

15 $1 - 2 \sin^2 \frac{1}{2}\theta$

Example 4

Solve the equation $3 \cos 2\theta + \sin \theta = 1$, for values of θ from $0°$ to $360°$ inclusive.

[The quadratic equation is liable to occur in various disguises. Here, $\sin \theta$ suggests that the equation may be a quadratic in $\sin \theta$, so we express $\cos 2\theta$ in terms of $\sin \theta$.]

We have $\cos 2\theta = 1 - 2 \sin^2 \theta$, so, substituting in the equation

$$3 \cos 2\theta + \sin \theta = 1$$

it follows that

$$3(1 - 2 \sin^2 \theta) + \sin \theta = 1$$

This is a quadratic equation for $\sin \theta$, and it is solved by factorisation.

$$3 - 6 \sin^2 \theta + \sin \theta = 1$$
$$\therefore \quad 6 \sin^2 \theta - \sin \theta - 2 = 0$$
$$\therefore \quad (3 \sin \theta - 2)(2 \sin \theta + 1) = 0$$
$$\therefore \quad \sin \theta = \tfrac{2}{3} \quad \text{or} \quad \sin \theta = -\tfrac{1}{2}$$

If $\sin \theta = \tfrac{2}{3}$,

$$\theta = 41.8° \quad \text{or} \quad 180° - 41.8° \quad \text{correct to one decimal place.}$$

If $\sin \theta = -\frac{1}{2}$,

$$\theta = 180° + 30° \quad \text{or} \quad 360° - 30°$$

Therefore the values of θ between $0°$ and $360°$ which satisfy the equation are $41.8°$, $138.2°$, $210°$, and $330°$.

Example 5

Prove that $\sin 3A = 3 \sin A - 4 \sin^3 A$.

The left-hand side of the identity may be written as $\sin (A + 2A)$, so by using the formula for $\sin (A + B)$ we have

$$\sin (A + 2A) = \sin A \cos 2A + \cos A \sin 2A$$

But the right-hand side of the identity to be proved is in terms of $\sin A$, and this suggests that $\cos 2A$ should be expressed in terms of $\sin A$. (We have only one formula for $\sin 2A$, so it must be used.) Therefore

$$\sin 3A = \sin A(1 - 2 \sin^2 A) + \cos A(2 \sin A \cos A)$$
$$= \sin A - 2 \sin^3 A + 2 \sin A \cos^2 A$$

Now $\cos^2 A$ must be expressed in terms of $\sin A$ by means of the identity $\cos^2 A = 1 - \sin^2 A$, therefore

$$\sin 3A = \sin A - 2 \sin^3 A + 2 \sin A(1 - \sin^2 A)$$
$$= \sin A - 2 \sin^3 A + 2 \sin A - 2 \sin^3 A$$
$$\therefore \quad \sin 3A = 3 \sin A - 4 \sin^3 A$$

A formula for $\cos 3A$ in terms of $\cos A$ may be obtained from the expansion of $\cos (2A + A)$. The proof is left as an exercise.

$$\cos 3A = 4 \cos^3 A - 3 \cos A$$

Exercise 18c

Nos. 1–6 in this exercise are intended to give the reader practice in using the trigonometrical identities introduced in this chapter. Do not use a calculator in these questions; in each case it is possible to give an exact answer. Leave surds in the answers where appropriate.

1 Evaluate:

(a) $2 \sin 15° \cos 15°$

(b) $\dfrac{2 \tan 22\frac{1}{2}°}{1 - \tan^2 22\frac{1}{2}°}$

(c) $2 \cos^2 75° - 1$

(d) $1 - 2 \sin^2 67\frac{1}{2}°$

(e) $\cos^2 22\frac{1}{2}° - \sin^2 22\frac{1}{2}°$

(f) $\dfrac{1 - \tan^2 15°}{\tan 15°}$

(g) $\dfrac{1 - 2 \cos^2 25°}{1 - 2 \sin^2 65°}$

(h) $\sec 22\frac{1}{2}° \, \mathrm{cosec} \, 22\frac{1}{2}°$

2 Find the values of sin 2θ and cos 2θ when:

(a) $\sin \theta = \frac{3}{5}$ (b) $\cos \theta = \frac{12}{13}$ (c) $\sin \theta = -\sqrt{3}/2$

3 Find the value of tan 2θ when:

(a) $\tan \theta = \frac{4}{3}$ (b) $\tan \theta = \frac{8}{15}$ (c) $\cos \theta = -\frac{5}{13}$

4 Find the values of cos x and sin x when cos $2x$ is:

(a) $\frac{1}{8}$ (b) $\frac{7}{25}$ (c) $-\frac{119}{169}$

5 Find the values of tan $\frac{1}{2}\theta$ when tan θ is:

(a) $\frac{3}{4}$ (b) $\frac{4}{3}$ (c) $-\frac{12}{5}$

6 If $t = \tan 22\frac{1}{2}°$, use the formula for tan 2θ to show that $t^2 + 2t - 1 = 0$. Deduce the value of tan $22\frac{1}{2}°$.

Solve the following equations for values of θ from $0°$ to $360°$ inclusive:

7 $\cos 2\theta + \cos \theta + 1 = 0$ **8** $\sin 2\theta = \sin \theta$

9 $\cos 2\theta = \sin \theta$ **10** $3 \cos 2\theta - \sin \theta + 2 = 0$

11 $\sin 2\theta \cos \theta + \sin^2 \theta = 1$ **12** $\sin \theta = 6 \sin 2\theta$

13 $2 \sin \theta (5 \cos 2\theta + 1) = 3 \sin 2\theta$ **14** $3 \tan \theta = \tan 2\theta$

15 $3 \cot 2\theta + \cot \theta = 1$ **16** $4 \tan \theta \tan 2\theta = 1$

17 Eliminate θ from the equations:

(a) $x = \cos \theta$, $y = \cos 2\theta$ (b) $x = 2 \sin \theta$, $y = 3 \cos 2\theta$

(c) $x = \tan \theta$, $y = \tan 2\theta$ (d) $x = 2 \sec \theta$, $y = \cos 2\theta$

Prove the following identities:

18 $\dfrac{\cos 2A}{\cos A + \sin A} = \cos A - \sin A$ **19** $\dfrac{\sin A}{\sin B} + \dfrac{\cos A}{\cos B} = \dfrac{2 \sin (A + B)}{\sin 2B}$

20 $\dfrac{\cos A}{\sin B} - \dfrac{\sin A}{\cos B} = \dfrac{2 \cos (A + B)}{\sin 2B}$ **21** $\tan A + \cot A = 2 \operatorname{cosec} 2A$

22 $\cot A - \tan A = 2 \cot 2A$

23 $\dfrac{1}{\cos A + \sin A} + \dfrac{1}{\cos A - \sin A} = \tan 2A \operatorname{cosec} A$

24 $\dfrac{\sin 2A}{1 + \cos 2A} = \tan A$ **25** $\cos 3A = 4 \cos^3 A - 3 \cos A$

26 $\operatorname{cosec} 2x - \cot 2x = \tan x$ **27** $\operatorname{cosec} 2x + \cot 2x = \cot x$

28 $\tan x = \sqrt{\dfrac{1 - \cos 2x}{1 + \cos 2x}}$ **29** $\sin 2x = \dfrac{2 \tan x}{1 + \tan^2 x}$

30 $\cos 2x = \dfrac{1 - \tan^2 x}{1 + \tan^2 x}$

18.4 The *t*-formulae

In the preceding section the following formulae for sin $2x$ and cos $2x$ were introduced:

$$\sin 2x = 2 \sin x \cos x$$
$$\cos 2x = \cos^2 x - \sin^2 x$$

It is possible to express both $\sin 2x$ and $\cos 2x$ in terms of $\tan x$ and there are many occasions when this is a very useful technique.

In the case of $\sin 2x$ we start by deliberately introducing a factor $\sin x/\cos x$, which is equal to $\tan x$.

$$\sin 2x = 2 \sin x \cos x$$

$$= 2 \frac{\sin x}{\cos x} \cos^2 x$$

$$= 2 \tan x \cos^2 x$$

$$= 2 \tan x \times \frac{1}{\sec^2 x}$$

This last step may seem rather peculiar; its purpose is to enable us to replace $\sec^2 x$ by $1 + \tan^2 x$ (see Section 17.6). Hence

$$\sin 2x = \frac{2 \tan x}{1 + \tan^2 x}$$

This identity is most frequently used in the form obtained by substituting θ for $2x$, i.e.

$$\sin \theta = \frac{2 \tan \frac{1}{2}\theta}{1 + \tan^2 \frac{1}{2}\theta}$$

$$\therefore \quad \boxed{\sin \theta = \frac{2t}{1 + t^2}} \quad \text{(where } t = \tan \tfrac{1}{2}\theta)$$

This is usually called the **t-formula** for $\sin \theta$. The corresponding t-formulae for $\cos \theta$ and $\tan \theta$ are left as exercises for the reader.

Qu. 1 Prove that, in the usual notation:

$$\boxed{\cos \theta = \frac{1 - t^2}{1 + t^2}}$$

Qu. 2 Prove that:

$$\boxed{\tan \theta = \frac{2t}{1 - t^2}}$$

Qu. 3 Use the t-formulae to solve the following equations, giving values of θ from $0°$ to $360°$ inclusive:
(a) $2 \cos \theta + 3 \sin \theta - 2 = 0$ (b) $7 \cos \theta + \sin \theta - 5 = 0$
(c) $3 \cos \theta - 4 \sin \theta + 1 = 0$ (d) $3 \cos \theta + 4 \sin \theta = 2$

18.5 The form $a \cos \theta + b \sin \theta$

Two applications of the identities of Section 18.2 follow in the next examples.

Example 6

Solve the equation $3 \cos \theta + 4 \sin \theta = 2$, for values of θ from $0°$ to $360°$, inclusive.

The solution is obtained by dividing both sides of the equation by some number, so as to leave it in the form

$$\cos \alpha \cos \theta + \sin \alpha \sin \theta = \text{constant}$$

Comparing this with

$$3 \cos \theta + \quad 4 \sin \theta = 2$$

it follows that

$$\frac{\cos \alpha}{3} = \frac{\sin \alpha}{4}, \quad \text{i.e.} \quad \tan \alpha = \frac{4}{3}$$

Using a calculator we find that $\alpha = 53.13°$, and from Figure 18.5 it follows that $\sin \alpha = \frac{4}{5}$ and $\cos \alpha = \frac{3}{5}$. Therefore we divide the original equation by 5, giving

$$\frac{3}{5} \cos \theta + \frac{4}{5} \sin \theta = \frac{2}{5}$$
$$\therefore \quad \cos \theta \cos \alpha + \sin \theta \sin \alpha = 0.4$$
$$\therefore \quad \cos (\theta - \alpha) = 0.4$$
$$\therefore \quad \theta - 53.13° = 66.42° \quad \text{or} \quad 293.58°$$

Therefore the roots of the equation in the range from $0°$ to $360°$ are $119.6°$ and $346.7°$, correct to the nearest tenth of a degree.†

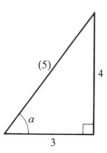

Figure 18.5

Qu. 4 What advantage is there in using the formula for $\cos (A - B)$, rather than that for $\sin (A + B)$ in Example 6?

† The figure in the second decimal place should be included in the intermediate working, in order to avoid errors due to premature approximation.

Example 7

Find the maximum and minimum values of $2 \sin \theta - 5 \cos \theta$, and the corresponding values of θ between $0°$ and $360°$.

This will be solved by writing

$$2 \sin \theta - 5 \cos \theta = k(\cos \alpha \sin \theta - \sin \alpha \cos \theta)$$

where k and α are to be found. Comparing the two forms of the expression,

$$\frac{\sin \alpha}{\cos \alpha} = \frac{5}{2}, \quad \text{i.e. } \tan \alpha = 2.5$$

From a calculator, it is found that $\alpha = 68.20°$; and from Figure 18.6, it follows that $\cos \alpha = 2/\sqrt{29}$, and $\sin \alpha = 5/\sqrt{29}$. So we may write

$$2 \sin \theta - 5 \cos \theta = \sqrt{29}\left(\frac{2}{\sqrt{29}} \sin \theta - \frac{5}{\sqrt{29}} \cos \theta\right)$$

$$= \sqrt{29}(\sin \theta \cos \alpha - \cos \theta \sin \alpha)$$

$$= \sqrt{29} \sin (\theta - \alpha)$$

Now the greatest value of $\sin x$ is 1, and this occurs when $x = 90°$, and the least value of $\sin x$ is -1, when $x = 270°$. (Values of x less than $0°$ or greater than $360°$ have been ignored.)

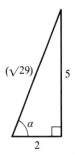

Figure 18.6

Therefore $\sqrt{29} \sin (\theta - \alpha)$ has a maximum value of $\sqrt{29}$ when $\theta - \alpha = 90°$; and it has a minimum value of $-\sqrt{29}$ when $\theta - \alpha = 270°$.

Therefore the maximum and minimum values of

$$2 \sin \theta - 5 \cos \theta$$

are $\sqrt{29}$ and $-\sqrt{29}$, and are given by

$$\theta = 90° + \alpha = 158.2° \quad \text{and} \quad \theta = 270° + \alpha = 338.2° \quad \text{respectively.}$$

Exercise 18d

Solve the following equations for values of θ from $0°$ to $360°$ inclusive:

1 $\sqrt{3}\cos\theta + \sin\theta = 1$ 2 $5\sin\theta - 12\cos\theta = 6$

3 $\sin\theta + \cos\theta = \frac{1}{2}$ 4 $\cos\theta - 7\sin\theta = 2$

5 $2\sin\theta + 7\cos\theta = 4$ 6 $3\tan\theta - 2\sec\theta = 4$

7 $4\cos\theta\sin\theta + 15\cos 2\theta = 10$ 8 $\cos\theta + \sin\theta = \sec\theta$

9 Prove that $\cos\theta - \sin\theta = \sqrt{2}\cos(\theta + 45°) = -\sqrt{2}\sin(\theta - 45°)$

10 Show that $\sqrt{3}\cos\theta - \sin\theta$ may be written as

   $2\cos(\theta + 30°)$ or $2\sin(60° - \theta)$

   Find the maximum and minimum values of the expression, and state the values of θ between $0°$ and $360°$ for which they occur.

11 Show that $3\cos\theta + 2\sin\theta$ may be written in the form $\sqrt{13}\cos(\theta - \alpha)$, where $\tan\alpha = \frac{2}{3}$. Hence find the maximum and minimum values of the function, giving the corresponding values of θ from $-180°$ to $+180°$.

12 Show that $3\cos\theta + 4\sin\theta$ may be expressed in the form $R\cos(\theta - \alpha)$, where α is acute. Find the values of R and α.

13 By expressing $\cos\theta + 2\sin\theta$ in the form $R\sin(\theta + \alpha)$, where α is acute, find the maximum and minimum values of the expression, giving the values of θ between $-180°$ and $180°$ for which they occur.

Find the maximum and minimum values of the following expressions, stating the values of θ, from $0°$ to $360°$ inclusive, for which they occur:

14 $\cos\theta + \sin\theta$ 15 $4\sin\theta - 3\cos\theta$ 16 $\sqrt{3}\sin\theta + \cos\theta$

17 $8\cos\theta - 15\sin\theta$ 18 $\sin\theta - 6\cos\theta$ 19 $\cos(\theta + 60°) - \cos\theta$

20 $3\sqrt{2}\cos(\theta + 45°) + 7\sin\theta$

18.6 Proof of the addition formulae, using vectors

In this section we shall use vectors, and in particular the scalar product of vectors (see Section 16.15), to give a more general proof of the formula

   $\cos(A - B) = \cos A\cos B + \sin A\sin B$

The diagram (Figure 18.7, over the page) shows A and B as acute angles, but the subsequent working is valid for angles of *any* magnitude.

In the diagram, $\overrightarrow{OP}$ and $\overrightarrow{OQ}$ are unit vectors, i.e. they are vectors whose length is one unit. $\overrightarrow{OP}$ is inclined at an angle A to the x-axis, and $\overrightarrow{OQ}$ is inclined at an angle B to the x-axis. Consequently the coordinates of the points P and Q are $(\cos A, \sin A)$ and $(\cos B, \sin B)$ respectively and the vectors $\overrightarrow{OP}$ and $\overrightarrow{OQ}$ can be written

   $\overrightarrow{OP} = \cos A\,\mathbf{i} + \sin A\,\mathbf{j}$ and $\overrightarrow{OQ} = \cos B\,\mathbf{i} + \sin B\,\mathbf{j}$

Taking the scalar product of these vectors, we have

   $\overrightarrow{OP}.\overrightarrow{OQ} = (\cos A\,\mathbf{i} + \sin A\,\mathbf{j}).(\cos B\,\mathbf{i} + \sin B\,\mathbf{j})$
   $= \cos A\cos B + \sin A\sin B$

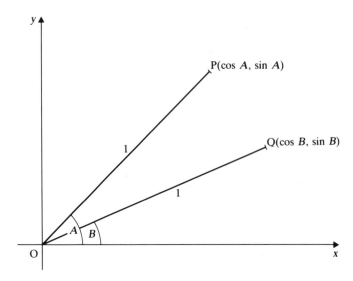

Figure 18.7

But, from the basic definition of the scalar product, we know that

$$\overrightarrow{OP}.\overrightarrow{OQ} = OP \times OQ \cos \angle POQ = 1 \times 1 \times \cos (A - B) = \cos (A - B)$$

Equating these two expressions for $\overrightarrow{OP}.\overrightarrow{OQ}$, we obtain

$$\cos (A - B) = \cos A \cos B + \sin A \sin B \qquad\qquad \ldots \text{ (1)}$$

To obtain the corresponding identity for $\cos (A + B)$, it is only necessary to replace B by $-B$, giving

$$\cos (A - (- B)) = \cos A \cos (- B) + \sin A \sin (- B)$$

and hence

$$\cos (A + B) = \cos A \cos B - \sin A \sin B$$

[Alternatively the proof above could be repeated with the angle B drawn in the fourth quadrant.]

The formulae for $\sin (A + B)$ can be obtained by replacing A in identity (1) by $90° - A$, which gives

$$\cos \{(90° - A) - B\} = \cos (90° - A) \cos B + \sin (90° - A) \sin B$$
$$\therefore \quad \cos \{90° - (A + B)\} = \cos (90° - A) \cos B + \sin (90° - A) \sin B$$

But $\sin (90° - \theta) = \cos \theta$ and $\cos (90° - \theta) = \sin \theta$, so

$$\sin (A + B) = \sin A \cos B + \cos A \sin B$$

The corresponding identity for $\sin (A - B)$ can then be obtained by replacing B by $-B$.

18.7 Introduction to the factor formulae

Factors are very useful, in algebra, for solving equations and simplifying expressions, and when dealing with trigonometrical ratios, it is often convenient to be able to factorise a sum of two terms. On the other hand, it is sometimes useful to express a product as a sum or difference of two terms, and it is to this that we turn first.

In Section 18.1 it was shown that

$$\cos (A + B) = \cos A \cos B - \sin A \sin B$$
$$\cos (A - B) = \cos A \cos B + \sin A \sin B$$

Adding,

$$\cos (A + B) + \cos (A - B) = 2 \cos A \cos B$$

and subtracting,

$$\cos (A + B) - \cos (A - B) = -2 \sin A \sin B$$

Now, keeping the formulae for $\cos (A + B)$ and $\cos (A - B)$ in mind, work through the next exercise.

Exercise 18e (Oral)

Express as a sum or difference of two cosines:

1 $-2 \sin x \sin y$ **2** $2 \cos x \cos y$

3 $2 \cos 3\theta \cos \theta$ **4** $-2 \sin (S + T) \sin (S - T)$

5 $2 \sin 5x \sin 3x$ **6** $2 \cos (x + y) \cos (x - y)$

7 $2 \cos \dfrac{A + B}{2} \cos \dfrac{A - B}{2}$ **8** $-2 \sin \dfrac{B + C}{2} \sin \dfrac{B - C}{2}$

9 $-2 \sin (x + 45°) \sin (x - 45°)$ **10** $2 \cos (2x + 30°) \cos (2x - 30°)$

Following the same method as before, we have

$$\sin (A + B) = \sin A \cos B + \cos A \sin B$$
$$\sin (A - B) = \sin A \cos B - \cos A \sin B$$

Adding,

$$\sin (A + B) + \sin (A - B) = 2 \sin A \cos B$$

and subtracting

$$\sin (A + B) - \sin (A - B) = 2 \cos A \sin B$$

Again, keeping the formulae for $\sin (A + B)$ and $\sin (A - B)$ in mind, work through the next exercise.

Exercise 18f (Oral)

Express as a sum or difference of two sines:

1 $2 \sin x \cos y$ 2 $2 \cos x \sin y$

3 $2 \sin 3\theta \cos \theta$ 4 $2 \sin (S + T) \cos (S - T)$

5 $2 \cos 5x \sin 3x$ 6 $2 \cos (x + y) \sin (x - y)$

7 $-2 \cos 4x \sin 2x$ 8 $2 \sin \dfrac{A + B}{2} \cos \dfrac{A - B}{2}$

9 $2 \cos \dfrac{A + B}{2} \sin \dfrac{A - B}{2}$ 10 $2 \sin \dfrac{R - S}{2} \cos \dfrac{R + S}{2}$

18.8 The factor formulae

We may now proceed to the question of factorising a sum or difference of two cosines or sines. The last section has indicated the method, for it was shown that

$$\cos (A + B) + \cos (A - B) = 2 \cos A \cos B$$
$$\cos (A + B) - \cos (A - B) = -2 \sin A \sin B$$
$$\sin (A + B) + \sin (A - B) = 2 \sin A \cos B$$
$$\sin (A + B) - \sin (A - B) = 2 \cos A \sin B$$

Here, the right-hand sides of the identities are in factors, but it would be more convenient if the left-hand sides were in the form $\cos P + \cos Q$, etc. Therefore let

$$P = A + B \quad \text{and} \quad Q = A - B$$

Adding,

$$P + Q = 2A \quad \therefore \quad A = \frac{P + Q}{2}$$

Subtracting,

$$P - Q = 2B \quad \therefore \quad B = \frac{P - Q}{2}$$

Substituting into the four identities above,

$$\cos P + \cos Q = 2 \cos \frac{P + Q}{2} \cos \frac{P - Q}{2}$$

$$\cos P - \cos Q = -2 \sin \frac{P + Q}{2} \sin \frac{P - Q}{2}$$

$$\sin P + \sin Q = 2 \sin \frac{P + Q}{2} \cos \frac{P - Q}{2}$$

$$\sin P - \sin Q = 2 \cos \frac{P + Q}{2} \sin \frac{P - Q}{2}$$

Remember how these identities were obtained: this will make it easier to remember them.

Example 8

Solve the equation $\sin 3x + \sin x = 0$, for values of x from $-180°$ to $+180°$, inclusive.

$$\sin 3x + \sin x = 0$$

therefore, using the formula for $\sin P + \sin Q$,

$$2 \sin 2x \cos x = 0$$
$$\therefore \quad \sin 2x = 0 \quad \text{or} \quad \cos x = 0$$

Now x may lie in the range from $-180°$ to $180°$, therefore $2x$ lies in the range from $-360°$ to $360°$.

If $\sin 2x = 0$,

$$2x = -360°, \ -180°, \ 0°, \ 180°, \ 360°$$
$$\therefore \quad x = -180°, \ -90°, \ 0°, \ 90°, \ 180°$$

If $\cos x = 0$, $\quad x = -90°, 90°$

Therefore the roots of the equation between $-180°$ and $+180°$, inclusive, are $-180°, \ -90°, 0°, 90°$ and $180°$.

Example 9

Solve the equation $\cos(x + 20°) - \cos(x + 80°) = 0.5$, for $0° \leqslant x \leqslant 360°$.

(The difference of the two cosines suggests using one of the above identities.)

$$\cos(x + 20°) - \cos(x + 80°) = 0.5$$
$$-2 \sin(x + 50°) \sin(-30°) = 0.5$$

But $\sin(-30°) = -\sin 30° = -\frac{1}{2}$.

$$\therefore \quad \sin(x + 50°) = 0.5$$
$$x + 50° = 30°, \ 150°, \ 390°, \ 510°, \ ...$$
$$x = -20°, \ 100°, \ 340°, \ ...$$

Therefore the roots of the equation between $0°$ and $360°$ are $100°$ and $340°$.

Example 10

Prove the identity

$$\cos^2 A - \cos^2 B = \sin(A + B) \sin(B - A)$$

[A neat method is to use $\cos^2 A = \frac{1}{2}(1 + \cos 2A)$, $\cos^2 B = \frac{1}{2}(1 + \cos 2B)$.]

$$\cos^2 A - \cos^2 B = \frac{1}{2}(\cos 2A - \cos 2B)$$
$$= \frac{1}{2}\{-2\sin(A+B)\sin(A-B)\}$$
$$\therefore \quad \cos^2 A - \cos^2 B = \sin(A+B)\sin(B-A)$$

Exercise 18g (Oral)

Express the following in factors:

1 $\cos x + \cos y$ **2** $\sin 3x + \sin 5x$

3 $\sin 2y - \sin 2z$ **4** $\cos 5x + \cos 7x$

5 $\cos 2A - \cos A$ **6** $\sin 4x - \sin 2x$

7 $\cos 3A - \cos 5A$ **8** $\sin 5\theta + \sin 7\theta$

9 $\sin(x + 30°) + \sin(x - 30°)$ **10** $\cos(y + 10°) + \cos(y - 80°)$

11 $\sin 3\theta - \sin 5\theta$ **12** $\cos(x + 30°) - \cos(x - 30°)$

13 $\cos \dfrac{3x}{2} - \cos \dfrac{x}{2}$ **14** $\sin 2(x + 40°) + \sin 2(x - 40°)$

15 $\cos(90° - x) + \cos y$ **16** $\sin A + \cos B$

17 $\sin 3x + \sin 90°$ **18** $1 + \sin 2x$

19 $\cos A - \sin B$ **20** $\frac{1}{2} + \cos 2\theta$

18.9 Further identities and equations

Example 11

Solve the equation $\cos 6x + \cos 4x + \cos 2x = 0$, for values of x from $0°$ to $180°$ inclusive.

[Remember that equations are very often solved by factorisation, so look to see whether any of the three terms is a factor of the sum of the other pair. Note that $\cos 4x$ is a factor of $\cos 6x + \cos 2x$, so group $\cos 6x$ and $\cos 2x$ together.]

$$\cos 4x + \cos 6x + \cos 2x = 0$$
$$\therefore \quad \cos 4x + 2\cos 4x \cos 2x = 0$$
$$\therefore \quad \quad \cos 4x(1 + 2\cos 2x) = 0$$
$$\therefore \quad \cos 4x = 0 \quad \text{or} \quad \cos 2x = -\frac{1}{2}$$

If $\cos 4x = 0$,

$$4x = 90°, 270°, 450°, 630°$$
$$\therefore \quad x = 22\frac{1}{2}°, 67\frac{1}{2}°, 112\frac{1}{2}°, 157\frac{1}{2}°$$

If $\cos 2x = -\frac{1}{2}$,

$$2x = 120°, 240°$$
$$\therefore \quad x = 60°, 120°$$

Therefore the roots of the equation in the range $0°$ to $180°$ are $22\frac{1}{2}°$, $60°, 67\frac{1}{2}°, 112\frac{1}{2}°, 120°, 157\frac{1}{2}°$.

Example 12

If A, B, C are the angles of a triangle, prove that

$$\cos A + \cos B + \cos C - 1 = 4 \sin \frac{A}{2} \sin \frac{B}{2} \sin \frac{C}{2}$$

Split the left-hand side into two pairs of terms. Now,

$$\cos A + \cos B = 2 \cos \frac{A+B}{2} \cos \frac{A-B}{2}$$

But since $A + B = 180° - C$,

$$\frac{A+B}{2} = 90° - \frac{C}{2}$$

$$\therefore \quad \cos \frac{A+B}{2} = \sin \frac{C}{2}$$

Seeing this factor $\sin(C/2)$ on the right-hand side, write

$$\cos C - 1 = -2 \sin^2 \frac{C}{2}$$

Therefore

$$\cos A + \cos B + \cos C - 1 = 2 \sin \frac{C}{2} \cos \frac{A-B}{2} - 2 \sin^2 \frac{C}{2}$$

$$= 2 \sin \frac{C}{2} \left(\cos \frac{A-B}{2} - \sin \frac{C}{2} \right)$$

On the right-hand side of the identity to be proved, $\sin(C/2)$ is multiplied by a function of A and B, so in the last bracket we must express $\sin(C/2)$ in terms of A and B. This has been done above.

$$\therefore \quad \cos A + \cos B + \cos C - 1 = 2 \sin \frac{C}{2} \left(\cos \frac{A-B}{2} - \cos \frac{A+B}{2} \right)$$

$$= -2 \left(\cos \frac{A+B}{2} - \cos \frac{A-B}{2} \right) \sin \frac{C}{2}$$

$$= -2 \left(-2 \sin \frac{A}{2} \sin \frac{B}{2} \right) \sin \frac{C}{2}$$

$$\therefore \quad \cos A + \cos B + \cos C - 1 = 4 \sin \frac{A}{2} \sin \frac{B}{2} \sin \frac{C}{2}$$

Exercise 18h

Prove the following identities:

1 $\dfrac{\cos B + \cos C}{\sin B - \sin C} = \cot \dfrac{B-C}{2}$

2 $\dfrac{\cos B - \cos C}{\sin B + \sin C} = -\tan \dfrac{B-C}{2}$

3 $\dfrac{\sin B + \sin C}{\cos B + \cos C} = \tan \dfrac{B+C}{2}$ **4** $\dfrac{\sin B - \sin C}{\sin B + \sin C} = \cot \dfrac{B+C}{2} \tan \dfrac{B-C}{2}$

5 $\sin x + \sin 2x + \sin 3x = \sin 2x \,(2 \cos x + 1)$
6 $\cos x + \sin 2x - \cos 3x = \sin 2x \,(2 \sin x + 1)$
7 $\cos 3\theta + \cos 5\theta + \cos 7\theta = \cos 5\theta (2 \cos 2\theta + 1)$
8 $\cos \theta + 2 \cos 3\theta + \cos 5\theta = 4 \cos^2 \theta \cos 3\theta$
9 $1 + 2 \cos 2\theta + \cos 4\theta = 4 \cos^2 \theta \cos 2\theta$
10 $\sin \theta - 2 \sin 3\theta + \sin 5\theta = 2 \sin \theta (\cos 4\theta - \cos 2\theta)$
11 $\cos \theta - 2 \cos 3\theta + \cos 5\theta = 2 \sin \theta (\sin 2\theta - \sin 4\theta)$
12 $\sin x - \sin (x + 60°) + \sin (x + 120°) = 0$
13 $\cos x + \cos (x + 120°) + \cos (x + 240°) = 0$

Solve the following equations, for values of x from $0°$ to $360°$ inclusive:

14 $\cos x + \cos 5x = 0$ **15** $\cos 4x - \cos x = 0$
16 $\sin 3x - \sin x = 0$ **17** $\sin 2x + \sin 3x = 0$
18 $\sin (x + 10°) + \sin x = 0$
19 $\cos (2x + 10°) + \cos (2x - 10°) = 0$
20 $\cos (x + 20°) - \cos (x - 70°) = 0$

Exercise 18i (Miscellaneous)

Do not use a calculator in nos. 1–6.

1 If $\sin A = \frac{5}{13}$, $\sin B = \frac{8}{17}$, where A and B are acute, find the values of:
(a) $\cos (A + B)$ (b) $\sin (A - B)$ (c) $\tan (A + B)$
2 If $\cos A = \frac{15}{17}$, $\sin B = \frac{20}{29}$, where A is reflex and B is obtuse, find the values of:
(a) $\sin (A + B)$ (b) $\cos (A - B)$ (c) $\cot (A - B)$
3 Find the values of:
(a) $\cos 80° \cos 20° + \sin 80° \sin 20°$

(b) $\dfrac{\tan 15° + \tan 30°}{1 - \tan 15° \tan 30°}$

(c) $\sin 40° \cos 50° + \sin 50° \cos 40°$
4 Find the values of $\sin x$ and $\cos x$ when $\cos 2x$ is:
(a) $\frac{1}{9}$ (b) $\frac{49}{81}$
5 Find the value of $\tan \theta$ when $\tan 2\theta$ is:
(a) $-\frac{20}{21}$ (b) $\frac{36}{77}$
6 If $\sin \theta = \frac{35}{37}$, where θ is acute, find the values of:
(a) $\sin 2\theta$ (b) $\cos 2\theta$

Solve the following equations, giving values of θ from $0°$ to $360°$ inclusive:

7 $\cos 2\theta + 5 \cos \theta = 2$ **8** $2 \sin 2\theta = 3 \sin \theta$
9 $\tan 2\theta + \tan \theta = 0$ **10** $4 \cos \theta - 3 \sin \theta = 1$
11 $3 \cos \theta + 2 \sin \theta = 2.5$

Eliminate θ from the following equations:

12 $x = 2 \cos 2\theta, \quad y = 3 \cos \theta$ **13** $x = 2 \tan \theta, \quad y = \tan 2\theta$

In nos. 14 and 15, using $t = \tan \frac{1}{2}\theta$, express in terms of t:

14 $3 \cos \theta + 4 \sin \theta + 5$ **15** $\sqrt{\left(\dfrac{1 + \sin \theta}{1 - \sin \theta}\right)}$

Find the maximum and minimum values of the following, giving the values of θ between $0°$ and $360°$ for which they occur:

16 $5 \cos \theta - 12 \sin \theta$ **17** $12 \cos \theta + 35 \sin \theta$ **18** $48 \cos \theta - 55 \sin \theta$

19 Prove that $\tan 3A = \dfrac{3 \tan A - \tan^3 A}{1 - 3 \tan^2 A}$

20 If $2A + B = 45°$, show that $\tan B = \dfrac{1 - 2 \tan A - \tan^2 A}{1 + 2 \tan A - \tan^2 A}$

Solve the following equations for values of θ from $0°$ to $180°$ inclusive:

21 $\cos \theta + \cos 3\theta + \cos 5\theta = 0$ **22** $\sin 2\theta + \sin 4\theta + \sin 6\theta = 0$
23 $\sin \theta - 2 \sin 2\theta + \sin 3\theta = 0$ **24** $\cos \frac{1}{2}\theta + 2 \cos \frac{3}{2}\theta + \cos \frac{5}{2}\theta = 0$
25 $\sin \theta + \cos 2\theta - \sin 3\theta = 0$

Prove the following identities. A, B, C are to be taken as the angles of a triangle.

26 $\sin A + \sin (B - C) = 2 \sin B \cos C$
27 $\cos A - \cos (B - C) = -2 \cos B \cos C$

28 $\sin A + \sin B + \sin C = 4 \cos \dfrac{A}{2} \cos \dfrac{B}{2} \cos \dfrac{C}{2}$

29 $\sin 2A + \sin 2B + \sin 2C = 4 \sin A \sin B \sin C$
30 $\tan A + \tan B + \tan C = \tan A \tan B \tan C$

Chapter 19

Further topics in trigonometry

19.1 Introduction

One of Euler's many contributions to mathematics is the invention of a standard notation for labelling triangles. In this notation the vertices are always labelled with capital letters, say A, B and C, and the same symbols are used to represent the sizes of the angles at these vertices. The corresponding lower case letters, a, b, c, are then used to represent the lengths of the sides opposite the vertices, i.e. the letter a is used to represent the length of the side BC (see Figure 19.1).

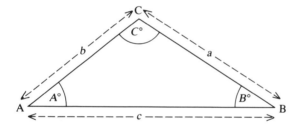

Figure 19.1

The traditional unit of measurement for angles is the degree (but it is not the only one, see Section 19.5); the degree has been used for over 2000 years. The traditional sub-unit is the minute, which is 1/60th of a degree, and the standard symbol for it is a small dash. So $35°\ 12'$ is equal to $35\frac{12}{60}°$; in decimals this becomes $35.2°$. For more awkward numbers a calculator can be used to convert the number of minutes into a decimal fraction of a degree.

In the next two sections Euler's notation will be used to introduce two important rules, the **sine rule** and the **cosine rule**. These rules are used to 'solve' triangles; that is, given sufficient data to define a unique triangle, the sine and cosine rules can be used to calculate the sizes of the remaining sides and angles.

19.2 The sine rule

In the triangle in Figure 19.2, CP is perpendicular to AB.

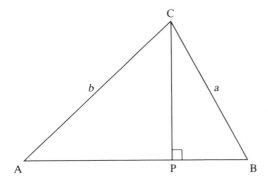

Figure 19.2

By elementary trigonometry the length of the altitude CP is equal to $b \sin A$ (from triangle APC) and it is also equal to $a \sin B$ (from triangle BPC). Equating these expressions, we have

$$a \sin B = b \sin A$$

and hence

$$\frac{a}{\sin A} = \frac{b}{\sin B}$$

Applying the same argument to the line from A, perpendicular to BC, we could obtain

$$\frac{b}{\sin B} = \frac{c}{\sin C}$$

Putting these expressions together, we have:

$$\boxed{\frac{a}{\sin A} = \frac{b}{\sin B} = \frac{c}{\sin C}}$$

This expression, which, by virtue of its symmetrical appearance, is easy to remember, is called the **sine rule**.

However, in drawing Figure 19.1, we have assumed that all the angles are acute; if one of them is obtuse, the proof must be modified. Suppose that B is the obtuse angle as shown in Figure 19.3 (over the page).

In *this* diagram, CP is the perpendicular line from C to AB *produced*. By elementary trigonometry $CP = a \sin \angle CBP = a \sin (180° - B)$. However

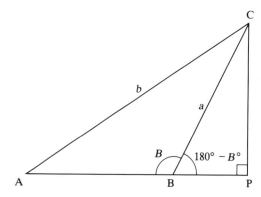

Figure 19.3

$\sin(180° - B)$ is equal to $\sin B$ and so we can write

$\qquad CP = a \sin B = b \sin A$

and proceed with the proof as before.

[See Exercise 19g, no. 16, for an alternative proof.]

Example 1

In triangle PQR, $r = 5.75$ and the sizes of angles P and Q are 42° and 65° respectively. Calculate the length of PR.

With these letters (see Figure 19.4), the sine rule becomes:

$$\frac{p}{\sin P} = \frac{q}{\sin Q} = \frac{r}{\sin R}$$

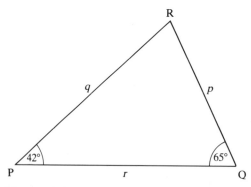

Figure 19.4

Notice that when two angles are given, the remaining angle can be calculated from the fact that the sum of the three angles of a triangle is

180°, so $R = 73°$. Substituting the data, and this value of R, we obtain

$$\frac{p}{\sin 42°} = \frac{q}{\sin 65°} = \frac{5.75}{\sin 73°}$$

In this example, the length of PR, i.e. q, is required. Making q the subject of the formula above, we obtain

$$q = \frac{5.75}{\sin 73°} \times \sin 65°$$

$$= 5.45, \quad \text{correct to three significant figures}$$

Example 2

In triangle ABC, $a = 4.73$, $c = 3.58$ and $C = 42° \, 12'$. Calculate the size of angle A.

Firstly we note that $42° \, 12' = 42\frac{12}{60}° = 42.2°$, and secondly, from Figure 19.5, we can see that two triangles can be drawn with these data. (It is very important that a sketch should be drawn, so that this sort of difficulty can be anticipated.)

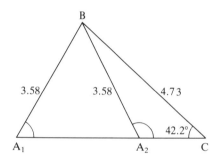

Figure 19.5

By the sine rule,

$$\frac{4.73}{\sin A} = \frac{b}{\sin B} = \frac{3.58}{\sin 42.2}$$

In this case, the middle term is superfluous; the other two terms give

$$\frac{\sin A}{4.73} = \frac{\sin 42.2°}{3.58}$$

$\therefore \quad \sin A = \dfrac{\sin 42.2°}{3.58} \times 4.73$

$$(= 0.8875)*$$

$\therefore \qquad A = 62.560° \quad \text{or} \quad 117.440°$

$$= 62.6° \quad \text{or} \quad 117.4°,$$

correct to the nearest tenth of a degree

There are two points to note in Example 2:

(1) The step marked with the asterisk indicates the figures which appear on a calculator at this stage; it is not necessary to write them down. (Indeed, to write them down, correct to four significant figures, and then to use the *corrected* figures to find A is poor calculator technique.)

(2) The alternative value of A, namely, $A = 117.4°$, follows from the fact that $\sin \theta = \sin(180° - \theta)$, i.e. in this case, $\sin 62.6° = \sin 117.4°$. If we inspect the diagram, we can see that both answers are perfectly reasonable, because the triangle $A_1 B A_2$ is isosceles.

A case like this one, where there are two possible answers, is called *the ambiguous case*.

The sine rule can be used when two angles are given (as in Example 1) or when one of the given sides is opposite the given angle (as in Example 2), but, as the reader should be able to see with a little experimentation, it is useless when the lengths of the three sides are given, or when two sides and the *included* angle (i.e. the angle between them) are given. In these circumstances we must turn to the cosine rule. [Some readers may prefer to work Exercise 19a, nos. 1–3 first.]

19.3 The cosine rule

There are several possible proofs of the cosine rule; this one uses the idea of the scalar product (see Section 16.15).

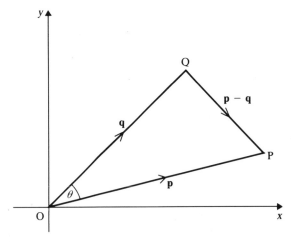

Figure 19.6

In the triangle OPQ (Figure 19.6), the angle POQ is equal to θ and $\overrightarrow{QP} = \mathbf{p} - \mathbf{q}$. Consider the scalar product $\overrightarrow{QP}.\overrightarrow{QP}$:

$$\overrightarrow{QP}.\overrightarrow{QP} = (\mathbf{p} - \mathbf{q}).(\mathbf{p} - \mathbf{q})$$
$$= \mathbf{p}.\mathbf{p} + \mathbf{q}.\mathbf{q} - 2\mathbf{p}.\mathbf{q}$$
$$= p^2 + q^2 - 2pq \cos \theta$$

But $\overrightarrow{QP}.\overrightarrow{QP}$ is equal to QP^2,

$\therefore$ $QP^2 = p^2 + q^2 - 2pq \cos \theta$

So, if we are given the values of p and q, and the size of the included angle θ, we can calculate the length of QP.

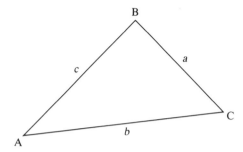

Figure 19.7

The formula looks neater, and it is easier to remember, if Euler's notation is used. If the triangle is re-lettered ABC, as in Figure 19.7, the cosine rule becomes

$$a^2 = b^2 + c^2 - 2bc \cos A$$

The letters a, b and c can be permuted to give the following alternative forms:

$b^2 = c^2 + a^2 - 2ca \cos B$
$c^2 = a^2 + b^2 - 2ab \cos C$

Example 3

In triangle PQR, $p = 14.3$, $r = 17.5$ and $Q = 25° \, 36'$. Calculate the length of side PR.

In this question we are given the lengths of two sides and the size of the included angle, so the cosine rule is appropriate. With these letters it takes the form

$q^2 = r^2 + p^2 - 2rp \cos Q$

Substituting the data gives

$q^2 = 17.5^2 + 14.3^2 - 2 \times 17.5 \times 14.3 \cos 25.6°$

Hence

$q = 7.71$,   correct to three significant figures

[On most calculators it should be possible to do the whole calculation without having to write down any of the intermediate working. If this is possible, it should be done, because mistakes are easily made when figures are transferred from the calculator to paper and *vice versa*. In case of difficulty, consult the calculator's instruction booklet.]

Example 4

In triangle XYZ, XY = 3.5, YZ = 4.5 and ZX = 6.5. Calculate the size of angle Y.

In this case the lengths of the three sides are given. The cosine rule can be used, but first it must be rearranged to make cos Y the subject.

$$y^2 = z^2 + x^2 - 2zx \cos Y$$
$$\therefore \quad 2zx \cos Y = z^2 + x^2 - y^2$$

and hence

$$\cos Y = \frac{z^2 + x^2 - y^2}{2zx}$$

Substituting the data,

$$\cos Y = \frac{3.5^2 + 4.5^2 - 6.5^2}{2 \times 3.5 \times 4.5}$$

$$\therefore \qquad Y = 108.0°, \quad \text{correct to the nearest tenth of a degree}$$

Once again, if you are using a calculator, the entire calculation should be done without writing down the intermediate steps. Be careful to press the 'equals' key when you have completed the top line (the calculator should display −9.75 at this stage), and, on most calculators, it is essential to enclose the bottom line in brackets, i.e. (2 × 3.5 × 4.5).

19.4 The area of a triangle

It is assumed that the reader is familiar with the elementary formula for △, the area of a triangle, namely,

$$\triangle = \tfrac{1}{2}bh$$

where b is the length of the base and h is the height of the triangle.

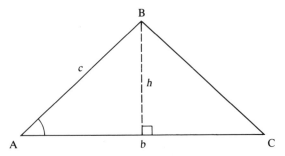

Figure 19.8

If we are given the lengths b and c and the size of the included angle A (see Figure 19.8), then the height, h, can be expressed as

$$h = c \sin A$$

and the formula for the area can be written

$$\triangle = \tfrac{1}{2}bc \sin A$$

[The reader should note that this formula can be used for both acute and obtuse angles.]

Example 5

In triangle PQR, $QR = 3.5$, $RP = 4$ and $PQ = 5$. Calculate the size of angle P and hence find the area of the triangle.

Rearranging the cosine rule (see Example 4),

$$\cos P = \frac{q^2 + r^2 - p^2}{2qr}$$

and substituting the data, i.e. $p = 3.5$, $q = 4$ and $r = 5$, we have

$$\cos P = \frac{16 + 25 - 12.25}{2 \times 4 \times 5}$$

$$= \frac{28.75}{40}$$

∴ $P = 44.0°$,   correct to the nearest tenth of a degree

The area of the triangle is given by

$$\triangle = \tfrac{1}{2}qr \sin P$$
$$= \tfrac{1}{2} \times 4 \times 5 \times \sin P$$
$$= 6.95, \quad \text{correct to three significant figures}$$

Note When no units have been explicitly stated, as in the example above, it is assumed that the same units have been used consistently throughout the question, e.g. if the lengths QR, RP and PQ are all given in cm, then the area of PQR is measured in cm^2.

Historical note The problem of calculating the area of a triangle when the lengths of the three sides are given is a very ancient one. The area can be calculated from the formula.

$$\triangle = \sqrt{\{s(s-a)(s-b)(s-c)\}}$$

where $s = \tfrac{1}{2}(a + b + c)$. This formula is usually known as Heron's formula, after Heron of Alexandria, who lived over two thousand years ago. However the formula was known even before Heron's time. (See also Exercise 19g, nos 17–20.)

Qu. 1 Calculate the area of the triangle in Example 3.
Qu. 2 Use Heron's formula (see *Historical note* above) to calculate the area of the triangle in Example 5.

Qu. 3 Calculate the areas of the triangles in which:
(a) $A = 60°$ $b = 3$ $c = 5$
(b) $C = 110°$ $a = 14$ $b = 11$
(c) $B = 90°$ $c = 8.6$ $b = 11.4$
(d) $a = 8$ $b = 11$ $c = 13$
(e) $a = 12.3$ $b = 14.1$ $c = 13.6$
(f) $a = 17.6$ $b = 16.9$ $c = 16.1$
(g) $a = 209$ $b = 313$ $c = 390$

Exercise 19a

Solve the following triangles:

1 (Sine formula, acute angled)
(a) $a = 12$ $B = 59°$ $C = 73°$
(b) $A = 75.6°$ $b = 5.6$ $C = 48.3°$
(c) $A = 73.2°$ $B = 61.7°$ $c = 171$
2 (Sine formula, obtuse angled)
(a) $A = 36°$ $b = 2.37$ $C = 49°$
(b) $A = 123.2°$ $a = 11.5$ $C = 37.1°$
(c) $a = 136$ $B = 104.2°$ $C = 43.1°$
3 (Sine formula, ambiguous case)
(a) $b = 17.6$ $C = 48° \ 15'$ $c = 15.3$
(b) $B = 129°$ $b = 7.89$ $c = 4.56$
(c) $A = 28° \ 15'$ $a = 8.5$ $b = 14.8$
4 (Cosine formula, acute angled)
(a) $a = 5$ $b = 8$ $c = 7$
(b) $a = 10$ $b = 12$ $c = 9$
(c) $a = 17$ $b = 13$ $c = 18$
5 (Cosine formula, acute angled)
(a) $A = 60°$ $b = 8$ $c = 15$
(b) $a = 14$ $B = 53°$ $c = 12$
(c) $a = 11$ $b = 9$ $C = 43.2°$
6 (Cosine formula, obtuse angled)
(a) $a = 8$ $b = 10$ $c = 15$
(b) $a = 11$ $b = 31$ $c = 24$
(c) $a = 27$ $b = 35$ $c = 46$
7 (Cosine formula, obtuse angled)
(a) $a = 17$ $B = 120°$ $c = 63$
(b) $A = 104° \ 15'$ $b = 10$ $c = 12$
(c) $a = 31$ $b = 42$ $C = 104° \ 10'$
8 Two points A and B on a straight coastline are 1 km apart, B being due east of A. If a ship is observed on bearings 167° and 205° from A and B respectively, what is its distance from the coastline?
9 A boat is sailing directly towards a cliff. The angle of elevation of a point on the top of the cliff and straight ahead of the boat increases from 10° to 15° as the ship sails a distance of 50 m. What is the height of the cliff?

10 A triangle is taken with sides 10, 11, 15 cm. By how much does its largest angle differ from a right angle?

11 A ship rounds a headland by sailing first 4 nautical miles on a course of 069° then 5 nautical miles on a course of 295°. Calculate the distance and bearing of its new position from its original position.

12 A motorist travelling along a straight level road in the direction 053° observes a pylon on a bearing of 037°; 800 m further along the road the bearing of the pylon is 296°. Calculate the distance of the pylon from the road.

19.5 Radians

The fact that there are 90 degrees in a right angle has been familiar to the reader since he or she began geometry; but it may not have been realised that the number is an arbitrary one which has come down to us from the Babylonian civilisation. Indeed, an attempt to introduce 100 degrees to the right angle was made after the French Revolution, but it was later dropped, and in 1938 a similar attempt was made by the Germans. The following example also illustrates the arbitrary nature of the number of degrees in a right angle.

Example 6

An arc AB of a circle, centre O, subtends an angle of $x°$ at O. Find the expressions in terms of x and the radius r, for (a) the length of the arc AB   (b) the area of the sector OAB (see Figure 19.9).

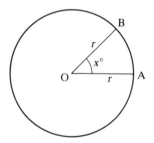

Figure 19.9

(a) The length of an arc of a given circle is proportional to the angle it subtends at the centre. But an angle of 360° is subtended by an arc of length $2\pi r$, therefore an angle of $x°$ is subtended by an arc of length

$$\frac{x}{360} \times 2\pi r$$

Therefore the length of arc AB is $(\pi/180)xr$.

(b) The area of a sector of a given circle is proportional to the angle at the centre. But a sector containing an angle of 360° is the whole circle, which has an area of πr^2, therefore a sector containing an angle of $x°$ has an area of

$$\frac{x}{360} \times \pi r^2$$

Therefore the area of the sector OAB is $\frac{1}{2}(\pi/180)xr^2$.

Thus, in both the length of an arc and the area of a sector, there appears a factor of $\pi/180$, which is due to the unit of measurement of the angle OAB. This suggests a new unit for measuring angles, which is called a **radian**, such that an

angle in radians $= \dfrac{\pi}{180} \times$ (angle in degrees)   . . . (1)

If we let θ radians equal x degrees, then, referring to Figure 19.9,

length of arc $AB = r\theta$

and

area of sector $OAB = \frac{1}{2}r^2\theta$

If, then, we construct an angle of 1 radian, the arc AB will be of length r, and so *an arc of a circle equal to the radius subtends at the centre an angle of 1 radian*. Radians are sometimes termed circular measure, and are denoted by rad. It follows from the relation (1) above, by putting the angle in degrees equal to 180, that

π rad $= 180°$

Hence 1 radian $= 57.296$ degrees and 1 degree $= 0.017\,453$ radians, both correct to five significant figures.

The use of radians extends far beyond finding lengths of arcs and areas of sectors. In later sections it is shown how they have applications in mechanics and calculus.

Exercise 19b

1 Convert to degrees:

(a) $\dfrac{\pi}{2}$ rad   (b) $\dfrac{\pi}{4}$ rad   (c) $\dfrac{\pi}{3}$ rad   (d) $\dfrac{2\pi}{3}$ rad

(e) $\dfrac{\pi}{6}$ rad   (f) $\dfrac{3\pi}{2}$ rad   (g) $\dfrac{5\pi}{2}$ rad   (h) 4π rad

(i) 5π rad   (j) $\dfrac{4\pi}{3}$ rad   (k) $\dfrac{7\pi}{2}$ rad   (l) $\dfrac{3\pi}{4}$ rad

2 Convert to radians, leaving π in your answer:
(a) 360° (b) 90° (c) 45° (d) 15°
(e) 60° (f) 120° (g) 300° (h) 270°
(i) 540° (j) 30° (k) 150° (l) 450°

3 What is the length of an arc which subtends an angle of 0.8 rad at the centre of a circle of radius 10 cm?

4 An arc of a circle subtends an angle of 1.2 rad at any point on the remaining part of the circumference. Find the length of the arc, if the radius of the circle is 4 cm.

5 An arc of a circle subtends an angle of 0.5 rad at the centre. Find the radius of the circle, if the length of the arc is 3 cm.

6 Find, in radians, the angle subtended at the centre of a circle of radius 2.5 cm by an arc 2 cm long.

7 What is the area of a sector containing an angle of 1.5 rad, in a circle of radius 2 cm?

8 The radius of a circle is 3 cm. What is the angle contained by a sector of area 18 cm²?

9 An arc subtends an angle of 1 rad at the centre of a circle, and a sector of area 72 cm² is bounded by this arc and the two radii. What is the radius of the circle?

10 The arc of a sector in a circle, radius 2 cm, is 4 cm long. What is the area of the sector?

Exercise 19c

1 Express in radians, leaving π in your answers:
(a) $22\frac{1}{2}°$ (b) 1080° (c) 12′ (d) 37° 30′

2 Express in degrees:
(a) $\frac{2\pi}{5}$ rad (b) $\frac{\pi}{36}$ rad (c) $\frac{7\pi}{12}$ rad (d) $\frac{7\pi}{2}$ rad

3 Find the length of an arc of a circle, which subtends an angle of 31° at the centre, if the radius of the circle is 5 cm.

4 The chord AB of a circle subtends an angle of 60° at the centre. What is the ratio of chord AB to arc AB?

5 An arc of a circle, radius 2.5 cm, is 3 cm long. Find the angle subtended by the arc at the centre:
(a) in radians (b) in degrees

6 A segment is cut off a circle of radius 5 cm by a chord AB, 6 cm long. What is the length of the minor arc AB?

7 What is the area of a sector containing an angle of 1.4 rad in a circle whose radius is 2.4 cm?

8 A chord AB subtends an angle of 120° at O, the centre of a circle with radius 12 cm. Find the area of:
(a) sector AOB (b) triangle AOB (c) the minor segment AB

9 An arc AB of a circle with radius 6 cm subtends an angle of 40° at the centre. Find the area bounded by the diameter BC, CA and the arc AB.

10 Two equal circles of radius 5 cm are situated with their centres 6 cm apart. Calculate what area lies within both circles.

11 A chord PQ of a circle with radius r, subtends an angle θ at the centre. Show that the area of the minor segment PQ is $\frac{1}{2}r^2(\theta - \sin\theta)$, and write down the area of the major segment PQ in terms of r and θ.

12 A circle of radius r is drawn with its centre on the circumference of another circle of radius r. Show that the area common to both circles is $2r^2(\pi/3 - \sqrt{3}/4)$.

19.6 Angular velocity

Someone who buys an electric motor is usually interested in the rate at which it goes, and they may be told that it does 12 000 revolutions per minute (rev min^{-1}). On the other hand the drum of a barograph turns at the rate of 49 degrees per day. In either case the rate of turning, which is called average angular velocity, is given by

$$\text{average angular velocity} = \frac{\text{angle turned}}{\text{time taken}}$$

Qu. 4 Find the average angular velocity of the second hand of a watch:
(a) in degrees per second ($°\,s^{-1}$)   (b) in rev min^{-1}
Qu. 5 Convert:
(a) 500 rev min^{-1} into $°\,s^{-1}$ (b) 1 rev week^{-1} into $°\,h^{-1}$

In many cases of turning, however, the angular velocity is not constant, so consider the average angular velocity in a small interval of time δt. If the angle turned through in this time is $\delta\theta$ radians,

$$\text{average angular velocity} = \frac{\delta\theta}{\delta t}\text{ rad s}^{-1}$$

But as $\delta t \to 0$,

$$\frac{\delta\theta}{\delta t} \to \frac{d\theta}{dt}$$

$\therefore$ average angular velocity $\to \dfrac{d\theta}{dt}$

$\dfrac{d\theta}{dt}$ is called **angular velocity** and is denoted by ω (the Greek letter omega). Therefore

$$\boxed{\omega = \frac{d\theta}{dt}}$$

[In motion in a straight line average velocity $= \dfrac{\text{displacement}}{\text{time}}$ and if a distance

δs is travelled in a time δt, average velocity $= \dfrac{\delta s}{\delta t}$. But $\dfrac{\delta s}{\delta t} \to \dfrac{ds}{dt}$ as $\delta t \to 0$ and so

the velocity at an instant is given by $v = \dfrac{ds}{dt}$. In this way there is a parallel

between linear motion and angular motion (see Chapter 5).]

If a particle moves in a circle of radius r with speed v and angular velocity ω about the centre, the relation between r, v, ω can be obtained from one of the results obtained in Section 19.5. If s is the distance of the particle measured along the circumference of the circle from a fixed point,

$$s = r\theta$$

Differentiating with respect to time (remember r is constant):

$$\frac{ds}{dt} = r\frac{d\theta}{dt}$$

$$\therefore \quad v = r\omega$$

Remember that ω must be measured in radians/unit time. Two sets of possible units for v, r, ω are shown in the table below:

v	r	ω
$m\,s^{-1}$	m	$rad\,s^{-1}$
$km\,h^{-1}$	km	$rad\,h^{-1}$

Example 7

A belt runs round a pulley attached to the shaft of a motor. If the belt runs at $0.75\ m\ s^{-1}$ and the radius of the pulley is 6 cm, find the angular velocity of the pulley (a) in $rad\ s^{-1}$ (b) in $rev\ min^{-1}$.

(a) Using the result $v = r\omega$,

$$\omega = \frac{75}{6} = 12.5\ rad\ s^{-1}$$

(b) $12.5\ rad\ s^{-1} = \dfrac{12.5}{2\pi}\ rev\ s^{-1}$

$$= \frac{12.5}{2\pi} \times 60\ rev\ min^{-1}$$

$$= 120\ rev\ min^{-1}, \text{ correct to 3 significant figures}$$

Exercise 19d

Use the result $v = r\omega$ where you can.

1 Express the angular velocity of the minute hand of a clock in:
(a) rev min^{-1} (b) deg s^{-1} (c) rad s^{-1}
2 A wheel is turning at 200 rev min^{-1}. Express this angular velocity in:
(a) deg s^{-1} (b) rad s^{-1}
3 The Earth rotates on its axis approximately $365\frac{1}{4}$ times in a year. Calculate its angular velocity in rad h^{-1}, correct to three significant figures.
4 A motor runs at 1200 rev min^{-1}. What is its angular velocity in rad s^{-1}? If the shaft of the motor is 2.5 cm in diameter, at what speed is a point on the circumference of the shaft moving?
5 A point on the rim of a wheel of diameter 2.5 m is moving at a speed of 44 m s^{-1} relative to the axis. At what rate in (a) rad s^{-1} (b) rev min^{-1}, is the wheel turning?
6 A belt runs round two pulleys of diameters 26.25 cm and 15 cm. If the larger rotates 700 times in a minute, find the angular velocity of the smaller in rad s^{-1}.
7 The Earth moves round the sun approximately in a circle of radius 150 000 000 km. Find its angular velocity in rad s^{-1} and obtain its speed along its orbit in km s^{-1}.
8 Taking the Earth to be a sphere of radius 6300 km which rotates about its axis once in 23.93 hours what error will be made in calculating the speed of a point on the equator, if it is assumed that the Earth rotates once in 24 hours? Express your answer in km h^{-1}, correct to two significant figures.

19.7 Inverse trigonometrical functions

Can you find an angle x, such that $\sin x = 0.5$? This sort of problem arises frequently in mathematics; indeed we have already met it earlier in this chapter. An answer can be easily obtained from a calculator. In this particular case, the angle is an angle in one of the 'standard' triangles described in Section 17.3, i.e. 30°. But this is not the complete solution; we can see from the graph of $y = \sin x$ (Figure 19.10), that 150° is also a possibility and, since $\sin x$ has a period of 360° (it repeats itself every 360°), we can add any multiple of 360°

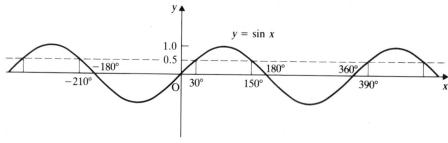

Figure 19.10

to these two angles. Hence there are infinitely many values of x which satisfy the equation $\sin x = 0.5$; they can be expressed, in degrees, in the form

$$x = 30° + n360° \quad \text{or} \quad x = 150° + n360°$$

where n is any integer, positive or negative.

If we were working in radians, this general solution would take the form

$$x = \frac{\pi}{6} + 2n\pi \quad \text{or} \quad x = \frac{5\pi}{6} + 2n\pi$$

Qu. 6 Write down the general solution, in degrees, of the equation $\cos x = -0.5$.

Qu. 7 Write down, in radians, the general solution of the equation $\tan x = 1$.

In advanced trigonometry, it is useful to have a standard abbreviation for the phrase 'the angle whose sine is x', etc. The usual abbreviation for this is arcsin x; and arccos x, arctan x are used for the inverses of the cos and tan functions. This is the standard notation on all microcomputers and it is also found on many pocket calculators, but the notation $\sin^{-1} x$, $\cos^{-1} x$ and $\tan^{-1} x$, is also used.

However, the fact that there are infinitely many angles, whose sines are x, causes some problems. For instance, if you were designing a pocket calculator, which of the infinitely many possible answers would you choose to show on the display? [Try finding arcsin, arccos and arctan of ± 0.2, ± 0.4, ± 0.8, etc., on your pocket calculator. Can you discover the principle which the manufacturer of your calculator is using to select the angle shown on the display?]

Another serious problem is that if we are intending to describe arcsin x, arccos x and arctan x, as *functions*, then we must ensure that the function has *exactly one value*, for any given value of x (see Section 3.8). Consequently, we must define these functions rather more carefully than we have done so far.

Definitions

(a) arcsin x is the angle (in radians) between $-\frac{1}{2}\pi$ and $+\frac{1}{2}\pi$, inclusive, whose sine is x.

(b) arccos x is the angle (in radians) between 0 and π, inclusive, whose cosine is x.

(c) arctan x is the angle (in radians) between $-\frac{1}{2}\pi$ and $+\frac{1}{2}\pi$, whose tangent is x.

The angles within these ranges are often called the **principal values.**

If desired, these definitions may be expressed in degrees, but for advanced work in trigonometry, radians are more common than degrees.

Qu. 8 Why is the range $-\frac{1}{2}\pi$ to $+\frac{1}{2}\pi$ unsuitable for arccos x?

Notice that, since there is no angle whose sine is greater than 1, an expression such as arcsin 2 is meaningless. The function arcsin x only makes sense if x is numerically smaller than (or equal to) 1; in other words, *the domain* of the function arcsin x is $\{x: -1 \leqslant x \leqslant +1\}$. The function arccos x has the same domain, but in the function arctan x, the variable x can take any (real) value, i.e. the domain of arctan x is $\mathbb{R}$ (see Figure 19.11).

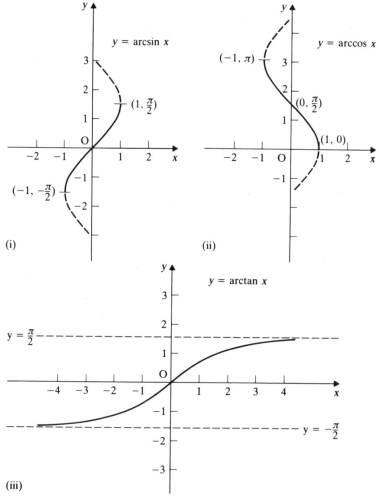

Figure 19.11

Like all inverse functions, the graphs of arcsin x, arccos x and arctan x are the reflections of the graphs of the corresponding functions in the line $y = x$.

In diagrams (i) and (ii), the solid parts of the graphs represent the principal values of arcsin x and arccos x respectively; the broken parts of the graphs represent the other values.

Exercise 19e

All the questions in this exercise use the angles in the 'standard' triangles (see Section 17.3). Do not use a calculator.

Write down the general solutions, *in degrees*, of the following equations:

1 $\sin x = 1/\sqrt{2}$ **2** $\cos x = 1$ **3** $\tan x = \sqrt{3}$
4 $\sin x = -1$ **5** $\cos x = -1/2$ **6** $\tan x = -1/\sqrt{3}$

Write down the general solutions, *in degrees*, of the following equations:

7 $\cos x = \frac{1}{2}$ **8** $\tan x = -1$
9 $\sin 2x = \frac{1}{2}$ **10** $\cos^2 x = \frac{3}{4}$

Write down the values, *in radians*, of:

11 $\arcsin(\sqrt{3}/2)$ **12** $\arccos(1/\sqrt{2})$ **13** $\arctan 1$
14 $\arcsin(-\frac{1}{2})$ **15** $\arccos(-\sqrt{3}/2)$ **16** $\arctan(-1)$
17 $\arcsin(-1)$ **18** $\arccos(-1)$ **19** $\arctan 0$
20 $\arccos 0$

19.8 Three-dimensional trigonometry

To begin with, it needs to be emphasised that some of the questions in this section will be very difficult without a clear figure. In general, the four following basic rules should be adopted:

(a) Parallel lines are drawn parallel.
(b) Vertical lines are drawn parallel to the sides of the paper.
(c) East–west lines are generally drawn parallel to the bottom of the paper, and north–south lines are drawn at an acute angle to east–west lines.
(d) All unseen lines should be dotted in.

In Figure 19.12, AB and CD are vertical posts. Notice that the angle NOE is marked a right angle, because this is what it represents.

Qu. 9 Copy Figure 19.12 and draw AC. Mark in all the right angles at A and C.

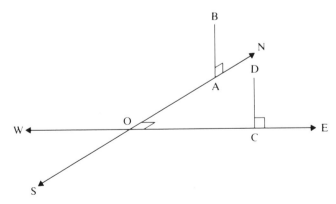

Figure 19.12

19.9 The angle between a line and a plane

When calculating the angle between a line and a plane, we are concerned with calculating the angle between two lines: the given line, and another line lying in the given plane. An infinite number of lines can be drawn, lying in the plane and passing through the point in which the given line meets the plane, and each line will yield a different angle. Which line should we take?

In Figure 19.13 the line QR meets the plane π in O. In order to find the angle between QR and π, take any point P on QR and drop a perpendicular PN to the plane; now join N to O and θ is the angle required. ON is the **projection** of OP onto the plane π.

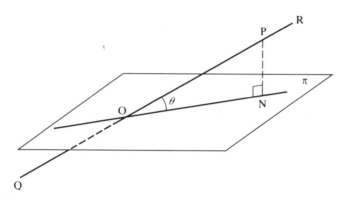

Figure 19.13

Qu. 10 Copy Figure 19.13 and draw any line in π and passing through O. Let M be the foot of the perpendicular from P to this line. Show that angle POM is greater than angle PON.

The results of Qu. 10 shows that θ is the *least* angle between QR and any line which can be drawn in π and passing through O.

Example 8

Figure 19.14 represents a rectangular box 9 cm × 6 cm × 6 cm with its lid open at an angle of 30°. Calculate the angle between BD′ and the plane CDD′C′.

BD′ meets the plane CDD′C′ in D′. Take any other point on BD′: B is an obvious point. Drop the perpendicular from B to the plane: BC. The angle we want is BD′C. Select triangle BD′C and mark in lengths (see Figure 19.15). We must calculate CD′ or BD′ first. CD′ is easier, so draw triangle CC′D′ and again mark in lengths.

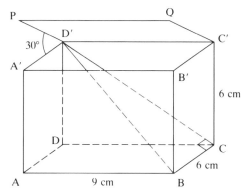

Figure 19.14

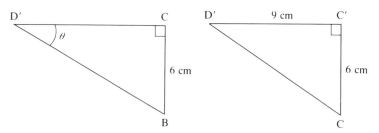

Figure 19.15

In triangle CC'D',

$$CD'^2 = 6^2 + 9^2 = 117$$
$$\therefore \quad CD' = \sqrt{117}\dagger$$

Now mark the length of CD' in triangle BCD'.

$$\tan \theta = \frac{6}{\sqrt{117}}$$
$$\therefore \quad \theta = 29.0°$$

Therefore the angle between BD' and the plane CDD'C' is 29.0°

Qu. 11 Calculate the angle between:
(a) BD' and the plane BCC'B'   (b) AC' and BD'
Qu. 12 Calculate the angle between BP and the plane ABCD.

---

† If a calculator is being used, intermediate calculations (such as $\sqrt{117}$) should not be evaluated, unless explicitly required by the question. Writing down intermediate values can lead to a build-up of rounding errors.

19.10 The angle between two planes

When calculating the angle between two planes we are again concerned with calculating the angle between two lines, one in each plane.

Referring to Figure 19.16, in order to find the angle between two planes π and π', we select a point C on their common line AB and draw lines PC and CQ in π and π', respectively, and at right angles to AB. PCQ is the angle we want. This angle is called the **dihedral** angle of the two planes.

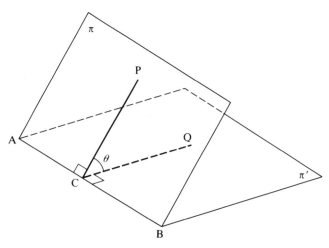

Figure 19.16

Qu. 13 Copy Figure 19.16 and draw a line PR parallel to AB; join CR. Let P', R' be the feet of the perpendiculars from P, R, respectively, to π'. Show that angle RCR' < angle PCQ.

Example 9

VABCD is a right pyramid on a square base ABCD of side 10 cm. Each sloping edge is 12 cm long. Calculate the angle between the faces VAB and VBC.

To obtain a good figure first represent the base ABCD as a rhombus, then dot in diagonals to meet at N. Put up the vertical NV and choose V so that AV does not coincide with DV (see Figure 19.17).

VB is the common line of the two planes. Draw AX perpendicular to VB, then, since the figure is symmetrical about VDB, CX is also perpendicular to VB. The angle we want is AXC, so we must work in triangle AXC.

First we want to find AX and AC.

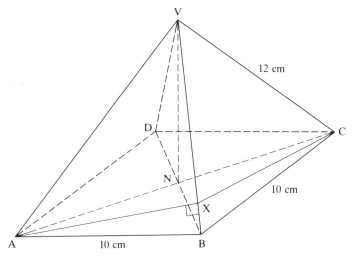

Figure 19.17

In triangle VAM (see Figure 19.18), $VM^2 = 12^2 - 5^2 = 119$.

$\therefore \quad VM = \sqrt{119}$ cm

Area of triangle $VAB = 5\sqrt{119} = \frac{1}{2} \times AX \times 12$.

$\therefore \quad AX = \dfrac{5\sqrt{119}}{6}$ cm

In triangle ABC (see Figure 19.18), $AC^2 = 10^2 + 10^2 = 200$.

$\therefore \quad AC = \sqrt{200} = 10\sqrt{2}$

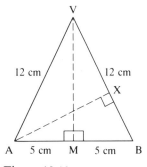 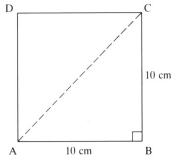

Figure 19.18

In triangle AXN (see Figure 19.19), $AN = \frac{1}{2}AC = 5\sqrt{2}$.

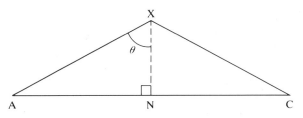

Figure 19.19

$$\sin \theta = \frac{AN}{AX} = \frac{5\sqrt{2}}{\frac{5}{6}\sqrt{119}} = 6\sqrt{\left(\frac{2}{119}\right)}$$

∴ $\theta = 51.06°$

∴ $\angle AXC = 102.1°$

Therefore the angle between the faces VAB and VCB is 102.1°.

Qu. 14 If, in Example 9, X is any point on VB, prove that triangle ABX ≡ triangle BCX. Hence prove that if AX is perpendicular to VB, then CX is also perpendicular to VB.

Qu. 15 If, in Example 9, Y is the mid-point of BC, show that VYN is the angle between VBC and ABCD, and calculate it.

Exercise 19f

1 A cuboid is formed by joining the vertices AA′, BB′, CC′, DD′ of two rectangles ABCD and A′B′C′D′. AB = 6 cm, BC = 6 cm, CC′ = 8 cm. X and Y are the mid-points of AD and CD, respectively. Calculate:
   (a) the angle between XB′ and the base ABCD
   (b) the angle between the plane XYB′ and the base ABCD
   (c) the angle between the plane BB′X and the plane BB′Y
2 A right pyramid VABCD stands on a rectangular base ABCD. AB = 6 cm, BC = 8 cm, and the height of the pyramid is 12 cm. Calculate:
   (a) the angle which a slant edge makes with the base
   (b) the angle which the slant face VAB makes with the base
   (c) the angle between the two opposite slant faces VBC and VAD
3 A hanging lamp is supported by three chains of equal length, fixed to points A, B, C in the ceiling which form an equilateral triangle of side 16 cm, and the lower ends are connected to a point 20 cm below the ceiling. Calculate:
   (a) the length of each chain
   (b) the angle which each chain makes with the ceiling
4 Two equal rectangles 3 m by 4 m are placed so that the longer sides XY coincide. The angle between their planes is 50°. Find the angle between the diagonals which pass through X.
5 A right pyramid stands on a square base of side 8 cm. The height of the pyramid is 10 cm. Calculate the angle between two adjacent faces.

6 Three mutually perpendicular lines meet at O and equal lengths OA, OB, OC are cut off. Find the inclination of ABC to ABO.

7 O is the middle point of the edge AD of a cube, of side 6 cm, whose faces ABCD, A'B'C'D' are similarly situated. Calculate:
   (a) the sine of the angle between the plane OCD' and the face CDD'C' of the cube
   (b) the sine of the angle between the edge DD' and the plane OC'D'

8 Calculate the vertical height and the slope of the slant edges and faces of a regular tetrahedron of side 8 cm, which stands on a horizontal base.

9 The roofs of an L-shaped house slope at 45°. What is the inclination to the horizontal of the line in which the two roofs meet?

10 In Figure 19.14, taking the same dimensions, calculate the angle between CP and the plane C'D'PQ.

11 A solid is formed by placing a pyramid with square base of side 15 cm and height 20 cm on top of a cuboid with the same base and the same height. Calculate the angle which a line drawn from the vertex of the pyramid to a bottom corner of the solid makes with the base.

12 In a regular tetrahedron ABCD, P is the mid-point of AB. Calculate the cosine of the angle between the planes PCD and BCD.

13 In a regular tetrahedron ABCD, Q is the middle point of AD. Find the angle between the line BQ and the plane DBC.

14 In a tetrahedron ABCD, $AC = 13$ cm, $AB = 12$ cm, $BC = 5$ cm, $CD = \sqrt{41}$ cm, $BD = 4$ cm, and $AD = 12$ cm. Calculate the cosine of the angle between the planes ABC and BDC.

15 Three adjacent edges of a rectangular box are $AB = a$ cm, $AD = b$ cm, and $AF = c$ cm. Find the angle between the planes BDF and BAD.

Exercise 19g (Miscellaneous)

1 Solve the following triangles:
   (a) $A = 60°$ $b = 8$ $c = 15$
   (b) $a = 14$ $B = 53°$ $c = 12$
   (c) $a = 11$ $b = 9$ $C = 43.2°$

2 Solve the triangles:
   (a) $a = 17$ $B = 120°$ $c = 63$
   (b) $A = 104° \ 15'$ $b = 10$ $c = 12$
   (c) $a = 31$ $b = 42$ $C = 104°$

3 Solve the triangles:
   (a) $c = 11.6$ $A = 54.2°$ $B = 26.4°$
   (b) $a = 4.96$ $b = 6.01$ $A = 31.2°$
   (c) $A = 20°$ $a = 15$ $c = 10$

4 Calculate the areas of the following triangles:
   (a) $x = 5$ $y = 8$ $z = 35°$
   (b) $x = 4$ $y = 5$ $z = 6$
   (c) $x = 25$ $y = 35$ $z = 9$

5 Convert to degrees:

(a) $\dfrac{2\pi}{5}$ (b) $\dfrac{5\pi}{6}$ (c) $\dfrac{3\pi}{8}$ (d) $\dfrac{7\pi}{12}$

6 Convert to radians, leaving π in your answers:
(a) 330°   (b) 50°   (c) 75°   (d) 24°

7 The area of a sector of a circle, diameter 7 cm, is 18.375 cm². What is the length of the arc of the sector?

8 A radar scanner rotates at a speed of 30 rev min⁻¹. Express this angular velocity in rad s⁻¹.

9 What is the angular velocity of the hour hand of a clock in:
(a) rev min⁻¹   (b) rad s⁻¹?

10 Two cog-wheels have radii 10 cm and 15 cm. If the larger wheel is turning with an angular velocity of 50 rad s⁻¹, what is the angular velocity of the smaller one when the teeth of the cog-wheels are engaged?

11 A circular coin is placed on a flat horizontal surface and held stationary while an identical coin, also placed on the horizontal surface, rolls around its perimeter, without slipping. Through how many radians does the second coin turn?

12 Investigate the effect on the cosine rule if, in the usual notation, a, b and c are given, and $c > a + b$.

13 Investigate the effect on the sine rule if, in the usual notation, a, b and A, are given, and:
(a) $a < b \sin A$ (b) $b \sin A < a < b$ (c) $b < a$

14 The lengths of the sides of a triangle are 10, x and $(x - 2)$. The side of length $(x - 2)$ is opposite an angle of 60°. Find the value of x.

15 In the triangle XYZ, $x = 29$, $y = 21$ and $z = 20$. Calculate:
(a) the area of the triangle
(b) the length of the perpendicular from Z to XY

16 Draw a triangle ABC and its circumcircle (i.e. the circle through the vertices A, B and C) marking the centre, O. Show that $\angle BOC = 2A$, where $\angle BAC = A$. By considering the isosceles triangle OBC, show that

$$\frac{a}{\sin A} = 2R$$

where R is the radius of the circumcircle.

$$\left[\text{Similarly it can be shown that } \frac{b}{\sin B} \text{ and } \frac{c}{\sin C} \text{ equal } 2R. \text{ This enables} \right.$$
us to prove a more general form of the sine rule (see Section 19.2), namely
$$\left. \frac{a}{\sin A} = \frac{b}{\sin B} = \frac{c}{\sin C} = 2R. \right]$$

17 In the cosine rule, substitute $\cos A = 2 \cos^2 \dfrac{A}{2} - 1$, and hence prove that

$$\cos \frac{A}{2} = \sqrt{\left\{ \frac{s(s-a)}{bc} \right\}} \text{ where } s = \tfrac{1}{2}(a + b + c).$$

18 In the cosine rule, substitute $\cos A = 1 - 2 \sin^2 \dfrac{A}{2}$, and hence prove that

$$\sin \frac{A}{2} = \sqrt{\left\{\frac{(s-b)(s-c)}{bc}\right\}}$$

19 Use the results of nos. 17 and 18 to prove Heron's formula for the area of a triangle.

$$\triangle = \sqrt{\{s(s-a)(s-b)(s-c)\}}$$

20 Prove Heron's formula by eliminating A from the formulae

$$a^2 = b^2 + c^2 - 2bc \cos A \quad \text{and} \quad \triangle = \tfrac{1}{2}bc \sin A$$

[*Hint* Use $\cos^2 A + \sin^2 A = 1$.]

Revision Exercise 3

1 Find the number of different arrangements that can be made using the eight letters of the word ROTATION.

Find the number of these arrangements in which the letters T are not consecutive. (L)

2 The registration number of a car consists of 3 letters of the alphabet followed by an integer, between 1 and 999 inclusive, followed by a letter of the alphabet, e.g. ABC 123 D, XYZ 78 A, PQR 5 S. Given that *all* 26 letters of the alphabet may be used and that any letter or digit may be repeated, find the total number of different registration numbers which could be formed. Find also in how many of these registration numbers the letters and digits are all different.

(Answers may be left in factor form.) (L)

3 The sum of the first ten terms of an arithmetic series is 60; the sum of the first twenty two terms is 220. Find the common difference and the first term of the series. (JMB)

4 The first four terms of an arithmetic progression are 2, $a - b$, $2a + b + 7$ and $a - 3b$ respectively, where a and b are constants. Find a and b and hence determine the sum of the first 30 terms of the progression. (L)

5 The coefficient of x in the binomial expansion of $(4 + x)^n$ equals the coefficient of x^3 in the binomial expansion of $(4 + x)^{n+1}$, where n is a positive integer. Find the value of n. (W)

6 Write down the coefficient c_r of x^r in the binomial expansion of $(1 + ax)^n$ and show that

$$\frac{c_{r+1}}{c_r} = \frac{a(n-r)}{r+1}$$

Given that the ratio of the coefficient of x^5 to that of x^4 is $8:1$ and that the ratio of the coefficient of x^{20} to that of x^{19} is $5:1$, find the values of a and n. (W)

7 When x is so small that x^3 and higher powers of x can be neglected, $(1 + 3x)^{1/2}$ may be expressed in the form

$$1 + ax + bx^2$$

where a and b are constants. Find the values of a and b. State the range of values of x for which the expansion is valid. (L)

8 Prove by induction that

$$\sum_{r=1}^{n} r^3 = \{\tfrac{1}{2}n(n+1)\}^2$$

Find

$$\sum_{r=1}^{n} (2r-1)^3$$

and show that it is a perfect square if $(2n^2 - 1)$ is a perfect square. (JMB)

418

9 Prove by induction, or otherwise, that

$$\sum_{r=1}^{n} \left(\frac{1}{4r^2 - 1} \right) = \frac{n}{2n + 1} \qquad \text{(JMB)}$$

10 The magnitudes of vectors **a** and **b** are 8 and 3 respectively, and the angle between the vectors is 60°. Sketch a diagram showing these vectors and the vector **a** − **b**. Calculate:
(a) the magnitude of **a** − **b**
(b) the resolved part of **a** in the direction of **b**   (JMB)

11 In $\triangle OPQ$, $\overrightarrow{OP} = 2\mathbf{p}$, $\overrightarrow{OQ} = 2\mathbf{q}$ and M and N are the mid-points of OP and OQ respectively.
(a) By expressing the vectors $\overrightarrow{PQ}$ and $\overrightarrow{MN}$ in terms of **p** and **q**, prove that $\overrightarrow{MN} = \frac{1}{2}\overrightarrow{PQ}$.
The lines PN and QM intersect at point G.
(b) Express, in terms of **p** and **q**, the vectors $\overrightarrow{PN}$ and $\overrightarrow{QM}$.
(c) Given that $\overrightarrow{GN} = \lambda\overrightarrow{PN}$, prove that $\overrightarrow{OG} = 2\lambda\mathbf{p} + (1 - \lambda)\mathbf{q}$.
(d) Given that $\overrightarrow{GM} = \mu\overrightarrow{QM}$, find $\overrightarrow{OG}$ in terms of μ, **p** and **q**.
(e) Hence prove that $\overrightarrow{OG} = \frac{2}{3}(\mathbf{p} + \mathbf{q})$.   (L)

12 The points P, Q have position vectors **p**, **q** relative to a fixed origin O. Show that the point R which divides the line joining PQ in the ratio $\lambda:(1 - \lambda)$ has position vector

$$\mathbf{r} = \lambda\mathbf{q} + (1 - \lambda)\mathbf{p}$$

Show on a diagram the relative positions of P, Q, R when $\lambda = 2$. The vertices A, B, C of a triangle have position vectors **a**, **b**, **c** respectively. The points D, E lie on AB, AC respectively and are such that $AD = 2DB$ and $2AE = EC$. Show that the point of intersection G of BE and CD has position vector

$$\frac{2\mathbf{a} + 4\mathbf{b} + \mathbf{c}}{7}$$

The line AG meets BC at F. Find the ratios:
(a) BF : FC   (b) AG : GF   (W)

13 Calculate the acute angle between the line with equation

$$\mathbf{r} = \begin{pmatrix} 2 \\ 6 \\ 1 \end{pmatrix} + t\begin{pmatrix} 1 \\ 3 \\ 2 \end{pmatrix}$$

and the z-axis, giving your answer correct to the nearest 0.1°.   (C)

14 The position vectors of three points A, B, C are given respectively by:

$$\mathbf{a} = \mathbf{i} + \mathbf{j} + 4\mathbf{k}$$
$$\mathbf{b} = 2\mathbf{i} - \mathbf{j} + 3\mathbf{k}$$
$$\mathbf{c} = 3\mathbf{i} - 3\mathbf{j}$$

Find the position vector of D, the fourth vertex of the parallelogram ABCD. Use the scalar (dot) product to determine, to the nearest degree, the acute angle between AB and BC.   (O & C)

15 The lines L and M are given respectively by the equations

$$\mathbf{r} = \begin{pmatrix} 2 \\ -3 \\ 1 \end{pmatrix} + s \begin{pmatrix} 1 \\ 2 \\ 2 \end{pmatrix} \quad \text{and} \quad \mathbf{r} = \begin{pmatrix} 8 \\ 5 \\ 13 \end{pmatrix} + t \begin{pmatrix} 3 \\ 2 \\ 6 \end{pmatrix}$$

Show that L and M intersect and find the position vector of A, their point of intersection.

Verify that L and M both lie in the plane Π given by the equation

$$2x - z = 3$$

The point B is (12, 5, 6) and the point C is the foot of the perpendicular from B to Π. Find the vector equation for BC and hence find the position vector of C. Show that C lies on L.   (JMB)

16 A transformation T of three dimensional space is defined by r′ = Mr, where

$$\mathbf{r} = \begin{pmatrix} x \\ y \\ z \end{pmatrix} \quad \mathbf{r'} = \begin{pmatrix} x' \\ y' \\ z' \end{pmatrix} \quad \text{and} \quad \mathbf{M} = \begin{pmatrix} -2 & 1 & 3 \\ 2 & 0 & -3 \\ -4 & 2 & 6 \end{pmatrix}$$

(a) Show that the plane $y = \lambda$ is transformed under T into a line L and that the direction of L is independent of λ. Specify this direction in terms of direction ratios.

(b) Show that the origin is the only invariant point under T.   (JMB)

17 Prove the identity $\dfrac{(\sin x + \cos x)^2}{\sin x \cos x} = 2 + \sec x \operatorname{cosec} x.$ (C)

18 (a) Simplify $\dfrac{\tan x + \cot x}{\operatorname{cosec} x}.$

(b) Find all the solutions, in the interval $0 \leqslant x \leqslant 2\pi$, of the equation $\cos 2x + \cos x = 0$.   (O & C)

19 (a) Find all the angles between 0° and 360° which satisfy the equation:

$$8 \sin x + 15 \cos x = 10$$

(b) Two acute angles, α and β, are such that $\tan \alpha = 4/3$ and $\tan(\alpha + \beta) = -1$. Without evaluating α or β,
(i) show that $\tan \beta = 7$,
(ii) evaluate $\sin \alpha$ and $\sin \beta$,
(iii) evaluate $\sin^2 2\alpha + \sin^2 2\beta$.   (C)

20 Express $\sqrt{6} \cos \theta - \sqrt{2} \sin \theta$ in the form $R \cos (\theta + \alpha)$ where $R > 0$ and $0 < \alpha < \frac{1}{2}\pi$.

Find the general solution, in radians, of the equation:

$$(\sqrt{6} \cos \theta - \sqrt{2} \sin \theta)^2 = 4 \qquad\qquad\qquad \text{(O)}$$

21 Find all the solutions in the interval $-\pi \leqslant \theta \leqslant \pi$ of the equation

$$2 \sin^2 \theta + 5 \cos \theta + 1 = 0$$

giving each solution in terms of π.

State the general solution of the equation.   (JMB)

22 Write down $\sin x + \sin 3x$ as a product of factors. Find in terms of π, the solutions of the equation

$$\sin x + \sin 3x = \sin 2x$$

which lie in the interval $-\pi < x \leqslant \pi$.

Find also the general solution of the equation.   (JMB)

23 Express $3 \sin x + 2 \cos x$ in the form $r \sin (x + \alpha)$, where r and α are constants, $r > 0$ and $0 < \alpha < 90°$.

Hence, or otherwise, find

(a) the least value of $(3 \sin x + 2 \cos x)^5$

(b) the solutions of the equation

$$3 \sin x + 2 \cos x = 1$$

for $0° < x < 360°$, giving your answers in degrees to 1 decimal place.   (L)

24 Solve the equation $9 \cos 2\theta + 6 \cos \theta + 5 = 0$ giving all the solutions in the range $0° < \theta < 360°$.   (W)

25 The pyramid VABCD has vertex V and a square base ABCD. Each side of the base has length 12 cm and the lengths of VA, VB, VC and VD are each 11 cm. The centre of the base is O and the mid-points of the sides AB and CD are P and Q respectively. Calculate:

(a) the height VO

(b) the size of the angle between edges VA and VC

(c) the length of the perpendicular from B to VA

(d) the size of the angle between the planes VAB and VAD

A sphere is placed inside the pyramid so that it touches the base and the four sloping faces. Calculate the size of the angle VPQ and hence, or otherwise, find the radius of the sphere.   (O)

Chapter 20

Derivatives of trigonometrical functions

20.1 Small angles

A glance at Figure 20.1 will show the reader that, for small acute angles, tan θ, θ and sin θ are practically equal.

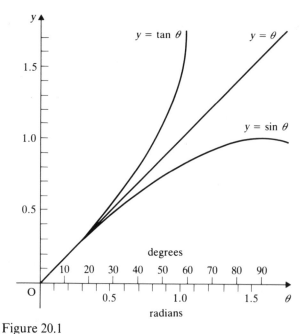

Figure 20.1

This is borne out by the following table:

Angle in degrees	10°	5°	1°
θ (radians)	0.174 532 9	0.087 266 5	0.017 453 3
tan θ	0.176 327 0	0.087 488 7	0.017 455 1
sin θ	0.173 648 2	0.087 155 7	0.017 452 4

We shall now consider this geometrically.

In Figure 20.2, the chord AB subtends an angle θ at the centre of a circle of radius r, and the tangent at B meets OA produced at D. Consider the three areas: triangle AOB, sector AOB, triangle DOB.

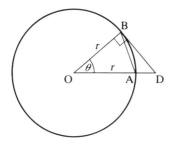

Figure 20.2

(a) In triangle AOB, two sides of length r include an angle θ, therefore its area is $\frac{1}{2}r^2 \sin \theta$ (see Section 19.4).
(b) From Section 19.5, the area of sector AOB is $\frac{1}{2}r^2\theta$.
(c) In triangle DOB, B is a right angle, therefore $BD = r \tan \theta$ and so its area is $\frac{1}{2}r^2 \tan \theta$.

From the figure it can be seen that

$$\text{triangle AOB} < \text{sector AOB} < \text{triangle DOB}$$
$$\therefore \quad \tfrac{1}{2}r^2 \sin \theta < \tfrac{1}{2}r^2\theta < \tfrac{1}{2}r^2 \tan \theta$$

But if we divide each term by $\frac{1}{2}r^2$ the order of magnitude is unchanged, therefore

$$\boxed{\sin \theta < \theta < \tan \theta}$$

providing θ is acute, as the figure requires. Again, if we divide each term by $\sin \theta$, the order of magnitude is unchanged, therefore

$$\frac{\sin \theta}{\sin \theta} < \frac{\theta}{\sin \theta} < \frac{\tan \theta}{\sin \theta}$$

But $\tan \theta = \sin \theta / \cos \theta$, therefore

$$1 < \frac{\theta}{\sin \theta} < \frac{1}{\cos \theta}$$

Now as $\theta \to 0$, $\cos \theta \to 1$,

$$\therefore \quad \frac{1}{\cos \theta} \to 1$$

Thus $\theta / \sin \theta$ lies between 1 and a function which approaches 1 as $\theta \to 0$.

$$\therefore \quad \boxed{\frac{\theta}{\sin\theta} \to 1 \quad \text{as} \quad \theta \to 0}$$

(See Chapter 3, Example 14 (p64) and Qu. 11 (p66).)

This limit (or, more strictly, $(\sin\theta)/\theta \to 1$ as $\theta \to 0$) is required in the next section for the differentiation of $\sin x$.

Another way of expressing the statement that $\theta/\sin\theta \to 1$ as $\theta \to 0$, is to say that, for small values of θ,

$$\boxed{\sin\theta \approx \theta}$$

An approximation for $\cos\theta$ is obtained from the identity

$$\cos\theta = 1 - 2\sin^2 \tfrac{1}{2}\theta$$

If θ is small, $\sin\tfrac{1}{2}\theta \approx \tfrac{1}{2}\theta$, therefore

$$\cos\theta \approx 1 - 2(\tfrac{1}{2}\theta)^2$$

Therefore, for small values of θ,

$$\boxed{\cos\theta \approx 1 - \tfrac{1}{2}\theta^2}$$

Example 1

Find the approximate value of $\dfrac{1 - \cos 2\theta}{\theta \tan\theta}$ when θ is small.

We cannot put $\theta = 0$, as the numerator and denominator would both be zero. Since $\cos\theta \approx 1 - \tfrac{1}{2}\theta^2$,

$$\cos 2\theta \approx 1 - \tfrac{1}{2}(2\theta)^2 = 1 - 2\theta^2$$

Therefore the numerator $\approx 2\theta^2$. But the denominator $\approx \theta^2$, since $\tan\theta \approx \theta$. Therefore, when θ is small,

$$\frac{1 - \cos 2\theta}{\theta \tan\theta} \approx \frac{2\theta^2}{\theta^2}$$

$$\therefore \quad \frac{1 - \cos 2\theta}{\theta \tan\theta} \approx 2 \quad \text{when } \theta \text{ is small}$$

Qu. 1 Find approximations for the following functions when θ is small:

(a) $\dfrac{\sin 3\theta}{2\theta}$

(b) $\dfrac{\sin 4\theta}{\sin 2\theta}$

(c) $\dfrac{1 - \cos\theta}{\theta^2}$

(d) $\dfrac{\theta \sin\theta}{1 - \cos 2\theta}$

(e) $\dfrac{\sin(\alpha + \theta)\sin\theta}{\theta}$

(f) $\dfrac{\sin(\alpha + \theta) - \sin\alpha}{\theta}$

(g) $\dfrac{\sin\theta \tan\theta}{1 - \cos 3\theta}$

(h) $\sin\theta \operatorname{cosec} \tfrac{1}{2}\theta$

(i) $\dfrac{\tan(\alpha + \theta) - \tan\alpha}{\theta}$

20.2 Derivatives of sin *x* and cos *x*

The graph of sin *x* may be sketched, as shown in Figure 20.3, and from it may be obtained a rough graph of its gradient. The gradient is zero at B, D, F, positive from A to B and from D to F, and negative from B to D, giving a graph like the one in Figure 20.4.

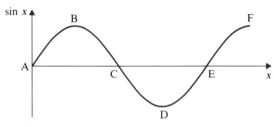

Figure 20.3

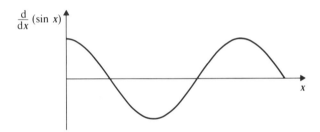

Figure 20.4

Qu. 2 Does Figure 20.4 resemble any graph you have met so far?
Qu. 3 Express sin *A* − sin *B* in factors. (See Section 18.8.)

We shall now find the derivative of sin *x* from first principles, using the definition in Section 4.8, that is

$$f'(x) = \lim_{h \to 0} \frac{f(x+h) - f(x)}{h}$$

[The reader is advised to review Section 4.8 before proceeding further.]

In this case, $f(x) = \sin x$, and so

$$f(x+h) - f(x) = \sin(x+h) - \sin x$$

Using the factor formula (see Qu. 3 above), this can be written:

$$f(x+h) - f(x) = 2 \cos \frac{x+h+x}{2} \sin \frac{h}{2}$$

$$\therefore \quad \frac{f(x+h) - f(x)}{h} = \frac{2 \cos \dfrac{2x+h}{2} \sin \dfrac{h}{2}}{h}$$

$$= \frac{\cos (x + \tfrac{1}{2}h) \sin \tfrac{1}{2}h}{\tfrac{1}{2}h} \qquad \qquad \cdots \ (1)$$

But we know that when $h \rightarrow 0$,

$$\cos(x + \tfrac{1}{2}h) \rightarrow \cos x \quad \text{and} \quad \frac{\sin \tfrac{1}{2}h}{\tfrac{1}{2}h} \rightarrow 1$$

Therefore, when $h \rightarrow 0$, the right-hand side of equation (1) tends to $\cos x$. So, for this function,

$$f'(x) = \cos x$$

In Leibnitz notation, this is written:

$$y = \sin x$$

$$\frac{dy}{dx} = \cos x$$

Or, more concisely,

$$\boxed{\frac{d}{dx}(\sin x) = \cos x}$$

Qu. 4 At what stage in the above is it necessary to have x in radians?
Qu. 5 Prove from first principles that

$$\boxed{\frac{d}{dx}(\cos x) = -\sin x}$$

Remember that these results hold only if x is in radians.

Example 2

Differentiate (a) $\sin(2x + 3)$ (b) $\cos^2 x$ (c) $\sin x°$.

(a) Let $y = \sin(2x + 3)$ and $t = 2x + 3$

then $y = \sin t$

$$\therefore \quad \frac{dy}{dx} = \cos t \quad \text{and} \quad \frac{dt}{dx} = 2$$

But $\dfrac{dy}{dx} = \dfrac{dy}{dt} \times \dfrac{dt}{dx} = (\cos t)2,$

$$\therefore \quad \frac{d}{dx}\{\sin(2x + 3)\} = 2\cos(2x + 3)$$

(b) Let $y = \cos^2 x$ and $t = \cos x$

then $y = t^2$

$$\frac{dy}{dx} = \frac{dy}{dt} \times \frac{dt}{dx} = 2t(-\sin x) = -2\cos x \sin x$$

$\therefore \quad \dfrac{d}{dx}(\cos^2 x) = -\sin 2x$

(c) Let $y = \sin x°$.   Now $x° = (\pi/180)x$ radians,

$\therefore \quad y = \sin \dfrac{\pi}{180}x$

Put $t = (\pi/180)x$ then $y = \sin t$.

$\dfrac{dy}{dx} = \dfrac{dy}{dt} \times \dfrac{dt}{dx} = (\cos t)\dfrac{\pi}{180} = \dfrac{\pi}{180}\cos \dfrac{\pi}{180}x = \dfrac{\pi}{180}\cos x°$

$\therefore \quad \dfrac{d}{dx}(\sin x°) = \dfrac{\pi}{180}\cos x°$

Qu. 6 Differentiate:
(a) $\cos 3x$ (b) $\sin^2 x$ (c) $2 \sin 2x$ (d) $\cos^3 x$

Example 3

Integrate (a) $\cos 2x$ (b) $3 \sin \frac{1}{2}x$.

The method used here is to change cos to sin, or sin to cos, and to determine the coefficient by differentiation:

(a) $\qquad \dfrac{d}{dx}(\sin 2x) = 2 \cos 2x$

$\therefore \qquad \dfrac{d}{dx}(\frac{1}{2}\sin 2x) = \cos 2x$

$\therefore \qquad \int \cos 2x \, dx = \frac{1}{2}\sin 2x + c$

(b) $\qquad \dfrac{d}{dx}(3 \cos \frac{1}{2}x) = -\frac{3}{2}\sin \frac{1}{2}x$

$\therefore \qquad \dfrac{d}{dx}(-2 \times 3 \cos \frac{1}{2}x) = 3 \sin \frac{1}{2}x$

$\therefore \qquad \int 3 \sin \frac{1}{2}x \, dx = -6 \cos \frac{1}{2}x + c$

Exercise 20a

1 Differentiate:
(a) $\cos 2x$ (b) $\sin 6x$ (c) $\cos (3x - 1)$
(d) $\sin (2x - 3)$ (e) $-3 \cos 5x$ (f) $2 \sin 4x$
(g) $-4 \sin \frac{3}{2}x$ (h) $2 \sin \frac{1}{2}(x + 1)$ (i) $\sin x^2$

2 Integrate:
(a) $\sin 3x$ (b) $\cos 3x$ (c) $2 \sin 4x$
(d) $2 \cos 2x$ (e) $-\frac{1}{2}\sin 6x$ (f) $6 \cos 4x$
(g) $\sin (2x + 1)$ (h) $3 \cos (2x - 1)$ (i) $\frac{2}{3}\sin \frac{1}{2}x$

3 Differentiate:
(a) $\sin^2 x$ (b) $4\cos^2 x$ (c) $\cos^3 x$
(d) $2\sin^3 x$ (e) $3\cos^4 x$ (f) $\sqrt{(\sin x)}$
(g) $\sqrt{(\cos x)}$ (h) $\cos^2 3x$ (i) $\sin^2 2x$
(j) $-2\sin^3 3x$ (k) $3\sin^4 2x$ (l) $\sqrt{(\sin 2x)}$

4 Differentiate:
(a) $x\cos x$ (b) $x\sin 2x$ (c) $x^2 \sin x$

(d) $\sin x \cos x$ (e) $\dfrac{\sin x}{x}$ (f) $\dfrac{\cos 2x}{x}$

(g) $\dfrac{x}{\sin x}$ (h) $\dfrac{x^2}{\cos x}$ (i) $\dfrac{\sin x}{\cos x}$

(j) $\cot x$ (k) $\dfrac{1}{\cos x}$ (l) $\operatorname{cosec} x$

5 A particle moves in a straight line such that its velocity in m s^{-1}, t s after passing through a fixed point O, is $3\cos t - 2\sin t$. Find:
(a) its distance from O after $\frac{1}{2}\pi$ s
(b) its acceleration after π s
(c) the time when its velocity is first zero

6 A particle is moving in a straight line in such a way that its distance from a fixed point O, t s after the motion begins, is $\cos t + \cos 2t$ cm. Find:
(a) the time when the particle first passes through O
(b) the velocity of the particle at this instant
(c) the acceleration when the velocity is zero

7 A particle moves in a straight line so that its distance from a fixed point O is given by

$$s = 3\cos 2t + 4\sin 2t$$

Show that the velocity v and the acceleration a are given by $v^2 + 4s^2 = 100$, $a + 4s = 0$. Hence find:
(a) the greatest distance of the particle from O
(b) the acceleration at this instant

8 The velocity at time t of a particle moving in a straight line is $6\cos 2t + \cos t$, and when $t = 0$, the particle is at O. Find:
(a) the time when v is first zero
(b) the distance from O at this instant
(c) the acceleration at the same instant

9 Find the area between the curve $y = \sin 3x$ and the x-axis between $x = 0$ and $x = \frac{1}{3}\pi$.

10 Sketch the curve $y = 1 + \cos x$ from $x = -\pi$ to $x = \pi$, and find the area enclosed by the curve and the x-axis between these limits.

11 Find the maximum value of $y = x + \sin 2x$ which is given by a value of x between 0 and $\frac{1}{2}\pi$. Sketch the graph of y for $0 \leqslant x \leqslant \frac{1}{2}\pi$ and find the area bounded by the curve, the x-axis and the line $x = \frac{1}{2}\pi$.

12 Find the maximum value of $y = 2\sin x - x$ which is given by a value of x between 0 and $\frac{1}{2}\pi$. Sketch the graph of y for values of x from 0 to π, and find the area between the curve, the x-axis and the line $x = \frac{1}{2}\pi$.

13 Show that $\frac{d}{dx}(\frac{1}{2}x - \frac{1}{4}\sin 2x) = \sin^2 x$ and deduce that

$$\int_0^\pi \sin^2 x \, dx = \frac{1}{2}\pi$$

14 Express $\cos^2 x$ in terms of $\cos 2x$, and hence show that

$$\int \cos^2 x \, dx = \frac{1}{2}x + \frac{1}{4}\sin 2x + c$$

15 Show that $\cos^3 x = \frac{1}{4}(\cos 3x + 3\cos x)$, and deduce that

$$\int \cos^3 x \, dx = \frac{1}{12}\sin 3x + \frac{3}{4}\sin x + c = \sin x - \frac{1}{3}\sin^3 x + c$$

16 By expressing $\sin^3 x$ in terms of $\sin x$ and $\sin 3x$, show that

$$\int \sin^3 x \, dx = \frac{1}{12}\cos 3x - \frac{3}{4}\cos x + c = \frac{1}{3}\cos^3 x - \cos x + c$$

17 Express $2\cos 5x \cos 3x$ as a sum of two cosines and hence evaluate

$$\int_0^{\pi/4} 2\cos 5x \cos 3x \, dx$$

20.3 Derivatives of tan *x*, cot *x*, sec *x*, cosec *x*

Using the derivatives of $\sin x$ and $\cos x$, those of the four other trigonometrical ratios can be obtained by writing

$$\tan x = \frac{\sin x}{\cos x} \qquad \cot x = \frac{\cos x}{\sin x}$$

$$\sec x = \frac{1}{\cos x} \qquad \text{cosec } x = \frac{1}{\sin x}$$

This is left as an exercise for the reader. The results are

$\dfrac{d}{dx}(\tan x) = \sec^2 x$	$\dfrac{d}{dx}(\cot x) = -\text{cosec}^2 x$
$\dfrac{d}{dx}(\sec x) = \sec x \tan x$	$\dfrac{d}{dx}(\text{cosec } x) = -\text{cosec } x \cot x$

Note
(a) the similarity of the pair of formulae on each line
(b) the associations between $\tan x$ and $\sec x$, and between $\cot x$ and $\text{cosec } x$. The same associations occur in the identities $1 + \tan^2 x = \sec^2 x$, $\cot^2 x + 1 = \text{cosec}^2 x$
(c) that the derivatives of ratios beginning with 'co', i.e. $\cos x$, $\cot x$, $\text{cosec } x$, all have a negative sign.

Exercise 20b

1 Differentiate:
  (a) $\tan 2x$ (b) $\cot 3x$ (c) $3 \sec 2x$
  (d) $2 \operatorname{cosec} \frac{1}{2}x$ (e) $-\tan (2x + 1)$ (f) $\frac{1}{3} \sec (3x - 2)$
  (g) $-2 \cot (3x + 2)$ (h) $\cot x^2$ (i) $\tan \sqrt{x}$

2 Differentiate:
  (a) $\tan^2 x$ (b) $\sec^2 x$ (c) $2 \cot^3 x$
  (d) $3 \operatorname{cosec}^2 x$ (e) $-\tan^2 2x$† (f) $\frac{1}{2} \cot^2 3x$
  (g) $\frac{1}{6} \sec^3 2x$ (h) $-2 \operatorname{cosec}^4 x$ (i) $\sqrt{(\tan x)}$

3 Differentiate:
  (a) $x \tan x$ (b) $\sec x \tan x$ (c) $x^2 \cot x$
  (d) $3x \operatorname{cosec} x$ (e) $\operatorname{cosec} x \cot x$ (f) $\dfrac{\tan x}{x}$
  (g) $\dfrac{\sec x}{x^2}$ (h) $\sin x - x \cos x$ (i) $x \sec^2 x - \tan x$

4 Integrate:
  (a) $\sec^2 2x$ (b) $3 \sec x \tan x$ (c) $-\operatorname{cosec}^2 \frac{1}{2}x$
  (d) $\frac{1}{3} \operatorname{cosec} 3x \cot 3x$ (e) $2 \sec^2 x \tan x$ (f) $\dfrac{1}{\cos^2 x}$
  (g) $\dfrac{\sin x}{\cos^2 x}$ (h) $\dfrac{1}{\sin^2 2x}$ (i) $\dfrac{\cos 2x}{\sin^2 2x}$

5 Sketch the graph of the curve $y = \sec^2 x - 1$ between $x = -\frac{1}{2}\pi$ and $x = \frac{1}{2}\pi$. Calculate the area enclosed by the curve, the x-axis and the line $x = \frac{1}{4}\pi$.
6 Find the volume generated by revolving the area bounded by the x-axis, the lines $x = \pm\frac{1}{4}\pi$ and the curve $y = \sec x$ about the x-axis.
7 Find the minimum values of the following functions which are given by values of x between 0 and $\frac{1}{2}\pi$:
  (a) $\tan x + 3 \cot x$ (b) $\sec x + 8 \operatorname{cosec} x$ (c) $6 \sec x + \cot x$
8 By expressing $\tan^2 x$ in terms of $\sec^2 x$, show that:
$$\int \tan^2 x \, dx = \tan x - x + c$$
9 Express $\cot^2 x$ in terms of $\operatorname{cosec}^2 x$ and hence integrate $\cot^2 x$.

Exercise 20c (Miscellaneous)

1 Find approximations for the following when θ is small:
  (a) $\dfrac{\sin \theta \tan \theta}{\theta^2}$ (b) $\dfrac{1 - \cos 2\theta}{\theta \sin 3\theta}$ (c) $\dfrac{\cos (\theta + \alpha) - \cos \alpha}{\theta}$

† The following method of working often overcomes the initial difficulty some students find with the chain rule:
$$\frac{d}{dx}(3 \sin^4 5x) = \frac{d}{dx}\{3(\sin 5x)^4\} = 3 \times 4(\sin 5x)^3 \times \cos 5x \times 5 = 60 \sin^3 5x \cos 5x.$$

2 Show that, if θ is small:

(a) $\sin\left(\frac{1}{6}\pi + \theta\right) \approx \frac{1}{2} + \frac{1}{2}\sqrt{3}\theta - \frac{1}{4}\theta^2$ (b) $\cos\left(\frac{1}{4}\pi + \theta\right) \approx \frac{1}{2}\sqrt{2}(1 - \theta - \frac{1}{2}\theta^2)$.

3 Differentiate:

(a) $\sin 3x$ (b) $\tan\frac{1}{2}x$ (c) $\cos x^2$

(d) $\sqrt{(\cos x)}$ (e) $2\operatorname{cosec}^3 x$ (f) $4\sin^2\frac{1}{2}x$

(g) $-3\sec^3 2x$ (h) $\sqrt{(\sin 2x)}$ (i) $3\tan^2 2x$

4 Integrate:

(a) $\cos 2x$ (b) $\sin(2x - 1)$ (c) $3\cos\frac{1}{2}x$

(d) $\sec^2\frac{1}{2}x$ (e) $\operatorname{cosec} x \cot x$ (f) $\sec 2x \tan 2x$

(g) $\dfrac{\cos x}{\sin^2 x}$ (h) $\dfrac{1}{\cos^2 2x}$ (i) $x\sin x^2$

5 Differentiate:

(a) $x\sin x$ (b) $\sin x \cos 2x$ (c) $x^2\tan^2 x$

(d) $\dfrac{\sec x}{x}$ (e) $\dfrac{\cos 2x}{\sin 3x}$ (f) $\sin x \tan 2x$

(g) $\dfrac{\sin x}{x^2}$ (h) $2\cos x + 2x\sin x - x^2\cos x$

6 Evaluate:

(a) $\displaystyle\int_0^{\pi/2} \sin 2x \, dx$ (b) $\displaystyle\int_{-\pi/3}^{\pi/6} \sec^2 x \, dx$

(c) $\displaystyle\int_0^{\pi} \sin^2 x \, dx$ (d) $\displaystyle\int_0^{\pi/4} \cos 3x \sin 5x \, dx$

7 Find:

(a) $\int \tan^2 x \, dx$ (b) $\int 2\cos 4x \cos 3x \, dx$

(c) $24\int \sin 7x \sin 5x \, dx$ (d) $\int (\sin x + \cos x)^2 \, dx$

8 If $x = a\cos\theta$, $y = b\tan\theta$, show that

$$\frac{d^2 y}{dx^2} = -\frac{b}{a^2}\operatorname{cosec}^3\theta$$

The remaining questions in this exercise revise the earlier chapters on trigonometry.

9 Convert to degrees:

(a) $\dfrac{\pi}{100}$ (b) $\dfrac{\pi}{5}$ (c) $\dfrac{5\pi}{3}$ (d) 7π

10 Convert to radians, leaving π in your answers:

(a) $10°$ (b) $15°$ (c) $330°$ (d) $400°$

11 Use a calculator to find the values of:

(a) $\sin(2 \text{ rad})$ (b) $\sec(0.5 \text{ rad})$ (c) $\tan(1.32 \text{ rad})$ (d) $\cos(2.98 \text{ rad})$

12 The area of a sector of a circle, radius 5 cm, is 20 cm^2. What is the length of the arc of the sector?

13 A sector with an area of $\frac{2}{3}$ cm^2 is bounded by an arc of length $\frac{5}{6}$ cm. What is the radius of the circle? Also find the angle contained by the sector, giving your answer in degrees.

14 A chord AB subtends a right angle at the centre of a circle of radius r. BC is a chord in the minor segment, inclined at 15° to BA. Show that the area bounded by the two chords and the arc AC is $\frac{1}{2}r^2(\frac{1}{6}\pi + \frac{1}{2}\sqrt{3} - 1)$.

15 The common chord of two circles of radii 13 cm and 37 cm is 24 cm long. Calculate the area common to both circles.

16 Draw, on the same diagram, the graphs of $y = x - 1$ and $y = \sin x$, where x is in radians, and $-\pi \leqslant x \leqslant +\pi$. Hence show that the equation

$$x = 1 + \sin x$$

has one root only. Estimate this root from your graph.

17 Draw the graph of $\cos 2\theta$ for values of θ from $-\frac{1}{2}\pi$ to $\frac{1}{2}\pi$. Use your graph to solve the equation $\cos^2 \theta = \frac{1}{2}(1 + \theta)$.

18 Draw the graph of $\cos 3\theta + \cos \theta$ for values of θ from 0 to π, and find the roots of the equation

$$2\cos 3\theta + 2\cos \theta + 1 = 0$$

in this range.

19 Without using a calculator, prove that

$$\sin 72° - \sin 144° - \sin 216° + \sin 288° = 0$$

20 Show that $\tan x + \cot x = 2 \operatorname{cosec} 2x$

Hence solve the equation

$$\tan x + \cot x = 4$$

for values of x between 0° and 360°.

Chapter 21

Coordinate geometry

21.1 Loci

'Percy the goat is tethered to a fixed point O by a rope which is 6 m long. If
Percy moves so that the rope is always taut, describe his path.' Readers will
have little difficulty deciding that the goat moves around a circle, centre O,
radius 6 m. (A scale drawing could be made, using a piece of string 6 cm long,
fixed at one end by a drawing-pin and with a pencil at the other end; as the
pencil moves, keeping the string taut, a circle can be drawn.)

Now consider this problem: 'Percy the goat is tethered by means of a ring
which can slide freely on a rope which is 6 m long. The ends of the rope are
attached to two fixed points A and B which are 4 m apart. Describe the goat's
path'. In this case there are probably few readers who could give the path a
name. However, a scale drawing could be made, using a piece of string 6 cm
long with its ends attached to two drawing pins which are fixed, 4 cm apart.
Use a pencil to trace the goat's path, being careful to keep the string taut. The
diagram should look something like Figure 21.1. Note that at all points on the
path, AP + PB = 6.

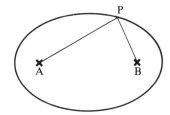

Figure 21.1

In this chapter, we shall use the techniques introduced earlier in the book to
investigate problems like this. In particular, the moving point P will be represented by a point in the Cartesian plane with coordinates (x, y) (we shall only
consider two-dimensional problems) and we shall endeavour to find an equation
which expresses, algebraically, the conditions governing the motion of P. (It is
customary, in this context, to use P to represent the *moving* point; any *fixed*

433

points are usually represented by A, B or C, although in many cases the origin O will be used as a fixed point.) The path traced out by the point P, as it moves according to the given conditions, is called the **locus** of P, and the equation satisfied by the coordinates of P is called the equation of the locus.

21.2 The equation of a locus

In the first of the introductory problems above, the given condition is $OP = 6$, so, if O is the origin, the equation of the locus can be obtained by applying Pythagoras' theorem in Figure 21.2.

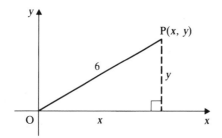

Figure 21.2

i.e. the equation of the locus is

$$x^2 + y^2 = 36$$

In the second problem, we shall take the two fixed points to be $(-2, 0)$ and $(2, 0)$, respectively (Figure 21.3).

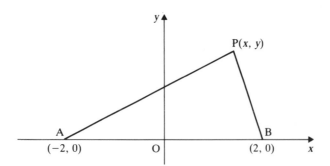

Figure 21.3

Applying the usual formula for the distance between two points we obtain

$$AP = \sqrt{\{(x + 2)^2 + y^2\}} \quad \text{and} \quad BP = \sqrt{\{(x - 2)^2 + y^2\}}$$

The condition which governs the movement of the point P is $AP + PB = 6$, so the equation of the locus is

$$\sqrt{\{(x + 2)^2 + y^2\}} + \sqrt{\{(x - 2)^2 + y^2\}} = 6$$

Qu. 1 Show that when the equation above is simplified it can be expressed as

$$\frac{x^2}{9} + \frac{y^2}{5} = 1$$

This curve is called an *ellipse*.

Example 1

Find the equation of the locus of a point P which moves so that it is equidistant from two fixed points A and B whose coordinates are (3, 2) and (5, −1) respectively.

Let P be the point (x, y). Expressed geometrically, the condition satisfied by P is

PA = PB

However, since we shall use Pythagoras' theorem to express the lengths of PA and PB in terms of x and y, it is neater to square this equation, obtaining

$PA^2 = PB^2$

Now

$$PA^2 = (x - 3)^2 + (y - 2)^2$$
$$PB^2 = (x - 5)^2 + (y + 1)^2$$

therefore the equation which must be satisfied by the coordinates of P is

$$(x - 3)^2 + (y - 2)^2 = (x - 5)^2 + (y + 1)^2$$
i.e. $x^2 - 6x + 9 + y^2 - 4y + 4 = x^2 - 10x + 25 + y^2 + 2y + 1$

Therefore the equation of the locus of points equidistant from (3, 2) and (5, −1) is $4x - 6y - 13 = 0$.

The locus is actually the perpendicular bisector (or mediator) of AB. Because of the close connection between the locus and the equation connecting the points lying on the locus, the equation itself is often referred to as the locus.

Qu. 2 Find the equation of the locus in Example 1 by using the fact that it is the perpendicular bisector of AB.

Note When drawing graphs it is often useful to take different scales on the two axes, but in coordinate geometry the scales must be the same or the figures will be distorted.

Example 2

Find the locus of a point P, whose distance from the point A(−1, 2) is twice its distance from the origin.

Let P(x, y) be a point on the locus (Figure 21.4), then

$$PA = 2PO$$

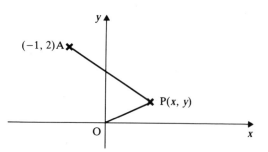

Figure 21.4

The lengths of PA and PO may be written down by the method of Section 2.2, but as both expressions involve a square root, it is neater to square first, giving

$$PA^2 = 4PO^2$$

$$\therefore \quad (x + 1)^2 + (y - 2)^2 = 4(x^2 + y^2)$$

$$\therefore \quad x^2 + 2x + 1 + y^2 - 4y + 4 = 4x^2 + 4y^2$$

Therefore the locus of P is $3x^2 + 3y^2 - 2x + 4y - 5 = 0$.

Exercise 21a

1 Find the equation of a circle with centre at the origin and radius 5 units.
2 What is the locus of a point which moves so that its distance from the point (3, 1) is 2 units?
3 What is the locus of a point which is equidistant from the origin and the point $(-2, 5)$?
4 What is the locus of a point which moves so that its distance from the point $(-2, 1)$ is equal to its distance from the point $(3, -2)$?
5 What is the distance of the point (x, y) from the line $x = -1$? Find the locus of a point which is equidistant from the origin and the line $x = -1$.
6 Find the locus of a point which is equidistant from the point $(0, 1)$ and the line $y = -1$.
7 Find the locus of a point which moves so that its distance from the point $A(-2, 0)$ is three times its distance from the origin.
8 A point P moves so that its distance from $A(2, 1)$ is twice its distance from $B(-4, 5)$. What is the locus of P?
9 Find the locus of a point which moves so that its distance from the point $(8, 0)$ is twice its distance from the line $x = 2$.
10 Find the locus of a point which moves so that its distance from the point $(2, 0)$ is half its distance from the line $x = 8$.
11 Find the locus of a point which moves so that the sum of the squares of its distances from the points $(-2, 0)$ and $(2, 0)$ is 26 units.

12 Find the locus of a point which moves so that it is equidistant from the point $(a, 0)$ and the line $x = -a$.

13 A is the point $(1, 0)$, and B is the point $(-1, 0)$. Find the locus of a point P which moves so that $PA + PB = 4$.

14 A is the point $(1, 0)$, and B is the point $(-1, 0)$, Find the locus of a point P which moves so that $PA - PB = 2$.

15 A rectangle is formed by the axes and the lines $x = 4$ and $y = 6$. Find the locus of a point which moves so that the sum of the squares of its distances from the axes is equal to the sum of the squares of its distances from the other two sides.

21.3 Tangents and normals

If a tangent touches a curve at the point P, the line through P perpendicular to the tangent is called a **normal**. (See Section 4.9.)

Example 3

Find the equations of the tangent and normal to the curve $y = 3x^2 - 8x + 5$, at the point where $x = 2$.

[The equation of a line can be found from its gradient and the coordinates of a point through which it passes. Therefore we begin by finding these.]

$$y = 3x^2 - 8x + 5$$

Therefore the gradient of the tangent, $\dfrac{dy}{dx}$, is given by

$$\frac{dy}{dx} = 6x - 8$$

At the point of contact $x = 2$, and so

$$\frac{dy}{dx} = 6 \times 2 - 8 = 4$$

The y-coordinate of the point of contact may be found by substituting $x = 2$ in the equation of the curve:

$$y = 3 \times 2^2 - 8 \times 2 + 5 = 1$$

Therefore the coordinates of the point of contact are $(2, 1)$.

Using the equation of a line in the form

$$y - y_1 = m(x - x_1)$$

the equation of the tangent is

$$y - 1 = 4(x - 2)$$

i.e. $4x - y - 7 = 0$

The normal is perpendicular to the tangent, and so its gradient is $-\frac{1}{4}$. Therefore its equation may be written

$$y - 1 = -\tfrac{1}{4}(x - 2)$$
i.e. $x + 4y - 6 = 0$

Thus the equations of the tangent and normal to the curve $y = 3x^2 - 8x + 5$ at the point (2, 1) are respectively $4x - y - 7 = 0$ and $x + 4y - 6 = 0$.

Note It should be emphasised that, when the equation of the tangent was found, the gradient of the curve *at* (2, 1) was used. If we had taken the gradient to be $6x - 8$, the equation $y - 1 = (6x - 8)(x - 2)$ would not have represented a straight line.

Example 4

Find the equations of the tangents to the curve $xy = 6$ which are parallel to the line $2y + 3x = 0$.

The gradient of the line $2y + 3x = 0$ is $-\frac{3}{2}$. Therefore we must find at what points on the curve $xy = 6$ the gradient is $-\frac{3}{2}$.

$$y = \frac{6}{x}$$

$$\therefore \quad \frac{dy}{dx} = -\frac{6}{x^2}$$

If $\quad \dfrac{dy}{dx} = -3/2$

$$-\frac{6}{x^2} = -\frac{3}{2}$$

$$\therefore \quad 3x^2 = 12, \quad \text{and so} \quad x^2 = 4$$

$$\therefore \quad x = \pm 2$$

When $x = 2$, $y = \frac{6}{2} = 3$; and when $x = -2$, $y = -\frac{6}{2} = -3$. Thus the gradient of the curve is $-\frac{3}{2}$ at the points (2, 3) and (−2, −3).

The equations of the tangents may be found from the form $y - y_1 = m(x - x_1)$:

$$y - 3 = -\tfrac{3}{2}(x - 2) \quad \text{and} \quad y + 3 = -\tfrac{3}{2}(x + 2)$$

Therefore the equations of the tangents to the curve $xy = 6$ which are parallel to the line $2y + 3x = 0$ are $3x + 2y - 12 = 0$ and $3x + 2y + 12 = 0$.

Sometimes questions about tangents may be solved without using calculus. Figure 21.5 shows a curve with a chord PQ passing through a fixed point P

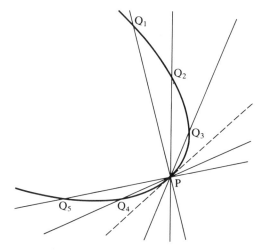

Figure 21.5

and a variable point Q. When P and Q are distinct, we must obtain distinct roots when the equations of the curve and PQ are solved simultaneously; and when P and Q coincide, producing a tangent, there will be a repeated root.

Example 5

Show that if the line $y = mx + c$ is a tangent to the curve $4x^2 + 3y^2 = 12$ then $c^2 = 3m^2 + 4$.

[If the line $y = mx + c$ is a tangent, then the point of contact must be given by an equation with a repeated root.]

Substituting $y = mx + c$ in the equation $4x^2 + 3y^2 = 12$, we obtain

$$4x^2 + 3(mx + c)^2 = 12$$
$$\therefore \quad 4x^2 + 3m^2x^2 + 6mxc + 3c^2 = 12$$
$$\therefore \quad (4 + 3m^2)x^2 + 6mcx + 3c^2 - 12 = 0$$

Now if the equation $ax^2 + bx + c = 0$ has equal roots then $b^2 = 4ac$ (see Section 11.2). Therefore if $y = mx + c$ is a tangent,

$$36m^2c^2 = 4(4 + 3m^2)(3c^2 - 12)$$
$$\therefore \quad 9m^2c^2 = 12c^2 - 48 + 9m^2c^2 - 36m^2$$
$$\therefore \quad 12c^2 = 36m^2 + 48$$

Therefore if $y = mx + c$ is a tangent to the curve $4x^2 + 3y^2 = 12$, then $c^2 = 3m^2 + 4$.

This means that the line $y = mx \pm \sqrt{(3m^2 + 4)}$ will touch the curve for all values of m. Hence we may find the tangents parallel to $y = 2x$, say by substituting $m = 2$, which gives $y = 2x \pm 4$.

Qu. 3 Find the equations of the tangents to the curve $4x^2 + 3y^2 = 12$ which are:

(a) parallel to $y = x$ (b) inclined at $60°$ to the x-axis

Qu. 4 Solve the following pairs of simultaneous equations:

(a) $y = x$, $y^2 = x^3 + x^2$ (b) $y = 2x$, $y^2 = x^3 + x^2$

What is the significance of the repeated root in each case?

Exercise 21b

1 Find the equations of the tangents and normals to the following curves at the points indicated:

(a) $y = x^2$, $(2, 4)$ (b) $y = 3x^2 - 2x + 1$,   where $x = 1$
(c) $y = x + 1/x$, $(-1, -2)$ (d) $y^2 = 4x$, $(1, -2)$
(e) $y = x^2 - 2x$, where $x = -2$ (f) $xy = 4$, where $y = 2$
(g) $y^3 = x^2$, $(1, 1)$

2 Show that the following lines touch the given curves and find the coordinates of the points of contact:

(a) $y^2 = 8x$, $y - 2x - 1 = 0$ (b) $x^2 + y^2 = 8$, $x - y - 4 = 0$
(c) $xy = 4$, $x + 9y - 12 = 0$ (d) $9x^2 - 4y^2 = 36$, $5x - 2y + 8 = 0$

3 At what points does the parabola $y = x^2 - 4x + 3$ cut the x-axis? Find the equations of the tangents and normals at these points.

4 Find the equations of the tangents at the points of intersection of the line $y = x + 1$ and the parabola $y = x^2 - x - 2$.

5 Find the equations of the normals to the curve $y = x^2 - 1$ at the points where it cuts the x-axis. What are the coordinates of the point of intersection of these normals?

6 Show that the equation of the tangent to the rectangular hyperbola $xy = c^2$ at the point (h, k) may be written $xk + yh - 2c^2 = 0$. Find the equation of the tangent which passes through the point $(0, c)$.

7 Show that, if the line $y = x + c$ is a tangent to the circle $x^2 + y^2 = 4$, then $c^2 = 8$.

8 Prove that the condition that the line $y = mx + c$ should touch the ellipse $x^2 + 4y^2 = 4$ is $c^2 = 4m^2 + 1$. Hence find the equations of the tangents to the ellipse which are parallel to the line $3x - 8y = 0$.

9 Show that the line $y = mx + c$ touches the hyperbola $b^2 x^2 - a^2 y^2 = a^2 b^2$ if $c^2 = a^2 m^2 - b^2$. Hence find the equations of the tangents to the hyperbola $9x^2 - 25y^2 = 225$ which are parallel to the line $x - y = 0$.

10 Find the condition that the line $lx + my + n = 0$ should touch the ellipse $b^2 x^2 + a^2 y^2 = a^2 b^2$.

21.4 The equation of a circle

We begin by obtaining the equation of a circle, radius r, with its centre at the origin.

We require an equation connecting the coordinates (x, y) of any point P on the circle (see Figure 21.6). Let N be the foot of the perpendicular from P to the x-axis, so that $ON = x$ and $NP = y$.

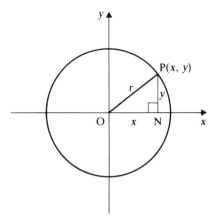

Figure 21.6

Then by Pythagoras' theorem,

$$ON^2 + NP^2 = r^2$$
$$\therefore \quad x^2 + y^2 = r^2$$

Therefore the equation of the circle, radius r, with its centre at the origin is

$$\boxed{x^2 + y^2 = r^2}$$

This is the simplest form in which the equation of a circle can be written, but now, to be quite general, consider the circle, radius r, whose centre is at the point $C(a, b)$.

Let $P(x, y)$ be any point on the circle, and draw CN and NP parallel to the x- and y-axes, as shown in Figure 21.7.

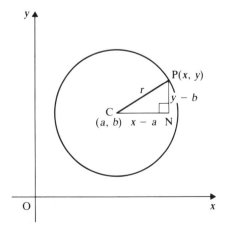

Figure 21.7

Now $CN = x - a$ and $NP = y - b$; but by Pythagoras' theorem in triangle CNP,

$$CN^2 + NP^2 = CP^2$$
$$\therefore \quad (x-a)^2 + (y-b)^2 = r^2$$

Therefore the equation of the circle, radius r, whose centre is at (a, b) is

$$\boxed{(x-a)^2 + (y-b)^2 = r^2}$$

Using this result, the equation of the circle with centre at $(4, -1)$ and radius 2 may be written

$$(x-4)^2 + (y+1)^2 = 2^2$$

Expanding the squares:

$$x^2 - 8x + 16 + y^2 + 2y + 1 = 4$$

Collecting the terms:

$$x^2 + y^2 - 8x + 2y + 13 = 0$$

The equation of a circle is often given in this form. Note that
(a) the coefficients of x^2 and y^2 are equal,
(b) the only other terms are linear (such as may occur in the equation of a straight line).

Qu. 5 Express the equation $(x-a)^2 + (y-b)^2 = r^2$ in the form

$$x^2 + y^2 + 2gx + 2fy + c = 0$$

Write down g, f, c, in terms of a, b, r.

Example 6

Find the radius and the coordinates of the centre of the circle
$2x^2 + 2y^2 - 8x + 5y + 10 = 0$.

[We may find the centre and radius if the equation is expressed in the form $(x-a)^2 + (y-b)^2 = r^2$.]

Divide both sides of the equation of the circle

$$2x^2 + 2y^2 - 8x + 5y + 10 = 0$$

by 2, in order to make the coefficients of x^2 and y^2 equal to 1:

$$x^2 + y^2 - 4x + \tfrac{5}{2}y + 5 = 0$$

Rearrange the terms, grouping those in x and y:

$$x^2 - 4x \quad + \quad y^2 + \tfrac{5}{2}y \qquad = -5$$

Complete the squares:

$$x^2 - 4x + 4 + y^2 + \tfrac{5}{2}y + (\tfrac{5}{4})^2 = -5 + 4 + \tfrac{25}{16}$$
$$\therefore \qquad (x-2)^2 + (y+\tfrac{5}{4})^2 = \tfrac{9}{16}$$
$$\therefore \qquad (x-2)^2 + (y+\tfrac{5}{4})^2 = (\tfrac{3}{4})^2$$

Comparing this with the equation of the circle, radius r, centre (a, b):

$$(x - a)^2 + (y - b)^2 = r^2$$

we obtain

$$a = 2 \quad b = -\tfrac{5}{4} \quad r = \tfrac{3}{4}$$

Therefore the radius is $\tfrac{3}{4}$ and the centre is at the point $(2, -\tfrac{5}{4})$.

Exercise 21c

1 Find the equations of the circles with the following centres and radii:
  (a) centre $(2, 3)$, radius 1 (b) centre $(-3, 4)$, radius 5
  (c) centre $(\tfrac{2}{3}, -\tfrac{1}{3})$, radius $\tfrac{2}{3}$ (d) centre $(0, -5)$, radius 5
  (e) centre $(3, 0)$, radius $\sqrt{2}$ (f) centre $(-\tfrac{1}{4}, \tfrac{1}{3})$, radius $\tfrac{1}{2}\sqrt{2}$
2 Find the radii and the coordinates of the centres of the following circles:
  (a) $x^2 + y^2 + 4x - 6y + 12 = 0$ (b) $x^2 + y^2 - 2x - 4y + 1 = 0$
  (c) $x^2 + y^2 - 3x = 0$ (d) $x^2 + y^2 + 3x - 4y - 6 = 0$
  (e) $2x^2 + 2y^2 + x + y = 0$ (f) $36x^2 + 36y^2 - 24x - 36y - 23 = 0$
  (g) $x^2 + y^2 - 2ax - 2by = 0$ (h) $x^2 + y^2 + 2gx + 2fy + c = 0$
3 Which of the following equations represent circles?
  (a) $x^2 + y^2 - 5 = 0$ (b) $x^2 + y^2 + 10 = 0$
  (c) $3x^2 + 2y^2 + 6x - 8y + 100 = 0$ (d) $ax^2 + ay^2 = 1$
  (e) $x^2 + y^2 + 8x + xy + 4 = 0$ (f) $x^2 + y^2 + bxy = 1$
  (g) $x^2 + y^2 + c = 0$ (h) $x^2 + dy^2 - 8x + 10y + 50 = 0$
  Which of them can represent circles if suitable values are given to the constants a, b, c, d?
4 Find the equation of the circle whose centre is at the point $(2, 1)$ and which passes through the point $(4, -3)$.
5 The points $(8, 4)$ and $(2, 2)$ are the ends of a diameter of a circle. Find the coordinates of the centre, and the radius. Deduce the equation of the circle.

21.5 Tangents to a circle

Elementary geometry will frequently help to simplify working in coordinate geometry, as the reader may have found in the last exercise. It provides a simple way of obtaining the equation of a tangent at a given point on a given circle, using the fact that a tangent is perpendicular to the radius through the point of contact. This method will be employed in the next example.

Example 7

Verify that the point $(3, 2)$ lies on the circle $x^2 + y^2 - 8x + 2y + 7 = 0$ and find the equation of the tangent at this point.

Substituting the coordinates $(3, 2)$ into the equation
$x^2 + y^2 - 8x + 2y + 7 = 0$,

L.H.S. $= 9 + 4 - 24 + 4 + 7 = 0 = $ R.H.S.

Therefore (3, 2) lies on the circle.

[The gradient of the tangent can be found from the gradient of the radius through (3, 2); and, in order to find this, we obtain the coordinates of the centre of the circle.]

The equation of the circle may be written

$$x^2 - 8x \qquad + y^2 + 2y \qquad = -7$$
$$\therefore \quad x^2 - 8x + 16 + y^2 + 2y + 1 \; = -7 + 16 + 1$$
$$\therefore \qquad\qquad (x - 4)^2 + (y + 1)^2 = 10$$

Therefore the centre of the circle is $(4, -1)$. Hence the gradient of the radius through (3, 2) is $\dfrac{(-1 - 2)}{(4 - 3)} = -3.$

Therefore the gradient of the tangent is $\frac{1}{3}$. Using the formula $y - y_1 = m(x - x_1)$, the equation of the tangent at (3, 2) is

$$y - 2 = \tfrac{1}{3}(x - 3)$$
$$\therefore \quad 3y - 6 = x - 3$$

Therefore the equation of the tangent to the circle at (3, 2) is $x - 3y + 3 = 0.$

Qu. 6 Verify that the given points lie on the following circles and find the equations of the tangents to the circles at these points:
(a) $x^2 + y^2 + 6x - 2y = 0$, (0, 0)
(b) $x^2 + y^2 - 8x - 2y = 0$, (3, 5)
(c) $x^2 + y^2 + 2x + 4y - 12 = 0$, $(3, -1)$
(d) $x^2 + y^2 + 2x - 2y - 8 = 0$, (2, 2)
(e) $2x^2 + 2y^2 - 8x - 5y - 1 = 0$, $(1, -1)$

Exercise 21d (Miscellaneous)

1 Find the locus of a point which is equidistant from the points $(4, -1)$ and (3, 7).
2 Find the locus of a point which is equidistant from the y-axis and the point (4, 0).
3 A point P moves so that its distance from the point (5, 0) is half its distance from the line $x - 8 = 0$. Find the locus of P.
4 Find the locus of a point which moves so that its distance from the origin is three times its distance from the line $x = a$.
5 Find the locus of a point which moves so that its distance from (2, 0) is twice its distance from $(-1, 0)$. Show that a point P, which moves so that the sum of the squares of the distances from P to the origin and the point $(-4, 0)$ is 16, describes the same locus.
6 If A is the point (2, 0) and B is $(-3, 0)$, find the locus of a point P which moves so that $AP^2 + 2BP^2 = 22.$
7 Find the equation of the circle on the line joining (a, b) to (c, d) as diameter.

8 A straight line of length 24 units moves with its ends on the axes. Find the locus of a point on the line which is:

(a) 12 units from the end on the x-axis

(b) 6 units from the end on the x-axis

9 A straight line of length 6 units moves with its ends A and B on the axes. Perpendiculars to the axes, erected at the points A and B, meet at P. Find the locus of P.

10 A and B are points on the x- and y-axes, and P is the mid-point of AB. Find the locus of P if the area of triangle AOB is 8 units.

11 Prove that the line $y = 2x$ is a tangent to the circle $x^2 + y^2 - 8x - y + 5 = 0$ and find the coordinates of the point of contact.

12 Show that the line $x - 2y + 12 = 0$ touches the circle $x^2 + y^2 - x - 31 = 0$ and find the coordinates of the point of contact.

13 The line $2x + 2y - 3 = 0$ touches the circle $4x^2 + 4y^2 + 8x + 4y - 13 = 0$ at A. Find the equation of the line joining A to the origin.

14 Find the equation of the circle whose centre is at the point $(5, 4)$ and which touches the line joining the points $(0, 5)$ and $(4, 1)$.

15 Find the equation of the tangent to the circle $x^2 + y^2 - 2x + y - 5 = 0$ at the point $(3, -2)$. If this tangent cuts the axes at A and B, find the area of triangle OAB.

Chapter 22

Further topics in coordinate geometry

22.1 Polar coordinates

If someone asks me at Harrow to tell her where Enfield is, I may reply that it is about 19 km east and 9 km north, or I might tell her that it is roughly 21 km away on a bearing N 60° E. These two descriptions of the position of Enfield correspond to the two systems of coordinates used in this book. The first is the basis of Cartesian coordinates and we have already met the second in the chapter on vectors. (See also Section 11.9.)

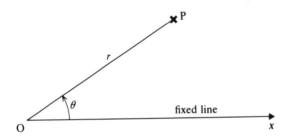

Figure 22.1

Let P be any point and let $OP = r$, where O is the origin (see Figure 22.1) and let OP make an angle θ with the x-axis, then r and θ are called the **polar coordinates** of the point P, and the coordinates may be written (r, θ). The x-axis is sometimes called the **initial line**, and the point O the **pole**.

It should be noticed that, while a bearing is usually measured in a clockwise sense from north, in mathematics the polar coordinate θ is normally represented in an anti-clockwise sense.

Thus in Figure 22.2 the coordinates of A are $(2, 30°)$ and those of B are $(3, 90°)$. A point may be described in different ways, for instance C may be written as $(2, 210°)$, $(2, -150°)$, $(-2, 30°)$ and so on. If, for any reason, a unique way of referring to each point is required, r may be taken to be positive and θ to lie in the range $-180° < \theta \leqslant 180°$.

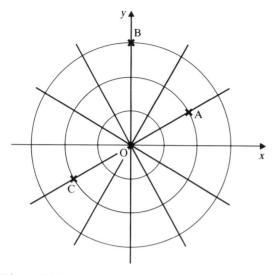

Figure 22.2

Example 1

Plot the curve whose polar equation is $r = a(1 + 2 \cos \theta)$.

Take values of θ, and calculate $1 + 2 \cos \theta$, as below.

θ	0°	30°	45°	60°	90°	120°	135°	150°	180°
$2 \cos \theta$	2	1.732	1.414	1	0	−1	−1.414	−1.732	−2
$1 + 2 \cos \theta$	3	2.732	2.414	2	1	0	−0.414	−0.732	−1

Plot these values (see Figure 22.3). Now if α is any angle, $\cos(-\alpha) = \cos \alpha$, therefore the same values of r will be obtained for negative values of θ. Thus the curve may be completed.

Example 2

Find the polar equation of a line such that the perpendicular to it from the origin is of length p and makes an angle α with the x-axis.

In Figure 22.4, N is the foot of the perpendicular from the origin to the line, and let P be any point (r, θ) on the line.

In the triangle ONP, N is a right angle and angle $PON = \theta - \alpha$ (or $\alpha - \theta$).

$\therefore \quad r \cos (\theta - \alpha) = p \quad$ (or $r \cos (\alpha - \theta) = p$)

Therefore, in either case, the polar equation of the line is $r \cos (\theta - \alpha) = p$.

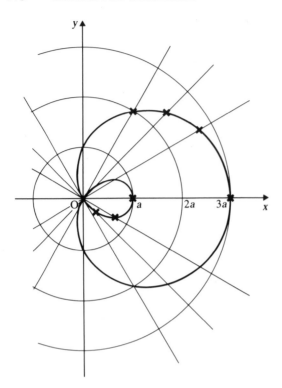

Figure 22.3

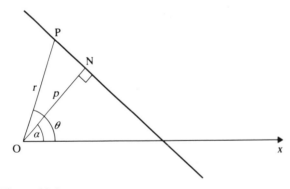

Figure 22.4

22.2 Relations between polar and Cartesian coordinates

In Figure 22.5, P is the point (x, y) in Cartesian coordinates and (r, θ) in polar coordinates, and PM is an ordinate.

Now, by the definitions of cosine and sine given in Section 17.1,

$$\cos \theta = \frac{x}{r} \quad \text{and} \quad \sin \theta = \frac{y}{r}$$

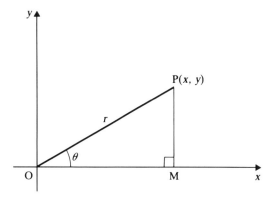

Figure 22.5

Therefore x and y are given in terms of r and θ by the equations

$$x = r \cos \theta \quad \text{and} \quad y = r \sin \theta$$

If, on the other hand, we are given the values of x and y, we can, by inspecting the diagram in Figure 22.5, write down the values of r and θ.

By Pythagoras' theorem,

$$r^2 = x^2 + y^2$$

$\therefore$ $$r = \pm \sqrt{(x^2 + y^2)}$$

In most cases the positive square root should be taken, but on some occasions it may be necessary to use the negative one. (For instance, in Example 1 on page 447, at the point $x = a$, $y = 0$, r is equal to $-a$.)

The angle θ can be found by elementary trigonometry. In Figure 22.5, θ is given by

$$\tan \theta = \frac{y}{x}$$

[Here again, care must be taken. For example, the point $x = -1$, $y = -1$, gives $\tan \theta = +1$, but in this case θ is equal to $-135°$, not $45°$; if in doubt, consult the diagram. Compare this with the modulus and arguments of a complex number (see Section 11.9).]

Example 3

Find the Cartesian equations of
(a) $r = a(1 + 2 \cos \theta)$ (b) $r \cos (\theta - \alpha) = p$.

(a) $r = a(1 + 2 \cos \theta)$

[The $\cos \theta$ suggests the relation $x = r \cos \theta$, so multiply through by r.]

$$\therefore \quad r^2 = a(r + 2r \cos \theta)$$
$$\therefore \quad x^2 + y^2 = a\{\sqrt{(x^2 + y^2)} + 2x\}$$
$$\therefore \quad x^2 + y^2 - 2ax = a\sqrt{(x^2 + y^2)}$$

Therefore the Cartesian equation of $r = a(1 + 2 \cos \theta)$ is

$$(x^2 + y^2 - 2ax)^2 = a^2(x^2 + y^2)$$

(b) $r \cos (\theta - \alpha) = p$

$\cos (\theta - \alpha)$ may be expanded (see Section 18.2),

$$\therefore \quad r \cos \theta \cos \alpha + r \sin \theta \sin \alpha = p$$

Therefore the Cartesian equation of $r \cos (\theta - \alpha) = p$ is

$$x \cos \alpha + y \sin \alpha = p$$

Note The perpendicular from the origin to this line is of length p and makes an angle α with the x-axis. This form of the equation of a straight line is known as the **normal** or **perpendicular** form.

Example 4

Find the polar equation of the circle whose Cartesian equation is $x^2 + y^2 = 4x$.

$$x^2 + y^2 = 4x$$

Put $x = r \cos \theta$, $y = r \sin \theta$, then

$$r^2 \cos^2 \theta + r^2 \sin^2 \theta = 4r \cos \theta$$
$$\therefore \qquad r^2 = 4r \cos \theta$$

Therefore the polar equation of the circle is $r = 4 \cos \theta$.

Exercise 22a

1 Sketch the curves given by the following polar equations:
(a) $r = a(1 + \cos \theta)$ (b) $r = a \cos 2\theta$ (c) $r = a(1 - \sin \theta)$
(d) $r = a \sin 3\theta$ (e) $r = a \sec \theta$ (f) $r = a \tan \theta$
(g) $r = a \cos \frac{1}{2}\theta$ (h) $r = a(1 + \sin 2\theta)$
2 Find the polar equations of the following loci:
(a) a circle, centre at the origin, radius a,
(b) a straight line through the origin, inclined at an angle α to the initial line,
(c) a straight line perpendicular to the initial line, at a distance a from the origin,
(d) a straight line parallel to the initial line at a distance a from it,

(e) a circle on the line joining the origin to $(a, 0)$ as a diameter,
(f) a circle, radius a, touching the initial line at the origin and lying above it,
(g) a circle, radius a, centre on the initial line at a distance c from the origin,
(h) a point which moves so that its distance from the origin is equal to its distance from the straight line $x = 2a$.
3 P_1 is the point (r_1, θ_1), P_2 is (r_2, θ_2) and $\theta_2 > \theta_1$. Show that the area of the triangle $OP_1 P_2$ is $\frac{1}{2} r_1 r_2 \sin(\theta_2 - \theta_1)$. Deduce that if the Cartesian coordinates of P_1 and P_2 are (x_1, y_1) and (x_2, y_2), then the area of $OP_1 P_2$ is $\frac{1}{2}(x_1 y_2 - x_2 y_1)$.
4 Deduce from the result of no. 3, that the area of the triangle $P_1(x_1, y_1)$, $P_2(x_2, y_2)$, $P_3(x_3, y_3)$ is

$$\tfrac{1}{2}\{(x_2 y_3 - x_3 y_2) + (x_3 y_1 - x_1 y_3) + (x_1 y_2 - x_2 y_1)\}$$

[If new axes are drawn at (x_3, y_3), the coordinates of P_1 and P_2 referred to them are $(x_1 - x_3, y_1 - y_3)$ and $(x_2 - x_3, y_2 - y_3)$.]
5 Obtain the polar equations of the following loci:
(a) $x^2 + y^2 = a^2$ (b) $x^2 - y^2 = a^2$ (c) $y = 0$
(d) $y^2 = 4a(a - x)$ (e) $x^2 + y^2 - 2y = 0$ (f) $xy = c^2$
6 Obtain the Cartesian equations of the following loci:
(a) $r = 2$ (b) $r = a(1 + \cos\theta)$ (c) $r = a\cos\theta$
(d) $2r^2 \sin 2\theta = c^2$ (e) $r = 4a\cot\theta\csc\theta$
7 Express the following straight lines in the form $x\cos\alpha + y\sin\alpha = p$. State the distance of each line from the origin and give the angle which the perpendicular from the origin makes with the x-axis.
(a) $x + \sqrt{3}y = 2$ (b) $x - y = 4$ (c) $3x + 4y - 10 = 0$
(d) $5x - 12y + 26 = 0$ (e) $x + 3y - 2 = 0$ (f) $ax + by + c = 0$

22.3 The distance of a point from a line

Given a point $P_1(x_1, y_1)$ and the line

$$ax + by + c = 0$$

we shall first find the distance, r, of P_1 from a point P_2 on the line, such that $\overrightarrow{P_1 P_2}$ makes an angle α with the x-axis (see Figure 22.6).

P_2 has coordinates $(x_1 + r\cos\alpha, y_1 + r\sin\alpha)$, but, as P_2 lies on the line $ax + by + c = 0$, its coordinates satisfy the equation, therefore

$$a(x_1 + r\cos\alpha) + b(y_1 + r\sin\alpha) + c = 0$$
$$\therefore \quad r(a\cos\alpha + b\sin\alpha) = -(ax_1 + by_1 + c)$$
$$\therefore \qquad r = -\frac{ax_1 + by_1 + c}{a\cos\alpha + b\sin\alpha} \qquad \cdots \ (1)$$

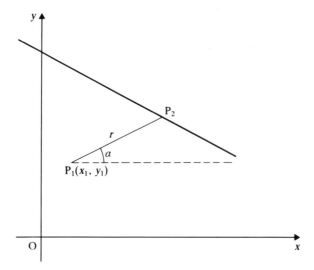

Figure 22.6

Now take the case when $P_1 P_2$ is perpendicular to the line $ax + by + c = 0$. The gradient of $ax + by + c = 0$ is $-a/b$, therefore the gradient of $P_1 P_2$ is b/a.

$$\therefore \quad \tan \alpha = \frac{b}{a}$$

$$\therefore \quad \sec^2 \alpha = 1 + \frac{b^2}{a^2} = \frac{a^2 + b^2}{a^2}$$

$$\therefore \quad \cos \alpha = \frac{a}{\sqrt{(a^2 + b^2)}}$$

and, since $\tan \alpha = b/a$,

$$\sin \alpha = \frac{b}{\sqrt{(a^2 + b^2)}}$$

so in the denominator of equation (1)

$$a \cos \alpha + b \sin \alpha = \left(\frac{a^2}{\sqrt{(a^2 + b^2)}} + \frac{b^2}{\sqrt{(a^2 + b^2)}} \right)$$

$$= \sqrt{(a^2 + b^2)}$$

$$\therefore \quad r = - \frac{ax_1 + by_1 + c}{\sqrt{(a^2 + b^2)}}$$

The numerator of this fraction (i.e. $ax_1 + by_1 + c$) will be zero if the point P_1 lies *on* the line, otherwise it will be positive when P_1 lies on one side of the line, and negative when it is on the other side. Since we are only interested in the length of the line $P_1 P_2$, we can ignore the sign; in other words, the perpendicular distance is

$$\left|\frac{ax_1 + by_1 + c}{\sqrt{(a^2 + b^2)}}\right|$$

Example 5

Find the distances from the line $2x + 3y - 6 = 0$ of the points
(a) $(1, 3)$, (b) $(-3, 4)$, (c) $(4, -2)$

The distance of (x_1, y_1) from the line $ax + by + c = 0$ is

$$\left|\frac{ax_1 + by_1 + c}{\sqrt{(a^2 + b^2)}}\right|$$

Therefore the distances of $(1, 3), (-3, 4), (4, -2)$ from $2x + 3y - 6 = 0$ are respectively:

(a) $\left|\dfrac{2 \times 1 + 3 \times 3 - 6}{\sqrt{(2^2 + 3^2)}}\right| = \dfrac{5}{\sqrt{13}}$

(b) $\left|\dfrac{2 \times (-3) + 3 \times 4 - 6}{\sqrt{(2^2 + 3^2)}}\right| = 0$

(c) $\left|\dfrac{2 \times 4 + 3 \times (-2) - 6}{\sqrt{(2^2 + 3^2)}}\right| = \dfrac{4}{\sqrt{13}}$

The formula is more easily remembered if two points are noticed:
(1) The numerator is obtained by substituting the coordinates of the point into the equation of the line (remember that the perpendicular distance is zero if the point lies on the line).
(2) The denominator is the square root of the sum of the squares of the coefficients.

Qu. 1 Find the distances of the given points from the following lines:
(a) $(3, 2)$, $3x - 4y + 4 = 0$ (b) $(2, -1)$, $5x + 12y = 0$
(c) $(0, -3)$, $x + 5y + 2 = 0$ (d) $(2, 5)$, $x + y - 1 = 0$
(e) $(-4, 2)$, $3y = 5x - 6$ (f) $(2, 1)$, $y = \frac{2}{3}x + \frac{1}{3}$
(g) $(0, a)$, $3y = 4x$ (h) (p, q), $3x + 4y - 3p = 0$
(i) (X, Y), $12x - 5y + 7 = 0$ (j) (x_1, y_1), $8x = 15y$

22.4 Parameters

Consider a circle, radius a, centre at the origin (see Figure 22.7). Let $P(x, y)$ be any point on the circle, and let the angle between PO and the x-axis be θ, then

$$x = a \cos \theta \quad \text{and} \quad y = a \sin \theta$$

These equations, which give the coordinates of any point on the curve in terms of θ, are called **parametric equations**, and θ is called a **parameter**.

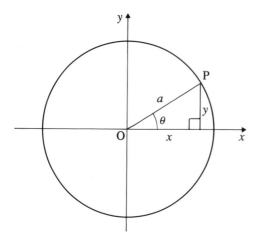

Figure 22.7

If we wish to refer to a particular point on the curve, a single number, the corresponding value of θ, will determine it. Thus $\theta = 60°$ gives the point $(a/2, \sqrt{3}a/2)$. On the other hand, if we were given a value of x, say $\frac{1}{2}a$, there are two corresponding points: $(a/2, \sqrt{3}a/2)$ and $(a/2, -\sqrt{3}a/2)$. Another advantage of parameters is that we may write down the coordinates of a general point on the curve $(a \cos \theta, a \sin \theta)$. If we wrote (x_1, y_1), we should also have to bear in mind the equation $x_1{}^2 + y_1{}^2 = a^2$.

Another example of parameters was used in Section 22.3. The point

$$(x_1 + r \cos \alpha, y_1 + r \sin \alpha)$$

lies on the straight line through (x_1, y_1) with gradient $\tan \alpha$, and in this case the parameter, r, is a distance. However, it is not always possible to give an easy interpretation of a parameter in terms of angles or distances.

Example 6

Plot the graph of the curve given parametrically by the equations $x = t^2 - 4$, $y = t^3 - 4t$, for values of t from -3 to $+3$.

A table of values is shown below.

t	-3	-2	-1	0	1	2	3
$x = t^2 - 4$	5	0	-3	-4	-3	0	5
$y = t^3 - 4t$	-15	0	3	0	-3	0	15

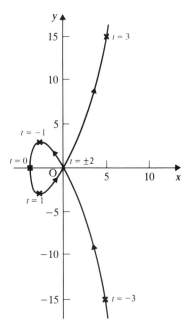

Figure 22.8

The graph has been plotted in Figure 22.8, and the values of the parameter, t, have been written against the corresponding points. The arrows indicate the direction of motion of a point on the curve as t increases from -3 to $+3$.

Example 7

Plot the curve given parametrically by $x = \sin \theta$, $y = \sin 2\theta$.

A few values of θ will give all the points we need.

θ	0	45°	90°	135°	180°
$x = \sin \theta$	0	0.7071	1	0.7071	0
$y = \sin 2\theta$	0	1	0	-1	0

Plotting these points and joining them by a curve we obtain the part of the curve in Figure 22.9 which lies to the right of the y-axis.

Now $\sin(-\alpha) = -\sin\alpha$, so that negative values of θ change the signs of x and y. Therefore the rest of the curve may be drawn in symmetrically.

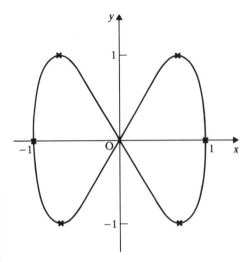

Figure 22.9

Example 8

Sketch the curve whose parametric form is

$$x = t^2 - 1$$
$$y = t^3$$

['Sketch' means draw a diagram displaying the principal features of the graph for all values of t, rather than 'plotting' it from a limited number of points. Graph paper is *not* normally used for this.]

First, find the points where the graph meets the axes.

It meets the y-axis when $x = 0$, i.e. when

$$t^2 - 1 = 0$$

hence

$$t^2 = 1$$
$$t = \pm 1$$

giving $y = \pm 1$.

So the graph meets the y-axis at $(0, 1)$ and $(0, -1)$.

It meets the x-axis when $t^3 = 0$, that is, at $(-1, 0)$.

Notice that, for all values of t, other than zero, x is greater than -1. Also, changing the sign of t does not affect x, but it reverses the sign of y, giving a pair of points placed symmetrically above and below the

x-axis. So the x-axis is a line of symmetry of the curve, with the branch of the curve for which $t > 0$ above the axis, and the branch for which $t < 0$ being its reflection in that axis.

The gradient of the curve is given by

$$\frac{dy}{dx} = \frac{dy}{dt} \bigg/ \frac{dx}{dt}$$

$$= \frac{3t^2}{2t}$$

$$= \frac{3t}{2}$$

This is zero when $t = 0$, i.e. at $(-1, 0)$, and it increases as t increases.

The sketch of the curve is shown in Figure 22.10.

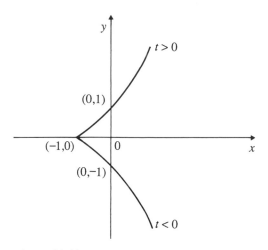

Figure 22.10

Qu. 2 Sketch the locus given by $x = t^2$, $y = 1 - t^2$, for real values of t. Is it the line $x + y = 1$?

The graph of the curve given parametrically by the equations $x = t^2 - 4$, $y = t^3 - 4t$ was plotted for values of t from -3 to $+3$ in Example 6. The question may well have risen in the reader's mind, 'What is the equation connecting x and y?' This can be found by eliminating t from the equations

$$x = t^2 - 4 \qquad y = t^3 - 4t$$

Notice that $y = tx$. Therefore we may substitute $t = y/x$ in either of the equations above. Choosing the simpler,

$$x = \frac{y^2}{x^2} - 4$$

$$\therefore \quad x^3 = y^2 - 4x^2$$

Therefore the Cartesian equation of the locus is $y^2 = x^2(x + 4)$.

Example 9

Find the Cartesian equation of the locus given parametrically by the equations $x = \sin \theta$, $y = \sin 2\theta$ (see Example 7).

$y = \sin 2\theta$, but $\sin 2\theta = 2 \sin \theta \cos \theta$, therefore

$$y = 2 \sin \theta \cos \theta$$
$$\therefore \quad y^2 = 4 \sin^2 \theta \cos^2 \theta$$

Now $x = \sin \theta$, therefore $1 - x^2 = \cos^2 \theta$, and so the Cartesian equation of the locus is $y^2 = 4x^2(1 - x^2)$.

The process of obtaining parametric equations from a given Cartesian equation is not so easy as the reverse, but one method is illustrated in the next example.

Example 10

Obtain parametric equations for the locus $y^2 = x^3 - x^2$.

Put $y = tx$ in the equation $y^2 = x^3 - x^2$, then

$$t^2 x^2 = x^3 - x^2$$
$$\therefore \quad t^2 = x - 1$$
$$\therefore \quad x = t^2 + 1$$

Therefore the locus may be represented by the parametric equations

$$x = t^2 + 1 \quad y = t^3 + t$$

Note This method is not suitable for all equations, but it works well when the terms are of degree n and $n - 1$.

Exercise 22b

1 Sketch the curves given parametrically by the equations:
   (a) $x = t^2 + 1$, $y = t + 2$ (b) $x = t^2$, $y = t^3$
   (c) $x = t$, $y = 1/t$ (d) $x = 1 + t$, $y = 3 - 2t$
   (e) $x = at^2$, $y = 2at$ (f) $x = t^2 + 1$, $y = t^3 + t$
   (g) $x = 2 \cos t$, $y = \sin t$ (h) $x = \sin t$, $y = \cos^3 t$

2 Find the values of the parameters and the other coordinates of the given points on the following curves:
(a) $x = t$, $y = 2/t$, where $y = 1\frac{1}{2}$
(b) $x = at^2$, $y = 2at$, where $x = \frac{9}{4}a$

(c) $x = \dfrac{1+t}{1-t}$, $y = \dfrac{2+3t}{1-t}$, where $y = -\frac{4}{3}$

(d) $x = a\cos\theta$, $y = b\sin\theta$, where $x = \frac{1}{2}a$
3 Find the Cartesian equations of the loci in no. 1.
4 By substituting $y = tx$, find parametric equations for the loci whose Cartesian equations are:
(a) $y^4 = x^5$ (b) $y = x^2 + 2x$ (c) $y^2 = x^2 + 2x$
(d) $x^2 = x^3 - y^3$ (e) $x^3 + y^3 = 3xy$
5 Show that the parametric equations
(a) $x = 1 + 2t$, $y = 2 + 3t$ (b) $x = 1/(2t - 3)$, $y = t/(2t - 3)$
both represent the same straight line, and find its Cartesian equation.
6 Show that the line given parametrically by the equations $x = (2 - t)/(1 + 2t)$, $y = (3 + t)/(1 + 2t)$ passes through the points $(6, 7)$ and $(-2, -1)$. Find the values of t corresponding to these points.
7 P is the variable point $(t^2, 3t)$ and O is the origin. Find the coordinates of Q, the mid-point of OP, and hence obtain the locus of Q as P varies.
8 The line joining the origin to the variable point $P(t, 1/t)$ meets the line $x = 1$ at Q. Find the locus of the mid-point of PQ.
9 Find the coordinates of the points nearest to the origin on the curve $x = t$, $y = 1/t$. What is their distance from the origin?
10 Find the equations of the chords joining the points with parameters p and q on the following curves:
(a) $x = t^2$, $y = 2t$ (b) $x = t$, $y = -1/t$
(c) $x = t^3$, $y = t$ (d) $x = t + 1/t$, $y = 2t$

Example 11

Find the equation of the tangent to the rectangular hyperbola $xy = c^2$ at the point $P(ct, c/t)$ and show that, if this tangent meets the axes at Q and R, then P is the mid-point of QR.

The gradient of the curve is given by

$$\frac{dy}{dx} = \frac{dy}{dt} \bigg/ \frac{dx}{dt}$$

But $y = c/t$

$$\therefore \quad \frac{dy}{dt} = -\frac{c}{t^2}$$

and $x = ct$,

$$\therefore \quad \frac{dx}{dt} = c$$

$$\therefore \quad \frac{dy}{dx} = \frac{-c/t^2}{c} = -\frac{1}{t^2}$$

Therefore the equation of the tangent at P is

$$yt^2 + x = 2ct$$

This tangent meets the axes at $Q(2ct, 0)$ and $R(0, 2c/t)$ therefore $P(ct, c/t)$ is the mid-point of QR.

Example 12

Find the coordinates of the points where the line $4x - 5y + 6a = 0$ cuts the curve given parametrically by $(at^2, 2at)$.

If the line $4x - 5y + 6a = 0$ meets the curve at the point $(at^2, 2at)$, then its coordinates must satisfy the equation of the line. Therefore

$$4at^2 - 10at + 6a = 0$$
$$\therefore \qquad 2t^2 - 5t + 3 = 0$$
$$\therefore \qquad (2t - 3)(t - 1) = 0$$
$$\therefore \qquad t = \tfrac{3}{2} \quad \text{or} \quad 1$$

Therefore the coordinates of the points of intersection are $(\tfrac{9}{4}a, 3a)$ and $(a, 2a)$.

Exercise 22c

1 Find the equations of the tangents and normals to the following curves at the given points:
(a) $x = t^2,\ y = t^3,\ (1, -1)$ (b) $x = t^2,\ y = 1/t,\ (\tfrac{1}{4}, 2)$
(c) $x = at^2,\ y = 2at,\ (a, -2a)$ (d) $x = ct,\ y = c/t,\ (-c, -c)$
(e) $x = t^2 - 4,\ y = t^3 - 4t,\ (-3, -3)$ (f) $x = 3\cos\theta,\ y = 2\sin\theta,\ (\tfrac{3}{2}, \sqrt{3})$
2 Find the equations of the tangents and normals to the following curves at the point whose parameter is t:
(a) $x = t^3,\ y = 3t^2$ (b) $x = at^2,\ y = 2at$
(c) $x = 4t^3,\ y = 3t^4$ (d) $x = ct,\ y = c/t$
(e) $x = a\cos t,\ y = b\sin t$ (f) $x = a\sec t,\ y = b\tan t$
3 Find the equations of the chords joining the points whose parameters are p and q on the following curves. Deduce the equations of the tangents at the points with parameter p by finding the limiting equations of the chords as q approaches p.
(a) $x = t^2,\ y = 2t$ (b) $x = 1/t,\ y = t^2$
(c) $x = ct,\ y = c/t$ (d) $x = a\cos t,\ y = b\sin t$
[*Hint* cancel a factor of $p - q$ in the gradients.]

4 Find the equation of the normal to the parabola $x = at^2$, $y = 2at$ at the point $(4a, 4a)$. Find also the coordinates of the point where the normal meets the curve again.

5 Find the coordinates of the point where the normal to the rectangular hyperbola $x = ct$, $y = c/t$ at $(2c, \frac{1}{2}c)$ meets the curve again.

6 Find the coordinates of the point where the tangent to the curve $x = 1/t$, $y = t^2$ at $(1, 1)$ meets the curve again.

7 Find the equation of the tangent to the parabola $y^2 = 4ax$ at the point $(at^2, 2at)$. For what values of t does the tangent pass through the point $(8a, 6a)$? Write down the equations of the tangents to the parabola from $(8a, 6a)$.

8 Find the equations of the tangents to the hyperbola $x = ct$, $y = c/t$ from the point $(\frac{3}{2}c, \frac{1}{2}c)$.

9 Find the equations of the normals to the parabola $x = at^2$, $y = 2at$ from the point $(14a, -16a)$.

10 The normal to the hyperbola $x = ct$, $y = c/t$ at the point P with parameter p meets the curve again at Q. Find the coordinates of Q.

11 Show that, if a tangent to the curve $x = 1/t$, $y = t^2$ meets the axes in A and B, then $PB = 2AP$.

12 Show that the tangent at the point with parameter t on the astroid $x = a \cos^3 t$, $y = a \sin^3 t$ is the line $y \cos t + x \sin t = a \sin t \cos t$. Show that the tangent meets the axes in points whose distance apart is a. Sketch the curve.

22.5 The parabola

As no new method is required, work on the parabola is given in the form of exercises. It is intended that any result proved may be used in later questions.

Definition

> The locus of a point equidistant from a given point and a given line is called a **parabola**. The given point is the **focus** and the given line the **directrix**.

Exercise 22d

1 Use compasses and graph paper to plot a parabola from the definition.

2 Given a parabola, draw axes with the x-axis through the focus, perpendicular to the directrix, and the origin where the x-axis meets the curve. Let the focus be $(a, 0)$ and show that the equation of the parabola is $y^2 = 4ax$. [It follows from the definition that the equation of the directrix is $x = -a$.]

3 Verify that the point $(at^2, 2at)$ lies on the parabola $y^2 = 4ax$ for all values of t, and that every point on the parabola is given thus.

4 Find the equations of the tangent and normal to the parabola $y^2 = 4ax$ at the point $(at^2, 2at)$.

In Figure 22.11, the tangent and normal at the point P on the parabola $y^2 = 4ax$ meet the x-axis at T and G, and the y-axis at T' and G'. PN is parallel to the y-axis. S is the focus. LD is the directrix and L is the foot of the perpendicular from P to the directrix.

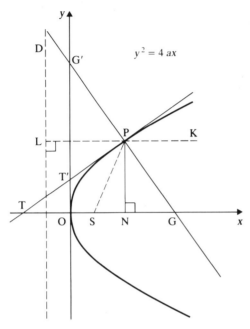

Figure 22.11

5 Show that ST' = T'L and deduce that:
   (a) $\angle$ LPT' = $\angle$ SPT' [use the definition of the curve]
   (b) $\angle$ SPG = $\angle$ KPG.
   [This proves the optical property of the parabola, i.e. that light from a point source at the focus is reflected in rays parallel to the axis.]
6 Show that L, T', S are collinear (i.e. lie on a straight line), and that LS is perpendicular to PT.
7 Show that TS = SP = SG.
8 Show that LPST is a rhombus and that LPGS is a parallelogram.
9 Show that NG = 2a.
10 If the parameters of the points P and Q are p and q, show that the tangents to the parabola meet at the point $(apq, ap + aq)$.
11 If PQ passes through the focus prove that, with the notation of no. 10, $pq = -1$.
12 Show that the tangents at the ends of a focal chord meet on the directrix.
13 Show that if the tangents at the ends of a focal chord meet the tangent at the vertex at U and V, then $\angle$ USV is a right angle.

14 Show that the locus of the mid-point of a focal chord is $y^2 = 2a(x - a)$.

15 Show that if the tangents to the parabola at P and Q meet on the line $x = ah$, then the locus of the mid-point of the chord PQ is $y^2 = 2a(x + ah)$.

Exercise 22e (Miscellaneous)

1 Show that at the points of intersection of the ellipse $4x^2 + 9y^2 = 36$ and the hyperbola $2x^2 - 3y^2 = 6$, their tangents are perpendicular to each other.

2 Sketch the curve whose polar equation is $r = a \cos 3\theta$.

3 Sketch the curve whose polar equation is $r = a(1 + \sin \theta)$ and from this obtain a sketch of the curve $r(1 + \sin \theta) = a$.

4 Find the polar equation of a parabola, taking the focus as the origin and the axis as the initial line.

5 Calculate the area of the triangle A(2, 5), B(3, −1), C(4, 6).

6 Find the polar equation of $(x^2 + y^2 + ax)^2 = a^2(x^2 + y^2)$ and the Cartesian equation of $r(1 + \sin \theta) = a$.

7 Find the equations of the tangents to the parabola $x = at^2$, $y = 2at$ from the point $(5a, 6a)$.

8 Find the coordinates of the point where the normal to the parabola $x = at^2$, $y = 2at$ at $(9a, 6a)$ meets the curve again.

9 Show that if the tangent at $P(t, t^3)$ to the curve $y = x^3$ meets the curve again at Q, then the y-axis divides PQ in the ratio $1 : 2$.

10 A tangent to the rectangular hyperbola $x = ct$, $y = c/t$ meets the axes at A and B. Show that the area of triangle AOB is constant.

Chapter 23

Variation and experimental laws

23.1 Variation

'Variation' in its mathematical sense is concerned with certain ways in which one variable depends on one or more others. The idea is bound up with ratio and proportion which the reader will have met in elementary arithmetic. Some readers may need to revise these ideas and to appreciate their power for the first time.

Proportion arises in arithmetic in a number of ways. For instance the circumference C of a circle is proportional to its radius r: this is usually expressed in the form of an equation,

$$C = 2\pi r$$

Sometimes a graph shows us that two variables are in proportion; for example Figure 23.1 shows the 'travel graph' of a car moving at a steady speed of

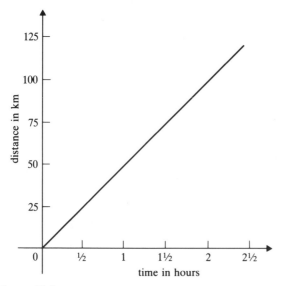

Figure 23.1

464

50 km h^{-1} along a road. Note that: (1) the gradient of the graph is uniform, (2) the straight line passes through the origin.

Yet another aspect of proportion, and indeed the most basic, is used in arithmetic when we use ratios.

To summarise, if y is proportional to x, then:
(a) $y = kx$, where k is some constant
(b) the graph of y against x is a straight line through the origin
(c) if x_1, y_1 and x_2, y_2 are corresponding values of x and y, then

$$\frac{y_1}{y_2} = \frac{x_1}{x_2}$$

Note that any one of these statements follows from either of the others. The equivalence of (a) and (b) is familiar from the work of Chapter 2. The equivalence of (b) and (c) can be seen by writing (c) in the form

$$\frac{y_1}{x_1} = \frac{y_2}{x_2}$$

which shows that (x_1, y_1) and (x_2, y_2) lie on the same straight line through the origin.

In the last paragraph we used the phrase,

'y is proportional to x'

Sometimes another phrase with exactly the same meaning is used instead, namely,

'y varies as x'

Other examples of variation will already be familiar to the reader. For instance, the area A of a circle is given in terms of its radius r by the equation

$$A = \pi r^2$$

Here A is *not* proportional to r, but it *is* proportional to r^2 and we express this by saying that 'A *varies* as the square of r'.

Another example is the volume V of a sphere in terms of its radius r. The equation connecting V and r is

$$V = \tfrac{4}{3}\pi r^3$$

Again V is *not* proportional to r, but it *is* proportional to r^3 and we express this by saying that 'V varies as the cube of r'.

Kinematics provides another example. If a distance of 60 km is travelled at a constant speed u km h^{-1}, the time t h is given by the equation

$$t = 60/u$$

We may say that t and u are inversely proportional, or we may express this by saying 't varies inversely as u'.

The 'inverse square law' may be familiar to the reader: one example of this is the force F exerted by the Earth on a given satellite at distance r from the centre of the Earth. The equation connecting F and r is

$$F = \frac{k}{r^2} \quad \text{(where } k \text{ is a constant)}$$

This may also be expressed by saying that 'F varies inversely as the square of r'.

Qu. 1 Express the following equations as statements involving the word 'varies':

(a) $s = 16t^2$ (b) $V = \pi r^3$ (c) $y = \dfrac{10}{x^2}$

(d) $T = \dfrac{\pi}{2\sqrt{2}}\sqrt{l}$ (e) $p = \dfrac{200}{V}$ (f) $T^2 = d^3$

Suppose that a number of spheres are made out of wood of uniform density. Then, unless we know the density of wood, we cannot calculate the mass M of one of these spheres from its diameter d. We can, however, say that

> M varies as the cube of d

or write

> $M = kd^3$ (where k is a constant)

Further, if M_1, d_1 and M_2, d_2 are the masses and diameters of two of the spheres,

$$M_1 = kd_1{}^3$$
$$M_2 = kd_2{}^3$$

so that, by division,

$$\frac{M_1}{M_2} = \frac{d_1{}^3}{d_2{}^3}$$

Now, if we know the mass and diameter of one of the spheres, this last equation provides us with a very convenient way of calculating the mass of any other when its diameter is known.

Example 1

A number of spheres are made out of wood of uniform density. The mass of sphere with diameter 7 cm is 0.11 kg. What is the mass of a sphere of diameter 9 cm?

As we have seen above, M varies as d^3. Hence if M_1, d_1 and M_2, d_2 are the masses and diameters of the two spheres,

$$\frac{M_1}{M_2} = \frac{d_1{}^3}{d_2{}^3}$$

It is often helpful to tabulate the data and it is worth noting that the algebra of the question is simplified if we place the *quantity to be found* in the line labelled (1):

	mass (kg)	diameter (cm)
(1)	M_1	9
(2)	0.11	7

Then substituting into the equation $M_1/M_2 = d_1{}^3/d_2{}^3$,

$$\frac{M_1}{0.11} = \frac{9^3}{7^3}$$

$$\therefore \quad M_1 = 0.11 \times \frac{9^3}{7^3}$$

$$= 0.23 \text{ to two significant figures}$$

Therefore the sphere of diameter 9 cm has a mass of 0.23 kg, correct to two significant figures.

[Example 1 illustrates the power of the method: an alternative way of tackling this question would have been to find the density of the wood from the data numbered (2) in the table.]

Qu. 2 In Example 1, what is the effect on M of:
(a) doubling d (b) trebling d?

We saw on page 466, that from the statement,

'M varies as the cube of d'

could be deduced the equation

$$\frac{M_1}{M_2} = \frac{d_1{}^3}{d_2{}^3}$$

which connects corresponding values M_1, d_1 and M_2, d_2. It is important for the following work to be able to convert a statement to an equation quickly and easily, so some more examples of this process follow.

If we are given that

'y varies as the square of x'

this is simply another way of saying

'y is proportional to x^2'

From this it follows immediately (see page 465) that:
(a) $y = kx^2$, where k is some constant
(b) the graph of y against x^2 is a straight line through the origin

(c) if x_1, y_1 and x_2, y_2 are corresponding values of x and y, then

$$\frac{y_1}{y_2} = \frac{x_1^2}{x_2^2}$$

On the other hand, if we are given that

'y varies *inversely* as the square of x'

this is simply another way of saying

'y is proportional to $\dfrac{1}{x^2}$'

from which it follows immediately that:
(a) $y = k/x^2$, where k is some constant
(b) the graph of y against $1/x^2$ is a straight line through the origin
(c) if x_1, y_1 and x_2, y_2 are corresponding values of x and y, then

$$\frac{y_1}{y_2} = \frac{1/x_1^2}{1/x_2^2}$$

or, multiplying numerator and denominator of the right-hand side by $x_1^2 x_2^2$,

$$\frac{y_1}{y_2} = \frac{x_2^2}{x_1^2}$$

Note that, in this case of *inverse* variation, the x's are upside down compared with the y's. 'Inverse' comes from the same root as 'invert', one meaning of which is to 'turn upside down'.

Qu. 3 Write down equations (i) with k's, (ii) with suffixes, similar to those above for the following statements:
(a) p varies as q
(b) p varies inversely as v
(c) v varies as the cube of x
(d) u varies as the square root of l
(e) F varies as the square of c
(f) H varies inversely as the square of d
(g) T varies inversely as the square root of g
(h) A varies as the nth power of s
(i) the cube of A varies as the square of v

Example 2

The length l of a simple pendulum varies as the square of the period T (time to swing to and fro). A pendulum 0.994 m long has a period of approximately 2 s. Find:
(a) the length of a pendulum whose period is 3 s
(b) an equation connecting l and T

(a) Tabulating the data:

	length (m)	period (s)
(1)	l	3
(2)	0.994	2

l varies as T^2.

$$\therefore \quad \frac{l_1}{l_2} = \frac{T_1^{\,2}}{T_2^{\,2}}$$

$$\therefore \quad \frac{l}{0.994} = \frac{3^2}{2^2}$$

$$\therefore \quad l = 0.994 \times \frac{9}{4}$$

$$= 2.236$$

Therefore the length of a pendulum whose period is 3 s is 2.24 m.

(b) Tabulating the data again, we enter l and T in the row numbered (1):

	length (m)	period (s)
(1)	l	T
(3)	0.994	2

Substituting in the same equation as before,

$$\frac{l}{0.994} = \frac{T^2}{2^2}$$

$$\therefore \quad l = 0.2485 T^2$$

Therefore the equation connecting l and T is $l \approx 0.25 T^2$.

Qu. 4 In Example 2, find the effect on l of:
(a) doubling T (b) trebling T
What is the effect on T of doubling l?
Qu. 5 Find the period of a pendulum whose length is 0.3 m from the data of Example 2. Time ten swings to and fro of such a pendulum and compare this with your answer.

Example 3

The weight w N of an astronaut varies inversely as the square of his distance d from the centre of the Earth. If an astronaut's weight on Earth is 792 N, what will his weight be at a height of 230 km above the Earth? Take the radius of the Earth to be 6370 km.

We tabulate the data:

	weight (N)	distance from the centre of the Earth (km)
(1)	w	$6370 + 230 = 6600$
(2)	792	6370

Now w varies inversely as d^2, so if w_1, d_1 and w_2, d_2 are corresponding values,

$$\frac{w_1}{w_2} = \frac{d_2^{\,2}}{d_1^{\,2}}$$

$$\therefore \quad \frac{w}{792} = \frac{6370^2}{6600^2}$$

$$\therefore \quad w = 792 \times \frac{6370^2}{6600^2}$$

$$= 737.7$$

Therefore the astronaut's weight would be 738 N.

To find the height above the Earth at which his weight would be halved, we again tabulate the data:

	weight (N)	distance from the centre of the Earth (km)
(1)	396	d
(2)	792	6370

Again using $w_1/w_2 = d_2^{\,2}/d_1^{\,2}$, for the new w_1, d_1,

$$\frac{396}{792} = \frac{6370^2}{d^2}$$

$$\therefore \quad d^2 = 2 \times 6370^2$$
$$\therefore \quad d = \sqrt{2} \times 6370$$
$$= 9010$$

Therefore the height above the Earth at which his weight would be halved is $9010 - 6370$ km $= 2640$ km.

Qu. 6 Find an equation in the form $w = k/d^2$ connecting the weight of the astronaut in Example 3 and his distance from the centre of the Earth.
Qu. 7 With the equation of Qu. 6, find the effect on w of:
(a) doubling d (b) trebling d

Qu. 8 Discuss whether the first of the following pairs of variables varies as some power of the second and, if so, state what power:
(a) the cost c of 100 copies of a book and the price p of one
(b) the cost C of a square of plywood and its side a
(c) the weight w of a spherical lead shot and its radius r
(d) the length l of a rectangle of given area and its breadth b
(e) the surface area S of a scale model and its length l
(f) the area A of an equilateral triangle and its side a
(g) the side a of an equilateral triangle and its area A
(h) the volume V of a regular tetrahedron and its side a
(i) the side a of a regular tetrahedron and its volume V

Exercise 23a

1 The area of a circular sector containing a given angle varies as the square of the radius of the circle. If the area of the sector is 2 cm^2 when the radius is 1.6 cm, find the area of the sector containing the same angle when the radius of the circle is 2.7 cm.
2 The distance of the horizon d km varies as the square root of the height h m of the observer above sea level. An observer at a height of 100 m above sea level sees the horizon at a distance of 35.7 km. Find the distance of the horizon from an observer 70 m above sea level.
   Also find an equation connecting d and h.
3 The length l cm of a simple pendulum varies as the square of its period T s. A pendulum with period 2 s is 99.4 cm long; find the length of a pendulum whose period is 2.5 s.
   What equation connects l and T?
4 Assuming that the length of paper in a roll of given dimensions varies inversely as the thickness of the paper, find the increase in length when the thickness of paper in a 100 m roll is decreased from 0.25 mm to 0.20 mm.
5 A certain type of hollow plastic sphere is designed in such a way that the mass varies as the square of the diameter. Three spheres of this type are made: one has mass 0.10 kg and diameter 9 cm; a second has diameter 14 cm; and a third has mass 0.15 kg. Find the mass of the second, the diameter of the third, and an equation connecting the mass m kg and the diameter d cm of spheres of this type.
6 The circumference C inches of a circle of radius r inches is given by the formula $C = 2\pi r$; if C_1, r_1 and C_2, r_2 are corresponding values of C, r,

$$\frac{C_1}{C_2} = \frac{r_1}{r_2} \qquad\qquad \cdot \ \cdot \ \cdot \ (1)$$

(a) What formula gives the circumference C cm of a circle of radius r m? Does equation (1) still hold?
(b) Given that 1 inch $= 2.54$ cm, what equation gives the circumference C cm of a circle of radius r inches? Does equation (1) still hold?
7 Boyle's law states that, under certain conditions, the pressure exerted by a given mass of gas is inversely proportional to the volume occupied by it.

The gas inside a cylinder is compressed by a piston in such a way that Boyle's law may legitimately be applied. When this happens, the volume is decreased from 200 cm^3 to 70 cm^3. If the original pressure of the gas is 9.8×10^4 N m^{-2}, find the final pressure of the gas.

8 The number of square carpet tiles needed to surface the floor of a hall varies inversely as the square of the length of a side of the tile used. If 2016 tiles of side 0.4 m would be needed to surface the floor of a certain hall, how many tiles of side 0.3 m would be required?

9 If the volume of a model 10 cm long is 72 cm^3, what is the volume of a similar model 6 cm long? What is the length of a similar model with volume 100 cm^3?

10 The square of the period (time to go round its orbit) of an Earth satellite varies as the cube of its mean distance from the centre of the Earth. The period of the Moon is 28 days and its mean distance from the centre of the Earth is 380 000 km. Find the period, to the nearest minute, of an Earth satellite whose mean distance from the surface of the Earth is 470 km, given that the radius of the Earth is 6370 km.

Also find an equation giving the period of an Earth satellite T hours in terms of its mean distance d km from the centre of the Earth.

23.2 Joint variation

So far we have only considered examples of variation where one variable, say y, varies as some power of another variable, say x. But there are many examples in science, engineering and everyday life when one variable depends on two or more others. For example, the volume V of a right circular cylinder is given in terms of its radius r and height h by the formula

$$V = \pi r^2 h$$

If we consider a metal rod of uniform circular cross-section which can be cut into lengths, we have a case of this law in which the radius is constant and so

the volume varies as the length

or, using the symbol '$\propto$' as an abbreviation for 'varies as',

$$V \propto h$$

On the other hand, if circular discs are cut out of sheet metal or plywood, h will be constant and so

the volume varies as the square of the radius

or $V \propto r^2$

To summarise, for a right circular cylinder,

if r is constant, $V \propto h$
if h is constant, $V \propto r^2$

In experimental work, if one variable depends on two or more others, it is most convenient to see how the first depends on each of the others in turn while the remainder are held constant. As an illustration of this, consider the discharge of water through a circular hole. The volume of water V will depend in some way on:

(a) the radius r of the hole
(b) the velocity v of the water
(c) the time t over which the discharge takes place.

It is found that
(1) if v, t are constant, $V \propto r^2$
(2) if t, r are constant, $V \propto v$
(3) if r, v are constant, $V \propto t$.

It will be seen that the equation

$$V = kr^2vt \quad (k \text{ constant})$$

satisfies the conditions (1), (2), (3) and hence it is natural to write

$$V \propto r^2vt$$

Qu. 9 Express the statement 'If z is constant, y varies as x; if x is constant, y varies as the cube of z', as a single equation.

Qu. 10 Write the statement, 'If h, t are constant, W varies as the square of r; if r, t are constant, W varies as h; if r, h are constant, W varies inversely as t', as a single statement using the sign '$\propto$'.

When one variable varies as two or more others, the word *jointly* is sometimes used. For example, with the data of the last paragraph, we might say that V varies jointly as v, t and the square of r.

Qu. 11 'The kinetic energy T of a flywheel varies jointly as its mass m and as the square of its radius r'. Express this statement:
(a) as an equation with a constant, k, (b) as a statement using the sign '$\propto$'.

Qu. 12 'F varies jointly as m and the square of v, and inversely as r'. Express this statement as an equation.

For purposes of calculation, we can rewrite statements in the form

$$A = k\frac{x^3}{t} \quad (\text{where } k \text{ is some constant})$$

in terms of the ratios of corresponding values A_1, x_1, t_1 and A_2, x_2, t_2 of the variables. We have

$$A_1 = k\frac{x_1^3}{t_1}$$

$$A_2 = k\frac{x_2^3}{t_2}$$

$$\therefore \frac{A_1}{A_2} = \frac{x_1^3/t_1}{x_2^3/t_2}$$

Multiplying numerator and denominator by $t_1 t_2$,

$$\frac{A_1}{A_2} = \frac{x_1{}^3 t_2}{x_2{}^3 t_1}$$

Note that A varies inversely as t, and that the ratio t_1/t_2 is 'upside down'.

Qu. 13 If x_1, y_1, z_1 and x_2, y_2, z_2 are corresponding values of x, y, z, write down equations connecting x_1, y_1, z_1 and x_2, y_2, z_2 when:
(a) z varies jointly as x and the square of y
(b) z varies as y and inversely as the square of x
(c) z varies as the cube of x and as the square of y
(d) z varies as x when y is constant and z varies as y when x is constant
(e) z varies as the square of x when y is constant and z varies as the square of y when x is constant.
(f) z varies as the square root of x when y is constant and inversely as y when x is constant

Example 4

The total sideways force experienced by a given car rounding a circular bend at a constant speed varies as the square of the speed of the car and inversely as the radius of the circle. A certain car goes round a bend of radius 50 m at 72 km h^{-1} and experiences a total sideways force of 12 kN. What sideways force will it experience on going round a bend of radius 30 m at 54 km h^{-1}?

Let the sideways force be F kN, the speed be v km h^{-1}, and the radius r m, then

$$F \propto \frac{v^2}{r}$$

Therefore, if F_1, v_1, r_1 and F_2, v_2, r_2 are corresponding values of F, v, r,

$$\frac{F_1}{F_2} = \frac{v_1{}^2/r_1}{v_2{}^2/r_2} = \frac{v_1{}^2 r_2}{v_2{}^2 r_1}$$

	F (kN)	v (km h^{-1})	r (m)
(1)	F	54	30
(2)	12	72	50

$$\therefore \quad \frac{F}{12} = \frac{54^2 \times 50}{72^2 \times 30}$$

$$\therefore \quad F = \frac{12 \times 3^2 \times 5}{4^2 \times 3}$$

$$= \frac{45}{4} = 11.25$$

Therefore the sideways force on the car will be approximately 11 kN.

23.3 Variation in parts

As an example of variation in parts, consider the cost of having a floor covered with lino tiles. First of all, a man and some materials have to be transported to the site. Here the cost of the man's time and the cost of the running of a van may be taken to vary as the distance s km from the firm's premises and so we may write this part of the cost as £ks, where k is some constant to be found. Second, there is the cost of materials and the man's time doing the job, which may be taken to vary as the area A m² of the floor, and so this part of the cost may be written £KA, where K is another constant to be determined. Hence, if the total cost is £C,

$$C = ks + KA$$

Let us suppose that the cost of two contracts is as given in the following table. How much would it cost to lay 40 m² of lino tiles at a distance of 75 km from the firm's premises?

cost £C	distance s km	area A m²
C	75	40
265	45	50
155	60	27

Substituting from the bottom two lines of the table into

$$C = ks + KA$$

we get

$$265 = 45k + 50K \qquad \qquad \ldots \ (1)$$
$$155 = 60k + 27K \qquad \qquad \ldots \ (2)$$

$4 \times (1) - 3 \times (2)$:

$$1060 - 465 = (200 - 81)K$$

$$\therefore \ K = \frac{595}{119} = 5$$

From (2):

$$155 = 60k + 135$$
$$\therefore \qquad k = \tfrac{1}{3}$$

Substituting $K = 5, \ k = \tfrac{1}{3}$,

$$C = \tfrac{1}{3}s + 5A$$

When $s = 75, \ A = 40$,

$$C = \tfrac{1}{3} \times 75 + 5 \times 40 = 225$$

Therefore the cost of laying 40 m² of tiles 75 km distant would be £225.

Qu. 14 The cost £C of manufacturing a certain number of wooden cubes for children is made up of two parts, one of which is constant and the other of which varies as the cube of the side x cm of a brick.
(a) Express the above statement in symbols.
(b) Find the cost of making 1000 $1\frac{1}{4}$ cm cubes if the same number of 2 cm and 1 cm cubes cost respectively £18 and £11.

Exercise 23b

1 The area of a sector of a circle varies jointly as the angle at the centre and the square of the radius. Given that the area of a sector containing an angle of 36° in a circle of radius 10 cm is 31.4 cm², find the area of a sector containing an angle of 72° in a circle of radius 5 cm.

2 The number of revolutions per minute of a bicycle wheel varies as the speed of the bicycle and inversely as the diameter of the wheel. A wheel of diameter 63 cm makes 151.5 revolutions per minute when the bicycle is moving at 18 km h⁻¹. Another bicycle has wheels of 35 cm diameter, how many revolutions per minute will one of its wheels make when the bicycle is moving at 30 km h⁻¹.

3 The flow of water through a circular orifice varies as the square of the diameter of the orifice and as the square root of the head of water. Given that 200 litres of water per second flow through an orifice of diameter 25 mm when the head of water is 4 m, find the flow of water through an orifice of diameter 10 mm when the head of water is 9 m.

4 The kinetic enery of a car (including passengers) varies jointly as the total mass and the square of the speed. A car of total mass 1000 kg travelling at 72 km h⁻¹ has a kinetic energy of 200 kJ. What is the kinetic energy of a car of total mass 1500 kg travelling at 108 km h⁻¹?

5 The volume of a given mass of gas varies directly as its absolute temperature and inversely as its pressure. At an absolute temperature of 283 K and a pressure of 73 cm of mercury, a certain mass of gas has volume 200 cm³. What will its volume be at standard temperature and pressure, i.e. absolute temperature 273 K and pressure 76 cm of mercury? Also find an equation which expresses the volume V cm³ of the gas in terms of its absolute temperature T K and its pressure p cm of mercury.

6 The rate at which an electric fire gives out heat varies as the square of the voltage and inversely as the resistance. If a fire with resistance 57.6 ohms gives out approximately 1 kW when the voltage is 240, at what rate will heat be given out by an electric fire with resistance 69 ohms when the voltage is 220? Also find an expression which gives (approximately) the output in kW of an electric fire of resistance R ohms when the voltage is V.

7 The frequency of the note emitted by a plucked wire of a certain type varies as the square root of the tension of the wire and inversely as its length. A wire of length 0.61 m under a tension of 31 N emits a note of frequency 130 hertz. What will be the frequency of the note emitted by a similar wire of length 0.25 m under a tension of 100 N? Find an equation which gives

the number of oscillations per second f in terms of the length l m and the tension F N.

8 When a note is produced by blowing across the top of a bottle with a circular mouth, the frequency of the note varies as the internal diameter of the mouth and inversely as the square root of the volume of the bottle. Blowing across a certain bottle, I obtain a note whose frequency is approximately 203 hertz. What is the frequency of the note I should obtain by blowing across the top of a bottle with four times the capacity, and with three-quarters the mouth diameter of the first?

9 The period of a simple pendulum varies as the square root of its length and inversely as the square root of the acceleration due to gravity. On the Earth, the period of a pendulum 99.4 cm long is 2 s. Assuming that the acceleration due to gravity on the surface of the Moon is one-sixth of that on the Earth, what would be the period of a pendulum 1 m long on the Moon?

10 The effectiveness of a spin drier is measured by the central acceleration at a point on the internal surface of the rotating drum. This acceleration varies as the internal diameter of the drum and as the square of its angular speed. Which would be the more effective: a spin drier with internal diameter 0.5 m running at an angular speed of 1600 rev min^{-1}, or one with internal diameter 0.3 m running at 2000 rev min^{-1}?

11 When a body is being uniformly accelerated, the distance travelled is the sum of two parts: one part varies as the time, the other varies as the square of the time. The distances travelled by a body in 2 s and 3 s from its original position are respectively 32 m and 57 m. How far will it travel from its original position in 4 s? Find an equation which gives the distance s m in terms of the time t s from its original position.

12 In good road conditions, the driver of a car moving at 30 km h^{-1} can stop the car in 11.4 m, and if the car is moving at 60 km h^{-1} it can be stopped in 33.6 m. This stopping distance is made up of two parts, one of which varies as the speed of the car, and the other of which varies as the square of the speed. In what distance can the driver stop the car if it is moving at 80 km h^{-1}? Find an equation which gives the stopping distance s m in terms of the speed v km h^{-1}.

If the car can just be stopped in 25 m, how fast is it moving?

23.4 Graphical determination of laws

A simple experiment is performed to investigate the relationship between the tension in an elastic band and its extension, by fixing the upper end and suspending bodies of different masses in turn from the lower end. The tension (y N) in the band (given by the weight of each body) is tabulated against the corresponding extension (x cm) measured to the nearest mm.

x	0	1	1.8	2.5	3.3	4.3	5.3
y	0	1	2	3	4	5	6

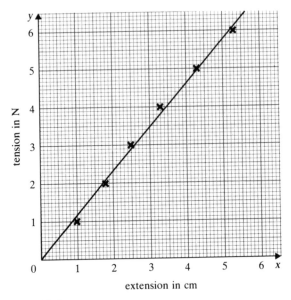

Figure 23.2

When these results are illustrated graphically (see Figure 23.2) we see that it is possible to draw a straight line about which the points are closely scattered; such a line is then drawn, and we make it pass through the origin since we know that $y = 0$ when $x = 0$.

A straight line through the origin of gradient m has the equation

$$y = mx$$

and, allowing for experimental error and the limited accuracy in measuring x, we may reasonably deduce this to be the relationship between the x and y of our experiment. Referring to the straight line drawn, when $x = 4$, $y \approx 4.6$, and its gradient $m \approx 4.6/4 = 1.2$ correct to 2 significant figures.

So by this experiment we have determined that the law connecting the tension in the given band (y N) and its extension (x cm) is

$$y \approx 1.2x$$

Qu. 15 A trolley accelerates down a slope from rest to v km h^{-1} in t s as shown by the following table. Determine graphically the law giving v in terms of t.

v	0	10	20	30	40	50	60
t	0	2.5	4.7	7.1	9.7	11.9	14.5

Example 5

The following estimate is received for printing copies of a pamphlet.

No. of copies	50	100	200	500
Cost in £	11.50	12.50	14.50	20.50

(a) Obtain a law giving the cost, £y, of x copies.
(b) Estimate the cost of 350 copies.

(a) A graph of the data (Figure 23.3) shows a straight line, so we assume that the printer has used a *linear* law connecting x and y to make his estimate, i.e. there is an equation connecting the variables of the form

$$y = mx + c$$

Now c is the intercept on the y-axis (see Section 2.7) and so we can refer to the graph to find that $c = 10.5$, and (from the triangle ABC) that the gradient

$$m = \frac{20.50 - 14.50}{500 - 200} = \frac{6}{300} = 0.02$$

Therefore the law is

$$y = 0.02x + 10.5$$

(b) When $x = 350$,

$$y = 0.02 \times 350 + 10.5$$
$$= 7.0 + 10.5$$
$$= 17.5$$

Therefore the cost of 350 copies is £17.50.

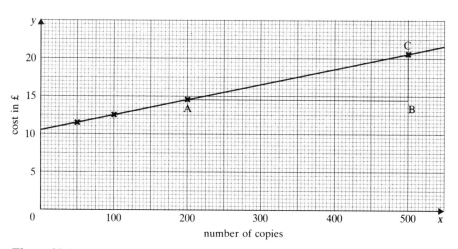

Figure 23.3

Qu. 16 From the solution of Example 5 (a), when $x = 0$, $y = 10.5$. What interpretation may be given to this result?

Note that in Figure 23.3 we have included the origin of the coordinates (that is to say each axis is calibrated *from zero*) and thus we were able to utilize the y-intercept to find c. This advantage must often be sacrificed in favour of the increased accuracy obtainable by using a larger scale; Example 6 demonstrates how the equation of a straight line is determined in these circumstances.

Example 6

Find the equation of the line $y = mx + c$ in Figure 23.4.

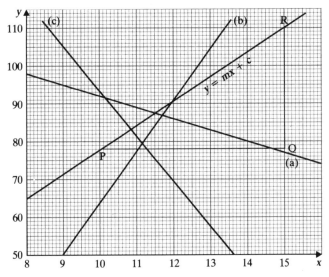

Figure 23.4

The gradient m is found from the triangle PQR (chosen so that the length of PQ is a whole number of units).

$$m = \frac{32}{5} = 6.4$$

Substituting in $y = mx + c$,

$$y = 6.4x + c$$

To find c, substitute the coordinates of a convenient point on the line, e.g. when $x = 10$, $y = 78$.

$$\therefore \quad 78 = 6.4 \times 10 + c$$
$$\therefore \quad c = 14$$

Therefore the required equation is $y = 6.4x + 14$.

Qu. 17 Find as accurately as possible the equations of the lines (a), (b), (c) in Figure 23.4. (Note that two of these lines have negative gradients.)

Qu. 18 The upper end of a coiled spring was fixed and bodies were hung in turn from the lower end. The masses of the bodies (*y* g) and the corresponding lengths of the spring (*x* cm) were recorded as follows:

x	8.4	9.5	10.1	11.0	11.7	12.6	13.5	14.3
y	30	40	50	60	70	80	90	100

Find a law giving *y* in terms of *x* over this range, and estimate the unstretched length of the spring.

23.5 Linear check of nonlinear laws

As we saw in Section 23.1, a nonlinear law connecting two variables may often be considered in such a way that it involves a linear relationship. For example, if we suspect that two variables *x* and *y* are inversely proportional, we wish to show that $xy = k$, where *k* is a constant, i.e. $y = k \times 1/x$; this may be done by plotting *y* against $1/x$ and seeing if the points lie close to a straight line through the origin.

To take another example, let us suppose that the designer of a car windscreen wishes to find out if the air resistance (*R* N) is proportional to the square, or the cube, of the velocity (*v* km h^{-1}); she carries out an experiment which yields the following results:

v	20	30	40	50
R	4	14	33	60

The reader may check from a rough sketch that the graph of *v* against *R* does no more than indicate that *R* might vary as some power of *v*, which is of no real assistance. This problem is dealt with in the following question.

Qu. 19 With the data of the preceding paragraph, plot the following graphs, letting 1 cm represent 5 N:
(a) *R* against v^2 (on the v^2-axis let 1 cm represent 200)
(b) *R* against v^3 (on the v^3-axis let 1 cm represent 10 000)
Deduce an approximate relationship giving *R* in terms of *v*.

Qu. 20 A marble was allowed to run down a sloping sheet of glass and the time (*t* s) taken to roll *s* m from rest was measured by a stop watch. The results were as follows:

s	1	2	3	4	5
t	1.4	2	2.5	2.8	3.2

Confirm that the law relating s and t is $s = kt^2$, and determine the values of the constant k to two significant figures.

23.6 Reduction of a law to linear form using logarithms

The method of Qu. 19 is severely limited, since we assume a relationship $R = kv^n$, then we guess some integral value of n and test for it. It would be better to employ a method which tests for any real rational value of n, and this is possible if we use logarithms. See Section 10.5.

Suppose that we wish to test the law

$$R = kv^n \qquad \qquad \text{. . . (1)}$$

where k and n are constants. If it is valid, then taking logarithms, base 10:

$$\begin{aligned} \lg R &= \lg (kv^n) \\ &= \lg v^n + \lg k \\ &= n \lg v + \lg k \qquad \qquad \text{. . . (2)} \end{aligned}$$

Writing $\lg R$ as y, $\lg v$ as x and $\lg k$ as c, (2) becomes

$$y = nx + c$$

which represents a straight line of gradient n.

Thus if we plot $\lg R$ against $\lg v$ and we obtain a set of nearly collinear points, this means that we have established the linear relationship (2) and confirmed the law (1); we then draw the 'best' straight line. Its gradient determines the value of the constant n, and the constant k is found from the y-intercept c, or by the method of Example 6.

Qu. 21 From the data of Qu. 19 the following table has been prepared:

$x = \lg v$	1.30	1.48	1.60	1.70
$y = \lg R$	0.60	1.15	1.52	1.78

Using a scale of 0.1 to 1 cm, plot $\lg R$ against $\lg v$ and deduce that $R \approx 0.0005v^3$ (see Example 6).

Example 7

The table below shows some data relating to the moons of the planet Jupiter:

	Io	Europa	Ganymede	Callisto
distance x (millions of km)	0.422	0.671	1.07	1.88
period T (days)	1.77	3.55	7.16	16.7

Plot a graph of lg x against lg T and hence express T in terms of x.

Use your formula to estimate:
(a) the period of another moon whose mean distance from the planet is 11.5 million km
(b) the distance of a moon whose period is 0.50 days

The table below shows values of $X(= \lg x)$ and $Y(= \lg T)$, correct to three significant figures:

	Io	Europa	Ganymede	Callisto
$X(= \lg x)$	−0.375	−0.173	0.0294	0.274
$Y(= \lg T)$	0.248	0.550	0.855	1.22

These values produce a straight line graph, as shown in Figure 23.5.

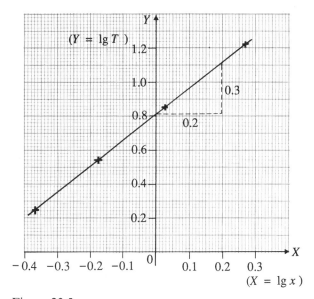

Figure 23.5

Since it is a straight line, we may deduce that X and Y are related by an equation of the form

$$Y = mX + c$$

where m is the gradient of the graph and c is its intercept on the Y-axis.

From the graph we can estimate that $m = 0.3 \div 0.2 = 1.5$, and $c = 0.81$.

Hence

$$Y = 1.5X + 0.81$$

Returning to the original variables, we have:

$$\lg T = 1.5 \lg x + 0.81$$

From a calculator, we can see that $0.81 = \lg 6.46$, so

$$\begin{aligned}\lg T &= 1.5 \lg x + \lg 6.46 \\ &= \lg x^{1.5} + \lg 6.46 \\ &= \lg (6.46x^{1.5})\end{aligned}$$

Hence

$$T = 6.46x^{1.5}$$

[As a check, put $x = 0.671$, the data for Europa, giving
$$\begin{aligned}T &= 6.46 \times 0.671^{1.5} \\ &= 3.55 \text{ to three significant figures.}]\end{aligned}$$

(a) If $x = 11.5$, then
$$\begin{aligned}T &= 6.46 \times 11.5^{1.5} \\ &= 250 \qquad \text{correct to two significant figures}\end{aligned}$$

[In view of the approximations already made, and the use of the graph, one should not claim an unreasonable degree of accuracy.]

A moon at a distance of 11.5 million km should have a period of approximately 250 days.

(b) If $T = 0.50$, then
$$\begin{aligned}0.50 &= 6.46 \times x^{1.5} \\ \therefore \quad x^{1.5} &= 0.0774 \\ \therefore \quad x &= 0.0774^{2/3} \\ &= 0.18 \qquad \text{correct to two significant figures}\end{aligned}$$

A moon with a period of 0.50 days should be at a mean distance of 0.18 million km.

Example 8

The frequency (f hertz) and the interval (x semitones) of each note of a C major scale are given in the table below; show that f, x are related by a law in the form $f = ka^x$ and determine the constants k, a.

Note	C	D	E	F	G	A	B	C
x	0	2	4	5	7	9	11	12
f	256	287	323	342	384	431	483	512

Assuming that $f = ka^x$, and taking logarithms to the base 10 of each side

$$\begin{aligned}\lg f &= \lg a^x + \lg k \\ \therefore \quad \lg f &= x \lg a + \lg k\end{aligned}$$

Writing $\lg f$ as y, $\lg a$ as m, $\lg k$ as c,

$$y = mx + c$$

This shows that we must, from the data, establish a linear relationship between x and $\lg f$. From the following table the points have been plotted in Figure 23.6 and the 'best' straight line has been drawn; we have confirmed that the law is of the form $f = ka^x$.

x	0	2	4	5	7	9	11	12
$y = \lg f$	2.408	2.458	2.509	2.534	2.584	2.634	2.684	2.709

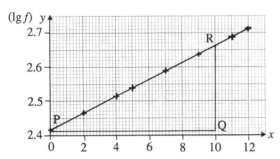

Figure 23.6

If we now consider the straight line in Figure 23.6 to have the equation $y = mx + c$, we see from the triangle PQR that its gradient

$$m = \lg a = \frac{0.25}{10} = 0.025$$

From a calculator, $a = 1.059$.

We may now write $y = 0.025x + c$.

From the graph, when $x = 0$, $y = 2.408$.

$\therefore$ $c = \lg k = 2.408$

From a calculator, $k = 256$.

Hence from the data we deduce the required law to be

$$f = 256 \times 1.059^x$$

Exercise 23c (Miscellaneous)

1 A round bolt with nominal diameter D mm has a countersunk head of diameter A mm. D and A are found to be as follows:

D	6.4	7.9	9.5	11.1	12.7	15.9	19.0	22.2	25.4
A	11.7	14.6	17.5	20.4	23.4	29.2	35.0	40.9	46.7

Find the linear equation giving A in terms of D. Does A vary as D?

2 The mass m kg of a 300 mm square of lead sheeting of thickness t mm is given as follows:

t	1.25	1.80	2.24	2.50	3.15	3.55
m	1.275	1.835	2.285	2.550	3.215	3.625

Obtain a linear relation giving m in terms of t.

3 A marble was dropped from a height h_1 cm and observed to rise to a height h_2 cm. Four such observations are given in the table below:

h_1	4	9	16	22
h_2	$1\frac{1}{2}$	3	$5\frac{1}{2}$	$7\frac{1}{2}$

Does it appear that there is a law connecting h_1, h_2? If so, what is it?

4 While some water was cooling, the temperature was recorded at minute intervals as follows:

Time t minutes	0	1	2	3	4	5	6
Temperature θ °C	62	61.5	61	60.5	60	59.5	59

Find an equation giving θ in terms of t. Can you expect this equation to hold over a wider range of values? Give reasons for your answer.

5 The periods and mean distances of some of the planets are given in the table below:

Period P days	87.97	224.7	365.3	687.0	4333	10 760
Mean distance s millions of km	58	108	150	228	778	1426

Find a law in the form $P = ks^n$.

6 For a certain survey in which n people are to be interviewed, a market research organisation calculates that it has an even chance of obtaining correct within $p\%$ the percentage in favour of the product concerned in the

survey. n and p are related as follows:

n	500	1000	2000	5000	10 000
p	1.51	1.07	0.75	0.48	0.34

Find how p varies with n.

7

x	1.0	1.5	2.0	2.5	3.0
y	12	30	72	173	416

The table shows corresponding values of variables x and y obtained in an experiment. Draw a straight line graph to verify that x and y are connected by a relationship of the form $y = ae^{bx}$, where a and b are constants.†
Using your graph obtain estimates of the values of a and b giving your answer to 2 significant figures.   (L)

8 Pairs of values, x and y, are obtained in an experiment as shown below:

x	10	20	40	75	100
y	136	334	824	1850	2710

It is believed that x and y are related by a law of the form

$$\lg y = m \lg x + c$$

where m and c are constants.
Write down a table of values for $\lg x$ and $\lg y$.
By drawing a graph, show that the law is approximately valid.
Estimate values of m and c giving your answers to 2 significant figures.
Using your values of m and c, express y in terms of x.   (L)

† e is the base of Napierian logarithms. See p195 and Chapter 26.

Chapter 24

Iterative methods for solving equations

24.1 Introduction

One of the most common tasks in mathematics is to solve an equation. In this book we have already solved a variety of different equations. We have solved quadratic equations by factorisation or by the formula, we have solved other polynomial equations by factorising them and we have solved some carefully selected trigonometrical equations.

Consider, however, the following problem. Figure 24.1 represents a circle, whose centre is at O, and whose radius is one unit. Can we find the value of θ, in radians, so that the area of the shaded segment is exactly 0.5 square units?

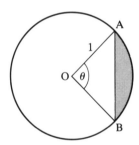

Figure 24.1

Since the angle θ is measured in radians, the area of the *sector* OAB is $\frac{1}{2}r^2\theta$, and since $r = 1$, this is just $\frac{1}{2}\theta$. The area of the *triangle*, OAB can be obtained from the standard formula, $\frac{1}{2}ab \sin C$; in this case $a = 1$, $b = 1$, and $C = \theta$, so the area of the triangle OAB is $\frac{1}{2} \sin \theta$. The area of the shaded segment is the difference of these two areas, i.e.

$$\tfrac{1}{2}\theta - \tfrac{1}{2} \sin \theta$$

The problem is to find the value of θ so that this area is 0.5 square units. In other words we need to solve the equation

$$\tfrac{1}{2}\theta - \tfrac{1}{2} \sin \theta = \tfrac{1}{2}$$

or $\quad \theta - \sin \theta = 1$

None of the methods for solving equations at our disposal (apart from drawing a graph) would enable us to solve this equation; indeed it is impossible to find an *exact* solution. However, there is no doubt that such an angle exists, and with a little experimentation using a calculator, it is possible to see that an *approximate* solution is $\theta = 2$.

In this chapter we shall develop methods by which approximate solutions to equations can be obtained. An approximate solution should not be despised, for it can be very useful, and, as in the example above, it may be the only solution available. The value of such an answer is greatly enhanced if it is possible to give an estimate of its degree of accuracy.

Later in the chapter we shall return to the equation $\theta - \sin \theta = 1$, but first we shall tackle a simpler problem, namely, can we find the square root of a given number without using the square root function on a calculator?

24.2 An iterative method for finding square roots

What is the square root of 18? Or, to put it another way, solve the equation $x^2 = 18$. Since we are not going to use the square root function on a calculator, the most sensible first step is to check through the 'square numbers'

   1,   4,   9,   16,   25,   36,   49,   ...

and note that $\sqrt{18}$ lies between 4 and 5, and that it is nearer 4 than 5. So we might say

   'the square root of 18 is 4, correct to the nearest whole number'

This at least gives an approximate answer and it indicates the degree of accuracy of this approximate answer.

We shall now use this 'first approximation' to obtain a better 'second approximation', and this in turn will be used to form an even better 'third approximation'. Such a procedure is called **successive approximation**, or **iteration**.

The method we shall use to find the successive approximations will depend upon the fact that if x is exactly equal to $\sqrt{18}$, then $18/x$ is exactly equal to $\sqrt{18}$. If x does *not* equal $\sqrt{18}$, then

   either x is less than $\sqrt{18}$, in which case $18/x$ is greater than $\sqrt{18}$,
   or x is greater than $\sqrt{18}$, in which case $18/x$ is less than $\sqrt{18}$.

In both cases, we can say that $\sqrt{18}$ lies between x and $18/x$.

Consequently, using $\sqrt{18} \approx 4$ as a 'first approximation', we know that $\sqrt{18}$ lies between 4 and 18/4, i.e. between 4 and 4.5, so we take as our 'second approximation' the mean of these two numbers, i.e.

$$\frac{1}{2}\left(4 + \frac{18}{4}\right) = 4.25$$

Now we repeat the process, using $\sqrt{18} \approx 4.25$. Once again we know that $\sqrt{18}$ must lie between 4.25 and 18/4.25, and so we take as our 'third approximation' the mean of *these* two numbers. In other words the third approximation is

$$\frac{1}{2}\left(4.25 + \frac{18}{4.25}\right) = 4.24265 \qquad \text{correct to six significant figures}$$

(The arithmetic at this stage is becoming rather heavy, and a calculator may be used to lighten the load. However, the square root function on the calculator is *not* allowed!)

We now have a very good approximate value of the square root of 18, and we know that the exact value lies between 4.24265 and 18/4.24265 (=4.24263). So we are now able to say that

$$\sqrt{18} = 4.243 \qquad \text{correct to four significant figures}$$

knowing that we are justified in claiming this degree of accuracy.

This procedure can be summed up as follows: writing x_r for the rth approximation, the $(r + 1)$th approximation is given by

$$x_{r+1} = \frac{1}{2}\left(x_r + \frac{18}{x_r}\right)$$

This is called an **iterative formula** for finding $\sqrt{18}$. More generally, the iterative formula for finding the square root of any positive number, N, is

$$x_{r+1} = \frac{1}{2}\left(x_r + \frac{N}{x_r}\right)$$

Qu. 1 Use the iterative formula above, to find the square roots of:
(a) 17   (b) 40   (c) 85   (d) 96
correct to four significant figures.

Historical note This method for calculating square roots is a very old one. It was used by the Babylonians more than three thousand years ago. Today it is frequently called Newton's algorithm, but this is hardly fair to those great, but nameless, mathematicians from Mesopotamia.

If a programmable calculator or a microcomputer is available, the reader should try to write programs to solve some of the equations in this chapter by iteration. Iterative methods are ideally suited to such an approach, because the same basic sequence of steps is repeated over and over again; this can be done very rapidly and accurately on a programmable calculator or a microcomputer.

24.3 Further iterative formulae

If we were given the iterative formula

$$x_{r+1} = \frac{1}{2}\left(x_r + \frac{18}{x_r}\right)$$

but we did not know how it had been constructed, would it be possible to discover the equation which it is designed to solve? The answer is 'Yes', provided the sequence

$$x_1, x_2, x_3, x_4, \ldots$$

tends to a limit. Suppose that $x_n \to X$, as $n \to \infty$, then for a large value of n, the iterative formula could be written

$$X = \frac{1}{2}\left(X + \frac{18}{X}\right)$$

This equation could then be simplified, as follows:

$$2X = X + \frac{18}{X}$$

$$\therefore \quad X = \frac{18}{X}$$

$$\therefore \quad X^2 = 18$$

So, as expected, we see that the equation which is solved by the iterative formula above is

$$x^2 = 18$$

Example 1

Starting with $x_1 = 4$, use the iterative formula

$$x_{r+1} = 5 - \frac{2}{x_r}$$

to find x_2, x_3, and x_4, giving these values correct to three significant figures. Find the equation which is solved by this iterative formula.

$$x_2 = 5 - \frac{2}{4}$$

$$= 4.5 \qquad \text{exactly}$$

$$x_3 = 5 - \frac{2}{4.5}$$

$$\approx 4.55556$$
$$= 4.56 \qquad \text{correct to three significant figures}$$

$$x_4 = 5 - \frac{2}{4.55556}$$

$$\approx 4.56098$$
$$= 4.56 \qquad \text{correct to three significant figures}$$

The successive values of x_r appear to be tending to a limit, namely 4.56.

[*Note* If you are using a calculator for the arithmetic, the successive values x_2, x_3, x_4 etc, should be retained on the calculator. It is poor technique to use the *corrected* value of x_r to calculate x_{r+1}. However, if you are answering an examination question which requires a specific degree of accuracy in presenting answers, you should always follow this instruction; it is usually there to simplify the task of marking the answer and it is very unwise to upset the examiner!]

To find the equation which this iterative formula solves, we write this limit as X, then, for large values of r, the iterative formula becomes

$$X = 5 - \frac{2}{X}$$

When this is simplified we obtain

$$X^2 - 5X + 2 = 0$$

So $x = 4.56$ is a root, correct to three significant figures, of the equation

$$x^2 - 5x + 2 = 0$$

[This equation is of course a quadratic equation, and using an iterative method to solve it is using a sledge-hammer to crack a nut. However, at this stage it is more convenient to use fairly simple equations for the examples. If this equation is solved by the formula, the solution would be

$$x = \frac{5 \pm \sqrt{17}}{2} = 4.56 \text{ or } 0.44 \qquad \text{correct to two decimal places}$$

The iterative formula has produced the first of these, but not the second. However, we could use the fact that the sum of the roots is 5 to calculate the second root, i.e. $5 - 4.56 = 0.44$.]

As we have seen above, if the sequence x_1, x_2, x_3, x_4, ... converges, then we can deduce the equation from the iterative formula. This suggests that if we have a given equation and we wish to construct a suitable iterative formula, all we need to do is to rearrange the equation in the form

$$x = f(x)$$

and the corresponding iterative formula will be

$$x_{r+1} = f(x_r)$$

Example 2

Form an iterative formula to solve the equation

$$x^3 - 5x + 1 = 0$$

and use it to find the root which lies between 0 and 1, correct to three significant figures.

The given equation can be arranged in the form

$$5x = x^3 + 1$$

$$x = \frac{x^3 + 1}{5}$$

consequently we shall take as the iterative formula

$$x_{r+1} = \frac{x_r^3 + 1}{5}$$

and, starting with $x_1 = 0$, we obtain

$$x_2 = \frac{1}{5} = 0.2$$

$$x_3 = \frac{1.008}{5} = 0.2016$$

$$x_4 = \frac{0.2016^3 + 1}{5}$$

$$= 0.201639 \quad \text{correct to six significant figures}$$

In view of the very small change from x_3 to x_4, it would be reasonable to conclude that we are now *very* near to the exact answer. Consequently we could claim, with some confidence, that the root of the equation is 0.202, correct to three significant figures.

However, the reader must not run away with the idea that *any* rearrangement of the original equation will yield a suitable iterative formula. Consider, for example, the following equation:

$$x^2 - 5x + 3 = 0$$

It is easy to verify that this has a root between 4 and 5.

The rearrangement

$$x = \frac{x^2 + 3}{5}$$

produces the iterative formula

$$x_{r+1} = \frac{x_r^2 + 3}{5}$$

If we start at $x_1 = 5$, the succeeding values of x_r, correct to four significant figures, are

$$x_2 = \frac{25 + 3}{5} = 5.6$$

$$x_3 = \frac{5.6^2 + 3}{5} = 6.872$$

$$x_4 = \frac{6.872^2 + 3}{5} = 10.04$$

$$x_5 = \frac{10.04^2 + 3}{5} = 20.78$$

These values of x_r are getting further and further away from the root we were expecting; we say the sequence $x_1, x_2, x_3, \ldots$ is *diverging*. However, the re-arrangement of the original equation was by no means the only possible one. Consider for example,

$$x = 5 - \frac{3}{x}$$

This gives the iterative formula

$$x_{r+1} = 5 - \frac{3}{x_r}$$

and if we start, as before, with $x_1 = 5$, we obtain

$$x_2 = 5 - \frac{3}{5} \qquad = 4.4$$

$$x_3 = 5 - \frac{3}{4.4} = 4.318$$

$$x_4 = 5 - \frac{3}{4.318} = 4.305$$

$$x_5 = 5 - \frac{3}{4.305} = 4.303$$

$$x_6 = 5 - \frac{3}{4.303} = 4.303$$

[The root given by the quadratic formula is 4.303.]

So this second arrangement has worked satisfactorily.

We can see from this that not all rearrangements of a given equation lead to a suitable iterative formula. We could decide to discard any iterative formula which produces a divergent sequence, but it would clearly be more satisfactory if we had some method for discriminating between a formula which produces a divergent sequence and one which produces a convergent sequence; we shall tackle this in the next section.

Exercise 24a

1 Use the iterative formula in Section 24.2 to find the square roots of:
  (a) 12   (b) 30   (c) 50   (d) 75
  giving your answers correct to three significant figures.

2 Use the iterative formula

$$x_{r+1} = \frac{2x_r}{3} + \frac{4}{x_r{}^2}$$

starting at $x_1 = 2$, to find x_2, x_3 and x_4, giving your answers correct to three significant figures. Find, in its simplest form, the equation which is solved by this iterative formula.

3 Adapt no. 2 so that it can be used to find $20^{1/3}$.

4 Show that the equation $x^2 - 5x + 1 = 0$ can be arranged as $x = (x^2 + 1)/5$, or, alternatively, as $x = 5 - 1/x$. Hence write down two possible iterative formulae which might be used for solving this quadratic, and, starting from $x_1 = 0.2$, find the values of x_2, x_3 and, x_4 which are produced by each of these iterative formulae.

Only one of these sequences appears to converge; use this sequence to write down the (two) roots of the quadratic equation.

5 The cubic equation $x^3 - 10x + 1 = 0$ can be rearranged in the form $x = (x^3 + 1)/10$.

Use this rearrangement to form an iterative formula and use it to find, correct to four significant figures, the root which lies between 0 and 1. (Start with $x_1 = 0$.)

6 Solve the equation in Section 24.1, that is $\theta = \sin \theta + 1$, by an iterative method, starting from $\theta = 2$. (θ is measured in *radians*.)

7 Show that the equation $x^2 - 8x + 10 = 0$, has a root between 1 and 2. Show that the iterative formula $x_{r+1} = 8 - 10/x_r$, can be formed from this equation, and, starting from $x_1 = 1$, calculate the values of x_2, x_3 and x_4. Comment on your results.

8 The iterative formulae

(a) $x_{r+1} = \dfrac{2x_r^3 + 10}{3x_r^2}$ and (b) $x_{r+1} = \dfrac{10}{x_r^2}$

can both be obtained by rearranging the equation $x^3 - 10 = 0$.

Starting from $x_1 = 2$, find the values of x_2, x_3 and x_4, which are produced by these iterative formulae. Only one of these sequences converges; use this one to find $\sqrt[3]{10}$, correct to four significant figures.

9 The fifth root of a real number N can be calculated from the iterative formula

$$x_{r+1} = \left(4x_r + \frac{N}{x_r^4} \right) \Big/ 5$$

Use this formula to find the fifth root of 50, correct to three significant figures. [*Hint* Start with $x_1 = 2$.]

10 The product of the roots of the quadratic equation

$$x^2 - px + q = 0$$

is q, so if x_r is an approximate value of one of the roots, the other could be written q/x_r. Use the fact that the sum of the roots of this quadratic equation is p to find a new approximation to the first root. Hence deduce the iterative formula

$$x_{r+1} = p - \frac{q}{x_r}$$

Use this iterative formula to solve the quadratic equation

$$x^2 - 7x + 3 = 0$$

giving your answers correct to three significant figures.

24.4 Iteration – the test for convergence

In the preceding sections we have seen that an iterative formula

$$x_{r+1} = f(x_r)$$

can be used to produce a sequence of values of x_r

$$x_1, x_2, x_3, x_4, \ldots$$

the value of x_1 being selected by trial and error. We have also seen (but not formally proved) that, provided the sequence tends to a limit, which we shall call X, then $x = X$ is a root of the equation

$$x = f(x)$$

In this section we shall examine the conditions under which we can expect the sequence $x_1, x_2, x_3, x_4, \ldots$ to converge. (Example 1 will be used as an illustration, so the reader is advised to read this example again before proceeding.)

Figure 24.2 shows the graphs of $y = x$ and $y = f(x)$, where $f(x) = 5 - 2/x$. The graphs intersect at P(X, Y).

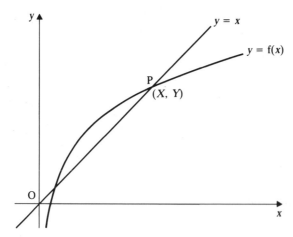

Figure 24.2

The x-coordinate of the point P, that is X, is a solution of the equation

$$x = f(x)$$

This is the root of the equation which we expect to obtain from the iterative formula

$$x_{r+1} = f(x_r)$$

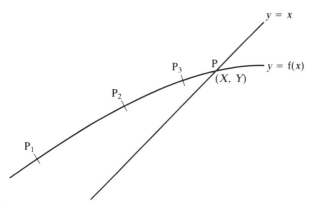

Figure 24.3

The diagram in Figure 24.3 shows an enlargement of the region around the point P in the previous diagram. It also shows the points $P_1, P_2, P_3, \ldots$, whose coordinates are $(x_1, y_1), (x_2, y_2), (x_3, y_3), \ldots$ respectively, where $x_1, x_2, x_3, \ldots$ are the successive approximations given by the iterative formula.

Since the point P_r, whose coordinates are (x_r, y_r), lies on the curve $y = f(x)$, the y-coordinate is given by

$$y_r = f(x_r)$$

and this in turn is equal to x_{r+1}, so the coordinates of P_r can be written (x_r, x_{r+1}). This lets us produce the following geometrical method for constructing the points $P_1, P_2, P_3, \ldots$ (see Figure 24.4). First mark the point (x_1, x_2), remembering that x_1 is selected on a trial-and-error basis. From P_1 draw a line

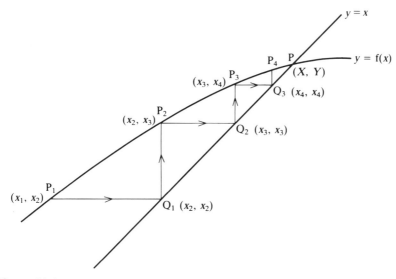

Figure 24.4

horizontally, i.e. parallel to the x-axis, and call the point where this meets the line, Q_1. The points P_1 and Q_1 have the same y-coordinate and Q_1 lies on the line $x = y$, so the coordinates of Q_1 are (y_1, y_1). But $y_1 = x_2$, so these coordinates could be written (x_2, x_2). From Q_1 we now draw a line vertically, i.e. parallel to the y-axis. The point where this meets the curve has the same x-coordinate as Q_1 and so its coordinates are (x_2, x_3). This is the point P_2. We now repeat the operation to construct the subsequent points $P_3, P_4, P_5, ...,$ but because space is limited, only the first few points are printed.

In the diagram we can see the points $P_1, P_2, P_3, ...$ getting closer and closer to the point P itself, and so the x-coordinates $x_1, x_2, x_3, ...$ will be getting closer and closer to X, or, to put it more formally, $x_r \to X$, as $r \to \infty$.

Although the function $f(x) = 5 - 2/x$ has been used in this illustration, a diagram like that in Figure 24.4 could be drawn for other functions *provided* $f'(x)$ *lies between 0 and* 1. If the gradient is greater than 1 the picture is quite different. Figure 24.5 shows the same construction applied to the graph of a function whose gradient is greater than 1. In this case, each step moves P_r further and further away from P.

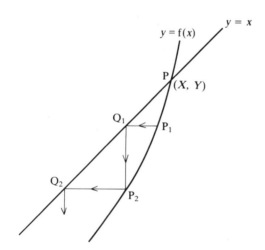

Figure 24.5

The diagrams in Figure 24.6 show the corresponding construction for graphs whose gradients are negative.

The first diagram (in which $-1 < f'(x) < 0$) shows the points $P_1, P_2, P_3, ...$ getting closer and closer to P; in other words, the sequence $x_1, x_2, x_3, ...$ converges when $|f'(x)| < 1$. In contrast the second diagram (in which $f'(x) < -1$) shows these points moving further and further away from P, and so the sequence $x_1, x_2, x_3, ...$ diverges when $|f'(x)| > 1$.

From these diagrams we can conclude that the sequence $x_1, x_2, x_3, ...$ will converge if $|f'(x)| < 1$. To ensure that this sequence converges rapidly, the initial

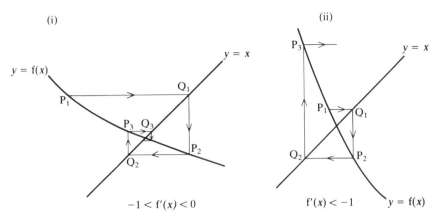

Figure 24.6

approximation should be as close as possible to the exact root and the function $f(x)$ should be selected so that $|f'(x)|$ is as small as possible.

[A more rigorous proof is beyond the scope of this book; any reader who wishes to know more should consult a more specialised textbook†. This topic usually comes under the heading 'numerical methods'.]

Example 3

Show that one of the iterative formulae

(a) $x_{r+1} = (x_r^2 + 3)/5$ (b) $x_{r+1} = 5 - 3/x_r$

produces a convergent sequence for $x \approx 5$, and the other does not.

In iterative formula (a)

$$f(x) = \frac{x^2 + 3}{5}$$

$$f'(x) = \frac{2x}{5}$$

hence

$$f'(5) = 2$$

Since $|f'(5)| > 1$, formula (a) will *not* produce a convergent sequence when $x \approx 5$.

In formula (b)

$$f(x) = 5 - \frac{3}{x}$$

$$f'(x) = \frac{3}{x^2}$$

† Dalton W 1991 *Numerical analysis – an intelligent approach to numerical computation*, Longman, for example.

hence

$$f'(5) = \frac{3}{25} = 0.12$$

In this case $|f'(5)| < 1$, so formula (b) *will* produce a convergent sequence when $x \approx 5$.

[*Note* These formulae were used earlier in this chapter, on pages 493–4.]

Exercise 24b

Which of the following iterative formulae should, according to the test in the preceding section, produce a convergent sequence, $x_1, x_2, x_3, \ldots$, in the region of the value of x indicated? (These iterative formulae were used in Exercise 24a.)

1 $x_{r+1} = \frac{1}{2}\left(x_r + \frac{12}{x_r}\right)$ $x \approx 3$ **2** $x_{r+1} = \frac{2x_r}{3} + \frac{4}{x_r^2}$ $x \approx 2$

3 $x_{r+1} = \frac{x_r^2 + 1}{5}$ $x \approx 0.2$ **4** $x_{r+1} = 5 - \frac{1}{x_r}$ $x \approx 0.2$

5 $x_{r+1} = \frac{x_r^3 + 1}{10}$ $x \approx 1$ **6** $\theta_{r+1} = \sin \theta_r + 1$ $\theta \approx 2$

7 $x_{r+1} = 8 - \frac{10}{x_r}$ $x \approx 1$ **8** $x_{r+1} = \frac{2x_r^3 + 10}{3x_r^2}$ $x \approx 2$

9 $x_{r+1} = \frac{10}{x_r^2}$ $x \approx 2$ **10** $x_{r+1} = \left(4x_r + \frac{50}{x_r^4}\right)\Big/ 5$ $x \approx 2$

24.5 The Newton-Raphson method

We now come to a particular method of iteration known as the Newton-Raphson method (it is frequently called Newton's method). Throughout this section we shall be considering the task of solving an equation of the form $F(x) = 0$ and the exact root we are seeking will be denoted by X.

As with all iterative methods, the first step is to find an approximate root. This can be done quite conveniently by drawing the graph of $y = F(x)$. The *exact* root is the x-coordinate of the point where the graph crosses the x-axis. Figure 24.7 shows the graph of $y = F(x)$ and the point $P(X, 0)$.

Now consider the enlargement of the region surrounding P, which is shown in Figure 24.8.

In this diagram, the point Q is near the point P and its x-coordinate x_r is an approximation to the exact root X, i.e. $x_r \approx X$. The coordinates of Q then are $(x_r, F(x_r))$. Newton's method consists of drawing a tangent to the curve at Q, and, if this line meets the x-axis at R, using the x-coordinate of R as the next

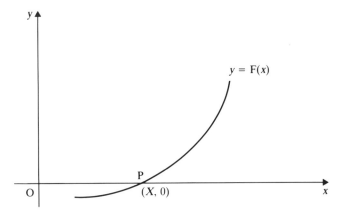

Figure 24.7

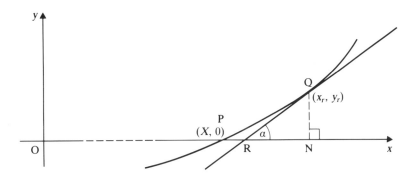

Figure 24.8

approximation to X. In other words R is the point $(x_{r+1}, 0)$. It is clear from the diagram that x_{r+1} will be a better approximation than x_r.

[The reader is advised to draw the corresponding diagram for a graph whose gradient is negative, and also to consider the effect of $F(x_r)$ being negative. From these diagrams the reader should be able to see that Newton's method will yield the desired approximation, provided $F'(x)$ is not zero near the exact root.]

From the diagram in Figure 24.8, we can produce a formula for x_{r+1}, in terms of the function $F(x)$ and x_r.

We know that

$$NQ = F(x_r)$$

and by elementary trigonometry

$$\frac{NQ}{RN} = \tan \alpha$$

i.e. $RN = \dfrac{NQ}{\tan \alpha}$

But, since the line RQ is the tangent to the curve at Q, $\tan \alpha$ is equal to the gradient at Q. In other words

$$\tan \alpha = F'(x_r)$$

So we can write

$$RN = \frac{F(x_r)}{F'(x_r)}$$

Now, from the diagram we can see that

$$OR = ON - RN$$

$$\therefore \quad OR = x_r - \frac{F(x_r)}{F'(x_r)}$$

and since Newton's method is to use the x-coordinate of R as the new approximation, we have

$$\boxed{x_{r+1} = x_r - \frac{F(x_r)}{F'(x_r)}}$$

Example 4

Verify that the equation $x^3 - 5x - 40 = 0$ has a root between $x = 3$ and $x = 4$. Use the Newton-Raphson method to find this root correct to three significant figures.

In this example,

$$F(x) = x^3 - 5x - 40$$

Putting $x = 3$ gives

$$F(3) = 27 - 15 - 40 = -28$$

and, putting $x = 4$,

$$F(4) = 64 - 20 - 40 = +4$$

Since $F(x)$ has changed sign between $x = 3$ and $x = 4$, the graph of the function must cross the x-axis in this interval, so there is a root between 3 and 4. (This assumes that $F(x)$ is continuous between these points; special care must be taken if $F(x)$ is known to have a discontinuity near the root being investigated.)

The Newton-Raphson iterative formula is

$$x_{r+1} = x_r - \frac{F(x_r)}{F'(x_r)}$$

and, in this case

$$F(x) = x^3 - 5x - 40$$

and, differentiating,

$$F'(x) = 3x^2 - 5$$

So, the iterative formula to solve this equation is

$$x_{r+1} = x_r - \frac{x_r^3 - 5x_r - 40}{3x_r^2 - 5}$$

As $|F(4)|$ is much smaller than $|F(3)|$, the root appears to be nearer 4 than 3, so we start with $x_1 = 4$, then

$$x_2 = 4 - \frac{64 - 20 - 40}{48 - 5}$$

$$= 4 - \frac{4}{43}$$

$$= 3.907$$

[*Note* The value of x_2 is printed here, correct to four significant figures. If you are using a calculator, each intermediate value should be stored in the memory for use in the next iteration. It is important to understand that calculating x_2 as accurately as possible from a particular value of x_1 does *not* mean that the root has been found to the same degree of accuracy; at this stage it would be unwise to claim that more than the first one or two significant figures have been determined.]

This value of x_2 should now be substituted into the Newton-Raphson formula. This gives

$$x_3 = 3.904(45)$$

In view of the very small change between x_2 and x_3, we could now safely claim that, correct to three significant figures, the root is 3.90.

This example illustrates some of the virtues of the Newton-Raphson formula. Firstly, provided $F'(x)$ is not zero near the root, it is unnecessary to check whether the sequence converges. Secondly, the sequence converges very rapidly; in other words it is only necessary to calculate a few values of x_r in order to get a very accurate answer.

Example 5

Use the Newton-Raphson formula to solve the equation

$$\theta - \sin \theta = 1$$

giving your answer correct to three significant figures.

504 Essential Pure Mathematics

[This is the equation which arose from the problem in Section 24.1.]
Firstly, the equation must be arranged in the form

$$\theta - \sin \theta - 1 = 0$$

and note that the function needed is

$$F(\theta) = \theta - \sin \theta - 1$$

and consequently

$$F'(\theta) = 1 - \cos \theta$$

The iterative formula we require is

$$\theta_{r+1} = \theta_r - \frac{\theta_r - \sin \theta_r - 1}{1 - \cos \theta_r}$$

Starting from $\theta_1 = 2$ (see Section 24.1, p488) and remembering that θ must be measured in radians,

$$\theta_2 = 2 - \frac{2 - \sin 2 - 1}{1 - \cos 2} = 1.93595$$

and

$$\theta_3 = 1.93456$$

and hence

$$\theta_4 = 1.93456$$

[These values have, for convenience, been rounded off to six significant figures.] As the changes in $\theta_2, \theta_3, \theta_4$, have been so small, we can fairly confidently conclude that, correct to three significant figures, the root is 1.93.

Extreme care should be taken when rounding off numbers which have already been rounded. If, in the example above, θ_2, θ_3 and θ_4 had been rounded to *four* significant figures, they would have read

$$\theta_2 = 1.936$$
$$\theta_3 = 1.935$$
$$\theta_4 = 1.935$$

Rounding θ_4 to *three* significant figures would have given (wrongly) 1.94.

Exercise 24c

Use the Newton-Raphson method to find the root of each of these equations which is near the given value. Give your answers correct to three significant figures.

1 $x^3 - 4x^2 - x - 12 = 0$ $x_1 = 5$ 2 $x^4 - 3x^3 - 10 = 0$ $x_1 = 3$
3 $2 \sin \theta = \theta$ $\theta_1 = 2$ 4 $x^3 - 5x^2 = 4$ $x_1 = 5$

5 $x^3 = 10x + 10$ $x_1 = 3.5$ **6** $3 \tan \theta + 4\theta = 6$ $\theta_1 = 1$
7 $x^4 - 4x^3 - x^2 + 4x - 10 = 0$ $x_1 = 4$ **8** $x^3 = 5x + 32$ $x_1 = 4$
9 Verify that the equation $x^3 - 2x - 5 = 0$ has a root between $x = 2$ and $x = 3$, and find this root correct to three significant figures.
10 Find, correct to three significant figures, the smallest positive root of $5x^5 = 5x + 1$.

Exercise 24d (Miscellaneous)

1 Use the iterative formula

$$x_{r+1} = \frac{1}{2}\left(x_r + \frac{N}{x_r}\right), \quad \text{where } N \in \mathbb{R}^+$$

to find the square roots of:
(a) 200 (b) 450 (c) 700 (d) 1000.

2 Repeat no. 1, using the Newton-Raphson method to solve equations of the form $x^2 - N = 0$.

3 Prove that the iterative formula formed by applying the Newton-Raphson method to the equation $x^2 - N = 0$ can be written

$$x_{r+1} = \frac{1}{2}\left(x_r + \frac{N}{x_r}\right)$$

(In other words prove that the iterative formula explained in Section 24.1 can be deduced from the Newton-Raphson formula.)

4 Prove that if X is an *exact* root of an equation $f(x) = 0$, then substituting $x_r = X$ in the Newton-Raphson formula gives $x_{r+1} = X$.

5 Verify that the equation $10 \cos x - x = 0$ has a root between $x = 1$ and $x = 2$. Using $x = \pi/2$ as a first approximation, show that the next approximation, given by applying Newton's formula once, is $5\pi/11$.

6 Sketch the graphs of $y = x$ and $y = \frac{1}{2}\cos x$, and, from your sketch, estimate the value of x such that $x = \frac{1}{2}\cos x$.
Use the iterative formula $x_{r+1} = \frac{1}{2}\cos x_r$ to solve this equation.

7 Solve the equation $x = \frac{1}{2}\cos x$ (see no. 6), by the Newton-Raphson method.

8 The equation $5x = \cos x$ has a root near $x = 0.5$. Solve this equation using the iterative formula $x_{r+1} = 0.2 \cos x_r$.
Sketch, on a large scale, the graphs of $y = x$ and $y = 0.2 \cos x$ near this root and mark the points $P_1(x_1, x_2)$, $Q_1(x_2, x_2)$, $P_2(x_2, x_3)$, $Q_2(x_3, x_3)$, $P_3(x_3, x_4)$, $Q_3(x_4, x_4)$, etc. (see Section 24.4) to illustrate that the sequence $x_1, x_2, x_3, \ldots$ converges.

9 Repeat no. 8 for the iterative formula $x_{r+1} = 10 - 15/x_r$, starting at $x_1 = 8$. Find the quadratic equation which is solved by this iterative formula and check your answer by applying the quadratic formula to this equation.

10 Show that the cubic equation $x^3 - 3x + 1 = 0$ can be arranged in the form

(a) $x = \frac{1}{3}(x^3 + 1)$ (b) $x = \dfrac{3x - 1}{x^2}$

By applying the test in Section 24.4, show that only one of these arrangements could be expected to produce a convergent iterative method, starting at $x_1 = 0.2$. Use this arrangement to solve the equation.

11 A cuboid has volume 100 cm^3, surface area 150 cm^2, and its length is twice its breadth. What are its dimensions?

12 When the height of water in a hemispherical bowl is h, the volume of water in the bowl is $\pi(rh^2 - \frac{1}{3}h^3)$, where r is the radius of the bowl. Find the height of the water when half the volume of the bowl is filled.

13 I invest £100 on January 1st for fifteeen consecutive years. If on January 1st of the next year the value of my savings is £2100, what rate of compound interest have I received?

14 A donkey is tied by a rope to a point on the circumference of a circular field of radius r. If the donkey is to be allowed to graze half the area of the field, how long should the rope be?

15 Show graphically, or otherwise, that the equation $x^3 - x - 1 = 0$ has only one root and find the integer n such that the root α satisfies $n < \alpha < n+1$. An iterative process for finding this root is defined by

$$x_1 = 1 \qquad x_{r+1} = (x_r + 1)^{1/3}$$

for all $r \in \mathbb{N}^+$. Obtain, to three places of decimals, the values of x_2 and x_3. Show, on a sketch graph, the line $y = x$ and the curve $y = (x + 1)^{1/3}$, indicating on the graph the relation between x_1, x_2, x_3 and the root α.   (L)

16 Find, by the Newton-Raphson method, the solution of the equation†

$$x^2 + 20 \ln x = 400$$

giving your answer correct to three significant figures. [*Hint* Let $x_1 = 15$.]
(O & C)

17 Show graphically that the equation $x^2 = 7 \lg x + 2.347$ has two real positive roots.

Taking $x = 2.2$ as an initial approximation to the larger of these roots, obtain a second approximation by writing the equation in the form $x = \sqrt{(7 \lg x + 2.347)}$ and using an iterative method.

Work to three decimal places and give your answer to two decimal places.
(O & C: MEI)

18 Using the Newton-Raphson process, solve the equation

$$\sqrt{x} + \sqrt{(x + 1)} + \sqrt{(x + 2)} = 5$$

giving your answer correct to three significant figures and showing that you have achieved this degree of accuracy.   (C)

19 A solution of the equation $x = f(x)$ is to be attempted using the iteration $x_{r+1} = f(x_r)$, starting with an initial estimate x_1. Draw sketch graphs showing $y = x$ and $y = f(x)$ to illustrate the following possibilities regarding the convergence towards, or divergence from, the root $x = a$.

(a) $x_1 > a$ and the successive iterates (approximations) steadily decrease, with the value a as a limit.

---

† The function ln x is the natural logarithm of x: in order to do this question the reader will need to know that its derivative is $1/x$, see Chapter 26.

(b) $x_1 > a$ and the successive iterates are alternately less than a and greater than a, but approach a as a limit.

(c) $x_1 > a$ and the successive iterates get steadily larger.

Use an iterative method to find a non-zero root of the equation $x = \arctan(2x)$ correct to 2 significant figures.   (C)

20 Show that the equation $x^3 - 6x + 1 = 0$ has a root between $x = 0$ and $x = 1$. Three possible rearrangements of the given equation in the form $x = F(x)$ are

$$x = \sqrt[3]{(6x - 1)}$$
$$x = \tfrac{1}{6}(x^3 + 1)$$
$$x = x^3 - 5x + 1$$

Only one of these rearrangements will provide an iterative method, of the form $x_{r+1} = F(x_r)$, which converges to the root between 0 and 1. Use this rearrangement to find this root correct to 3 significant figures.   (C)

Revision Exercise 4

1 In triangle ABC, angle B is $\pi/6$ radians and angle A is almost a right-angle, so that $A = (\frac{1}{2}\pi - x)$, where x is small. Show that

$$BC/AC \approx 2 - x^2 \qquad \text{(C)}$$

2 Given that x is so small that terms in x^3 and higher powers of x may be neglected, show that

$$11 \sin x - 6 \cos x + 5 = A + Bx + Cx^2$$

and state the values of the constants A, B and C. (L)

3 The finite region R lies in the first quadrant, being bounded by the curve $y = \cos x + \frac{1}{2} \sin 2x$, the x-axis for $0 \leqslant x \leqslant \pi/2$ and the y-axis. Find the area of R.

The region R is rotated through four right-angles about the x-axis. Prove that the volume of the solid of revolution generated is

$$\pi(15\pi + 32)/48$$

Find the corresponding volume when R is rotated about the line $y = -1$.
(O & C)

4 The function f is defined for the domain $0 \leqslant x \leqslant \pi/3$ by $f(x) = 2 \sec x$. State the range of f and sketch the graph of f.

The region bounded by the curve with equation $y = f(x)$, the coordinate axes and the line $x = \pi/3$ is rotated through 2π radians about the x-axis. Calculate the volume of the solid of revolution formed, giving your answer to three significant figures. (O)

5 A particle moves along the x-axis. At time t seconds its displacement from the origin O is x metres, where

$$x = 2 \sin^2 t - 2 \sin t + 1$$

Find, in terms of π, the four values of t in the interval $0 \leqslant t \leqslant 2\pi$ at which the particle is stationary. Calculate the exact values of the displacement and of the acceleration for these values of t.

Find also the total distance travelled by the particle during the interval $0 \leqslant t \leqslant 2\pi$. (JMB)

6 A curve is given parametrically by

$$x = \sin t, \quad y = \cos^3 t \qquad -\pi < t \leqslant \pi$$

Show that

(a) $-1 \leqslant x \leqslant 1$ and $-1 \leqslant y \leqslant 1$

(b) $\dfrac{dy}{dx} = a \sin 2t$ where a is a constant, and give the value of a.

Find the value of dy/dx when $x = 0$ and show that the curve has points of inflexion where $t = -3\pi/4$, $-\pi/4$, $\pi/4$ and $3\pi/4$. Sketch the curve. (L)

7 The points A, B have coordinates $(1, -2)$ and $(4, 2)$ respectively and P is the point (x, y). Show that $AP^2 = x^2 + y^2 - 2x + 4y + 5$ and derive a similar expression for BP^2. Given that P moves in such a way that $AP = 2BP$, show that the locus of P is a circle.

Calculate the radius and the coordinates of the centre of this circle. (W)

8 Show that the equation of the tangent to the curve $y = x^3$ at the point (c, c^3) is $y = 3c^2 x - 2c^3$.

A tangent to the curve intercepts the Ox and Oy axes at P and Q respectively. Given that the triangle OPQ has area 32/3, find the possible equations of the tangent. (W)

9 Show that the line $y = mx + 2/m$ is a tangent to the curve $y^2 = 8x$ for all values of m and find, in terms of m, the coordinates of P, the point of contact of the line with the curve.

Find the value of m for which the line is also a tangent to the curve $x^2 + y = 0$, and if m has this value, find the coordinate of Q, the point of contact of the line with the curve $x^2 + y = 0$.

Assuming m to have the value calculated above, find the coordinates of R, the point where PQ crosses the x-axis. (AEB)

10 (a) The parametric equations of a curve are

$$x = 4 + t^2 \qquad y = 3 + 2t$$

    (i) Express dy/dx in terms of t.

    (ii) A point P on the curve has parameter p. Given that the tangent at P passes through the origin, find the possible values of p.

    (iii) Find the values of t at the points of intersection of the curve with the line $2y + x = 7$.

    (iv) Obtain the Cartesian equation of the curve.

(b) The Cartesian equation of a certain curve can be written in the form

$$(x - 1)^2 + (y - 3)^2 = 1$$

Given that x is defined parametrically by $x = 1 + \cos \theta$, and that $y = 2$ when $\theta = \pi/2$, express y in terms of θ. (C)

11 (a) The parametric equations of a curve are

$$x = t^2 - 2t \qquad y = 2t - 11$$

    (i) Find the coordinates of the point where the curve intersects the x-axis.

    (ii) Obtain the Cartesian equation of the curve.

(b) The parametric equations of a curve are

$$x = t + 1/t \qquad y = t - 1/t$$

    (i) Find dy/dx in terms of t, and hence find the values of t for which $dy/dx = 3$.

    (ii) P and Q are points on the curve at which the values of t are 2 and $\frac{1}{2}$ respectively. The tangents at P and Q meet at a point R. Find the coordinates of R. (C)

12 With respect to a fixed origin O, the points A and B have coordinates $(-4, 0)$ and $(12, 12)$ respectively. The mid-point of AB is M. Find an equation of the line in the plane of the coordinate axes Ox and Oy which passes through M and is perpendicular to AB.

Hence, or otherwise, find, in Cartesian form, an equation of the circle which passes through O, A and B. (L)

13 Sketch the curve C given by the equation $xy = 1$. A line of gradient m, where $m \neq 0$, passes through the point A(3, 0) and meets C at points P and Q. Show that the x-coordinates of P and Q are the roots of the equation

$$mx^2 - 3mx - 1 = 0$$

(i) Find the set of values of m for which this equation has real unequal roots. Find also the (non-zero) value for m for which the roots are equal, and hence, or otherwise, find the equation of the tangent to C from the point A.
(ii) Show that the mid-point M of PQ lies on the line $x = 3/2$. Show on your diagram the possible positions of M on this line. Indicate the part of the line which corresponds to positive values of m.   (JMB)

14 Prove that the equation of the normal to the parabola $y^2 = 4ax$ at the point P(at^2, $2at$) is

$$y + tx = 2at + at^3$$

The normal at P meets the x-axis at G and the line through P parallel to the y-axis meets the x-axis at H. Prove that the length GH is constant as t varies.

The midpoint of PG is M. The line through M perpendicular to PG cuts PH at Q. Prove that the coordinates of Q are (at^2, $at - a/t$) and determine a Cartesian equation for the locus of Q as t varies.   (O)

15 (a) Sketch the curve

$$r = 3 + \cos 3\theta \qquad (-\pi < \theta \leqslant \pi)$$

[An accurate plot is not required, but your sketch should show the maximum and minimum values of r and where they are attained.]
(b) Sketch the curve whose equation in polar coordinates is

$$r = a \sin^2 (2\theta)$$

where a is a positive constant, and $-\pi < \theta \leqslant \pi$.
[An accurate plot is not required, but your sketch should show clearly the shape of the curve near the pole, and the point(s) where r attains its maximum value.]   (C, part Q)

16 The length L, in metres, of 16 mm film on a spool of overall diameter d, in centimetres, is suspected to satisfy a relation of the form

$$L = kd^n$$

The following results were obtained by measuring the length of film wound on 5 spools of varying diameter.

L (in m)	32	98	128	392	512
d (in cm)	2.0	3.5	4.0	7.0	8.0

(a) Plot on graph paper, ln L against ln d.
(b) Explain why your graph indicates that a relation of the above form exists.
(c) Estimate from your graph the constants k and n.
[NB ln means logarithm base e, see Chapter 10, page 195.]   (AEB)

17 The period of oscillation, T seconds, of a heavy weight attached to a wire of length l metres was investigated for $2 \leqslant l \leqslant 8$. The results are shown below:

l	2	3	4	5	6	7	8
T	2.81	3.47	4.01	4.49	4.98	5.29	5.63

It is believed that l and T are related by an equation of the form $T = kl^n$, where k and n are positive constants. Plot values of $\ln T$ against $\ln l$ and hence state, giving reasons, whether or not l and T are related by an equation of the given form.
By taking suitable readings from your graph, estimate the values of k and n to 1 significant figure. (L)

18 Kepler's third law of planetary motion states that T, the period of revolution of a planet round the Sun, is dependent upon R, the mean distance of the planet from the Sun. Given that this relationship can be expressed in the form

$$T = aR^b$$

where a and b are constants,
  (i) express the relationship in a form suitable for drawing a straight line graph,
 (ii) use the data below to draw a straight line graph,
(iii) estimate the values of a and b, giving your results to two significant figures,
 (iv) estimate the period of revolution of the planet Neptune whose mean distance from the Sun is 4497 million km.

Planet	Distance from the Sun R (10^6 km)	Period T (days)
Venus	108	225
Earth	150	365
Mars	228	687
Jupiter	778	4330
Saturn	1427	10752

(C)

19 The variables x and y are known to satisfy an equation of the form

$$y = a + b\sqrt{x}$$

where a and b are constants. Corresponding approximate values of x and y (each rounded to one decimal place) were obtained experimentally and are given in the following table.

x	3.2	6.8	16.0	25.2	33.6	40.4
y	4.0	5.0	6.6	8.2	9.0	9.8

By drawing a suitable linear graph, estimate the values of a and b, giving both answers to one decimal place. (JMB)

20 The variables x and y are known to satisfy an equation of the form

$$y = ab^x$$

where a and b are constants. For five different values of x, corresponding approximate values of y were obtained experimentally and are given in the following table.

x	2.0	2.5	3.0	3.5	4.0
y	11.3	18.5	27.1	44.5	70.4

By drawing a suitable linear graph, estimate the values of a and b, giving both answers to one decimal place. (JMB)

21 Sketch on a single diagram the graphs of $y = x^2 - 4$ and $y = 1/x$. Hence show that the equation $x^3 - 4x - 1 = 0$ has three real roots. For each of these roots, state the integer closest to that root. Use the iteration

$$x_{n+1} = \frac{1}{x_n^2 - 4}$$

to calculate the root closest to zero, giving your answer correct to 4 decimal places. (C)

22 Show that the equation

$$x^3 + 3x - 1 = 0$$

has a root α between 0 and 1 and use linear interpolation to obtain a first approximation x_1 to α. Confirm that

$$x = 1/(x^2 + 3)$$
$$\text{and} \quad x = (1 - 3x)^{1/3}$$

are both rearrangements of the equation. Further, by considering suitable derivatives, show that only one of the corresponding iterative formulae

$$x_{n+1} = 1/(x_n^2 + 3)$$
$$\text{and} \quad x_{n+1} = (1 - 3x_n)^{1/3}$$

is likely to converge to α starting from x_1.

Use that formula to find α correct to two decimal places. (AEB)

23 Given that $f(\theta) = \theta - \sqrt{(\sin \theta)}$, $0 < \theta < \frac{1}{2}\pi$, show that

(a) the equation $f(\theta) = 0$ has a root lying between $\frac{1}{4}\pi$ and $\frac{3}{10}\pi$,

(b) $f'(\theta) = 1 - \dfrac{\cos \theta}{2\sqrt{(\sin \theta)}}$

(c) Taking $\frac{3}{10}\pi$ as a first approximation to this root of the equation $f(\theta) = 0$, use the Newton-Raphson procedure once to find a second approximation, giving your answer to 2 decimal places.

(d) Show that $f'(\theta) = 0$ when $\sin \theta = \sqrt{5} - 2$. (L)

24 A chord divides a circle, centre O, into two regions whose areas are in the ratio $2:1$. Prove that the angle θ, subtended by this chord at O, satisfies the equation $f(\theta) = 0$, where

$$f(\theta) = \theta - \sin\theta - 2\pi/3$$

Using the same axes, sketch for $0 \leqslant \theta \leqslant \pi$, the graphs of

$$y = \theta - 2\pi/3 \quad \text{and} \quad y = \sin\theta$$

By taking $5\pi/6$ as a first approximation to the positive root of the equation $f(\theta) = 0$, apply the Newton-Raphson procedure once to obtain a second approximation, giving your answer to three decimal places.   (L)

25 (a) Find a positive integer n such that the cubic equation

$$x^3 - 8x - 2 = 0$$

has a root in the interval $(n, n+1)$†

(b) Use the Newton-Raphson method to find this root, proving that your answer is correct to three significant figures.

(c) Give reasons why this is the only positive root of the equation.

(d) Show, by performing the iterative process, that

$$x_{n+1} = (8x_n + 2)^{1/3} \quad (n = 1, 2, ...) \text{ with } x_1 = 3$$

also gives this root of the equation.

(e) State, with reasons, which method you would choose for obtaining this root.   (O & C)

† See 'Mathematical notation', page xv.

Chapter 25

Techniques of integration

25.1 Introduction

In earlier chapters, we dealt with the differentiation of powers of x, polynomials, products and quotients, composite functions, trigonometrical functions, and we also discussed implicit functions and parameters.

Now that we come to extend the scope of integration we find that it is not, unfortunately, merely a matter of putting into reverse the techniques for differentiation; we have learned a technique for differentiating $(3x^2 + 2)^4$ as it stands, but can we integrate this function without first expanding it? Even consider the simple function x^n, we can differentiate this whenever $n \in \mathbb{Q}$, but we must bear in mind the gap which remains to be filled later in this book when we discover how to deal with $\int x^{-1} \, dx$.

Integration is, in fact, less susceptible than differentiation to concise systematic treatment. It presents a broad front, and the reader's experience of it will gradually expand, so that by quick recognition of an increasing number of forms of *integrand* (i.e. the function to be integrated) there is developed the power to discriminate between the many possible lines of attack.

25.2 Integration by inspection

The very first thing to search for in any but the simplest integrands is the presence of a function and its derivative; with this, we may often guess the integral to be a certain composite function, check by differentiation, and adjust the numerical factor. Two examples follow to illustrate this method.

Example 1

Find the following integrals:
(a) $\int (3x + 7)^4 \, dx$
(b) $\int x(3x^2 + 2)^4 \, dx$

(a) We need to recognise that the integrand of $\int (3x + 7)^4 \, dx$, that is

$$(3x + 7)^4$$

probably arises from differentiating $(3x + 7)^5$. When we examine this, we find (from the chain rule) that

$$\frac{d}{dx}(3x + 7)^5 = 5(3x + 7)^4 \times 3$$

$$= 15(3x + 7)^4$$

Hence

$$\int (3x + 7)^4\, dx = \tfrac{1}{15}(3x + 7)^5 + c$$

(b) In the second integral, $(3x^2 + 2)^4$ probably comes from differentiating $(3x^2 + 2)^5$, the extra factor x being part of the derivative of $3x^2 + 2$. When we differentiate this expression, we find:

$$\frac{d}{dx}\{(3x^2 + 2)^5\} = 5(3x^2 + 2)^4 \times 6x = 30x(3x^2 + 2)^4$$

$$\therefore \quad \frac{d}{dx}\left\{\frac{1}{30}(3x^2 + 2)^5\right\} = x(3x^2 + 2)^4$$

Hence

$$\int x(3x^2 + 2)^4\, dx = \frac{1}{30}(3x^2 + 2)^5 + c$$

Example 2

Find $\int \sin^2 4x \cos 4x\, dx$.

[We note that $\cos 4x$ is a constant $\times$ the derivative of $\sin 4x$, and we deduce that the integral is a function of $\sin 4x$.]

$$\frac{d}{dx}\{\sin^3 4x\} = 3(\sin 4x)^2 \times \cos 4x \times 4 = 12 \sin^2 4x \cos 4x$$

Hence

$$\int \sin^2 4x \cos 4x\, dx = \frac{1}{12} \sin^3 4x + c$$

Qu. 1 Differentiate:

(a) $(2x^2 + 3)^4$ (b) $\sqrt{(x^2 - 2x + 1)}$ (c) $\dfrac{1}{(2x - 1)^2}$ (d) $\sin(4x - 7)$

Qu. 2 Find the following integrals, and check by differentiation:
(a) $\int x(x^2 + 1)^2\, dx$ (b) $\int (2x + 1)^4\, dx$
(c) $\int \tfrac{1}{2} \sin 3x\, dx$ (d) $\int x^2 \sqrt{(x^3 + 1)}\, dx$

25.3 Odd powers of sin x, cos x

Pythagoras' theorem in the forms

$$\cos^2 x + \sin^2 x = 1, \quad \cot^2 x + 1 = \operatorname{cosec}^2 x \quad \text{and} \quad 1 + \tan^2 x = \sec^2 x$$

(see Section 17.6), may be used to change some integrands to a form susceptible to integration by inspection. In particular, it enables us to integrate odd powers of sin x and cos x.

Example 3

■ Find $\int \sin^5 x \, dx$.

$$\begin{aligned}
\int \sin^5 x \, dx &= \int \sin^4 x \sin x \, dx \\
&= \int (1 - \cos^2 x)^2 \sin x \, dx \\
&= \int (\sin x - 2 \cos^2 x \sin x + \cos^4 x \sin x) \, dx \\
\therefore \quad \int \sin^5 x \, dx &= -\cos x + \tfrac{2}{3} \cos^3 x - \tfrac{1}{5} \cos^5 x + c
\end{aligned}$$

Qu. 3 Find:
(a) $\int \sin^3 x \, dx$ (b) $\int \cos^5 x \, dx$

Qu. 4 Find $\int \sec x \tan^3 x \, dx$. $\left[\text{Remember } \dfrac{d}{dx}(\sec x) = \sec x \tan x. \right]$

25.4 Even powers of sin x, cos x

Two very important formulae derived from the double angle formulae are:

$$\cos^2 x = \tfrac{1}{2}(1 + \cos 2x) \quad \text{and} \quad \sin^2 x = \tfrac{1}{2}(1 - \cos 2x)$$

(See Section 18.3.)

Their use in integrating even powers of sin x and cos x is illustrated in the latter part of the next exercise which also gives practice in the use of other formulae.

Exercise 25a

1 Differentiate:

(a) $(5x^2 - 1)^3$ (b) $\dfrac{1}{(2x^2 - x + 3)^2}$ (c) $\sqrt[3]{(x^2 + 4)}$

(d) $\cot 5x$ (e) $\cos(5x - 1)$ (f) $\sin^2 \dfrac{x}{3}$

(g) $\tan \sqrt{x}$ (h) $\sec^2 2x$ (i) $\sqrt{\operatorname{cosec} x}$

Find the following integrals in nos. 2–4:

2 (a) $\int x(x^2 - 3)^5 \, dx$ (b) $\int (3x - 1)^5 \, dx$

(c) $\int x(x + 2)^2 \, dx$ (d) $\int \dfrac{x}{(x^2 + 1)^2} \, dx$

(e) $\int \dfrac{x+1}{(x^2+2x-5)^3}\,dx$

(f) $\int (2x-3)(x^2-3x+7)^2\,dx$

(g) $\int \dfrac{2x}{(4x^2-7)^2}\,dx$

(h) $\int 2x\sqrt{(3x^2-5)}\,dx$

(i) $\int (x^3+1)^2\,dx$

(j) $\int \dfrac{x^2-1}{\sqrt{(x^3-3x)}}\,dx$

(k) $\int \dfrac{x-1}{(2x^2-4x+1)^{3/2}}\,dx$

(l) $\int (2x^2-1)^3\,dx$

3 (a) $\int 3\cos 3x\,dx$
(b) $\int \sin(2x+3)\,dx$
(c) $\int \cos x \sin x\,dx$
(d) $\int \frac13 \cos 2x\,dx$
(e) $\int \sin 3x \cos^2 3x\,dx$
(f) $\int \sec^2 x \tan^2 x\,dx$
(g) $\int \sec^5 x \tan x\,dx$
(h) $\int \cos x \sqrt{\sin x}\,dx$
(i) $\int x\,\mathrm{cosec}^2 x^2\,dx$

(j) $\int \dfrac{\cos\sqrt x}{\sqrt x}\,dx$
(k) $\int \mathrm{cosec}^3 x \cot x\,dx$

4 (a) $\int \cos^3 x\,dx$
(b) $\int \cos^5 \dfrac{x}{2}\,dx$
(c) $\int \sin^3 2x\,dx$

(d) $\int \cos^3(2x+1)\,dx$
(e) $\int \sin^5 x \cos^2 x\,dx$
(f) $\int \cos^3 x \sin^3 x\,dx$
(g) $\int \sec^4 x\,dx$
(h) $\int \mathrm{cosec}\, x \cot^3 x\,dx$
(i) $\int \tan^5 x \sec x\,dx$

5 Express:

(a) $\sin^2 \dfrac{x}{2}$ in terms of $\cos x$ (b) $\cos^2 3x$ in terms of $\cos 6x$

6 Find:

(a) $\int \cos^2 x\,dx$ (b) $\int \sin^2 \dfrac{x}{2}\,dx$ (c) $\int \cos^2 3x\,dx$

7 Express $\sin^4 x$ in terms of $\cos 2x$, and $\cos^2 2x$ in terms of $\cos 4x$. Show that $\int \sin^4 x\,dx = \frac38 x - \frac14 \sin 2x + \frac1{32}\sin 4x + c$.
8 Find $\int \cos^4 x\,dx$.
9 Find the following integrals:

(a) $\int \sin^2 x\,dx$ (b) $\int \cos^2 \dfrac{x}{3}\,dx$ (c) $\int \sin^4 2x\,dx$ (d) $\int \cos^4 \dfrac{x}{2}\,dx$

10 Write down a formula for $\cos x$ in terms of $\cos \dfrac{x}{2}$, and show that

$$\int \dfrac{1}{1+\cos x}\,dx = \tan \dfrac{x}{2} + c$$

25.5 Changing the variable

In Example 1 part (b) we found that

$$\int x(3x^2 + 2)^4 \, dx = \frac{1}{30}(3x^2 + 2)^5 + c$$

The integral is a function of $(3x^2 + 2)$. If we write $3x^2 + 2$ as u, then the integral is a function of u; this suggests that we might make the substitution $u = 3x^2 + 2$ in the integrand, and *integrate with respect to u*. Let us see how this can be done.

Let

$$y = \int x(3x^2 + 2)^4 \, dx$$

then

$$\frac{dy}{dx} = x(3x^2 + 2)^4$$

If $u = 3x^2 + 2$, x may be expressed as a function of u. Then, by the chain rule,

$$\frac{dy}{du} = \frac{dy}{dx} \times \frac{dx}{du}$$

$$\therefore \quad \frac{dy}{du} = x(3x^2 + 2)^4 \frac{dx}{du}$$

Integrating with respect to u,

$$y = \int x(3x^2 + 2)^4 \frac{dx}{du} \, du$$

But $\quad u = 3x^2 + 2$

$$\therefore \quad \frac{du}{dx} = 6x \quad \text{and} \quad \frac{dx}{du} = \frac{1}{6x}$$

$$\therefore \quad \int x(3x^2 + 2)^4 \, dx = \int x(3x^2 + 2)^4 \frac{1}{6x} \, du$$

$$= \int \tfrac{1}{6}u^4 \, du$$

$$= \tfrac{1}{30}u^5 + c$$

$$= \tfrac{1}{30}(3x^2 + 2)^5 + c$$

Qu. 5 Find $\int \sin^2 4x \cos 4x \, dx$; put $u = \sin 4x$.
Qu. 6 Find $\int \sin^5 x \, dx$; put $u = \cos x$.

Comparing the foregoing text and questions with the solutions of Examples 1, 2 and 3, it might appear that we have merely introduced a more cumbersome technique; however, the power of changing the variable lies in its application to a wide class of integrals not susceptible to the method of integration by inspection.

In general, let $f(x)$ be a function of x, and let

$$y = \int f(x)\, dx$$

Then

$$\frac{dy}{dx} = f(x)$$

If u is a function of x, then by the chain rule

$$\frac{dy}{du} = \frac{dy}{dx} \times \frac{dx}{du}$$

$$\therefore \qquad \frac{dy}{du} = f(x)\frac{dx}{du}$$

$$\therefore \qquad y = \int f(x)\frac{dx}{du}\, du$$

$$\therefore \qquad \boxed{\int f(x)\, dx = \int f(x)\frac{dx}{du}\, du}$$

Thus an integral with respect to x may be transformed into an integral with respect to a related variable u, by using the above result, and substituting for $f(x)$ and $\dfrac{dx}{du}$ in terms of u.

Example 4

Find $\int x\sqrt{(3x-1)}\, dx$.

Sidework:

$$\int x\sqrt{(3x-1)}\frac{dx}{du}\, du = \int \frac{1}{3}(u^2+1)u\frac{2u}{3}\, du \qquad \text{Let } \sqrt{(3x-1)}=u$$

$$= \int \left(\tfrac{2}{9}u^4 + \tfrac{2}{9}u^2\right) du \qquad\qquad x = \tfrac{1}{3}(u^2+1)$$

$$= \tfrac{2}{45}u^5 + \tfrac{2}{27}u^3 + c \qquad\qquad \frac{dx}{du} = \frac{2u}{3}$$

$$= \tfrac{2}{135}u^3(3u^2+5) + c$$

$$\therefore \qquad \int x\sqrt{(3x-1)}\, dx = \tfrac{2}{135}(3x-1)^{3/2}(9x+2) + c$$

Qu. 7 Find the following integrals, using the given change of variable:
(a) $\int x\sqrt{(2x+1)}\, dx$ $\qquad \sqrt{(2x+1)} = u$
(b) $\int x\sqrt{(2x+1)}\, dx$ $\qquad 2x+1 = u$
(c) $\int x(3x-2)^6\, dx$ $\qquad 3x-2 = u$

Exercise 25b

Find the following integrals, using the given change of variable:

1 $\int 3x\sqrt{(4x-1)}\,dx$ $\sqrt{(4x-1)}=u$ 2 $\int x\sqrt{(5x+2)}\,dx$ $5x+2=u$

3 $\int x(2x-1)^6\,dx$ $2x-1=u$ 4 $\int \dfrac{x}{\sqrt{(x-2)}}\,dx$ $\sqrt{(x-2)}=u$

5 $\int (x+2)(x-1)^4\,dx$ $x-1=u$ 6 $\int (x-2)^5(x+3)^2\,dx$ $x-2=u$

7 $\int \dfrac{x(x-4)}{(x-2)^2}\,dx$ $x-2=u$ 8 $\int \dfrac{x-1}{\sqrt{(2x+3)}}\,dx$ $\sqrt{(2x+3)}=u$

9 $\int x\sqrt{(3x-4)}\,dx$ $\sqrt{(3x-4)}=u$ 10 $\int x(x+5)^6\,dx$ $x+5=u$

25.6 Definite integrals and changing the limits

The method of changing the variable is also applicable to definite integrals. It is usually more convenient to change the limits to those of the new variable at the same time.

As a reminder that one must be ever watchful for the presence of a function and its derivative in an integrand, two examples of this type are also given here.

Example 5

Evaluate $\displaystyle\int_{1/2}^{3} x\sqrt{(2x+3)}\,dx$.

Sidework:

$$\int_{x=1/2}^{x=3} x\sqrt{(2x+3)}\,\frac{dx}{du}\,du\dagger = \int_{4}^{9} \tfrac{1}{2}(u-3)u^{1/2}\tfrac{1}{2}\,du \qquad \text{Let } 2x+3=u$$
$$x = \tfrac{1}{2}(u-3)$$

$$= \int_{4}^{9} (\tfrac{1}{4}u^{3/2} - \tfrac{3}{4}u^{1/2})\,du \qquad \frac{dx}{du} = \tfrac{1}{2}$$

$$= \left[\tfrac{1}{10}u^{5/2} - \tfrac{1}{2}u^{3/2}\right]_{4}^{9}$$

x	u
3	9
$\tfrac{1}{2}$	4

$$= (24.3 - 13.5) - (3.2 - 4)$$
$$= 11.6$$

† The reader should note that, in practice, this integral will of course first be written down as given (i.e. as an integral with respect to x). When it is decided to change the variable, dx is changed to $\dfrac{dx}{du}\,du$; it is then necessary to specify that the limits are still those of x.

Example 6

Evaluate (a) $\displaystyle\int_2^3 \frac{x}{\sqrt{(x^2-3)}}\,dx$ (b) $\displaystyle\int_0^{\pi/4} \cos^3 x \sin x\,dx$

(a) $\displaystyle\int_2^3 \frac{x}{\sqrt{(x^2-3)}}\,dx = \left[(x^2-3)^{1/2}\right]_2^3$

$$= (9-3)^{1/2} - (4-3)^{1/2}$$
$$= \sqrt{6} - 1$$

(b) $\displaystyle\int_0^{\pi/4} \cos^3 x \sin x\,dx = \left[-\tfrac{1}{4}\cos^4 x\right]_0^{\pi/4}$

$$= (-\tfrac{1}{4}\times\tfrac{1}{4}) - (-\tfrac{1}{4})$$
$$= -\tfrac{1}{16} + \tfrac{1}{4}$$
$$= \tfrac{3}{16}$$

Exercise 25c

Evaluate the following definite integrals by changing the variable and the limits:

1 $\displaystyle\int_2^3 x\sqrt{(x-2)}\,dx$ **2** $\displaystyle\int_0^1 x(x-1)^4\,dx$

3 $\displaystyle\int_1^2 \frac{x}{\sqrt{(2x-1)}}\,dx$ **4** $\displaystyle\int_1^2 (2x-1)(x-2)^3\,dx$

Evaluate the following definite integrals either by writing down the integral as a function of x, or by using the given change of variable:

5 $\displaystyle\int_0^{\pi/6} \sec^4 x \tan x\,dx$ $(\sec x = u)$

6 $\displaystyle\int_0^{\pi/2} \sin^5 x\,dx$ $(\cos x = u)$

Evaluate:

7 (a) $\displaystyle\int_0^{1/2} \frac{x}{\sqrt{(1-x^2)}}\,dx$ (b) $\displaystyle\int_0^4 2x\sqrt{(4-x)}\,dx$

8 (a) $\displaystyle\int_{-1}^0 x(x^2-1)^4\,dx$ (b) $\displaystyle\int_0^{\pi/4} \sec^4 x\,dx$

9 Calculate the area enclosed by the curve $y = x/\sqrt{(x^2-1)}$, the x-axis, $x=2$ and $x=3$.

10 Calculate the area under $y = \sin^3 x$ from $x=0$ to $x=2\pi/3$.

25.7 Integration using the inverse trigonometrical functions

The inverse trigonometrical functions were introduced in Section 19.7. Some readers may need to revise this topic before proceeding further; Qu. 8–11 are included for this purpose.

Qu. 8 The following angles lie between 0 and 90° inclusive. Express them in degrees, and in radians in terms of π:

(a) $\tan^{-1} 1$ (b) $\sin^{-1} \frac{1}{2}$ (c) $\frac{1}{2} \sin^{-1} 1$ (d) $\cos^{-1} \frac{1}{2}$

(e) $\frac{1}{2} \cos^{-1} \frac{1}{2}$ (f) $\cos^{-1} 1$ (g) $2 \cos^{-1} \frac{\sqrt{3}}{2}$ (h) $\frac{1}{3} \cos^{-1} 0$

(i) $\frac{2}{3} \cot^{-1} 1$ (j) $\sec^{-1} 2$ (k) $2 \operatorname{cosec}^{-1} \sqrt{2}$

Qu. 9 Express the following angles in radians, leaving π in the answers:
(a) 20°   (b) 70°   (c) 150°   (d) 300°   (e) 405°

Qu. 10 Express the following angles in degrees:
(a) 1 rad   (b) 0.03 rad   (c) 1.25 rad
(d) 0.715 rad   (e) $\pi/5$ rad

Qu. 11 Express the following (acute) angles in radians:
(a) $2 \sin^{-1} 0.6$ (b) $\tan^{-1} 1.333$ (c) $\frac{2}{3} \cos^{-1} 0.3846$

The inverse sine function may be written as arcsin x, or as $\sin^{-1} x$. Both forms are in current use and both will be used in this book to familiarise the reader with them.

The expression $\sqrt{(1 - x^2)}$ may be reduced to a simpler form by changing the variable to u, where $x = \sin u$; thus

$$\sqrt{(1 - x^2)} = \sqrt{(1 - \sin^2 u)} = \sqrt{\cos^2 u} = \cos u$$

This is used in the following example.

Example 7

Find $\displaystyle\int \frac{1}{\sqrt{(1 - x^2)}} \, dx.$

Sidework:

$$\int \frac{1}{\sqrt{(1 - x^2)}} \frac{dx}{du} \, du = \int \frac{1}{\sqrt{(1 - \sin^2 u)}} \cos u \, du \qquad \text{Let } x = \sin u$$

$$= \int \frac{1}{\cos u} \cos u \, du \qquad\qquad \frac{dx}{du} = \cos u$$

$$= \int 1 \, du$$

$$= u + c$$

$$= \arcsin x + c$$

25.8 $\int \dfrac{1}{\sqrt{(a^2 - b^2 x^2)}}\,dx$

The reader should check that the integral found in Example 7 is not susceptible to the change of variable $\sqrt{(1 - x^2)} = u$; $\int \dfrac{1}{\sqrt{(1 - x^2)}}\,dx$ merely becomes $\int \dfrac{-1}{\sqrt{(1 - u^2)}}\,du$. However, changes of variable involving a trigonometrical substitution, such as was successfully applied in this case, open the way to finding a very important group of integrals. Here are two examples of the type of substitution we shall be using.

If $x = 5 \sin u$,

$$\sqrt{(25 - x^2)} = \sqrt{(25 - 25 \sin^2 u)} = \sqrt{\{25(1 - \sin^2 u)\}} = 5 \cos u$$

If $x = \dfrac{\sqrt{3}}{2} \sin u$,

$$\sqrt{(3 - 4x^2)} = \sqrt{(3 - 4 \times \tfrac{3}{4} \sin^2 u)} = \sqrt{\{3(1 - \sin^2 u)\}} = \sqrt{3} \cos u$$

Qu. 12 Reduce each of the following to the form $k \cos u$, and give u in terms of x in each case:

(a) $\sqrt{(9 - x^2)}$ (b) $\sqrt{(1 - 25x^2)}$ (c) $\sqrt{(4 - 9x^2)}$ (d) $\sqrt{(7 - x^2)}$

We see that to deal with $\sqrt{(a^2 - b^2 x^2)}$ we write

$$a^2 - b^2 x^2 \quad \text{as} \quad a^2 - a^2 \sin^2 u$$

thus $b^2 x^2 = a^2 \sin^2 u$, and $x = (a/b) \sin u$. Note that $u = \arcsin(bx/a)$ and, for the substitution to be valid, and of use, u must be real and not $\pi/2$, so $|bx| < |a|$; this condition is implicit in $\sqrt{(a^2 - b^2 x^2)}$ being real and not zero.

Example 8

Find $\int \dfrac{1}{\sqrt{(9 - 4x^2)}}\,dx$.

Sidework:

$$\int \frac{1}{\sqrt{(9 - 4x^2)}} \frac{dx}{du}\,du = \int \frac{1}{\sqrt{(9 - 9 \sin^2 u)}} \times \frac{3}{2} \cos u\,du \qquad \begin{array}{l} 9 - 4x^2 \\ 9 - 9 \sin^2 u \end{array}$$

$$= \int \frac{1}{3 \cos u} \times \frac{3}{2} \cos u\,du \qquad\qquad \text{Let } x = \tfrac{3}{2} \sin u$$

$$= \int \tfrac{1}{2}\,du \qquad\qquad\qquad\qquad \frac{dx}{du} = \frac{3}{2} \cos u$$

$$= \tfrac{1}{2} u + c$$

$$= \frac{1}{2} \arcsin \left(\frac{2x}{3} \right) + c$$

Qu. 13 Find the following integrals:

(a) $\int \dfrac{1}{\sqrt{(4-x^2)}}\,dx$ (b) $\int \dfrac{1}{\sqrt{(1-3x^2)}}\,dx$ (c) $\int \dfrac{1}{\sqrt{(16-9x^2)}}\,dx$

Qu. 14 Prove that $\displaystyle\int \dfrac{1}{\sqrt{(a^2-b^2x^2)}}\,dx = \dfrac{1}{b}\arcsin\left(\dfrac{bx}{a}\right) + c$

25.9 $\displaystyle\int \dfrac{1}{a^2+b^2x^2}\,dx$

In Section 25.8 we made use of Pythagoras' theorem in the form $\cos^2 u + \sin^2 u = 1$; we shall now find that an alternative form, $1 + \tan^2 u = \sec^2 u$, helps to effect other useful changes of variable.

Qu. 15 Find $\displaystyle\int \dfrac{1}{1+x^2}\,dx$ by taking x as $\tan u$.

Qu. 16 Reduce each of the following to the form $k\sec^2 u$, and give u in terms of x in each case:
(a) $9 + x^2$ (b) $1 + 4x^2$ (c) $25 + 9x^2$ (d) $3 + x^2$

Qu. 17 Find the following integrals:

(a) $\int \dfrac{1}{4+x^2}\,dx$ (b) $\int \dfrac{1}{1+16x^2}\,dx$

Example 9

Evaluate $\displaystyle\int_{\sqrt{3}/2}^{3/2} \dfrac{1}{3+4x^2}\,dx$.

Sidework:

$$\int_{x=\sqrt{3}/2}^{x=3/2} \dfrac{1}{3+4x^2}\dfrac{dx}{du}\,du \qquad \begin{array}{l} 3+4x^2 \\ 3+3\tan^2 u \end{array}$$

$$= \int_{\pi/4}^{\pi/3} \dfrac{1}{3(1+\tan^2 u)}\dfrac{\sqrt{3}}{2}\sec^2 u\,du \qquad \text{Let } x = \dfrac{\sqrt{3}}{2}\tan u$$

$$= \int_{\pi/4}^{\pi/3} \dfrac{\sqrt{3}}{6}\,du \qquad\qquad \dfrac{dx}{du} = \dfrac{\sqrt{3}}{2}\sec^2 u$$

$$= \left[\dfrac{\sqrt{3}u}{6}\right]_{\pi/4}^{\pi/3}$$

$$= \dfrac{\sqrt{3}}{6}\left(\dfrac{\pi}{3}-\dfrac{\pi}{4}\right)$$

$$= \dfrac{\sqrt{3}\pi}{72}$$

x	$\tan u$	u
$\dfrac{3}{2}$	$\sqrt{3}$	$\dfrac{\pi}{3}$
$\dfrac{\sqrt{3}}{2}$	1	$\dfrac{\pi}{4}$

The reader should have little difficulty proving the general form of the integrals in the last two sections, namely:

$$\int \frac{1}{\sqrt{(a^2 - b^2 x^2)}} \, dx = \frac{1}{b} \sin^{-1} \left(\frac{bx}{a} \right) + c$$

and

$$\int \frac{1}{a^2 + b^2 x^2} \, dx = \frac{1}{ab} \tan^{-1} \left(\frac{bx}{a} \right) + c$$

These results may be quoted (except in examination questions with explicit instructions to do otherwise).

Exercise 25d

1 Express the following in the form $k \cos u$, and give u in terms of x in each case:

(a) $\sqrt{(16 - x^2)}$ (b) $\sqrt{(1 - 9x^2)}$ (c) $\sqrt{(9 - 4x^2)}$ (d) $\sqrt{(10 - x^2)}$

2 Find the following integrals:

(a) $\displaystyle\int \frac{1}{\sqrt{(25 - x^2)}} \, dx$ (b) $\displaystyle\int \frac{1}{\sqrt{(1 - 4x^2)}} \, dx$

(c) $\displaystyle\int \frac{1}{\sqrt{(4 - 9x^2)}} \, dx$ (d) $\displaystyle\int \frac{1}{\sqrt{(3 - x^2)}} \, dx$

3 Express the following in the form $k \sec^2 u$, and give u in terms of x in each case:

(a) $16 + x^2$ (b) $1 + 9x^2$ (c) $4 + 3x^2$ (d) $2 + x^2$

4 Find the following integrals:

(a) $\displaystyle\int \frac{1}{25 + x^2} \, dx$ (b) $\displaystyle\int \frac{1}{1 + 36x^2} \, dx$

(c) $\displaystyle\int \frac{1}{16 + 3x^2} \, dx$ (d) $\displaystyle\int \frac{1}{5 + x^2} \, dx$

5 Find the following integrals:

(a) $\displaystyle\int \frac{1}{9 + 2x^2} \, dx$ (b) $\displaystyle\int \frac{3}{\sqrt{(4 - 5x^2)}} \, dx$

(c) $\displaystyle\int \frac{1}{\sqrt{(3 - 2x^2)}} \, dx$ (d) $\displaystyle\int \frac{2}{3 + 5x^2} \, dx$

6 Evaluate the following integrals, leaving π in your answers:

(a) $\displaystyle\int_1^{\sqrt{3}} \frac{2}{1 + x^2} \, dx$ (b) $\displaystyle\int_0^{\sqrt{2}} \frac{1}{\sqrt{(4 - x^2)}} \, dx$

(c) $\displaystyle\int_{1/2}^1 \frac{3}{\sqrt{(1 - x^2)}} \, dx$ (d) $\displaystyle\int_0^3 \frac{1}{9 + x^2} \, dx$

7 (a) Find $\int \dfrac{1}{\sqrt{(9-x^2)}}\,dx$ using   (i) $x = 3\sin u$ (ii) $x = 3\cos u$

(b) Evaluate $\displaystyle\int_{3/2}^{3} \dfrac{1}{\sqrt{(9-x^2)}}\,dx$ using   (i) $x = 3\sin u$ (ii) $x = 3\cos u$

8 Find the following integrals, using the given change of variable:

(a) $\int \dfrac{1}{\sqrt{\{4-(x+1)^2\}}}\,dx$ $x + 1 = 2\sin u$

(b) $\int \dfrac{1}{9+(x-3)^2}\,dx$ $x - 3 = 3\tan u$

9 Find the following integrals:

(a) $\int \dfrac{1}{(x+3)^2+25}\,dx$ (b) $\int \dfrac{1}{\sqrt{\{4-(x-1)^2\}}}\,dx$

(c) $\int \dfrac{1}{3(x-2)^2+5}\,dx$ (d) $\int \dfrac{1}{\sqrt{\{9-3(x+1)^2\}}}\,dx$

10 (a) $2x^2 - 12x + 21$ may be written $2(x^2 - 6x + 9) + 21 - 18 = 2(x-3)^2 + 3$.
Write the following expressions in the form $a(x+b)^2 + c$ (see Section 11.3):
(i) $x^2 - 6x + 16$ (ii) $3x^2 - 12x + 14$ (iii) $2x^2 - 4x + 5$
(b) Find the following integrals:

(i) $\int \dfrac{1}{x^2 - 2x + 5}\,dx$ (ii) $\int \dfrac{1}{2x^2 + 4x + 11}\,dx$

(iii) $\int \dfrac{1}{x^2 - 4x + 13}\,dx$ (iv) $\int \dfrac{1}{4x^2 - 8x + 7}\,dx$

25.10 Integration by parts

We have learned the importance of recognising such integrals as

$$\int 2x \cos(x^2 + 2)\,dx = \sin(x^2 + 2) + c$$

When, however, the integrand is the product of two functions of x but is not susceptible to this treatment, e.g. $\int x \cos x\,dx$, we may often successfully apply a technique known as *integration by parts*; this is based upon the idea of differentiating the product of two functions of x. (See p147.)

If u and v are two functions of x,

$$\frac{d}{dx}(uv) = v\frac{du}{dx} + u\frac{dv}{dx}$$

Integrating each side with respect to x,

$$uv = \int v \frac{du}{dx} dx + \int u \frac{dv}{dx} dx$$

$$\therefore \quad \boxed{\int u \frac{dv}{dx} dx = uv - \int v \frac{du}{dx} dx}$$

Example 10

Find $\int x \cos x \, dx$.

Sidework:

$$\int u \frac{dv}{dx} dx = uv - \int v \frac{du}{dx} dx$$

Let $u = x$

$$\int x \cos x \, dx = x \sin x - \int \sin x \times 1 \, dx$$

Let $\dfrac{dv}{dx} = \cos x$

$$= x \sin x + \cos x + c$$

$$\therefore \quad v = \sin x$$

This method can of course only be attempted if the factor chosen as $\dfrac{dv}{dx}$ can be integrated; Example 10 illustrates the fact that its successful application usually depends upon the *correct choice of u*, since it is this which determines whether $\int v \dfrac{du}{dx} dx$ is easier to tackle than the original integral.

To some integrals it is necessary to apply the method of integration by parts more than once, as is illustrated in the next example.

Example 11

Find $\int x^2 \sin x \, dx$.

Sidework:

$$\int x^2 \sin x \, dx = x^2(-\cos x) - \int -\cos x \times 2x \, dx$$

Let $u = x^2$

$$= -x^2 \cos x + \int 2x \cos x \, dx$$

Let $\dfrac{dv}{dx} = \sin x$

$$\therefore \quad v = -\cos x$$

$$\int 2x \cos x \, dx = 2x \sin x - \int \sin x \times 2 \, dx$$

Let $u = 2x$

$$= 2x \sin x + 2 \cos x + c$$

$$\therefore \int x^2 \sin x \, dx = -x^2 \cos x + 2x \sin x + 2 \cos x + c$$

Let $\dfrac{dv}{dx} = \cos x$

$$= 2x \sin x + (2 - x^2) \cos x + c$$

$$v = \sin x$$

Exercise 25e

Find the following integrals:

1 $\int 2x \sin x \, dx$ 2 $\int x \sin 2x \, dx$
3 $\int x \cos(2x + 1) \, dx$ 4 $\int x(x + 1)^7 \, dx$
5 $\int x^2 \cos 3x \, dx$ 6 $\int x^2 \sin x \cos x \, dx$
7 $\int (x \cos x)^2 \, dx$ 8 $\int x \sin x \cos x \, dx$
9 $\int x \tan^{-1} x \, dx$ 10 $\int x(1 - x^2)^6 \, dx$
11 $\int \sin x \cos x \, dx$ 12 $\int t \sin^2 t \, dt$
13 Show that $\int x \sin^{-1} x \, dx = \frac{1}{4}(2x^2 - 1) \sin^{-1} x + \frac{1}{4}x\sqrt{(1 - x^2)} + c$
     (*Hint* Substitute $x = \sin \theta$.)

14 Evaluate $\displaystyle\int_0^{\pi/2} x \cos x \, dx$

15 Evaluate $\displaystyle\int_0^{\pi} t \cos^2 t \, dt$

Exercise 25f (Miscellaneous)

Find the integrals nos. 1–20, which are arranged by types in the order in which they occur in the chapter:

1 $\int x^2 \sqrt{(x^3 - 1)} \, dx$ 2 $\displaystyle\int \frac{x}{(x^2 - 1)^3} \, dx$ 3 $\int \sin 2x \cos^2 2x \, dx$

4 $\int \sec^2 x \sqrt{\cot x} \, dx$ 5 $\int \cos^3 4x \, dx$ 6 $\displaystyle\int \sin^2 \frac{x}{3} \, dx$

7 $\int \cos^4 2x \, dx$ 8 $\int \sqrt{(1 - \cos x)} \, dx$ 9 $\displaystyle\int \sin \frac{x}{3} \cos^2 \frac{x}{6} \, dx$

10 $\int \cos 3x \cos 2x \, dx$ 11 $\displaystyle\int x(3x - 7)^4 \, dx$ 12 $\displaystyle\int \frac{x}{\sqrt{(5 + x)}} \, dx$

13 $\displaystyle\int \frac{1}{\sqrt{(6 - 5x^2)}} \, dx$ 14 $\displaystyle\int \frac{1}{1 + 8x^2} \, dx$ 15 $\displaystyle\int \frac{1}{\sqrt{(5 - 4x - x^2)}} \, dx$

16 $\displaystyle\int \frac{1}{3x^2 + 6x + 5} \, dx$ 17 $\displaystyle\int \frac{x + 1}{\sqrt{(5 - x^2)}} \, dx$ 18 $\int \sqrt{(9 - x^2)} \, dx$

19 $\displaystyle\int \frac{1}{(4 - x^2)^{3/2}} \, dx$ 20 $\displaystyle\int \frac{1}{x^2 \sqrt{(16 - x^2)}} \, dx$

21 Find (a) $\displaystyle\int \frac{x}{\sqrt{(1 - x^2)}} \, dx$ (b) $\displaystyle\int \frac{2}{1 + x^2} \, dx$ (c) $\int x\sqrt{(1 - x^2)} \, dx$

        (d) $\displaystyle\int \frac{2}{\sqrt{(1 - x^2)}} \, dx$ (e) $\displaystyle\int \frac{2 - x}{\sqrt{(1 - x^2)}} \, dx$

Find the integrals nos. 22–45:

22 $\displaystyle\int \frac{x+2}{\sqrt{(3x-1)}}\,dx$
23 $\int \frac{1}{2}x\sqrt{(x^2+2)}\,dx$
24 $\displaystyle\int \frac{1}{x^2\sqrt{(1-x^2)}}\,dx$

25 $\displaystyle\int \cos^2\frac{x}{2}\sin^3\frac{x}{2}\,dx$
26 $\displaystyle\int \frac{x}{3\sqrt{(4-x^2)}}\,dx$
27 $\displaystyle\int \frac{3}{\sqrt{(36-x^2)}}\,dx$

28 $\int (x-1)^2(x+3)^5\,dx$
29 $\displaystyle\int \frac{x^2}{\sqrt{(4-x^2)}}\,dx$
30 $\displaystyle\int \frac{2+x}{\sqrt{(9-x^2)}}\,dx$

31 $\displaystyle\int \frac{1}{3x^2-12x+16}\,dx$
32 $\displaystyle\int \sin^2\frac{x}{5}\,dx$
33 $\int \sqrt{(\cos 3x+1)}\,dx$

34 $\int \sqrt{(4-x^2)}\,dx$
35 $\int \sec^5 x\tan x\,dx$
36 $\displaystyle\int \frac{x^2}{\sqrt{(4-9x^6)}}\,dx$

37 $\int \sin^5 2x\,dx$
38 $\displaystyle\int \frac{1}{(1+x^2)^2}\,dx$
39 $\displaystyle\int \sin\frac{3x}{2}\cos\frac{5x}{2}\,dx$

40 $\displaystyle\int \frac{\tan x}{\sqrt{(\cos 2x+1)}}\,dx$
41 $\displaystyle\int \frac{x}{1+x^4}\,dx$
42 $\int \cos x\sqrt{\cos 2x}\,dx$

43 $\displaystyle\int \frac{1}{x\sqrt{(x^2-9)}}\,dx$

44 $\displaystyle\int \frac{1}{(1-x)\sqrt{(1-x^2)}}\,dx$ $\left(\text{Put } x=\cos u; \text{ show integral}=\cot\frac{u}{2}+c.\right)$

Evaluate nos. 45–49:

45 $\displaystyle\int_0^3 2x\sqrt{(5x+1)}\,dx$
46 $\displaystyle\int_{\pi/4}^{\pi/2} \cos x\,\mathrm{cosec}^3 x\,dx$
47 $\displaystyle\int_0^\pi \sin\frac{x}{2}\cos\frac{x}{2}\,dx$

48 $\displaystyle\int_0^{\pi/2} x\sin x\,dx$
49 $\displaystyle\int_0^\pi x^2\sin x\cos x\,dx$

Chapter 26

Exponential and logarithmic functions

26.1 Exponential functions

The word *exponent* is often used instead of *index*, and functions in which the variable is in the index (such as 2^x, $10^{\sin x}$) are called **exponential functions**.

26.2 The graph of $y = a^x$

Let us first consider the function 2^x. A table of values and the graph of $y = 2^x$ are shown below.

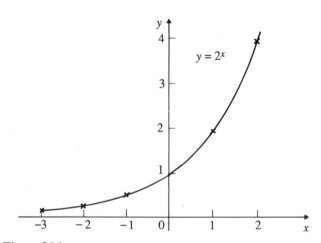

Figure 26.1

Table of values, $y = 2^x$:

x	-3	-2	-1	0	1	2
2^x	$\frac{1}{8}$	$\frac{1}{4}$	$\frac{1}{2}$	1	2	4

As $x \to -\infty$, $2^x \to 0$, and so the curve approaches the x-axis but does not meet it.

Qu. 1 Copy and extend the table opposite to include values of 1.5^x (from $x = -3$ to $x = +3$), and of 2.5^x, 3^x (both from $x = -2$ to $x = +2$). Sketch, with the same axes, the graphs of $y = 1^x$, $y = 1.5^x$, $y = 2^x$, $y = 2.5^x$, $y = 3^x$. What do you notice about the gradient of $y = a^x$ at $(0, 1)$ as a takes different values greater than 1? How would you deduce the shape of the graph of $y = (\frac{1}{2})^x$ from Figure 26.1?

26.3 The gradient of $y = a^x$ at $(0, 1)$; a limit

We shall confine our attention for the time being to exponential functions of the form a^x, where a is taken to be a constant real number greater than 1. Since $a^0 = 1$, the graph of $y = a^x$ (Figure 26.2) passes through the point $A(0, 1)$, and we let the gradient of the curve at this point be m.

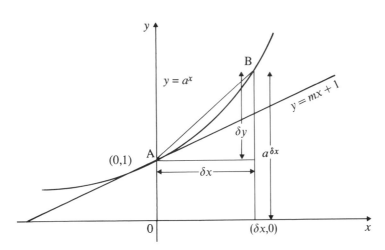

Figure 26.2

With the usual notation, if B is the point $(\delta x, a^{\delta x})$, then the gradient of AB is

$$\frac{\delta y}{\delta x} = \frac{a^{\delta x} - 1}{\delta x}$$

Now as $\delta x \to 0$, the gradient of AB $\to m$.

It follows that the limit, as $\delta x \to 0$, of $\dfrac{a^{\delta x} - 1}{\delta x}$ is m, the gradient of $y = a^x$ at $(0, 1)$.

Qu. 2 Investigate this limit, using a calculator, for $a = 2$ and $a = 3$.

26.4 The form of $\dfrac{d}{dx}(a^x)$

The limit just established enables us to investigate the gradient of $y = a^x$ at any point $P(x, y)$ on the curve. With the usual notation, if Q is the point $(x + \delta x, y + \delta y)$,

$$y + \delta y = a^{x + \delta x}$$

$$\therefore \qquad \delta y = a^{x + \delta x} - a^x = a^x(a^{\delta x} - 1)$$

$$\therefore \quad \text{the gradient of PQ,} \ \frac{\delta y}{\delta x} = a^x \left(\frac{a^{\delta x} - 1}{\delta x} \right) \qquad \qquad \cdots \quad (1)$$

Now as $\delta x \to 0$, the gradient of PQ $\to$ the gradient of the tangent at P; also, since we have shown that

$$\left(\frac{a^{\delta x} - 1}{\delta x} \right) \to m, \text{ the gradient at } (0, 1)$$

then the R.H.S. of (1) $\to ma^x$.

$$\therefore \quad \frac{dy}{dx} = ma^x$$

Thus $\qquad \boxed{\dfrac{d}{dx}(a^x) = ma^x, \text{ where } m \text{ is the gradient of } y = a^x \text{ at the point } (0, 1)}$

We have already noted (see Qu. 1) that, as a increases, the gradients of the curves $y = a^x$ at $(0, 1)$ increase; for every value of a there is an appropriate value of m, and it is reasonable to suppose that we should be able to express m in terms of a. However for the time being we must be satisfied with some numerical approximations for m which we will now proceed to find.

26.5 Approximate derivatives of 2^x and 3^x

The following table was used to draw the graphs of $y = 2^x$ and $y = 3^x$ in Figure 26.3; $y = m_2 x + 1$ and $y = m_3 x + 1$ are the respective tangents at $(0, 1)$.

Table of values for $y = 2^x$ and $y = 3^x$:

x	-2	$-\frac{3}{2}$	-1	$-\frac{1}{2}$	$-\frac{1}{4}$	0	$\frac{1}{4}$	$\frac{1}{2}$	1	$\frac{2}{3}$	2
2^x	0.25	0.35	0.5	0.71	0.84	1	1.19	1.41	2	2.83	4
3^x	0.11	0.19	0.33	0.58	0.76	1	1.32	1.73	3	5.20	9

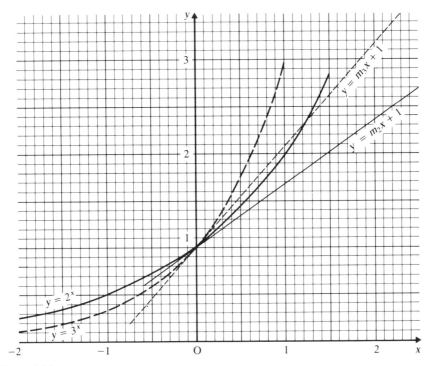

Figure 26.3

Qu. 3 (a) Measure the gradients of the two tangents in Figure 26.3, (compare them with your answers to Qu. 2) and deduce approximate expressions for $\dfrac{d}{dx}(2^x)$ and $\dfrac{d}{dx}(3^x)$.

(b) Now calculate the gradient of $y = 2^x$ where $x = 1$, and the gradient of $y = 3^x$ where $x = \frac{1}{2}$. Check from the graph.

Qu. 4 Tangents were drawn to a graph of $y = 2^x$, and their gradients were measured and entered in the following table:

x	-3	-2	-1	0	1	$\frac{3}{2}$	2	$\frac{5}{2}$
$y = 2^x$	0.125	0.25	0.5	1	2	2.83	4	5.66
$\dfrac{dy}{dx}$	0.08	0.18	0.37	0.62	1.33	1.90	2.82	3.68

Confirm graphically that these results indicate that $\dfrac{dy}{dx} \propto y$, and deduce an approximate expression for $\dfrac{d}{dx}(2^x)$.

26.6 The exponential function e^x

It has been established in the previous section that

$$\frac{d}{dx}(2^x) \approx 0.7 \times 2^x$$

and

$$\frac{d}{dx}(3^x) \approx 1.1 \times 3^x$$

Since, in general, $\frac{d}{dx}(a^x) = ka^x$, these results suggest that for simplicity we should find a value of a between 2 and 3 for which $k = 1$; this number is called e, its value is approximately 2.718 28, and it will be found to play a vital part in the further development of mathematics from this point.

Let us now summarise what we know about e.

Definition

> e is the number such that the gradient of $y = e^x$ at $(0, 1)$ is 1.
> e^x is called the **exponential function.**

Thus $$\frac{d}{dx}(e^x) = e^x$$

Also $$\int e^x \, dx = e^x + c$$

Since x may be any real number, the *domain* of the exponential function is $\mathbb{R}$. However e^x is always positive, so the *range* of the exponential function is $\mathbb{R}^+$. (See Section 3.8.)

Qu. 5 Use a calculator to verify that the limit of $(e^{\delta x} - 1)/\delta x$, as δx tends to zero, is 1.

Example 1

Find $\frac{dy}{dx}$ when $y = e^{3x^2}$.

[Here we have a composite function of x. This example is written out in full as a reminder of the technique involved, but the reader should be able to differentiate in one step.]

$$y = e^{3x^2}$$

Let $u = 3x^2$ then $y = e^u$

$$\therefore \quad \frac{du}{dx} = 6x \quad \text{and} \quad \frac{dy}{du} = e^u$$

Now, by the chain rule, $\dfrac{dy}{dx} = \dfrac{dy}{du} \times \dfrac{du}{dx} = e^u \times 6x.$

$$\therefore \quad \frac{dy}{dx} = 6x\, e^{3x^2}$$

Example 2

Find (a) $\int e^{x/2}\, dx$ (b) $\int x^2 e^{x^3}\, dx$

(a) Since $\dfrac{d}{dx}(e^{x/2}) = \tfrac{1}{2}e^{x/2}$ then $\int e^{x/2}\, dx = 2e^{x/2} + c.$

(b) Since $\dfrac{d}{dx}(e^{x^3}) = 3x^2 e^{x^3}$ then $\int x^2 e^{x^3}\, dx = \tfrac{1}{3}e^{x^3} + c.$

Qu. 6 Differentiate with respect to x:
(a) e^{4x} (b) e^{x^2} (c) e^{2x^3} (d) e^{-x^2} (e) $e^{\tan x}$ (f) $e^{\sqrt{x}}$
Qu. 7 Find the following integrals, and check by differentiation:
(a) $\int x\, e^{x^2}\, dx$ (b) $\int \sin x\, e^{\cos x}\, dx$ (c) $\int 2e^{x/3}\, dx$
(d) $\int 3e^{2x}\, dx$ (e) $\int \tfrac{1}{2}x\, e^{3x^2}\, dx$ (f) $\int \operatorname{cosec}^2 2x\, e^{\cot 2x}\, dx$

Exercise 26a

1 Make sketches of the graphs of the following functions:
 (a) e^{2x} (b) 2^{-x} (c) $2^{1/x}$ (d) 2^{x^2} (e) $3e^x$ (f) e^{x+1}
2 With the same axes, sketch the graphs of $y = e^{\sin x}$ and $y = e^{\cos x}$; are these functions periodic?
 (a) Is the function $e^{\sin x}$ odd, even or neither?
 (b) Is the function $e^{\cos x}$ odd, even or neither?
3 Is the function e^{-x^2} odd, even or neither? If its domain is $\mathbb{R}$, what is its range? Sketch the graph of $y = e^{-x^2}$.
4 Draw the graph of $y = 2.5^x$, taking values of x from -2 to $+2$. Draw the tangents to the curve at the points given by $x = -\tfrac{3}{2}, -1, -\tfrac{1}{2}, 0,$ $\tfrac{1}{2}, 1, \tfrac{3}{2}$, measure their gradients, and confirm graphically that $\dfrac{dy}{dx} = ky.$

Deduce an approximate expression for $\dfrac{d}{dx}(2.5^x).$

Differentiate with respect to x in nos. 5–7.

5 (a) $4e^x$ (b) e^{3x} (c) e^{2x+1} (d) e^{2x^2}

6 (a) $e^{\cos x}$ (b) $e^{\sec x}$ (c) $e^{3\tan x}$ (d) $e^{\sin 2x}$

7 (a) $x^2 e^x$ (b) $\dfrac{e^x}{x}$ (c) $\dfrac{x}{2} e^{\sin x}$ (d) $e^{x^2}\operatorname{cosec} x$

8 Find the following integrals:

(a) $\int 3e^{x/2}\,dx$ (b) $\int e^{-x}\,dx$ (c) $\int e^{x/3}\,dx$

(d) $\int 2e^{3x-1}\,dx$ (e) $\displaystyle\int \frac{x}{2} e^{x^2}\,dx$ (f) $\int x^2 e^{-x^3}\,dx$

(g) $\int \sin x\, e^{\cos x}\,dx$ (h) $\int (1+\tan^2 x)\, e^{\tan x}\,dx$ (i) $\displaystyle\int \frac{e^{\cot x}}{\sin^2 x}\,dx$

(j) $\int x^{-2} e^{1/x}\,dx$

9 Find the equation of the tangent to the curve $y = e^x$ at the point given by $x = a$. Deduce the equation of the tangent to the curve which passes through the point $(1, 0)$.

10 Find the volume of the solid generated by rotation about the x-axis of the area enclosed by $y = e^x$, the axes, $x = 1$.

26.7 Further theory of logarithms

Since a logarithm is an index (or exponent), the discussion of exponential functions leads naturally to further consideration of logarithms. It is advisable at this stage to restate some of the ideas covered in Chapter 10.

Definition

> The logarithm of b to the base a, written $\log_a b$, is the power to which the base must be raised to equal b.

Thus since $10^2 = 100,$ $2 = \lg 100,$

and if $a^x = b,$ $x = \log_a b.$

The reader should already be familiar with the following basic rules:

> $\log_c (ab) = \log_c a + \log_c b$
> $\log_c (a/b) = \log_c a - \log_c b$
> $\log_c (a^n) = n \log_c a$

Remember also that if $y = \log_a x$ then $x = a^y$, and that if we eliminate y from these two equations, we obtain

$$x = a^{\log_a x}$$

On the other hand, eliminating x gives

$$y = \log_a(a^y)$$

We shall now show that $\log_a b = \dfrac{\log_c b}{\log_c a}$.

Let $x = \log_a b$,

$\therefore \quad a^x = b$

Taking logarithms to the base c of each side,

$$\log_c(a^x) = \log_c b$$

$\therefore \qquad x \log_c a = \log_c b$

$\therefore \qquad\qquad x = \dfrac{\log_c b}{\log_c a}$

i.e.
$$\boxed{\log_a b = \dfrac{\log_c b}{\log_c a}}$$

Qu. 8 Express as a single logarithm:
(a) $2\log_{10} a - \tfrac{1}{3}\log_{10} b + 2$
(b) $\log_c(1+x) - \log_c(1-x) + A$ where $A = \log_c B$

Qu. 9 Express in terms of $\log_c a$:

(a) $\log_c(2a)$ (b) $\log_c a^2$ (c) $\log_c \dfrac{1}{a}$ (d) $\log_c \dfrac{2}{a}$

(e) $\log_c \sqrt{a}$ (f) $\log_c \dfrac{a}{2}$ (g) $\log_c \dfrac{1}{a^2}$ (h) $\log_c(2a)^{-1}$

26.8 Natural logarithms

Logarithms to the base e are called *natural logarithms*, or *Napierian logarithms*, in honour of John Napier, a Scotsman, who published the first table of logarithmic sines in 1614. It is not surprising that the idea of logarithms was discovered independently at about the same time by Joost Bürgi, a Swiss; there was a pressing need to reduce labour involved in computation, especially in astronomy and navigation.

Napier's first publication on this topic fired the imagination of Henry Briggs, who visited him to discuss the practical application of the discovery; the fruit of this meeting was the eventual introduction of logarithms to the base 10, or *common logarithms*, for computation. However, it should be remembered that neither Napier nor Bürgi put forward the concept of a *base*, with the logarithm as an index; this idea does not appear to have been fully developed until about the middle of the eighteenth century. The choice of e as the base, though less convenient than 10 for computation, provides a new function $\log_e x$ of fundamental importance.

Exercise 26b

Express as a single logarithm:

1 $2\lg a - 2 + \lg 2a$ 　　　 2 $3\log_e x + 3 - \log_e 3x$
3 $4\log_e(x-3) - 3\log_e(x-2)$ 　 4 $\frac{1}{2}\log_e(1+y) + \frac{1}{2}\log_e(1-y) + \log_e k$

Express in terms of $\log_e a$:

5 $\log_e 3a$ 　 6 $\log_e a^3$ 　 7 $\log_e(a/3)$ 　 8 $\log_e(1/a^3)$
9 $\log_e(3/a)$ 　 10 $\log_e(\frac{1}{3}a^{-1})$ 　 11 $\log_e(\sqrt[3]{a})$

Express as the sum or difference of logarithms:

12 $\log_e \cot x$ 　 13 $\log_e \tan^2 x$ 　 14 $\log_e(x^2-4)$ 　 15 $\log_e\sqrt{\left(\dfrac{x+1}{x-1}\right)}$

Notation

The notation $\log_e x$ has the great virtue that it emphasises that the base of the logarithms is e. However, in recent years $\ln x$ has been universally adopted as the standard abbreviation (the n signifying that these are Napierian, or perhaps natural logarithms). From here onwards we shall use this notation exclusively.

Qu. 10 Express as a single term:

(a) $\ln x + \ln y - 1$ 　　 (b) $\ln\left(\dfrac{e^3}{x}\right) + \ln\left(\dfrac{x}{e}\right)$

In the function $\ln x$, the independent variable x *must* be a positive real number (it must not be zero, nor must it be negative), in other words the *domain* of the logarithmic function is $\mathbb{R}^+$ (or some subset of $\mathbb{R}^+$). When $x > 1$, $\ln x$ is positive, it is zero when $x = 1$ and it is negative when $0 < x < 1$; its *range*, in other words, is $\mathbb{R}$. In this context, if the domain is not explicitly stated, it should always be assumed that it has been chosen so that only logarithms of positive numbers are required. For example, in the function $\ln(1+x)$, it should be assumed that $x > -1$, or again, in the function $\ln(2-x)$, it should be assumed that $x < 2$ is intended.

The reader is strongly advised to commit the following important identities to memory:

$$\ln(e^x) = x \quad \text{and} \quad e^{\ln x} = x$$

Qu. 11 Simplify:
(a) $e^{2\ln x}$ 　 (b) $e^{-\ln x}$ 　 (c) $e^{(1/2)\ln x}$
(d) $\ln(e^{\sin x})$ 　 (e) $\frac{1}{2}\ln(e^{x^2})$ 　 (f) $\ln(\sqrt{e^x})$

26.9 The derivative of ln x

Figure 26.4 shows the graph of $y = \ln x$ (or $x = e^y$); this curve is the reflection in the line $y = x$ of the graph of $y = e^x$ (which is shown as a dotted curve). This is to be expected because $\ln x$ and e^x are inverse functions (see Section 3.16).

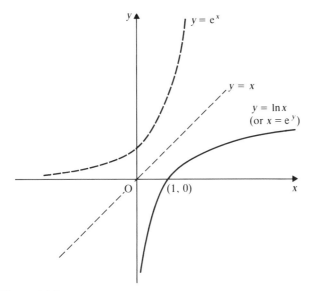

Figure 26.4

To find $\dfrac{d}{dx}(\ln x)$, we write $y = \ln x$ as

$$x = e^y$$

Differentiating each side with respect to x,†

$$\frac{d}{dx}(x) = \frac{d}{dy}(e^y) \times \frac{dy}{dx}$$

$$\therefore \qquad 1 = e^y \frac{dy}{dx}$$

$$\therefore \qquad \frac{dy}{dx} = \frac{1}{e^y} = \frac{1}{x}$$

$$\therefore \qquad \boxed{\frac{d}{dx}(\ln x) = \frac{1}{x}}$$

Example 3

Find $\dfrac{dy}{dx}$ if:

(a) $y = \ln 2x$ (b) $y = \ln x^2$ (c) $y = \ln (x^2 + 2)$ (d) $y = \ln \dfrac{x}{\sqrt{(x^2 + 1)}}$

† Or we may differentiate each side with respect to y.

$$\frac{dx}{dy} = e^y = x, \qquad \therefore \quad \frac{dy}{dx} = 1 \bigg/ \frac{dx}{dy} = \frac{1}{x}.$$

(a) $y = \ln 2x = \ln 2 + \ln x$

$\therefore \quad \dfrac{dy}{dx} = \dfrac{1}{x}$

(b) $y = \ln x^2 = 2 \ln x$

$\therefore \quad \dfrac{dy}{dx} = \dfrac{2}{x}$

(c) $y = \ln (x^2 + 2)$

Let $u = x^2 + 2$ then $y = \ln u$

$\dfrac{du}{dx} = 2x$ and $\dfrac{dy}{du} = \dfrac{1}{u}$

$\therefore \quad \dfrac{dy}{dx} = \dfrac{dy}{du} \times \dfrac{du}{dx} = \dfrac{1}{u} \times 2x$

$\therefore \quad \dfrac{dy}{dx} = \dfrac{2x}{x^2 + 2}$

(d) $y = \ln \dfrac{x}{\sqrt{(x^2 + 1)}} = \ln x - \dfrac{1}{2} \ln (x^2 + 1)$

$\therefore \quad \dfrac{dy}{dx} = \dfrac{1}{x} - \dfrac{1}{2} \times \dfrac{2x}{x^2 + 1} = \dfrac{x^2 + 1 - x^2}{x(x^2 + 1)}$

$\therefore \quad \dfrac{dy}{dx} = \dfrac{1}{x(x^2 + 1)}$

Qu. 12 Differentiate with respect to x:
(a) e^{x^2} (b) $\ln (x^2 - 2)$ (c) $\ln \sin^2 x$ (d) $\ln \sin (x^2)$

Qu. 13 If $y = \ln \{x \sqrt{(x + 1)}\}$ find $\dfrac{dy}{dx}$ (a) by differentiating the logarithm of a product as it stands   (b) by first writing y as the sum of two logarithms.

Qu. 14 Differentiate with respect to x:
(a) $\ln (3x)$ (b) $\ln (4x)$ (c) $\ln (3x + 1)$
(d) $\ln (2x^3)$ (e) $\ln (x^3 - 2)$ (f) $\ln (x - 1)^3$

26.10 $\dfrac{d}{dx}(a^x)$ and $\displaystyle\int a^x \, dx$

In Section 26.4 we found that $\dfrac{d}{dx}(a^x) = ma^x$, m being the gradient of $y = a^x$ at $(0, 1)$. When $a = e$, $m = 1$; we can now find m for other values of a.

Let $y = a^x$, then

$\ln y = \ln a^x = x \ln a$

Differentiating with respect to x (and using the chain rule):

$$\frac{d}{dy}(\ln y) \times \frac{dy}{dx} = \frac{d}{dx}(x \ln a)$$

$$\therefore \qquad \frac{1}{y} \times \frac{dy}{dx} = \ln a$$

$$\therefore \qquad \frac{dy}{dx} = y \ln a$$

$$\therefore \qquad \boxed{\frac{d}{dx}(a^x) = a^x \ln a} \qquad \qquad \dots \quad (1)$$

Qu. 15 Find $\dfrac{d}{dx}(4^x)$ reproducing the above method in full. Find the gradient of the curve $y = 4^x$ at $(2, 16)$.

Qu. 16 Find the gradient at $(0, 1)$ of the following curves, to four decimal places:
(a) $y = 2^x$ (b) $y = 3^x$
(Compare with Qu. 3 on page 533.)

Qu. 17 Differentiate with respect to x:
(a) 10^x (b) 2^{3x+1}

It follows from (1) that:

$$\int a^x \ln a \, dx = a^x + k$$

$$\therefore \qquad \boxed{\int a^x \, dx = \frac{a^x}{\ln a} + c}$$

Qu. 18 Find $\dfrac{d}{dx}(5^x)$ and deduce $\int 5^x \, dx$.

Qu. 19 Find $\dfrac{d}{dx}(2^{x^2})$ and deduce $\int x \, 2^{x^2} \, dx$.

Qu. 20 Find the following integrals:
(a) $\int 3^{2x} \, dx$ (b) $\int x^2 \, e^{x^3} \, dx$ (c) $\int 2^{\tan x} \sec^2 x \, dx$

Exercise 26c

1 Differentiate with respect to x:

(a) $\ln (4x)$ (b) $4 \ln x$ (c) $\ln (2x - 3)$ (d) $\ln \dfrac{x-1}{2}$

(e) $\ln x^4$ (f) $\ln (x^2 - 1)$ (g) $\ln 3x^2$ (h) $3 \ln x^2$

(i) $\ln (x + 1)^2$ (j) $\ln \dfrac{1}{x}$ (k) $\ln (\frac{1}{2}x)$ (l) $\ln \sqrt{x}$

(m) $\ln \dfrac{1}{2x}$ (n) $\ln \dfrac{2}{x}$ (o) $\ln x^{-2}$ (p) $\lg x$

2 Differentiate with respect to x:
  (a) $\ln \cos x$ (b) $\ln \sin^2 x$ (c) $\ln \tan 3x$
  (d) $\ln \cos^3 2x$ (e) $\ln (2 \cot^2 x)$ (f) $\ln (3 \cos^2 2x)$

  (g) $\ln \tan \dfrac{x}{2}$ (h) $\ln \sec x$ (i) $\ln (\sec x + \tan x)$

  (j) $\ln \operatorname{cosec} (x^2)$ (k) $\ln \dfrac{\sin x + \cos x}{\sin x - \cos x}$

3 Find:

  (a) $\dfrac{d}{dx} \ln \sqrt{\dfrac{1-x}{1+x}}$ (b) $\dfrac{d}{dx} \ln \{x\sqrt{(x^2 - 1)}\}$

  (c) $\dfrac{d}{dx} \ln \dfrac{(x+1)^2}{\sqrt{(x-1)}}$ (d) $\dfrac{d}{dx} \ln \{x + \sqrt{(x^2 - 1)}\}$

4 Differentiate with respect to x:

  (a) $x \ln x$ (b) $x^2 \ln x$ (c) $\dfrac{\ln x}{x}$ (d) $\dfrac{\ln x}{x^2}$

  (e) $\dfrac{x}{\ln x}$ (f) $(\ln x)^2$ (g) $\ln (\ln x^k)$ (h) $\ln (e^{\sin x})$

5 Differentiate with respect to x:
  (a) 5^x (b) 2^{x^2} (c) 3^{2x-1} (d) $e^{\ln x}$

6 (a) Find $\dfrac{d}{dx} (3^x)$ and deduce $\int 3^x \, dx$.

  (b) Find $\dfrac{d}{dx} (2^{x^2})$ and deduce $\int x \, 2^{x^2} \, dx$.

7 Find the following integrals:
  (a) $\int 10^x \, dx$ (b) $\int 2^{3x} \, dx$ (c) $\int x \, 3^{x^2} \, dx$ (d) $\int 2^{\cos x} \sin x \, dx$

8 Find $\dfrac{d}{dx} (x \ln x)$ and deduce $\int \ln x \, dx$.

9 Find $\dfrac{d}{dx} (x \, 2^x)$ and deduce $\int x \, 2^x \, dx$.

10 Find (a) $\dfrac{d}{dx} \ln (x - 2)$ (b) $\dfrac{d}{dx} \ln (2 - x)$

  Sketch on the same axes the graphs of $\ln (x - 2)$, $\ln (2 - x)$, $y = \dfrac{1}{x - 2}$.

11 Sketch on the same axes the following curves:

(a) $y = \ln x$, $y = \ln(-x)$, $y = \dfrac{1}{x}$

(b) $y = \ln \dfrac{1}{x}$, $y = \ln\left(-\dfrac{1}{x}\right)$, $y = -\dfrac{1}{x}$

(c) $y = \ln(x-3)$, $y = \ln(3-x)$, $y = \dfrac{1}{x-3}$

(d) $y = \ln\left(\dfrac{1}{x-3}\right)$, $y = \ln\left(\dfrac{1}{3-x}\right)$, $y = \dfrac{1}{3-x}$

12 Given that $x \in \mathbb{R}^+$, write down the range of the following functions:
(a) $y = \ln(1 + x^2)$ (b) $y = \ln(1/x)$
Sketch the graph of each of these functions.

26.11 $\displaystyle\int \frac{f'(x)}{f(x)}\,dx$

The result $\displaystyle\int x^n\,dx = \frac{x^{n+1}}{n+1} + c$ holds for all rational values of n, except $n = -1$;

this hitherto puzzling gap may now be filled. Since we have established that

$\dfrac{d}{dx}(\ln x) = \dfrac{1}{x}$, it follows that

$$\int \frac{1}{x}\,dx = \ln x + c$$

or $\quad\boxed{\displaystyle\int \frac{1}{x}\,dx = \ln(kx)}\quad$ where $\quad c = \ln k$

Example 4

Find the following integrals:

(a) $\displaystyle\int \frac{1}{2x}\,dx$ (b) $\displaystyle\int \frac{1}{2x-1}\,dx$

(a) $\displaystyle\int \frac{1}{2x}\,dx = \frac{1}{2}\int \frac{1}{x}\,dx$

$\qquad = \tfrac{1}{2}\ln x + c$
$\qquad = \ln(k\sqrt{x})\qquad$ where $c = \ln k$

(b) $\displaystyle\int \frac{1}{2x-1}\,dx$

This is best tackled in reverse by guessing the form of the integral.

$$\frac{d}{dx}\{\ln(2x-1)\} = \frac{2}{2x-1}$$

$$\therefore \quad \int \frac{1}{2x-1}\,dx = \tfrac{1}{2}\ln(2x-1)+c$$

Qu. 21 Find the following integrals:

(a) $\displaystyle\int \frac{2}{x}\,dx$ (b) $\displaystyle\int \frac{1}{3x}\,dx$ (c) $\displaystyle\int \frac{1}{3x-2}\,dx$ (d) $\displaystyle\int \frac{1}{3x-6}\,dx$

Qu. 22 Find the following integrals:

(a) $\displaystyle\int \frac{1}{2x+3}\,dx$ using the substitution $u = 2x+3$

(b) $\displaystyle\int \frac{1}{1-x}\,dx$ using the substitution $u = 1-x$

Qu. 23 Evaluate $\displaystyle\int_1^2 \frac{3}{x}\,dx$.

An integral of the form $\displaystyle\int \frac{f'(x)}{f(x)}\,dx$ may be reduced to the form $\displaystyle\int \frac{1}{u}\,du$, by the substitution $u = f(x)$.

$$\int \frac{f'(x)}{f(x)}\,dx = \int \frac{f'(x)}{f(x)} \times \frac{dx}{du}\,du$$

$$= \int \frac{f'(x)}{u} \times \frac{1}{f'(x)}\,du$$

$$= \int \frac{1}{u}\,du$$

$$= \ln u + c$$

$$= \ln f(x) + c$$

Hence

$$\boxed{\int \frac{f'(x)}{f(x)}\,dx = \ln\{k\,f(x)\}}$$

From now onwards we must be prepared to recognise, in yet another form, the integrand involving a function of x and its derivative. As before, such an integral may be found by substitution, or usually it may be written down at once.

Example 5

Find $\int \dfrac{x}{x^2+1}\,dx.$

Since $\dfrac{d}{dx}\ln(x^2+1) = \dfrac{2x}{x^2+1},$

$\int \dfrac{x}{x^2+1}\,dx = \tfrac{1}{2}\ln(x^2+1) + c$

$\qquad\qquad = \ln\{k\sqrt{(x^2+1)}\}$ \qquad where $k = \ln c$

Qu. 24 Find the following integrals:

(a) $\displaystyle\int \dfrac{x^2}{(x^3-2)^2}\,dx$ \qquad (b) $\int x^2 \cos(x^3)\,dx$ \qquad (c) $\int x^2\,e^{x^3}\,dx$

(d) $\displaystyle\int \dfrac{x^2}{x^3-2}\,dx$ \qquad (e) $\displaystyle\int \dfrac{x-1}{x^2-2x}\,dx$ \qquad (f) $\displaystyle\int \dfrac{2x}{3-x^2}\,dx$

(g) $\int \cot x\,dx$

Qu. 25 Find $\displaystyle\int \dfrac{x}{x-1}\,dx$

(a) using the substitution $u = x-1$
(b) by first dividing the numerator by the denominator.

26.12 $\displaystyle\int_a^b \dfrac{1}{x}\,dx$ when a, b are negative

An important point must be cleared up. Reference to Figure 26.4 reminds us that as the value of x goes from 0 to $+\infty$, the value of $\ln x$ goes from $-\infty$ to $+\infty$; $\ln x$ *is not defined for negative values of* x. This presents us with an apparent paradox which may be demonstrated in graphical terms as follows.

Referring to the graph of $y = 1/x$ in Figure 26.5 (page 546) it is apparent that the two shaded areas are equal in magnitude and of opposite sign. However, we soon get into trouble if we seek to evaluate the appropriate integral with the negative limits; thus, is it true to say that

$$\int_{-2}^{-1} \dfrac{1}{x}\,dx = \left[\ln x\right]_{-2}^{-1}$$

$$= \text{'}\ln(-1) - \ln(-2)\text{'}?$$

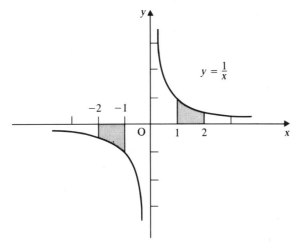

Figure 26.5

We could now write this as $\ln\left(\dfrac{-1}{-2}\right) = \ln\frac{1}{2} = \ln 2^{-1} = -\ln 2$, and thus obtain

a correct figure for the area, but the working is not valid, since the expression '$\ln(-1) - \ln(-2)$' is meaningless.

We surmount this difficulty as soon as we realise that *for negative values of x,* although $\ln x$ is not defined, $\ln(-x)$ *does exist*, and

$$\frac{d}{dx}\ln(-x) = \frac{-1}{-x} = \frac{1}{x} \qquad \text{(See Figure 26.6.)}$$

$$\boxed{\text{Thus, if } a \text{ and } b \text{ are negative, } \int_a^b \frac{1}{x}\,dx = \left[\ln(-x)\right]_a^b}$$

Using the modulus sign, we could write this as

$$\boxed{\int_a^b \frac{1}{x}\,dx = \left[\ln|x|\right]_a^b}$$

This form of the result could be used for a and b both positive *and* for a and b both negative; notice however that a and b must not have opposite signs.

Hence the left-hand shaded area in Figure 26.5 $\displaystyle = \int_{-2}^{-1} \frac{1}{x}\,dx$

$$= \left[\ln|x|\right]_{-2}^{-1}$$

$$= \ln 1 - \ln 2$$

$$= -\ln 2$$

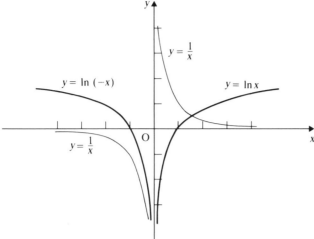

Figure 26.6

Qu. 26 Evaluate:

(a) $\displaystyle\int_{-4}^{-3} \frac{1}{x}\,dx$ (b) $\displaystyle\int_{-1}^{-1/2} \frac{1}{x}\,dx$

Qu. 27 Evaluate $\displaystyle\int_{-4}^{-2} \frac{1}{x}\,dx$, using the change of variable $x = -u$.

Qu. 28 Can any meaning be assigned to $\displaystyle\int_{-2}^{+2} \frac{1}{x}\,dx$?

Example 6

Find the area enclosed by the curve $y = \dfrac{1}{x-2}$ and
(a) the lines $x = 4$, $x = 5$, and the x-axis,
(b) the line $x = 1$, and the axes. (Figure 26.7.)

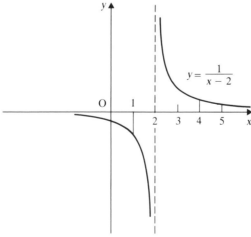

Figure 26.7

(a) The required area $= \displaystyle\int_4^5 \frac{1}{x-2}\,dx$

$$= \left[\ln{(x-2)} \right]_4^5$$

$$= \ln 3 - \ln 2$$
$$= \ln \tfrac{3}{2}$$

(b) Between $x = 0$ and $x = 1$, $(x - 2)$ is negative and so $\ln{(x - 2)}$ is meaningless. Consequently we use

$$\int \frac{1}{x-2}\,dx = \ln|x-2| + c$$

as follows:

The required area $= \displaystyle\int_0^1 \frac{1}{x-2}\,dx$

$$= \left[\ln|x-2| \right]_0^1$$

$$= \ln 1 - \ln 2$$
$$= -\ln 2$$

Qu. 29 Find $\dfrac{d}{dx}\{\ln{(x-3)}\}$ and $\dfrac{d}{dx}\{\ln{(3-x)}\}$.

Qu. 30 Sketch the curve $y = \dfrac{1}{x-3}$, and evaluate:

(a) $\displaystyle\int_5^6 \frac{1}{x-3}\,dx$ (b) $\displaystyle\int_{-2}^2 \frac{1}{x-3}\,dx$

Qu. 31 Sketch the curve $y = \dfrac{1}{2-x}$ and evaluate $\displaystyle\int_3^5 \frac{1}{2-x}\,dx$.

Exercise 26d

1 Find the following integrals:

(a) $\displaystyle\int \frac{1}{4x}\,dx$ (b) $\displaystyle\int \frac{5}{x}\,dx$ (c) $\displaystyle\int \frac{1}{2x-3}\,dx$

(d) $\displaystyle\int \frac{1}{2x+8}\,dx$ (e) $\displaystyle\int \frac{1}{3-2x}\,dx$ (f) $\displaystyle\int \frac{x}{1-x^2}\,dx$

(g) $\displaystyle\int \frac{3x}{x^2-1}\,dx$ (h) $\displaystyle\int \frac{2x+1}{x^2+x-2}\,dx$ (i) $\displaystyle\int \frac{2x-3}{3x^2-9x+4}\,dx$

(j) $\int \dfrac{x}{x+2}\,dx$ (k) $\int \dfrac{3x}{2x+3}\,dx$ (l) $\int \dfrac{2x}{3-x}\,dx$

(m) $\int \dfrac{x-1}{2-x}\,dx$ (n) $\int \dfrac{3-2x}{x-4}\,dx$ (o) $\int \tan x\,dx$

(p) $\int \cot \dfrac{x}{2}\,dx$ (q) $\int \cot (2x+1)\,dx$ (r) $\int -\tan \dfrac{x}{3}\,dx$

2 (a) Sketch the curves $y = \ln(2x-1)$ and $y = \ln(1-2x)$.

  (b) Find $\dfrac{d}{dx}\ln(2x-1)$ and $\dfrac{d}{dx}\ln(1-2x)$.

  (c) Evaluate $\displaystyle\int_1^2 \dfrac{1}{2x-1}\,dx$ and $\displaystyle\int_{-2}^0 \dfrac{1}{2x-1}\,dx$.

3 Sketch the curve $y = \dfrac{1}{x-4}$ and evaluate:

  (a) $\displaystyle\int_1^2 \dfrac{1}{x-4}\,dx$ (b) $\displaystyle\int_5^6 \dfrac{1}{x-4}\,dx$

4 (a) Find $\dfrac{d}{dx}\ln\left(\dfrac{1}{3-x}\right)$ and $\dfrac{d}{dx}\ln\left(\dfrac{1}{x-3}\right)$.

  (b) Sketch on the same axes the graphs of $y = -\ln(3-x)$, $y = -\ln(x-3)$, $y = 1/(3-x)$, and find the area enclosed by the latter, the lines $x = 5$, $x = 6$, and the x-axis.

  (c) Find the area under $y = 1/(3-x)$ from $x = 0$ to $x = 1$.

5 Evaluate the following:

  (a) $\displaystyle\int_2^8 \dfrac{1}{2x}\,dx$ (b) $\displaystyle\int_1^{4/3} \dfrac{1}{3x-2}\,dx$ (c) $\displaystyle\int_1^3 \dfrac{1}{x-5}\,dx$

  (d) $\displaystyle\int_3^5 \dfrac{1}{1-2x}\,dx$ (e) $\displaystyle\int_{-0.25}^{0.25} \dfrac{1}{2x+1}\,dx$ (f) $\displaystyle\int_{-\sqrt{2}}^0 \dfrac{x}{x^2+2}\,dx$

  (g) $\displaystyle\int_0^3 \dfrac{2x-1}{x^2-x+1}\,dx$ (h) $\displaystyle\int_4^6 \dfrac{x}{x-2}\,dx$ (i) $\displaystyle\int_{-7}^{-5} \dfrac{x+1}{x+3}\,dx$

  (j) $\displaystyle\int_{-0.5}^0 \dfrac{2-x}{x-1}\,dx$ (k) $\displaystyle\int_{\pi/3}^{\pi/2} \cot \theta\,d\theta$ (l) $\displaystyle\int_0^{\pi/6} \tan 2x\,dx$

  (m) $\displaystyle\int_{\pi/6}^{\pi/4} \dfrac{\sec^2 \theta}{\tan \theta}\,d\theta$

26.13 Further integration by parts

Example 7

Find $\displaystyle\int_0^1 x\,e^{2x}\,dx$.

$$\int_0^1 x\,e^{2x}\,dx = \left[\frac{1}{2}x\,e^{2x}\right]_0^1 - \int_0^1 \frac{1}{2}e^{2x}\,dx$$

$$= \frac{1}{2}e^2 - \left[\frac{1}{4}e^{2x}\right]_0^1$$

$$= \tfrac{1}{2}e^2 - [\tfrac{1}{4}e^2 - \tfrac{1}{4}]$$

$$= \tfrac{1}{4}(e^2 + 1)$$

Some functions can be integrated by parts, even though they are not products, by inserting an extra factor of 1, as follows:

$$\int \ln x\,dx = \int 1 \times \ln x\,dx$$

$$= x\ln x - \int x \times \left(\frac{1}{x}\right) dx$$

$$= x\ln x - \int 1\,dx$$

$$= x\ln x - x + c$$

Or again:

$$\int \tan^{-1} x\,dx = \int 1 \times \tan^{-1} x\,dx$$

$$= x\tan^{-1} x - \int x \times \left(\frac{1}{1+x^2}\right) dx$$

$$= x\tan^{-1} x - \frac{1}{2}\int \frac{2x}{1+x^2}\,dx$$

$$= x\tan^{-1} x - \tfrac{1}{2}\ln(1+x^2) + c$$

Exercise 26e

Find the following integrals:

1 $\int x^2 \ln x\,dx$ **2** $\int x^2 e^{-x}\,dx$ **3** $\int x^3 e^x\,dx$
4 $\int \ln 2x\,dx$ **5** $\int \sin^{-1}(3x)\,dx$ **6** $\int t^3 e^{-t^2}\,dt$

Evaluate:

7 $\displaystyle\int_0^1 x\,e^{-x}\,dx$ **8** $\displaystyle\int_1^{e^2} \ln x\,dx$ **9** $\displaystyle\int_0^1 \sin^{-1} x\,dx$

10 $\displaystyle\int_0^1 t^2 e^t\,dt$ **11** $\displaystyle\int_0^2 \theta\,e^{2\theta}\,d\theta$ **12** $\displaystyle\int_1^9 \sqrt{y}\ln y\,dy$

13 $\displaystyle\int_1^e z(\ln z)^2 \, dz$ **14** $\displaystyle\int_1^2 t^2 \ln t \, dt$ **15** $\displaystyle\int_0^1 y\,e^{-3y} \, dy$

16 Find the area bounded by the curve $y = 250x^2\,e^{5x}$, the x-axis, and the lines $x = 0$ and $x = 1$.

17 Find the area bounded by the curve $y = \ln x$, the x-axis, and the lines $x = 1$ and $x = e$.

18 Given that $I = \int e^x \sin x \, dx$, show, by applying integration by parts twice, that:

$$I = -e^x \cos x + e^x \sin x - \int e^x \sin x \, dx$$

Hence show that $I = \frac{1}{2} e^x(\sin x - \cos x) + c$.

19 Using the method of no. 18, find $\int e^{-x} \sin x \, dx$.

20 Using the method of no. 18, evaluate $\displaystyle\int_0^{\pi/2} e^{2x} \cos x \, dx$.

26.14 The exponential series

The expansion of functions of a variable as series has considerable theoretical and practical importance. There are some problems that are most easily tackled by means of series, for instance estimating the value of the constant e, and there are problems in science and engineering which have no practicable solution except by series. Further, the development of computers has considerably added to the practical importance of approximate numerical solutions to problems. So far in this book only the function $(1 + x)^n$ has been expanded in a series and in this chapter two more functions, e^x and $\ln(1 + x)$ will be considered.

The fundamental property of the function e^x is that

$$\frac{d}{dx}(e^x) = e^x$$

If two assumptions are made:

(a) that e^x can be expanded as a series of ascending powers of x and
(b) that the nth derivative of such a series is the sum to infinity of the nth derivatives of the individual terms,

it is easy to find the coefficients of the terms in the series.

Suppose that

$$e^x = a_0 + a_1 x + a_2 x^2 + a_3 x^3 + \ldots + a_n x^n \ldots \qquad\qquad \text{. . . (1)}$$

Differentiating (1) once, twice, and three times respectively,

$$e^x = a_1 + 2a_2 x + 3a_3 x^2 + \ldots + na_n x^{n-1} + \ldots \qquad\qquad \text{. . . (2)}$$

$$e^x = 2a_2 + 3 \times 2a_3 x + \ldots + n(n-1)a_n x^{n-2} + \ldots \qquad \text{. . . (3)}$$

$$e^x = 3 \times 2a_3 + \ldots + n(n-1)(n-2)a_n x^{n-3} + \ldots \qquad \text{. . . (4)}$$

Differentiating (1) n times,

$$e^x = n!a_n + \ldots \qquad\qquad \ldots\ \ (5)$$

Now substituting $x = 0$ in (1), (2), (3), (4), (5),

$$1 = a_0$$
$$1 = a_1$$
$$1 = 2a_2$$
$$1 = 3 \times 2a_3$$
$$1 = n!a_n$$

Substituting the values we have just found for a_0, a_1, a_2, a_3, a_n into series (1),

$$e^x = 1 + x + \frac{x^2}{2!} + \frac{x^3}{3!} + \ldots + \frac{x^n}{n!} + \ldots$$

This series is often denoted by **exp x**. It can be shown that it is valid for all values of x.

Example 8

Find the value of e correct to four places of decimals.

Substituting $x = 1$ in the series for e^x,

$$e^1 = 1 + 1 + \frac{1}{2!} + \frac{1}{3!} + \ldots + \frac{1}{r!} + \ldots$$

The working is shown, although readers may prefer to use a calculator, if available. Each term in the series, after the first, is obtained from the previous one by dividing by 1, 2, 3, ..., 9, ... respectively. The working has been taken to five places of decimals. The value obtained for e is 2.7183, correct to four places of decimals.

1.000 00
1.000 00
0.500 00
0.166 67
0.041 67
0.008 33
0.001 39
0.000 20
0.000 02(5)
0.000 00
2.718 28

It can be shown that e is irrational, and it can also be shown that e is *transcendental*, that is, e satisfies no algebraic equation in the form:

$$a_0 + a_1 x + \ldots + a_n x^n = 0$$

where the coefficients $a_0, a_1, \ldots, a_n$ are integers.

Example 9

Find the first four terms in the expansions in ascending powers of x of
(a) e^{1-x^2} (b) e^{x-x^2}, giving the general term in (a).

(a) $e^{1-x^2} = e^1 \times e^{-x^2}$

$$= e\left\{1 + (-x^2) + \frac{(-x^2)^2}{2!} + \frac{(-x^2)^3}{3!} + \dots + \frac{(-x^2)^r}{r!} + \dots\right\}$$

$\therefore \quad e^{1-x^2} = e\{1 - x^2 + \tfrac{1}{2}x^4 - \tfrac{1}{6}x^6 + \dots + (-1)^r x^{2r}/r! + \dots\}$

(b) $e^{x-x^2} = 1 + (x - x^2) + \frac{(x - x^2)^2}{2!} + \frac{(x - x^2)^3}{3!} + \dots$

$$= 1 + x - x^2 + \tfrac{1}{2}x^2 - x^3 + \dots + \tfrac{1}{6}x^3 + \dots$$

$\therefore \quad e^{x-x^2} = 1 + x - \tfrac{1}{2}x^2 - \tfrac{5}{6}x^3 + \dots$

26.15 The logarithmic series

The geometric series $1 - u + u^2 - u^3 + \dots$ has a sum to infinity (see Section 14.6) of $1/(1 + u)$. So we may write:

$$\frac{1}{1 + u} = 1 - u + u^2 - u^3 + \dots$$

Assuming that the integral of the sum of an infinite series is the sum of the integrals of its terms, integrate between 0 and x:

$$\ln(1 + x) = x - \frac{x^2}{2} + \frac{x^3}{3} - \frac{x^4}{4} + \dots$$

The nth term of the geometric series is $(-1)^{n-1}u^{n-1}$ so that the nth term of the logarithm series is $(-1)^{n-1}x^n/n$. Since the geometric series only has a sum if $|u| < 1$, we should expect that the logarithmic series would be valid when $|x| < 1$ but it can also be shown that the series has a sum when $x = 1$. Thus

$$\ln(1 + x) = x - \frac{x^2}{2} + \frac{x^3}{3} - \dots + (-1)^{n-1}\frac{x^n}{n} + \dots$$

provided $-1 < x \leqslant 1$.

Note that if x is replaced by $-x$ in this series,

$$\ln(1 - x) = -x - \frac{x^2}{2} - \frac{x^3}{3} - \dots - \frac{x^n}{n} - \dots$$

provided $-1 \leqslant x < 1$.

Example 10

Expand as series in ascending powers of x:
(a) $\ln(2 + x)$ (b) $\ln(2 + x)^3$

(a) $\ln (2 + x) = \ln \{2(1 + \tfrac{1}{2}x)\}$
$\qquad\qquad = \ln 2 + \ln (1 + \tfrac{1}{2}x)$

$$= \ln 2 + \tfrac{1}{2}x - \frac{(\tfrac{1}{2}x)^2}{2} + \ldots + (-1)^{n-1}\frac{(\tfrac{1}{2}x)^n}{n} + \ldots$$

$\therefore \quad \ln (2 + x) = \ln 2 + \dfrac{x}{2} - \dfrac{x^2}{8} + \ldots + (-1)^{n-1}\dfrac{x^n}{2^n \times n} + \ldots$

The expansion is valid if $-1 < \tfrac{1}{2}x \leqslant 1$, i.e. if $-2 < x \leqslant 2$.

(b) $\ln (2 + x)^3 = 3 \ln (2 + x)$.

Therefore, using the result of part (a),

$$\ln (2 + x)^3 = 3 \ln 2 + \frac{3x}{2} - \frac{3x^2}{8} + \ldots + (-1)^{n-1}\frac{3x^n}{2^n \times n} + \ldots$$

Again, this expansion is valid if $-2 < x \leqslant 2$.

Other series have been devised for the calculation of logarithms and one of these will now be obtained.

$$\ln (1 + x) = \quad x - \frac{x^2}{2} + \frac{x^3}{3} - \frac{x^4}{4} + \ldots + \frac{x^{2n-1}}{2n-1} - \frac{x^{2n}}{2n} + \ldots$$

$$\ln (1 - x) = -x - \frac{x^2}{2} - \frac{x^3}{3} - \frac{x^4}{4} - \ldots - \frac{x^{2n-1}}{2n-1} - \frac{x^{2n}}{2n} - \ldots$$

The expansions are valid if $-1 < x \leqslant 1$, $-1 \leqslant x < 1$, respectively, so for both to be valid, $-1 < x < 1$.

Subtracting,

$$\ln \left(\frac{1+x}{1-x}\right) = 2 \left(x + \frac{x^3}{3} + \ldots + \frac{x^{2n-1}}{2n-1} + \ldots\right)$$

Dividing by 2 and writing

$$\frac{1}{2}\ln \left(\frac{1+x}{1-x}\right) = \ln \sqrt{\left(\frac{1+x}{1-x}\right)}$$

we obtain

$$\ln \sqrt{\left(\frac{1+x}{1-x}\right)} = x + \frac{x^3}{3} + \ldots + \frac{x^{2n-1}}{2n-1} + \ldots$$

provided $-1 < x < +1$.

The advantage of this series may be seen by attempting to calculate, say, ln 1.5 by two methods.

(a) Substitute $x = \tfrac{1}{2}$ in

$\ln (1 + x) = x - \tfrac{1}{2}x^2 + \tfrac{1}{3}x^3 - \ldots + (-1)^{n-1}x^n/n + \ldots$

$\ln 1.5 \quad = \tfrac{1}{2} - \tfrac{1}{8} + \tfrac{1}{24} - \tfrac{1}{64} + \tfrac{1}{160} - \tfrac{1}{384} + \tfrac{1}{896} - \tfrac{1}{2048} + \ldots$

(b) Substitute $x = \frac{1}{5}$ in

$$\ln\left(\frac{1+x}{1-x}\right) = 2\left\{x + \frac{1}{3}x^3 + \frac{1}{5}x^5 + \ldots + x^{2n-1}/(2n-1) + \ldots\right\}$$

$\ln 1.5 \qquad = 2(\frac{1}{5} + \frac{1}{375} + \frac{1}{15625} + \ldots)$

$\qquad\qquad = 0.4055 \qquad$ to four places of decimals

It is clear that the value correct to four places of decimals can be obtained far more rapidly by the second series.

Note that, using $\lg 1.5 = \lg e \times \ln 1.5$, the value of $\lg 1.5$ can be obtained.

Exercise 26f

1 Use the expansion $\exp x$ to find the values of:
(a) $e^{0.1}$ (b) $1/e$ (c) $\sqrt{e}$
giving your answers correct to four places of decimals.

In nos. 2–5, expand the functions of x as far as the fourth non-zero terms and give the general terms:

2 e^{x^3} **3** $\sqrt[3]{(e^x)}$ **4** $(1/e^x)^2$ **5** e^{2+x}
6 Expand the following functions in ascending powers of x, giving the first three or four terms, as indicated, and the general term. State the ranges of values of x for which the expansions are valid.
(a) $\ln(3+x)$, (4)   (b) $\ln(1-\frac{1}{2}x)$, (4)   (c) $\ln(2-5x)$, (4)

(d) $\ln(1-x^2)$, (4)   (e) $\ln\left(\frac{3+x}{3-x}\right)$, (3)   (f) $\ln\left(\frac{4-3x}{4+3x}\right)$, (3)

Find the first three terms and the general terms in the expansions of the functions below. State the necessary restrictions on the values of x.

7 $\ln\left(\frac{2-x}{3-x}\right)$ **8** $\ln\frac{1}{3-4x-4x^2}$

9 $\ln\left\{\frac{(1+4x)^3}{(1+3x)^4}\right\}$ **10** $\ln\sqrt{(x^2+3x+2)}$

Exercise 26g (Miscellaneous)

1 Prove that $\log_a b = 1/(\log_b a)$, where $a, b \in \mathbb{R}^+$. Solve the equation

$$\log_2 x + \log_x 2 = 2.5$$

2 Prove that $\log_a x = \frac{\log_b x}{\log_b a}$.

Given that $\lg 3 = 0.4771$ and that $\lg e = 0.4343$, calculate the value of $\ln 0.3$, giving your answer correct to three significant figures.

3 Given that $2 \log_y x + 2 \log_x y = 5$, show that $\log_y x$ is either $\frac{1}{2}$ or 2. Hence find all pairs of values of x and y which satisfy simultaneously the equation above and the equation $xy = 27$.   (JMB)

4 (a) The functions f_1 and f_2, each with domain $D = \{x: x \in \mathbb{R}, x > -1\}$, are defined by

$$f_1(x) = \ln (x + 1) \qquad f_2(x) = x^2 + 1$$

For each function state the range. Show that an inverse function f_1^{-1} exists and, using the same axes, sketch the graphs of $y = f_1(x)$ and $y = f_1^{-1}(x)$. Show that an inverse function f_2^{-1} does not exist and suggest an interval such that f_2, restricted to this interval, will have an inverse function.

   (b) Functions g_1 and g_2, each with domain $\mathbb{R}$, are defined by

$$g_1(x) = \ln (1 + x^2) \qquad g_2(x) = 1 + x$$

Given that $g_1 g_2$ and $g_2 g_1$ are the composite functions defined on $\mathbb{R}$, find expressions for $g_1 g_2(x)$ and $g_2 g_1(x)$ and state whether each of these functions is odd, even or neither.   (L)

5 Functions f and g are defined as follows:

$$f: x \mapsto e^{-x} \quad (x \in \mathbb{R}^+) \qquad g: x \mapsto \frac{1}{1 - x} \quad (x \in \mathbb{R}, x < 1)$$

Give the ranges of f, g and gf.

Give definitions of the inverse functions f^{-1}, g^{-1} and $(gf)^{-1}$ in a form similar to the above definitions.   (C)

6 Show, by means of a sketch graph, or otherwise, that the equation

$$e^{2x} + 4x - 5 = 0$$

has only one real root, and that this root lies between 0 and 1.
Starting with the value 0.5 as a first approximation to this root, use the Newton-Raphson method to evaluate successive approximations, showing the stages of your work and ending when two successive approximations give answers which, when rounded to two decimal places, agree.   (C)

7 The function f with domain $\mathbb{R}$ is defined by $f(x) = e^{\cos x}$.
   (a) Prove that f is periodic and state the period.
   (b) Determine whether f is an odd function, an even function or a function which is neither odd nor even.
   (c) Sketch the graph of $y = e^{\cos x}$ for $-2\pi \leqslant x \leqslant 2\pi$.
   (d) State, with reason, whether the inverse function f^{-1} exists.
   (e) If f^{-1} does not exist, determine a subset D of $\mathbb{R}$ which is the domain of a function g, with $g(x) = f(x)$, $x \in D$, and g^{-1} exists.   (L)

Chapter 27

Partial fractions

27.1 Introduction

When we add algebraic fractions, $\dfrac{1}{x-1}+\dfrac{1}{x+1}$ for example, we first find the common denominator, $(x-1)(x+1)$ in this case, and proceed as follows:

$$\frac{1}{x-1}+\frac{1}{x+1}=\frac{x+1}{(x-1)(x+1)}+\frac{x-1}{(x-1)(x+1)}$$

$$=\frac{x+1+x-1}{(x-1)(x+1)}$$

$$=\frac{2x}{(x-1)(x+1)}$$

We have now reached the stage when the reverse process is of value. Given a fraction such as $\dfrac{5}{x^2+x-6}$ whose denominator factorises, we may split it up into its component fractions, writing it as $\dfrac{1}{x-2}-\dfrac{1}{x+3}$; it is now said to be in **partial fractions**. Just one example of the several applications of this must suffice for the present. No change of variable yet discussed would enable us to find $\displaystyle\int\frac{5}{(x-2)(x+3)}\,dx$ as it stands, but using partial fractions,

$$\int\frac{5}{(x-2)(x+3)}\,dx=\int\left\{\frac{1}{x-2}-\frac{1}{x+3}\right\}dx$$

$$=\ln(x-2)-\ln(x+3)+c$$

$$=\ln\left\{\frac{k(x-2)}{x+3}\right\}$$

Qu. 1 Express each of the following as a single fraction:

(a) $\dfrac{1}{1-x}+\dfrac{2}{1+x}$ (b) $\dfrac{2x-1}{x^2+1}-\dfrac{1}{x+1}$ (c) $\dfrac{3}{(x-1)^2}+\dfrac{1}{x-1}+\dfrac{2}{x+1}$

557

Qu. 2 Express in partial fractions:

(a) $\dfrac{4}{(x-2)(x+2)}$ (b) $\dfrac{1}{1-x^2}$ (c) $\dfrac{1}{2\times 3}$ (d) $\dfrac{1}{n(n+1)}$

Unfortunately most partial fractions cannot be obtained by trial and error quite as easily as those in Qu. 2. The reader need only consider attempting Qu. 1 in reverse, to be convinced that we need some technique to find partial fractions; we shall find that this involves us in handling algebraic identities, so we must discuss these briefly.

27.2 Identities

Let us first distinguish clearly between an *equation* and an *identity*. $x^2 = 4$ is an *equation*, which is satisfied only by the two values $x = \pm 2$. But

$$x^2 - 4 \equiv (x+2)(x-2)$$

and

$$x^2 + 2x - 2 \equiv (x+1)(x-1) + 2(x+1) - 3$$

are both **identities**, and for them the L.H.S. = R.H.S. *for any value of* x; moreover, if the R.H.S. is multiplied out, the coefficients of x^2, x and the constant term will be identical on each side.

Example 1

Find the values of the constants A, B, C such that

$$5x + 3 \equiv Ax(x+3) + Bx(x-1) + C(x-1)(x+3)$$

First method
Collecting like terms on the R.H.S.

$$5x + 3 \equiv (A+B+C)x^2 + (3A-B+2C)x - 3C$$

Equating coefficients of x^2,

$$0 = A + B + C \qquad \qquad \text{. . . (1)}$$

Equating coefficients of x,

$$5 = 3A - B + 2C \qquad \qquad \text{. . . (2)}$$

Equating constant terms,

$$3 = -3C \qquad \qquad \text{. . . (3)}$$

From (3), $C = -1$, and substituting this value into (1) and (2), and solving these equations simultaneously, we obtain $A = 2$, and $B = -1$.

Second method

$$5x + 3 \equiv Ax\,(x + 3) + Bx(x - 1) \quad + C(x - 1)(x + 3)$$

Putting $x = 0$,

$$3 = \quad 0 \quad + \quad 0 \quad - \quad 3C\dagger$$
$$\therefore \qquad C = -1$$

Putting $x = -3$,

$$-15 + 3 = \quad 0 \quad + B(-3)(-4) + \quad 0$$
$$\therefore \qquad -12 = \quad 12B$$
$$\therefore \qquad B = -1$$

Putting $x = 1$,

$$5 + 3 = A \times 1 \times 4 + \quad 0 \quad + \quad 0$$
$$\therefore \qquad A = 2$$

It should be noted that the identity holds for *any* value of x, but we have chosen those particular values which make all but one term on the R.H.S. vanish each time.

Qu. 3 $2x^2 + 9x - 10 \equiv A(x - 3)(x + 4) + B(x + 2)(x + 4) + C(x + 2)(x - 3)$.
(a) Obtain three equations in A, B, C by substituting $x = -1$, 0, 1 in this identity.
(b) Find the values of A, B, C by substituting more convenient values of x.
Qu. 4 Find the values of the constants A, B, C in the following identities:
(a) $22 - 4x - 2x^2 \equiv A(x - 1)^2 + B(x - 1)(x + 3) + C(x + 3)$, using the first method in Example 1,
(b) $5x + 31 \equiv A(x + 2)(x - 1) + B(x - 1)(x - 5) + C(x - 5)(x + 2)$, using the second method in Example 1,
(c) $13x - 11 \equiv A(3x - 2) + B(2x + 1)$.
Qu. 5 Put $x = 1$ to find the value of A in the identity

$$x^2 + x + 7 \equiv A(x^2 + 2) + (Bx + C)(x - 1)$$

Now substitute any other values of x to find B and C.

The substitution method is fast, but often it may be combined with the method of equating coefficients for greater speed and simplicity (e.g. having found A in Qu. 5, equate coefficients of x^2 to find B). The latter method also gives us a deeper insight into the nature of identities. Let us consider the statement

$$x^2 - 5x + 8 \equiv A(x + 3) + B(x - 1)^2$$

Applying the method of substitution we obtain $A = 1$, $B = 2$; however, when A and B are given these values we do *not* have an identity!

This apparently alarming breakdown is readily explained when we apply the method of equating coefficients. This shows that for only *two* unknowns we

† This should be compared with equation (3) on page 558.

have the *three* equations, $B = 1$, $A - 2B = -5$, and $3A + B = 8$, which are not consistent. Thus we cannot find values for A and B to form the 'identity' given above.

Since we shall soon be concerned with forming identities, the method of equating coefficients will be a valuable check that the number of unknown constants introduced corresponds to the number of equations to be satisfied.

Qu. 6 Can values of A, B, C be found which make the following pairs of expressions identical?
(a) $2x + 3$ and $A(x + 1)(x - 2) + B(x + 1)^2 + C$,
(b) $x^2 - 8x + 30$ and $A(x - 3)^2 + B(x + 2)$.

Exercise 27a

1 Express each of the following as a single fraction:

(a) $\dfrac{3}{x + 3} - \dfrac{2}{x - 2}$ (b) $\dfrac{1}{(x + 2)^2} - \dfrac{2}{x + 2} + \dfrac{1}{3x - 1}$

(c) $\dfrac{4}{2 + 3x^2} - \dfrac{1}{1 - x}$ (d) $\dfrac{3}{x^2 + 1} - \dfrac{1}{x - 1} + \dfrac{2}{(x - 1)^2}$

2 Express in partial fractions:

(a) $\dfrac{2x}{(3 + x)(3 - x)}$ (b) $\dfrac{a}{a^2 - b^2}$ (c) $\dfrac{1}{5 \times 6}$ (d) $\dfrac{1}{p(1 - p)}$

3 Use the first method of Example 1 to find the values of the constants A, B, C in the following identities:
(a) $31x - 8 \equiv A(x - 5) + B(4x + 1)$
(b) $8 - x \equiv A(x - 2)^2 + B(x - 2)(x + 1) + C(x + 1)$
(c) $71 + 9x - 2x^2 \equiv A(x + 5)(x + 2) + B(x + 2)(x - 3) + C(x - 3)(x + 5)$
(d) $2x^3 - 15x^2 - 10 \equiv A(x - 2)(x + 1) + B(x + 1)(2x^2 + 1) + C(2x^2 + 1)(x - 2)$

4 Use the second method of Example 1 to find the values of the constants A, B, C in the following identities:
(a) $2x - 4 \equiv A(3 + x) + B(7 - x)$
(b) $8x + 1 \equiv A(3x - 1) + B(2x + 3)$
(c) $4x^2 + 4x - 26 \equiv A(x + 2)(x - 4) + B(x - 4)(x - 1) + C(x - 1)(x + 2)$
(d) $17x^2 - 13x - 16 \equiv A(3x + 1)(x - 1) + B(x - 1)(2x - 3) + C(2x - 3)(3x + 1)$

5 Can values of A, B, C, D be found which make the following pairs of expressions identical?
(a) $2x^2 - 22x + 53$ and $A(x - 5)(x - 3) + B(x - 3)(x + 2) + C(x + 2)(x - 5)$
(b) $x + 7$ and $A(x - 2) + B(x + 1)^2$
(c) $3x^2 + 7x + 11$ and $(Ax + B)(x + 2) + C(x^2 + 5)$
(d) $x + 1$ and $A(x - 2) + B(x^2 + 1)$
(e) $x^3 + 2x^2 - 4x - 2$ and $(Ax + B)(x - 2)(x + 1) + C(x + 1) + D(x - 2)$

6 Find the values of A, B, C if $x^3 - 1$ is expressed in the form
$$(x - 1)(Ax^2 + Bx + C)$$
Factorise:
(a) $x^3 + 1$ (b) $x^3 - 8$ (c) $x^3 + 27$ (d) $8x^3 - 27$ (e) $27x^3 + 125$

27.3 Type I – denominator with only linear factors

We shall find that in the more straightforward cases which we have to deal with at this stage, partial fractions fall into three main types; each will be illustrated by a worked example, and the reader is strongly advised to work through the questions following each of these, before going on to consider the next type.

In practice, a question of considerable length and complexity may depend upon the correct determination of partial fractions in the early stages; to avoid fruitless labour at a later date, the habit of *checking* partial fractions should be firmly established from the start, and they should be combined into one fraction mentally, the numerator obtained being checked with the original.

First we deal with a fraction whose denominator consists of only linear factors.

Example 2

Express $\dfrac{11x + 12}{(2x + 3)(x + 2)(x - 3)}$ in partial fractions.

Let $\dfrac{11x + 12}{(2x + 3)(x + 2)(x - 3)} \equiv \dfrac{A}{2x + 3} + \dfrac{B}{x + 2} + \dfrac{C}{x - 3}$

where A, B, C are constants to be found. It follows that:

$$\dfrac{11x + 12}{(2x + 3)(x + 2)(x - 3)}$$

$$\equiv \dfrac{A(x + 2)(x - 3) + B(x - 3)(2x + 3) + C(2x + 3)(x + 2)}{(2x + 3)(x + 2)(x - 3)}$$

$\therefore \quad 11x + 12 \equiv A(x + 2)(x - 3) + B(x - 3)(2x + 3) + C(2x + 3)(x + 2)$

Putting $x = 3$,

$$33 + 12 = \quad\quad 0 \quad\quad + \quad\quad 0 \quad\quad + C \times 9 \times 5$$
$$\therefore \quad\quad C = 1$$

Putting $x = -2$,

$$-22 + 12 = \quad\quad 0 \quad\quad + B \times (-5) \times (-1) + \quad\quad 0$$
$$\therefore \quad\quad -10 = 5B$$
$$\therefore \quad\quad B = -2$$

Putting $x = -\frac{3}{2}$,

$$-\tfrac{33}{2} + 12 = A \times \tfrac{1}{2} \times \tfrac{-9}{2} \quad + \quad 0 \quad + \quad 0$$
$$\therefore \quad\quad -\tfrac{9}{2} = -\tfrac{9}{4}A$$
$$\therefore \quad\quad A = 2$$

$$\therefore \quad \dfrac{11x + 12}{(2x + 3)(x + 2)(x - 3)} \equiv \dfrac{2}{2x + 3} - \dfrac{2}{x + 2} + \dfrac{1}{x - 3}$$

$$\left[\text{Since} \quad \text{R.H.S.} \equiv \frac{2(x+2)(x-3) - 2(x-3)(2x+3) + (2x+3)(x+2)}{(2x+3)(x+2)(x-3)} \right.$$

we check the coefficients in the numerator. $\Big]$

Check   Coefficient of $x^2 = 2 - 4 + 2 = 0$
          Coefficient of $x = -2 + 6 + 7 = 11$
          Constant term $= -12 + 18 + 6 = 12$

Qu. 7 Express in partial fractions:

(a) $\dfrac{6}{(x+3)(x-3)}$ (b) $\dfrac{x}{(2+x)(2-x)}$ (c) $\dfrac{x-1}{3x^2 - 11x + 10}$

(d) $\dfrac{3x+1}{(x+2)(x+1)(x-3)}$ (e) $\dfrac{3-4x}{2+3x-2x^2}$

27.4 Type II – denominator with a quadratic factor

Fractions which can be split solely into partial fractions are necessarily *proper*, by which is meant that *the degree of the numerator is less than the degree of the denominator**. Moreover, the partial fractions themselves are always proper.

Bearing this in mind we can now discover how to deal with a fraction having in the denominator a quadratic factor which does not factorise.

Let $\dfrac{3x+1}{(x-1)(x^2+1)} \equiv \dfrac{A}{x-1} + \dfrac{\textit{numerator}}{x^2+1}$

Then $3x + 1 \equiv A(x^2 + 1) + \textit{numerator} \times (x-1)$

From our previous work on identities, we see, by equating coefficients that there are *three* equations to be satisfied. It follows that there are *three* constants to determine,† and therefore the *numerator* must contain two of them; thus the only way to write the second partial fraction, so that it is proper, is in the form

$$\frac{Bx + C}{x^2 + 1}$$

* With an improper fraction, we divide first, and we obtain a quotient and partial fraction, thus

$$\frac{x^2 + x + 1}{(x-1)(x+2)} \equiv 1 + \frac{3}{(x-1)(x+2)} \equiv 1 + \frac{1}{x-1} - \frac{1}{x+2},$$

and

$$\frac{x^3 + 2x^2 - 7x - 18}{x^2 - 9} \equiv x + 2 + \frac{2x}{(x+3)(x-3)} \equiv x + 2 + \frac{1}{x+3} + \frac{1}{x-3}.$$

† In general, the number of constants to be found is the same as the degree of the denominator of the original fraction.

Example 3

Express $\dfrac{3x+1}{(x-1)(x^2+1)}$ in partial fractions.

Let $\quad \dfrac{3x+1}{(x-1)(x^2+1)} \equiv \dfrac{A}{x-1} + \dfrac{Bx+C}{x^2+1}$

$\therefore \qquad\qquad 3x+1 \equiv A(x^2+1) + (Bx+C)(x-1)$

Putting $x=1$: $\quad 4 = 2A+0 \qquad \therefore \quad A=2$

Putting $x=0$: $\quad 1 = A-C \qquad \therefore \quad 1 = 2-C \qquad \therefore \quad C=1$

Equating coefficients of x^2: $\quad 0 = A+B \qquad \therefore \quad B=-2$

$\therefore \quad \dfrac{3x+1}{(x-1)(x^2+1)} \equiv \dfrac{2}{x-1} + \dfrac{1-2x}{x^2+1} \equiv \dfrac{2}{x-1} - \dfrac{2x-1}{x^2+1}$

Check   Coefficient of $x^2 = 2-2 = 0$
              Coefficient of $x = -(-2-1) = +3$
              Constant term $= 2-1 = +1$

Qu. 8 Express in partial fractions:

(a) $\dfrac{6-x}{(1-x)(4+x^2)}$ (b) $\dfrac{4}{(x+1)(2x^2+x+3)}$

(c) $\dfrac{5x+2}{(x+1)(x^2-4)}$ (d) $\dfrac{3+2x}{(2-x)(3+x^2)}$

27.5 Type III – denominator with a repeated factor

Here we take as an example $\dfrac{1}{(x+2)(x-1)^2}$.

Written as $\dfrac{1}{(x+2)(x^2-2x+1)}$ this suggests Type II and the partial

fractions $\dfrac{A}{x+2} + \dfrac{Bx+K}{x^2-2x+1}$. Certainly we have the correct number of con-

stants to be found to identify this expression with the original fraction; however, the denominator of the second partial fraction factorises, and so we have not gone far enough.

$$\dfrac{Bx+K}{(x-1)^2} \equiv \dfrac{B(x-1)+B+K}{(x-1)^2}$$

$$\equiv \dfrac{B}{x-1} + \dfrac{B+K}{(x-1)^2}$$

Writing C for $B + K$, we obtain

$$\frac{Bx + K}{(x - 1)^2} \equiv \frac{B}{x - 1} + \frac{C}{(x - 1)^2}$$

This indicates the appropriate form when we have a repeated factor. (See also Qu. 10.)

Example 4

Express $\dfrac{1}{(x + 2)(x - 1)^2}$ in partial fractions.

Let $\dfrac{1}{(x + 2)(x - 1)^2} \equiv \dfrac{A}{x + 2} + \dfrac{B}{x - 1} + \dfrac{C}{(x - 1)^2}$

$\therefore \quad \dfrac{1}{(x + 2)(x - 1)^2} \equiv \dfrac{A(x - 1)^2 + B(x - 1)(x + 2) + C(x + 2)}{(x + 2)(x - 1)^2}$

$\therefore \qquad 1 \equiv A(x - 1)^2 + B(x - 1)(x + 2) + C(x + 2)$

Putting $x = -2$: $1 = 9A$ $\therefore$ $A = \frac{1}{9}$

Putting $x = 1$: $1 = 3C$ $\therefore$ $C = \frac{1}{3}$

Equating coefficients of x^2: $0 = A + B$ $\therefore$ $B = -\frac{1}{9}$

$\therefore \quad \dfrac{1}{(x + 2)(x - 1)^2} \equiv \dfrac{1}{9(x + 2)} - \dfrac{1}{9(x - 1)} + \dfrac{1}{3(x - 1)^2}$

Check   Expressing the R.H.S. as a single fraction with denominator $(x + 2)(x - 1)^2$, the numerator is
$\frac{1}{9}\{(x - 1)^2 - (x + 2)(x - 1) + 3(x + 2)\}$.

Coefficient of $x^2 = \frac{1}{9}(1 - 1) = 0$
Coefficient of $x = \frac{1}{9}(-2 - 1 + 3) = 0$
Constant term $= \frac{1}{9}(1 + 2 + 6) = 1$

Qu. 9 Express in partial fractions:

(a) $\dfrac{x + 1}{(x + 3)^2}$ (b) $\dfrac{2x^2 - 5x + 7}{(x - 2)(x - 1)^2}$

Qu. 10 Find the values of A, B, C, D, if

$$\frac{x^3 - 10x^2 + 26x + 3}{(x + 3)(x - 1)^3} \equiv \frac{A}{x + 3} + \frac{B}{x - 1} + \frac{C}{(x - 1)^2} + \frac{D}{(x - 1)^3}$$

27.6 Improper fractions

As already implied, an *improper* fraction is one whose *numerator is of degree equal to, or greater than, that of the denominator*. To deal with this we first divide the numerator to obtain a quotient and a proper fraction, and then split the latter into partial fractions. Thus

$$\frac{x^4 - 2x^3 - x^2 - 4x + 4}{(x-3)(x^2+1)} \equiv x + 1 + \frac{x^2 - 2x + 7}{(x-3)(x^2+1)}, \text{ etc.}$$

Often, instead of doing long division, it is quicker to proceed as follows:

$$\frac{2x^2+1}{(x-1)(x+2)} \equiv \frac{2(x^2+x-2)-2x+5}{x^2+x-2} \equiv 2 + \frac{5-2x}{(x-1)(x+2)}, \text{ etc.}$$

Qu. 11 Express the following in the form of a quotient and a proper fraction:

(a) $\dfrac{x^3 + 2x^2 - 2x + 2}{(x-1)(x+3)}$

(b) $\dfrac{3x^2 - 2x - 7}{(x-2)(x+1)}$

Qu. 12 Express in partial fractions:

(a) $\dfrac{x^2 - 7}{(x-2)(x+1)}$ (b) $\dfrac{x^3 - x^2 - 4x + 1}{x^2 - 4}$

Exercise 27b

Express in partial fractions:

1 (a) $\dfrac{x-11}{(x+3)(x-4)}$ (b) $\dfrac{x}{25-x^2}$

(c) $\dfrac{3x^2 - 21x + 24}{(x+1)(x-2)(x-3)}$ (d) $\dfrac{4x^2 + x + 1}{x(x^2-1)}$

2 (a) $\dfrac{5x^2 - 10x + 11}{(x-3)(x^2+4)}$ (b) $\dfrac{2x^2 - x + 3}{(x+1)(x^2+2)}$

(c) $\dfrac{3x^2 - 2x + 5}{(x-1)(x^2+5)}$ (d) $\dfrac{11x}{(2x-3)(2x^2+1)}$

3 (a) $\dfrac{x-5}{(x-2)^2}$ (b) $\dfrac{5x+4}{(x-1)(x+2)^2}$

(c) $\dfrac{5x^2+2}{(3x+1)(x+1)^2}$ (d) $\dfrac{x^4 + 3x - 1}{(x+2)(x-1)^2}$

4 (a) $\dfrac{3x^3 + x + 1}{(x-2)(x+1)^3}$ (see Qu. 10)   (b) $\dfrac{3x^2 + 2x - 9}{(x^2-1)^2}$

5 (a) $\dfrac{x^3 + 2x^2 - 10x - 9}{x^2 - 9}$ (b) $\dfrac{3(x^2-3)}{(x-1)(x+2)}$

6 $\dfrac{3x+7}{x(x+2)(x-1)}$ **7** $\dfrac{3}{x^2(x+2)}$ **8** $\dfrac{68+11x}{(3+x)(16-x^2)}$

9 $\dfrac{2x+1}{x^3-1}$ **10** $\dfrac{2x^2+39x+12}{(2x+1)^2(x-3)}$

27.7 Summation of series

An introduction to the summation of series was given in Chapter 14. There are some series which may be summed by the use of partial fractions; the method of application is illustrated in the following example.

Example 5

(a) Express $\dfrac{2}{n(n+1)(n+2)}$ in partial fractions, and (b) deduce that

$$\frac{1}{1\times2\times3}+\frac{1}{2\times3\times4}+\ldots+\frac{1}{n(n+1)(n+2)}=\frac{1}{4}-\frac{1}{2(n+1)(n+2)}$$

(a) Let $\dfrac{2}{n(n+1)(n+2)}\equiv\dfrac{A}{n}+\dfrac{B}{n+1}+\dfrac{C}{n+2}$

$\therefore$ $2\equiv A(n+1)(n+2)+B(n+2)n+Cn(n+1)$

Putting $n=0$: $2=2A$ $\therefore$ $A=1$

Putting $n=-1$: $2=-B$ $\therefore$ $B=-2$

Putting $n=-2$: $2=2C$ $\therefore$ $C=1$

$\therefore$ $\dfrac{2}{n(n+1)(n+2)}\equiv\dfrac{1}{n}-\dfrac{2}{n+1}+\dfrac{1}{n+2}$

Check   Coefficient of $n^2=1-2+1=0$
          Coefficient of $n=3-4+1=0$
          Constant term $=2$

(b) If $S=\dfrac{1}{1\times2\times3}+\dfrac{1}{2\times3\times4}+\ldots+\dfrac{1}{n(n+1)(n+2)}$

$2S\equiv\dfrac{2}{1\times2\times3}+\dfrac{2}{2\times3\times4}+\ldots+\dfrac{2}{n(n+1)(n+2)}$

[From part (a) it follows that

$$2S\equiv\left(\frac{1}{1}-\frac{2}{2}+\frac{1}{3}\right)+\left(\frac{1}{2}-\frac{2}{3}+\frac{1}{4}\right)+\left(\frac{1}{3}-\frac{2}{4}+\frac{1}{5}\right)+\ldots$$

$$+\left(\frac{1}{n}-\frac{2}{n+1}+\frac{1}{n+2}\right)$$

We see that the majority of terms when grouped three together in a different way, such as $\frac{1}{3} - \frac{2}{3} + \frac{1}{3}$, have zero sum. We then have to pick out those terms which remain at the beginning and at the end, and this is most easily done if we set out the working in columns.]

From part (a)
$$\frac{2}{1 \times 2 \times 3} = \frac{1}{1} - \frac{2}{2} + \frac{1}{3}$$

$$\frac{2}{2 \times 3 \times 4} = \frac{1}{2} - \frac{2}{3} + \frac{1}{4}$$

$$\frac{2}{3 \times 4 \times 5} = \frac{1}{3} - \frac{2}{4} + \frac{1}{5}$$

. . . .

$$\frac{2}{(n-2)(n-1)n} = \frac{1}{n-2} - \frac{2}{n-1} + \frac{1}{n}$$

$$\frac{2}{(n-1)n(n+1)} = \frac{1}{n-1} - \frac{2}{n} + \frac{1}{n+1}$$

$$\frac{2}{n(n+1)(n+2)} = \frac{1}{n} - \frac{2}{n+1} + \frac{1}{n+2}$$

Adding,
$$2S = \frac{1}{2} - \frac{1}{n+1} + \frac{1}{n+2}$$

$$= \frac{1}{2} - \frac{1}{(n+1)(n+2)}$$

$$S = \frac{1}{4} - \frac{1}{2(n+1)(n+2)}$$

The reader should also note that as $n \to \infty$, $\dfrac{1}{2(n+1)(n+2)} \to 0$.

Thus the infinite series $\dfrac{1}{1 \times 2 \times 3} + \dfrac{1}{2 \times 3 \times 4} + \dfrac{1}{3 \times 4 \times 5} + \ldots$

is *convergent*, and its *sum to infinity* is $\frac{1}{4}$ (see Section 15.4).

Qu. 13 Show that $\dfrac{1}{1 \times 2} + \dfrac{1}{2 \times 3} + \dfrac{1}{3 \times 4} + \ldots + \dfrac{1}{n(n+1)} = 1 - \dfrac{1}{n+1}$.

27.8 Integration

We have already shown in Section 27.1 how partial fractions may be applied to integration. Two more examples follow.

Example 6

Find $\int \dfrac{2x-1}{(x+1)^2}\,dx.$

Let $\dfrac{2x-1}{(x+1)^2} \equiv \dfrac{A}{x+1} + \dfrac{B}{(x+1)^2}$

We find that $A = 2 \qquad B = -3$

$\therefore \quad \displaystyle\int \dfrac{2x-1}{(x+1)^2}\,dx = \int \left\{ \dfrac{2}{x+1} - \dfrac{3}{(x+1)^2} \right\} dx$

$$= 2\ln(x+1) + 3(x+1)^{-1} + c$$

Qu. 14 Find (a) $\displaystyle\int \dfrac{1}{x^2-9}\,dx$ (b) $\displaystyle\int \dfrac{2x+2}{(2x-3)^2}\,dx$

Qu. 15 (a) Find $\displaystyle\int \dfrac{x}{4-x^2}\,dx$ without using partial fractions.

(b) Find this integral using partial fractions.

Example 7

Evaluate $\displaystyle\int_{2}^{3} \dfrac{5+x}{(1-x)(5+x^2)}\,dx$ correct to three significant figures.

Let $\dfrac{5+x}{(1-x)(5+x^2)} \equiv \dfrac{A}{1-x} + \dfrac{Bx+C}{5+x^2}$

We find that $A = 1 \qquad B = 1 \qquad C = 0$

$\therefore \quad \displaystyle\int_{2}^{3} \dfrac{5+x}{(1-x)(5+x^2)}\,dx = \int_{2}^{3} \left\{ \dfrac{1}{1-x} + \dfrac{x}{5+x^2} \right\} dx$

$$= \left[-\ln(x-1) + \tfrac{1}{2}\ln(5+x^2) \right]_{2}^{3}$$

$$= (-\ln 2 + \tfrac{1}{2}\ln 14) - (-\ln 1 + \tfrac{1}{2}\ln 9)$$
$$= \tfrac{1}{2}\ln 14 - \ln 2 - \ln 3$$
$$= -0.472$$

(correct to three significant figures)

Example 7 also revises an important point. If $x < 1$,

$$\int \dfrac{1}{1-x}\,dx = -\ln(1-x) + c$$

However, if $x > 1$, as the limits show to be the case here,

$$\int \frac{1}{1-x} dx = -\ln(x-1) + c \qquad \text{(See Section 26.12.)}$$

Both cases can be covered by writing

$$\int \frac{1}{1-x} dx = -\ln|1-x| + c$$

Qu. 16 Can $\displaystyle\int_0^2 \frac{5+x}{(1-x)(5+x^2)} dx$ be evaluated?

Qu. 17 Evaluate (a) $\displaystyle\int_2^3 \frac{x-4}{(x+2)(x-1)} dx$ \qquad (b) $\displaystyle\int_1^2 \frac{3x^2+2x+2}{(x+1)(x^2+2)} dx$

Exercise 27c

1 Express $\dfrac{2}{n(n+2)}$ in partial fractions, and deduce that

$$\frac{2}{1\times 3} + \frac{2}{2\times 4} + \frac{2}{3\times 5} + \dots + \frac{2}{n(n+2)} = \frac{3}{2} - \frac{2n+3}{(n+1)(n+2)}$$

2 Express $\dfrac{n+3}{(n-1)n(n+1)}$ in partial fractions, and deduce that

$$\frac{5}{1\times 2\times 3} + \frac{6}{2\times 3\times 4} + \frac{7}{3\times 4\times 5} + \dots + \frac{n+3}{(n-1)n(n+1)} = \frac{3}{2} - \frac{n+2}{n(n+1)}$$

3 For the series given in no. 2 write down (a) the nth term, (b) the sum of the first n terms, (c) the limit of this sum as $n \to \infty$.

4 Prove that the series $\dfrac{2}{1\times 2} + \dfrac{2}{2\times 3} + \dfrac{2}{3\times 4} + \dots$ is convergent, and find its sum to infinity.

5 Find the sum of the first n terms of the following series:

(a) $\dfrac{1}{1\times 4} + \dfrac{1}{2\times 5} + \dfrac{1}{3\times 6} + \dots$

(b) $\dfrac{1}{2\times 4} + \dfrac{1}{4\times 6} + \dfrac{1}{6\times 8} + \dots$

(c) $\dfrac{1}{3\times 6} + \dfrac{1}{6\times 9} + \dfrac{1}{9\times 12} + \dots$

(d) $\dfrac{1}{2\times 6} + \dfrac{1}{4\times 8} + \dfrac{1}{6\times 10} + \dots$

(e) $\dfrac{1}{1\times 3\times 5} + \dfrac{1}{2\times 4\times 6} + \dfrac{1}{3\times 5\times 7} + \dots$

(f) $\dfrac{1}{3 \times 4 \times 5} + \dfrac{2}{4 \times 5 \times 6} + \dfrac{3}{5 \times 6 \times 7} + \ldots$

6 Find the sum of the first n terms of the following series, remembering that $2n - 1$, $2n + 1$, etc. are odd for all integral values of n:

(a) $\dfrac{2}{1 \times 3} + \dfrac{2}{3 \times 5} + \dfrac{2}{5 \times 7} + \ldots$

(b) $\dfrac{1}{1 \times 3 \times 5} + \dfrac{1}{3 \times 5 \times 7} + \dfrac{1}{5 \times 7 \times 9} + \ldots$

(c) $\dfrac{2}{1 \times 3 \times 5} + \dfrac{3}{3 \times 5 \times 7} + \dfrac{4}{5 \times 7 \times 9} + \ldots$

7 Find the following integrals:

(a) $\displaystyle\int \dfrac{1}{x(x-2)}\,dx$

(b) $\displaystyle\int \dfrac{1}{(x+3)(5x-2)}\,dx$

(c) $\displaystyle\int \dfrac{7x+2}{3x^3 + x^2}\,dx$

(d) $\displaystyle\int \dfrac{x}{16 - x^2}\,dx$

(e) $\displaystyle\int \dfrac{1}{x^2 - 4x - 5}\,dx$

(f) $\displaystyle\int \dfrac{x-2}{x^2 - 4x - 5}\,dx$

(g) $\displaystyle\int \dfrac{2x^2 + 2x + 3}{(x+2)(x^2+3)}\,dx$

(h) $\displaystyle\int \dfrac{22 - 16x}{(3+x)(2-x)(4-x)}\,dx$

(i) $\displaystyle\int \dfrac{4x - 33}{(2x+1)(x^2-9)}\,dx$

(j) $\displaystyle\int \dfrac{5x+2}{(x-2)^2(x+1)}\,dx$

Exercise 27d (Miscellaneous)

Note that this exercise contains a mixture of integrals; some need partial fractions, others can be done by inspection, or by quoting standard results.

1 $\displaystyle\int \dfrac{1}{1+x^2}\,dx$

2 $\displaystyle\int \dfrac{x}{1+x^2}\,dx$

3 $\displaystyle\int \dfrac{1+x}{1+x^2}\,dx$

4 $\displaystyle\int \dfrac{1}{1-x^2}\,dx$

5 $\displaystyle\int \dfrac{x}{1-x^2}\,dx$

6 $\displaystyle\int \dfrac{x}{\sqrt{(1-x^2)}}\,dx$

7 $\displaystyle\int \dfrac{1}{\sqrt{(1-x^2)}}\,dx$

8 $\displaystyle\int \dfrac{1+x}{\sqrt{(1-x^2)}}\,dx$

9 $\displaystyle\int \dfrac{1}{1-x}\,dx \quad (x < 1)$

10 $\displaystyle\int \dfrac{1}{1-x}\,dx \quad (x > 1)$

11 $\displaystyle\int \dfrac{x}{1+x}\,dx$

12 $\displaystyle\int \dfrac{1}{(1-x)^2}\,dx$

13 $\displaystyle\int \dfrac{x}{(1-x)^2}\,dx$

Evaluate the following, correct to three significant figures:

14 $\displaystyle\int_3^5 \frac{2}{x^2 - 1} \, dx$

15 $\displaystyle\int_{-1}^0 \frac{2}{(1 - x)(1 + x^2)} \, dx$

16 $\displaystyle\int_2^3 \frac{x - 9}{x(x - 1)(x + 3)} \, dx$

17 $\displaystyle\int_0^3 \frac{13x + 7}{(x - 4)(3x^2 + 2x + 3)} \, dx$

18 Find the volume of the solid generated when the area under $y = \dfrac{1}{x - 2}$ from $x = 3$ to $x = 4$ is rotated through four right angles about the x-axis. If the solid is made of material of uniform density, where is its centre of gravity?

Revision Exercise 5 (Integration)

This exercise covers all the methods of integration the reader has met in this book. Most examining boards provide a list of approved standard integrals and the reader may find it helpful to have this to hand while working through the exercise. Some questions are more difficult than the reader may need for examination purposes.

Nos. 1–7 summarise the main methods dealt with in chapters 25, 26, 27.

Nos. 8–12 gather together the integrals of some trigonometrical functions and inverse functions, to enable the reader to take stock of his or her power of handling these integrals.

Nos. 13–15 are designed to develop discrimination in choice of method. These questions test the essential skill, recognition of form, and the more experienced reader may confine his or her attention to these questions, together with some of the less obvious integrals in nos. 8–12.

Find the integrals in nos. 1–6.

1 (a) $\int x\sqrt{(x^2+1)}\,dx$ (b) $\int \dfrac{x^2+1}{\sqrt{(x^3+3x-4)}}\,dx$ (c) $\int \cos^5 u\,du$

(d) $\int \sec^6 \theta\,d\theta$ (e) $\int \sec x \tan^5 x\,dx$ (f) $\int x \sin x^2\,dx$

(g) $\int \dfrac{\sec^2 \sqrt{x}}{\sqrt{x}}\,dx$ (h) $\int x(2x^2+3)^{-1}\,dx$ (i) $\int \dfrac{x}{e^{x^2}}\,dx$

(j) $\int \tan \dfrac{\theta}{2}\,d\theta$

2 Change of variable:

(a) $\int x\sqrt{(2x-3)}\,dx$ (b) $\int 2x(3x-1)^7\,dx$ (c) $\int \dfrac{y(y-8)}{(y-4)^2}\,dy$

(d) $\int \dfrac{1}{\sqrt{(4-5y^2)}}\,dy$ (e) $\int \dfrac{1}{3+9u^2}\,du$ (f) $\int \dfrac{1}{u^2-6u+17}\,du$

(g) $\int \dfrac{1}{\sqrt{(7+4x-2x^2)}}\,dx$ (h) $\int \sqrt{(4-y^2)}\,dy$

3 Involving exponential and logarithmic functions:

(a) $\int e^{3x}\,dx$ (b) $\int 10^y\,dy$ (c) $\int \dfrac{x^2}{e^{x^3}}\,dx$

(d) $\int \dfrac{1}{3x}\,dx$ (e) $\int \dfrac{1}{3x+4}\,dx$ (f) $\int \dfrac{1}{3-2x}\,dx$ $(x>\tfrac{3}{2})$

572

(g) $\int \dfrac{1}{3x+9}\,dx$ (h) $\int \dfrac{1}{1-x^2}\,dx$ (i) $\int \ln x\,dx$

(j) $\int e^{\sqrt{x}}\,dx$ (write as $\int x^{1/2} x^{-1/2} e^{x^{1/2}}\,dx$)

4 Partial fractions:

(a) $\int \dfrac{2}{9-x^2}\,dx$ (b) $\int \dfrac{1}{y(y-3)}\,dy$ (c) $\int \dfrac{1}{x^3-x^2}\,dx$

(d) $\int \dfrac{x}{(4-x)^2}\,dx$ (e) $\int \dfrac{2-x^2}{(x+1)^3}\,dx$ (f) $\int \dfrac{(x-2)^2}{x^3+1}\,dx$

5 Integration by parts:

(a) $\int x \cos \dfrac{x}{2}\,dx$ (b) $\int \dfrac{x}{2} e^x\,dx$ (c) $\int y \operatorname{cosec}^2 y\,dy$

(d) $\int 2y(1-3y)^6\,dy$ (e) $\int x\,3^x\,dx$ (f) $\int x \ln 2x\,dx$

(g) $\int \ln t\,dt$ (h) $\int \tan^{-1} 3x\,dx$ (i) $\int x^3 \sin x\,dx$

6 Splitting the numerator:

(a) $\int \dfrac{2x-1}{4x^2+3}\,dx$ (b) $\int \dfrac{1-4y}{\sqrt{(1+2y-y^2)}}\,dy$

7 Evaluate the following:

(a) $\displaystyle\int_{1/3}^{2/3} \dfrac{1}{\sqrt{(4-9x^2)}}\,dx$ (b) $\displaystyle\int_{1}^{\sqrt{2}} \dfrac{1}{8+y^2}\,dy$

(c) $\displaystyle\int_{5}^{\infty} \dfrac{1}{(x-3)^2}\,dx$ (d) $\displaystyle\int_{-1}^{+1} \dfrac{1}{2x-3}\,dx$

8 Find the following integrals:

(a) $\int \sin 5x\,dx$ (b) $\int \cos \dfrac{x}{3}\,dx$ (c) $\int \tan 5x\,dx$ (d) $\int \cot \tfrac{1}{2}x\,dx$

9 Find the following integrals:

(a) $\int \sec^2 \dfrac{x}{3}\,dx$ (b) $\int \operatorname{cosec}^2 4x\,dx$ (c) $\int \sin^2 x\,dx$

(d) $\int \cos^2 x\,dx$ (e) $\int \tan^2 x\,dx$ (f) $\int \cot^2 x\,dx$

10 Find the following integrals:
(a) $\int \sin^3 x\,dx$
(b) $\int \cos^3 x\,dx$†
(c) $\int \tan^3 x\,dx$ (use Pythagoras' theorem)
(d) $\int \cot^3 x\,dx$ (use Pythagoras' theorem)†

† The change of variable $y = \tfrac{1}{2}\pi - x$ may be used.

11 Find the following integrals ((a) and (b) by expressing the integrands in terms of cos 2x, cos 4x, the remainder by using Pythagoras' theorem):

(a) $\int \sin^4 x \, dx$ (b) $\int \cos^4 x \, dx$ (c) $\int \tan^4 x \, dx$

(d) $\int \csc^4 x \, dx$ (e) $\int \sec^4 x \, dx$ (f) $\int \cot^4 x \, dx$

12 Find the following integrals using integration by parts:

(a) $\int \sin^{-1} x \, dx$ (b) $\int \cos^{-1} x \, dx$

(c) $\int \tan^{-1} x \, dx$ (d) $\int \cot^{-1} x \, dx$

Find the integrals in nos. 13–15.

13 (a) $\int \dfrac{1}{3+4x^2} \, dx$ (b) $\int \dfrac{x}{\sqrt{(5+8x^2)}} \, dx$ (c) $\int \dfrac{x}{2+3x^2} \, dx$

(d) $\int x\sqrt{(3+x^2)} \, dx$ (e) $\int \dfrac{x+1}{3+2x^2} \, dx$ (f) $\int \dfrac{x-2}{x^2-4x+7} \, dx$

14 (a) $\int \dfrac{1}{\sqrt{(4-5x^2)}} \, dx$ (b) $\int \dfrac{x}{\sqrt{(1-3x)}} \, dx$ (c) $\int \dfrac{2}{9-x^2} \, dx$

(d) $\int \dfrac{3}{(16-x)^2} \, dx$ (e) $\int x\sqrt{(6-x^2)} \, dx$ (f) $\int \dfrac{3x}{4-x^2} \, dx$

(g) $\int \sqrt{(4-x^2)} \, dx$ (h) $\int \dfrac{x}{\sqrt{(7-2x^2)}} \, dx$

15 (a) $\int \cos x° \, dx$ (b) $\int x \sin 2x \cos 2x \, dx$

(c) $\int \sec \dfrac{\theta}{2} \csc \dfrac{\theta}{2} \, d\theta$ (d) $\int \cos^6 x \sin^5 x \, dx$

(e) $\int y \sec^2 y \, dy$ (f) $\int x \sin x \, dx$

(g) $\int x \sin x^2 \, dx$ (h) $\int u^2 \cos u \, du$

(i) $\int \sin^2 y \cos^2 y \, dy$ (j) $\int \sin 5x \cos 2x \, dx$

Chapter 28

Curve sketching

Curve sketching is a very useful mathematical skill. It should not be confused with *plotting* a curve, which usually involves plotting a small number of points on graph paper and joining them up with a smooth curve.

Sketching is usually done on plain paper, and the object is to convey an overall impression of the graph's behaviour. If possible, the points where the graph crosses the axes should be shown, together with any stationary points. The asymptotes, if there are any, should also be shown (see Example 5).

We start the chapter with a revision of finding stationary points by differentiation. We then introduce a more advanced technique, the second derivative test, for distinguishing between maximum and minimum points.

28.1 Local maxima and minima – the first derivative test

We have already met the first derivative test in Chapter 6. The diagrams in Figure 28.1 illustrate (i) a local maximum and (ii) a local minimum. (The + and − signs indicate the sign of the gradient.)

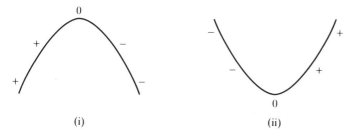

(i)   (ii)

Figure 28.1

At a turning point, $\dfrac{dy}{dx} = 0$ *and it changes sign*; in the case of a maximum (see Figure 28.1 (i)) it changes from + to − as x increases, whereas at a minimum it changes from − to + (see Figure 28.1(ii)).

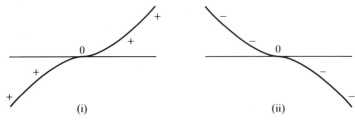

Figure 28.2

If however $\dfrac{dy}{dx} = 0$ but does *not* change sign, then we have a **stationary point of inflexion** (see Figure 28.2).

The first derivative test is very easy to apply, especially if one makes a habit of factorising the derived function, as the next two examples show.

Example 1

Investigate the stationary points on the graph of

$$y = x^2 e^{-x}$$

and sketch the curve.

$$y = x^2 e^{-x}$$

When $x = 0$, $y = 0$: for all other values of x, y is positive. When x tends to infinity y tends to zero, and when x tends to minus infinity, y becomes infinite.

$$\frac{dy}{dx} = 2xe^{-x} - x^2 e^{-x}$$

$$= (2x - x^2)e^{-x}$$
$$= x(2 - x)e^{-x}$$

From this we can see that $\dfrac{dy}{dx}$ is zero when $x = 0$ and when $x = 2$. We know that e^{-x} is always positive, so the sign of the gradient is determined by the other factors. By inspection, we can see that $\dfrac{dy}{dx}$ is negative when $x < 0$, and that between 0 and 2, $\dfrac{dy}{dx}$ is positive. When $x > 2$, $\dfrac{dy}{dx}$ is negative again.

Therefore there is a local minimum at $(0, 0)$, and a local maximum at $(2, 4e^{-2})$. The curve can now be sketched (see Figure 28.3).

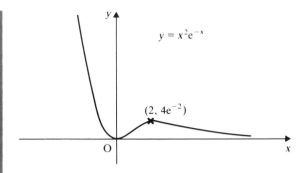

Figure 28.3

Example 2

Investigate the stationary values of the function

$$f(x) = x^3 - 3x^2 + 3x$$

and sketch the graph of $y = f(x)$.

In this case,

$$\begin{aligned} f'(x) &= 3x^2 - 6x + 3 \\ &= 3(x^2 - 2x + 1) \\ &= 3(x - 1)^2 \end{aligned}$$

We can see that $f'(1)$ is zero, but as $(x - 1)^2$ is a square, it can never be negative. In other words, the gradient of $y = f(x)$ is zero at $x = 1$, but everywhere else it is positive. Therefore there is a point of inflexion at $(1, 1)$ (see Figure 28.4).

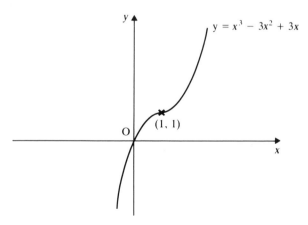

Figure 28.4

Qu. 1 Investigate the stationary values of the function xe^{-x} and sketch the graph of $y = xe^{-x}$.

28.2 Local maxima and minima – the second derivative test

The second derivative test depends on the fact that if the gradient of a curve $y = f(x)$ is *increasing* with x, the rate of change of the gradient is *positive*; if the gradient is *decreasing*, its rate of change is *negative*. To put it another way, let us consider the graph of $\dfrac{dy}{dx}$ plotted against x, bearing in mind that the gradient of *this* curve is given by $\dfrac{d^2 y}{dx^2}$; if $\dfrac{dy}{dx}$ is increasing with x, the gradient, $\dfrac{d^2 y}{dx^2}$, is positive; if $\dfrac{dy}{dx}$ is decreasing, $\dfrac{d^2 y}{dx^2}$ is negative.

Looking back to Figure 28.1, we see that at a local maximum, the gradient is decreasing (it is changing from a positive value, through zero, to a negative value as x increases); so at such a point the derivative *of the gradient function* is negative. In other words, if $y = f(x)$ and

> if $\dfrac{dy}{dx}$ is zero and $\dfrac{d^2 y}{dx^2}$ is *negative* at $x = a$, then y has a (local) maximum at $x = a$;

on the other hand:

> if $\dfrac{dy}{dx}$ is zero and $\dfrac{d^2 y}{dx^2}$ is *positive* at $x = a$, then y has a (local) minimum at $x = a$.

Figure 28.5 shows (as a continuous curve) a graph representing $y = f'(x)$, with positive gradient at $x = a$, i.e. $f''(a) > 0$, and $f'(a) = 0$. The dashed curve represents the corresponding graph of $y = f(x)$, showing a minimum when $x = a$.

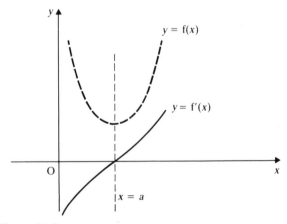

Figure 28.5

Qu. 2 Draw a diagram, like Figure 28.5, illustrating the graphs of $y = f'(x)$ and $y = f(x)$, with $f''(a) < 0$ and $f'(a) = 0$.

Example 3

Use the second derivative test to investigate the stationary values of the function xe^{-x}.

Let $\quad y = xe^{-x}$

$\therefore \quad \dfrac{dy}{dx} = e^{-x} - xe^{-x}$

$= (1 - x)e^{-x}$

From this we can see that there is a stationary value of $1/e$ when $x = 1$.

$\dfrac{d^2 y}{dx^2} = -e^{-x} - e^{-x} + xe^{-x}$

$= -2e^{-x} + xe^{-x}$

When $x = 1$, $\dfrac{d^2 y}{dx^2} = -2e^{-1} + e^{-1} = -e^{-1}$. This is negative, so by the second derivative test, there is a local maximum of $1/e$ when $x = 1$.

It is important to understand that no conclusion can be drawn from the second derivative test when $\dfrac{d^2 y}{dx^2}$ is zero. (It is a common mistake to think that there is always a point of inflexion in this case. If the reader has any doubts on this point, consider $y = x^4$; both $\dfrac{dy}{dx}$ and $\dfrac{d^2 y}{dx^2}$ are zero at $x = 0$, but the function clearly has a minimum at this point.)

Although examination papers frequently direct the candidate to use the second derivative test (and it is a foolish candidate who ignores the examiner's instructions), if you are free to choose your own method, the first derivative test is often the simpler one to use.

28.3 Points of inflexion

We have already met *stationary* points of inflexion, see Figure 28.2. In Figure 28.2(i), the gradient is positive everywhere except at the stationary point, where it is zero, i.e. at this point the gradient has a minimum value. In Figure 28.2(ii), the gradient is negative everywhere except at the stationary point, where it is zero, so at this point the gradient has a maximum value. In general, a point of inflexion is a point where the gradient has a local maximum

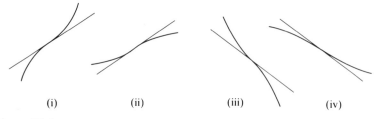

(i)   (ii)   (iii)   (iv)

Figure 28.6

or minimum value. Figure 28.6 shows some points of inflexion for which $\frac{dy}{dx} \neq 0$.

Looking at Figure 28.6(i), we see that the gradient is always positive; it is decreasing as it approaches the point of inflexion, and after that it increases again, i.e. the *gradient* has a *minimum* value at this point of inflexion. The reader should analyse the other diagrams similarly. (On a graph, a point of inflexion is easily recognised, because the graph 'crosses its own tangent' at such a point.)

Points of inflexion are easily located by applying the first derivative test to the gradient function, i.e.

---

at a point of inflexion $\frac{d^2 y}{dx^2}$ is zero *and it changes sign*

[In the case of $y = x^4$, mentioned at the end of Section 28.2, the second derivative, namely $12x^2$, does not change sign at $x = 0$.]

Example 4

Find the points of inflexion of the function $y = \dfrac{48}{12 + x^2}$ and sketch its graph.

We are given $y = \dfrac{48}{12 + x^2}$, so in this case,

$$\frac{dy}{dx} = \frac{-96x}{(12 + x^2)^2}$$

From this we can see that $\dfrac{dy}{dx}$ is zero when $x = 0$, and that its sign changes from positive to negative as x passes through zero, so there is a local maximum at this point. The maximum value of the function is 4.

To find the points of inflexion, we differentiate again:

$$\frac{d^2y}{dx^2} = \frac{-96}{(12+x^2)^2} + \frac{96 \times 4x^2}{(12+x^2)^3}$$

$$= 96\left(\frac{-(12+x^2)+4x^2}{(12+x^2)^3}\right)$$

$$= 96\left(\frac{3x^2-12}{(12+x^2)^3}\right)$$

$$= \frac{288(x-2)(x+2)}{(12+x^2)^3}$$

From this we can see that $\dfrac{d^2y}{dx^2}$ is zero at $x = \pm 2$, and that it changes sign at these points. Hence there are points of inflexion at $(-2, 3)$ and $(+2, 3)$.

In order to sketch the curve, notice that y is always positive and that it tends to zero as x tends to infinity. Also, this is an even function, so its graph is symmetrical about the y-axis (see Figure 28.7).

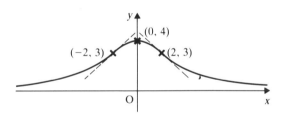

Figure 28.7

Qu. 3 Find the point of inflexion on $y = 2x^3 - 18x^2 + 12x + 80$.

Exercise 28a

Find the nature of the stationary points of:

1 $y = x(x-3)^2$ **2** $y = x + \dfrac{4}{x^2}$ **3** $y = x - 2 + \dfrac{1}{x-3}$ **4** $y = x - \ln x$

Find the points of inflexion in nos. 5 and 6.

5 $y = x^4 - 54x^2$ **6** $y = x^4 - 4x^3 + 6x^2 - 4x$.
7 Sketch the graphs of nos. 1–6.

In nos. 8–11, find the maxima and minima of the functions of θ in the interval $0 \leqslant \theta \leqslant 2\pi$:

8 $\sin \theta + \frac{1}{2} \sin 2\theta$. Sketch the graph.

9 $(\sin \theta)/(1 + \sin \theta)$. Sketch the graph.

10 $\ln \cos \theta - \cos \theta$.

11 $\cos \theta - \frac{1}{3} \cos 3\theta$. Sketch the graph.

12 Find the turning point of the function $x \, e^{-x}$ and determine its nature. Show that there is a point of inflexion when $x = 2$ and sketch the curve.

13 Find the turning point of the function $10 \arctan x - \frac{1}{2}x^2$ and sketch the curve.

14 Show that the function $x \ln x$ has a minimum at $(1/e, -1/e)$. Given that $x \ln x \to 0$ as $x \to 0$, sketch the graph of the function.

15 Show that $e^x \cos x$ has turning points at intervals of π in x. Distinguish between maxima and minima and show that these values are in a geometrical progression with common ratio $-e^\pi$.

28.4 Rational functions of two quadratics

In this section we shall be concerned with rational functions of two quadratics, that is, functions of the form

$$\frac{ax^2 + bx + c}{Ax^2 + Bx + C}$$

where a, b, c, A, B, C are constants.

Example 5

Sketch the curve $y = \dfrac{(x-1)(x+2)}{(x+1)(x-3)}$.

First note the following:

(a) when $y = 0$, $x = 1$ or $x = -2$;

(b) when $x = 0$, $y = \frac{2}{3}$;

(c) when $x = -1$ or $x = 3$, the denominator of the fraction is zero so that there is no corresponding value of y; the function is *discontinuous* at these points. If x differs from -1 or 3 by a small amount, the denominator is small and so y is large. Therefore $y \to \infty$ as $x \to -1$ and $x \to 3$;

(d) given any value of x, other than -1 or 3, there exists one and only one value of y. Note that since the equation can be arranged as a quadratic in x, there are in general two values of x corresponding to each value of y;

(e) the sign of y may be determined by inspecting the signs of the factors $x + 2$, $x + 1$, $x - 1$, $x - 3$;

	$x < -2$	$-2 < x < -1$	$-1 < x < 1$	$1 < x < 3$	$3 < x$
$x + 2$	$-$	$+$	$+$	$+$	$+$
$x + 1$	$-$	$-$	$+$	$+$	$+$
$x - 1$	$-$	$-$	$-$	$+$	$+$
$x - 3$	$-$	$-$	$-$	$-$	$+$
y	$+$	$-$	$+$	$-$	$+$

The shading in Figure 28.8 denotes the regions where the graph cannot lie.

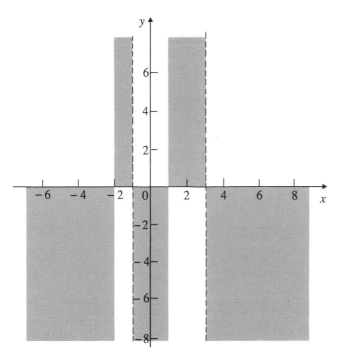

Figure 28.8

(f) The expression

$$\frac{x^2 + x - 2}{x^2 - 2x - 3}$$

is an improper fraction and, as in Section 27.6, it can be written in the form

$$\frac{(x^2 - 2x - 3) + 3x + 1}{x^2 - 2x - 3} = 1 + \frac{3x + 1}{x^2 - 2x - 3}$$

When x tends to $\pm\infty$, the term $(3x + 1)/(x^2 - 2x - 3)$ tends to zero, and hence y tends to 1. For large positive values of x this extra term is positive, so y is just larger than 1. For values of x which are large in magnitude, but negative, the extra term is negative, so y is just smaller than 1.

The line $y = 1$, together with the lines $x = -1$ and $x = 3$, are called **asymptotes**. (The asymptotes are shown as broken lines in Figure 28.9.)

It is possible for the curve to cross the asymptote $y = 1$, indeed, if we put $y = 1$, we find:

$$1 = \frac{x^2 + x - 2}{x^2 - 2x - 3}$$

Hence:

$$x^2 + x - 2 = x^2 - 2x - 3$$
$$\therefore \qquad 3x = -1$$
$$\therefore \qquad x = -\tfrac{1}{3}$$

Therefore, the graph crosses the asymptote $y = 1$ at the point $(-\tfrac{1}{3}, 1)$.

The graph is shown in Figure 28.9

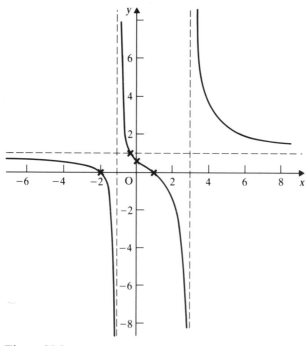

Figure 28.9

An asymptote is a line which a curve approaches when either x or y is very large; sometimes both x and y will be large.

In Example 5, the asymptotes were parallel to the axes but this is not always the case. The graph of $y = x + 1/x$, for example, has one asymptote $x = 0$ (when $x \to 0$ and $y \to \infty$) and another $y = x$ (when x is very large).

Example 6

Prove that $(3x - 9)/(x^2 - x - 2)$ cannot lie between two certain values. Illustrate graphically.

Let $\quad y = \dfrac{3x - 9}{x^2 - x - 2}$

then

$$(x^2 - x - 2)y = 3x - 9$$
$$\therefore \quad yx^2 - x(y + 3) + 9 - 2y = 0 \qquad \qquad \text{. . . (1)}$$

We can regard this as a quadratic equation in x, where, using the notation of Section 11.2, $a = y$, $b = -(y + 3)$ and $c = 9 - 2y$.

This quadratic will have no real roots if its discriminant (i.e. $b^2 - 4ac$) is negative, that is, if

$$\{-(y + 3)\}^2 - 4y(9 - 2y) < 0$$
$$\therefore \quad y^2 + 6y + 9 - 36y + 8y^2 < 0$$
$$\therefore \qquad \qquad 9y^2 - 30y + 9 < 0$$
$$\therefore \qquad \qquad 3(3y - 1)(y - 3) < 0$$
$$\therefore \quad \tfrac{1}{3} < y < 3$$

Therefore there are no real values of x when $\tfrac{1}{3} < y < 3$.

Now $y = \dfrac{3(x - 3)}{(x + 1)(x - 2)}$, and we may proceed as in Example 5.

(a) If $y = 0$, $x = 3$.
(b) If $x = 0$, $y = 4\tfrac{1}{2}$.
(c) The lines $x = -1$ and $x = 2$ are asymptotes; the function is discontinuous when $x = -1$ and $x = 2$.
(d) There is only one value of y for each value of x.
(e) The sign of y is obtained:

	$x < -1$	$-1 < x < 2$	$2 < x < 3$	$3 < x$
$x + 1$	$-$	$+$	$+$	$+$
$x - 2$	$-$	$-$	$+$	$+$
$x - 3$	$-$	$-$	$-$	$+$
y	$-$	$+$	$-$	$+$

(f) As $x \to \infty$, $y \to 0$, so the line $y = 0$ is an asymptote.

(g) The values of x corresponding to $y = \frac{1}{3}$ and $y = 3$ are found from equation (1).

[Note that $y = \frac{1}{3}$ and $y = 3$ make the discriminant '$b^2 - 4ac$' $= 0$, so that equation (1) on page 585 has equal roots. The sum of the roots is $(y + 3)/y$, therefore $x = \frac{1}{2}(y + 3)/y$.] When $y = \frac{1}{3}$, $x = 5$; when $y = 3$, $x = 1$.

Our findings are shown in Figure 28.10 and the curve has been sketched in Figure 28.11.

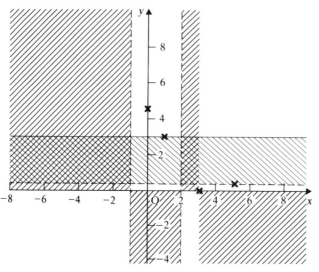

Figure 28.10

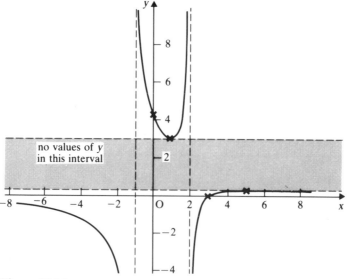

Figure 28.11

Example 7

Sketch the curve $y = \dfrac{2x}{x^2 + 1}$.

(a) The curve cuts the axes only at $(0, 0)$.
(b) As a quadratic in x, the equation is $x^2 y - 2x + y = 0$.
For real values of x,

$$(-2)^2 - 4y^2 \geqslant 0$$
$$\therefore \quad 4 - 4y^2 \geqslant 0$$
$$\therefore \quad 4(1 - y^2) \geqslant 0$$
$$\therefore \quad 4(1 - y)(1 + y) \geqslant 0$$
$$\therefore \quad -1 \leqslant y \leqslant +1$$

(c) When $y = -1$, $x = -1$, and when $y = +1$, $x = +1$. Therefore $(-1, -1)$ is a minimum and $(1, 1)$ a maximum.
(d) As $x \to \infty$, $y \to 0$, so the line $y = 0$ is an asymptote.
(e) Since $x^2 + 1$ is positive, x and y have the same sign; $x^2 + 1$ is never zero, so the function is continuous.

The curve has been sketched in Figure 28.12.

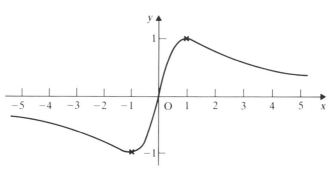

Figure 28.12

Exercise 28b

Sketch the following curves.

1 $y = \dfrac{x - 2}{x + 3}$ **2** $y = \dfrac{x}{x - 1}$ **3** $y = \dfrac{x}{x^2 - 1}$

4 $y = \dfrac{x^2}{x^2 - 1}$ **5** $y = \dfrac{2x - 4}{(x - 1)(x - 3)}$ **6** $y = \dfrac{(x - 1)(x + 3)}{(x - 2)(x + 2)}$

For each of the following curves, find the intervals within which y *cannot* lie.
Illustrate graphically.

7 $y = \dfrac{4}{(x-1)(x-3)}$ **8** $y = \dfrac{3x-6}{x(x+6)}$

Find the turning points of the following, and sketch the curves.

9 $y = \dfrac{x^2 - 4x}{x^2 - 4x + 3}$ **10** $y = \dfrac{x^2 + 4x - 5}{x + 7}$

28.5 Some tests for symmetry

The remainder of this chapter is devoted to further aids to curve sketching,
and the most useful of these is symmetry.

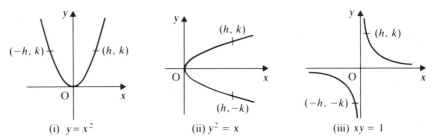

(i) $y = x^2$ (ii) $y^2 = x$ (iii) $xy = 1$

Figure 28.13

First consider the graph of $y = x^2$ (Figure 28.13 (i)), which is symmetrical about
the y-axis. If the point (h, k) lies on the curve, we have $k = h^2$, and so the point
$(-h, k)$ also lies on the curve. In general, if an equation is unaltered by replacing
x by $-x$, the curve is symmetrical about the y-axis. The graphs of all *even*
functions are symmetrical about the y-axis.

Similarly, if the equation of a curve is unaltered by replacing y by $-y$, there
is symmetry about the x-axis (Figure 28.13 (ii)).

Figure 28.13 (iii) represents the curve $xy = 1$, which has *rotational* symmetry
about a *point*, the origin. If (h, k) lies on the locus, so does $(-h, -k)$. In general,
if an equation is unaltered when x and y are replaced by $-x$ and $-y$ respectively, the curve will have rotational symmetry about the origin. The graphs of
all *odd* functions have rotational symmetry about the origin.

Qu. 4 Which of the following show symmetry about (i) the y-axis (ii) the x-axis
(iii) the origin?
(a) $4x^2 + y^2 = 1$ (b) $y^2 = x(x+1)$
(c) $x^5 + y^5 = 5xy^2$ (d) $x^2 - 3xy + y^2 = 1$
(e) $y^2 = x^2(x+1)(x-1)$ (f) $x^2y - x + y^3 = 0$
(g) $y^2 = \cos x$ (h) $\tan y = \sin x$

Example 8

Sketch the curve $x^2 - y^2 = 1$.

(a) The equation shows symmetry about both axes and the origin.
(b) Since $y^2 = x^2 - 1$, y is not real when x is numerically less than 1.
(c) When $y = 0$, $x = \pm 1$.
(d) As x increases in magnitude, so does y.
(e) On differentiation

$$2y\frac{dy}{dx} = 2x$$

$$\therefore \quad \frac{dy}{dx} = \frac{x}{y} \quad \text{(where } y = \pm\sqrt{(1 - x^2)}\text{)}$$

$$\therefore \quad \text{as} \quad x \to \pm 1 \quad \frac{dy}{dx} \to \infty$$

and

$$\therefore \quad \text{as} \quad x \to \pm\infty \quad \frac{dy}{dx} \to \pm 1$$

(f) Since $y^2 = x^2 - 1$, when x, y are large, y^2 is nearly equal to x^2. Thus the lines $y = \pm x$ are asymptotes.

The curve has been sketched in Figure 28.14

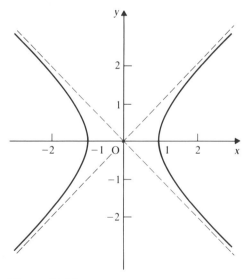

Figure 28.14

28.6 The form $y^2 = f(x)$

If an equation can be expressed in the form $y^2 = f(x)$, then it will have a number of special features. Since y^2 cannot be negative, x must be limited to values for which f(x) is non-negative; for any such value we can write $y = \pm\sqrt{f(x)}$, so the graph will be symmetrical about the x-axis.

Example 9

Sketch the graph of $y^2 = x(x-2)^2$.

The factor $(x-2)^2$ is never negative so the sign of the R.H.S. is determined by the factor x. So x must be greater than, or equal to, zero to obtain real values of y. Also, y is zero at $x = 0$ and $x = 2$.

Consider $y^2 = x(x-2)^2$. Taking the square root, we have

$$y = \pm x^{1/2}(x-2)$$
$$= \pm(x^{3/2} - 2x^{1/2})$$

$$\therefore \quad \frac{dy}{dx} = \pm(\tfrac{3}{2}x^{1/2} - x^{-1/2})$$

$$= \pm\frac{3x-2}{2x^{1/2}}$$

From this we can see that $\frac{dy}{dx} = 0$ when $x = \frac{2}{3}$, and that

as $x \to 0$ $\frac{dy}{dx} \to \infty$

as $x \to 2$ $\frac{dy}{dx} \to \pm\sqrt{2}$

and

as $x \to \infty$ $\frac{dy}{dx} \pm \infty$

The graph of $y^2 = x(x-2)^2$ is shown in Figure 28.15.

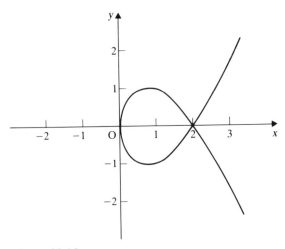

Figure 28.15

[It should be noted that the equation $y^2 = x(x-2)^2$ cannot be regarded as a rule for expressing y as a *function* of x, because there are *two* values of y for each value of x. However $y = +\sqrt{x(x-2)}$ and $y = -\sqrt{x(x-2)}$ could be regarded as two functions whose graphs could be combined to produce the graph of $y^2 = x(x-2)^2$.]

Qu. 5 Find the gradient of
(a) $y^2 = x(x-2)(x-4)$ (b) $y^2 = x^2(x+2)$
at the points where the graphs cut the x-axis.

Sketch the curves by the method of Example 9.

28.7 Simple changes of axes

The equation of a circle, centre $C(a, b)$ and radius r, is (see Section 21.4)

$$(x-a)^2 + (y-b)^2 = r^2$$

and the equation of an equal circle, centre the origin, is

$$x^2 + y^2 = r^2$$

Therefore, if new axes CX and CY were taken parallel to Ox and Oy, the equation of the former would become

$$X^2 + Y^2 = r^2$$

This is equivalent to making the substitutions

$$X = x - a \qquad Y = y - b$$

or, as is often more convenient,

$$x = X + a \qquad y = Y + b$$

These relationships may easily be verified from a diagram.

Such a change of axes is sometimes helpful in curve sketching. Thus

$$(y-1)^2 = 4(x+2)$$

becomes

$$Y^2 = 4X$$

referred to parallel axes through $(-2, 1)$ and the curve is now easily drawn, as in Figure 28.16 (over the page).

Note that the equation $y = ax^2 + bx + c$ may be written

$$y + \frac{b^2}{4a} - c = a\left(x + \frac{b}{2a}\right)^2$$

Referred to parallel axes through $\left(-\dfrac{b}{2a}, -\dfrac{b^2 - 4ac}{4a}\right)$ the equation becomes

$$Y = aX^2$$

which is a parabola (see Section 22.5).

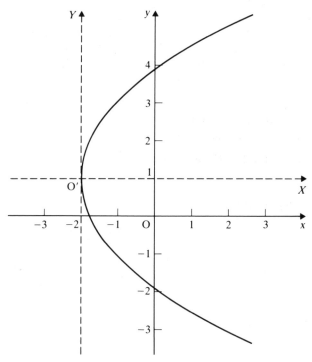

Figure 28.16

Example 10

Sketch the function $1 + 2 \sin (\theta + \frac{1}{4}\pi)$ for values of θ from 0 to 2π.

Write $y = 1 + 2 \sin (\theta + \frac{1}{4}\pi)$
∴ $y - 1 = 2 \sin (\theta + \frac{1}{4}\pi)$

With the substitutions

$$\Theta = \theta + \tfrac{1}{4}\pi \quad \text{and} \quad Y = y - 1 \qquad \qquad \text{. . . (1)}$$

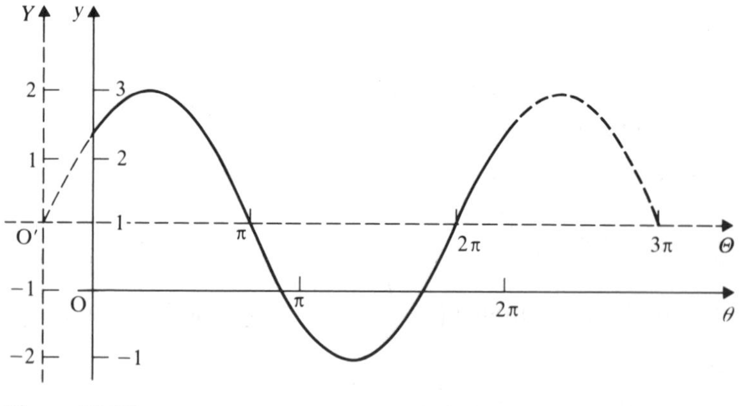

Figure 28.17

the equation becomes

$$Y = 2 \sin \Theta$$

The graph of $Y = 2 \sin \Theta$ has been sketched in Figure 28.17. Writing $\theta = y = 0$ in equations (1), the origin of the θ, y axes is found to be $(\frac{1}{4}\pi, -1)$, referred to the Θ, Y axes. The θ, y axes were then drawn to pass through this point.

28.8 The form $y = 1/f(x)$

Example 11

Sketch on the same axes the graphs of:
(a) $y = (x + 1)(2x - 3)$ (b) $y = 1/\{(x + 1)(2x - 3)\}$.

(a) The graph of $f(x) = (x + 1)(2x - 3)$ is a parabola meeting the x-axis at $(-1, 0)$ and $(1\frac{1}{2}, 0)$. As $x \to \pm \infty$, $y \to +\infty$. See the broken line in Figure 28.18.

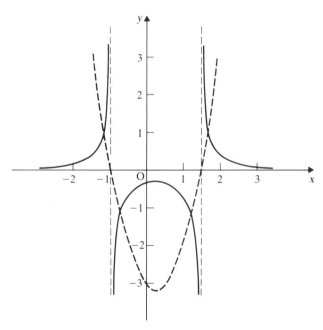

Figure 28.18

(b) The reciprocal of $f(x)$ is sketched as follows:
   (i)   the signs of $f(x)$ and $1/f(x)$ are the same,
   (ii) as $f(x) \to \infty$, $1/f(x) \to 0$ and vice versa,
   (iii) when $f(x) = \pm 1$, $1/f(x)$ has the same value.

The two graphs are shown in Figure 28.18.

Exercise 28c

Sketch the graphs of:

1 $y = 1 + \sin x$ **2** $y = 1 - \cos x$

3 $y = \operatorname{cosec} x$ **4** $y = \dfrac{1}{1 + \cos x}$

5 $y - 2 = (x - 3)^2$ **6** $y = 1 + 1/x$

7 $y = \dfrac{1}{x^2 - 1}$ **8** $y = \dfrac{1}{x^2 + 1}$

9 $y^2 = x + 2$ **10** $y^2 = 4 - x$
11 $y^2 = x^2(2 - x)^3$ **12** $y^2 = (x^2 - 1)(4 - x^2)$

Exercise 28d (Miscellaneous)

Sketch the curves in nos. 1–4:

1 $2x^2 + y^2 = 4$ **2** $2x^2 - y^2 = 4$
3 $x^2 y = 1$ **4** $x^2 y^2 = 4$
5 Sketch, on the same axes, the graphs of:

$$y = (x - 3)(x + 2) \quad \text{and} \quad y = \frac{1}{(x - 3)(x + 2)}$$

6 Sketch, on the same axes, the graphs of:

$$y = x^2 + 25 \quad \text{and} \quad y = \frac{1}{x^2 + 25}$$

7 Given that $y(x - 1) = x^2 + 3$, where x is real, show that y cannot take any value between -2 and 6.
Find the asymptotes of the curve $y = (x^2 + 3)/(x - 1)$ and sketch the curve, showing the coordinates of the turning points.   (C)
8 Given that $f(x) = x - 1 + 1/(x + 1)$, x real, $x \neq 1$, find the values of x for which $f'(x) = 0$. Sketch the graph of f, showing the coordinates of the turning points and indicating clearly the form of the graph when $|x|$ becomes large.   (JMB)
9 Show that the graph of $y = (x^2 - 1)/(x^2 + 4x)$ has no real stationary points and sketch this graph.   (JMB)
10 The domain of the function f is the set $D = \{x : x \in \mathbb{R}, \ x \neq -1, \ x \neq 1\}$. The function $f : D \rightarrow \mathbb{R}$ is defined by

$$f(x) = \frac{x^2}{(x - 1)(x + 1)}$$

Find the coordinates of the maximum point on the graph of f and state the equation of each of the asymptotes of the graph.
Sketch the graph showing in particular how the curve approaches each of its asymptotes.   (L)

Chapter 29

Differential equations

29.1 The general problem

An equation containing any *differential coefficients* such as $\dfrac{dy}{dx}, \dfrac{d^2y}{dx^2}$, is called a *differential equation*; a solution of such an equation is an equation relating x and y and containing no differential coefficients.

Given the differential equation $\dfrac{dy}{dx} = 3$, we obtain the *general solution* $y = 3x + c$, which is the equation of all straight lines of gradient 3. If the data also includes the fact that $y = 5$ when $x = 1$, we can determine that $c = 2$, and we obtain the *particular solution* $y = 3x + 2$.

Thus, in simple graphical terms,

(a) a **differential equation** defines some property common to a family of curves,
(b) the **general solution**, involving one or more arbitrary constants, is the equation of *any* member of the family,
(c) a **particular solution** is the equation of *one* member of the family.

Consider the differential equation $\dfrac{dy}{dx} = x$. We can easily solve this with our existing knowledge, but before we do so, consider for a moment what this differential equation tells us: it says that, for any value of x, the gradient is equal to x. The information is illustrated in Figure 29.1

The solution of the differential equation is

$$y = \tfrac{1}{2}x^2 + c$$

(in this context, the constant of integration, c, is usually called 'an **arbitrary constant**'). Equations of this form represent parabolas with the y-axis as the axis of symmetry (see Figure 29.2).

As with the family of lines $y = 3x + c$, above, if we are given some further information, say when $x = 0$, $y = 2$, then we can find c and identify the particular parabola with this property, in this case $y = \tfrac{1}{2}x^2 + 2$.

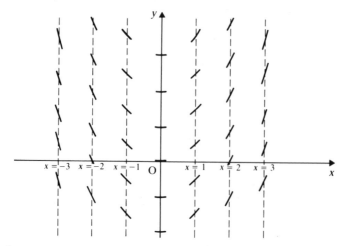

Figure 29.1

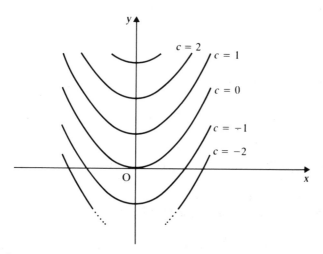

Figure 29.2

Qu. 1 Find the general solution of $\dfrac{d^2 y}{dx^2} = 0$. What is the particular solution given by $\dfrac{dy}{dx} = 3$, and $y = -2$ when $x = 1$?

Qu. 2 Find the general solution of $\dfrac{dy}{dx} = 3x^2$. Illustrate with a sketch.

Qu. 3 For any circle centre the origin, $\dfrac{dy}{dx} = -\dfrac{x}{y}$. Solve this equation by writing it as $y\dfrac{dy}{dx} = -x$. $\left(\text{What is } \dfrac{d}{dx}(y^2)? \right)$

Qu. 4 Find the general solution of $\dfrac{d^2 s}{dt^2} = a$, where a is a constant. What does this become, given the initial conditions $s = 0$ and $\dfrac{ds}{dt} = u$ when $t = 0$?

Definition

> The **order** of a differential equation is determined by the highest differential coefficient present.

Thus the equations in Qu. 1 and 4 are of the second order, whereas those in Qu. 2 and 3 are of the first order.

Since each step of integration introduces one arbitrary constant, it is in general true that the order of a differential equation gives us the number of arbitrary constants in the general solution.

This suggests that from an equation involving x, y, and n arbitrary constants there may be formed (by differentiating n times and eliminating the constants) a differential equation of order n.

Qu. 5 Form differential equations by differentiating and eliminating the constants A, B from the following:
(a) $y = Ax + B$ (b) $y = Ax$ (c) $r = A \cos \theta$
(d) $xy = A$ (e) $y = A\,e^x$ (f) $y = e^{Bx}$
(g) $y = A\,e^{Bx}$ (h) $y = A \ln x$ (i) $x = \tan(Ay)$

Qu. 6 Confirm the given general solution of each of the following differential equations:

(a) $\dfrac{d^2 y}{dx^2} - \dfrac{dy}{dx} - 2y = 0$ $y = A\,e^{2x} + B\,e^{-x}$

(b) $\dfrac{d^2 x}{dt^2} - 4\dfrac{dx}{dt} + 4x = 0$ $x = e^{2t}(A + Bt)$

We must now classify some of the simpler forms of differential equations.

29.2 First order – separating the variables

The solutions of $\dfrac{dy}{dx} = f(x)$ and $\dfrac{dy}{dx} = f(y)$ $\left(\text{which may be written } \dfrac{dx}{dy} = \dfrac{1}{f(y)}\right)$ depend upon the integrals $\int f(x)\,dx$ and $\int \dfrac{1}{f(y)}\,dy$. There are other differential equations equally susceptible to direct integration once they have been written in a suitable form.

Consider

$$\frac{dy}{dx} = xy \qquad\qquad \dots \text{ (1)}$$

We write this as

$$\frac{1}{y}\frac{dy}{dx} = x$$

then integrating each side with respect to x,

$$\int \frac{1}{y}\frac{dy}{dx}\,dx = \int x\,dx$$

$$\left[\text{But from Section 25.5 we know that } \int f(y)\,dy = \int f(y)\frac{dy}{dx}\,dx. \right]$$

$$\therefore \quad \int \frac{1}{y}\,dy = \int x\,dx \qquad\qquad \dots \text{ (2)}$$

$$\therefore \quad \ln y + c = \tfrac{1}{2}x^2$$

If we write $c = \ln k$, this becomes:

$$\ln y + \ln k = \tfrac{1}{2}x^2$$

and hence

$$\ln (ky) = \tfrac{1}{2}x^2 \quad \text{ or } \quad y = A\,e^{x^2/2}$$

Note how the arbitrary constant of integration appears in different forms; we have written c as $\ln k$, and A as $1/k$.

Now let us look back at (1) and (2) in the above working. The symbols dx, dy have as yet no meaning for us in isolation; they have been used only in composite symbols such as $\frac{dy}{dx}, \frac{d}{dx}f(x), \int f(x)\,dx$. However, in the present circumstances it is convenient to think of dx as an 'x-factor', and dy as a 'y-factor', and proceed direct from (1) to (2) by 'separating the variables' and adding the integral sign. The intervening lines provide the justification for this.

Example 1

Solve $x^2\dfrac{dy}{dx} = y(y-1)$.

$$x^2\frac{dy}{dx} = y(y-1)$$

Separating the variables,

$$\int \frac{1}{y(y-1)}\,dy = \int \frac{1}{x^2}\,dx$$

$$\therefore \quad \int \left\{ \frac{1}{y-1} - \frac{1}{y} \right\} dy = \int \frac{1}{x^2}\,dx$$

$$\therefore \quad \ln(y-1) - \ln y + c = -\frac{1}{x}$$

Write $c = \ln k$, giving

$$\ln \frac{k(y-1)}{y} = -\frac{1}{x}$$

or $\qquad k(y-1) = y\,e^{-1/x}$

Qu. 7 Solve the following differential equations, and check solutions by differentiation and elimination of arbitrary constants:

(a) $\dfrac{dy}{dx} = \dfrac{x}{y}$ (b) $\dfrac{dy}{dx} = \dfrac{y}{x}$ (c) $\dfrac{dx}{dy} = xy$

(d) $x\dfrac{dy}{dx} = \tan y$ (e) $e^{-x}\dfrac{dy}{dx} = y^2 - 1$ (f) $\sqrt{(x^2+1)}\dfrac{dy}{dx} = \dfrac{x}{y}$

Qu. 8 $v\dfrac{dv}{ds} = a$, where a is a constant. Solve this equation given that $v = u$ when $s = 0$.

Since Newton's time, many physical problems have been expressed in terms of differential equations (readers who are studying applied mathematics or physics have probably met some already). Solving, or at least attempting to solve, a differential equation is a very common task for a scientist, and nowadays the problem frequently arises in other disciplines, such as economics. What follows is an important application of the subject in physics.

It is known that radioactive substances decay at a rate which is proportional to the amount of the radioactive substance present. If we use x to represent the amount present at time t, we can express this in the form of a differential equation, namely,

$$\frac{dx}{dt} = -kx \qquad \text{where } k \text{ is a positive constant}$$

For different substances, the rate of decay is different; it is usual to quote the *half-life* of the substance, that is, the time it takes for half of the original quantity to decay. For radium the half-life is about 1600 years. We shall now solve the differential equation, that is, express x as a function of t, and hence find the value of k. We shall then use the solution to find the percentage of a given sample of radium which would still exist after a lapse of 200 years in storage.

[Remember, in the following working, to distinguish between the arbitrary constant of integration A (or x_0), and k, a constant which is determined by the half-life of radium.]

$$\frac{dx}{dt} = -kx$$

Separating the variables gives

$$\int \frac{1}{x} dx = \int -k\, dt$$

and integrating,

$$\ln x = -kt + c$$
$$\therefore \quad x = e^{-kt+c}$$
$$= e^c \times e^{-kt}$$

and replacing e^c by A, we can write

$$x = A\, e^{-kt}$$

This is a general solution of the differential equation. (This particular differential equation is extremely common, and, unless specific instructions to the contrary are given, the solution $x = A\, e^{-kt}$ may be quoted.) We now continue with the solution.

When $t = 0$, $x = A$, in other words A is the original value of x. It is convenient to write this as x_0, so

$$x = x_0 e^{-kt}$$

Now, we are told that when $t = 1600$, $x = \frac{1}{2}x_0$, consequently

$$\tfrac{1}{2}x_0 = x_0 e^{-1600k}$$
$$\therefore \quad \tfrac{1}{2} = e^{-1600k}$$
$$\text{i.e.} \quad e^{1600k} = 2$$

Taking natural logarithms,

$$1600k = \ln 2,$$

$$k = \frac{\ln 2}{1600}$$

Hence the solution can be expressed

$$x = x_0 e^{-(\ln 2/1600)t}$$

This, in turn, can be written

$$x = x_0 (e^{\ln 2})^{-t/1600}$$

but $e^{\ln 2} = 2$, (see Section 26.8; this step is extremely common in this topic), hence

$$x = x_0 2^{-t/1600}$$

[We can verify by inspection that when $t = 1600$, $x = \frac{1}{2}x_0$. It is important to check your work like this whenever possible.]

Finally, when $t = 200$,

$$x = x_0 2^{-1/8}$$
$$= 0.917x_0$$

In other words, after 200 years, 91.7% of the original radioactive radium still exists.

Exercise 29a

1 By differentiating and eliminating the constants A and B from the following equations, form differential equations:
(a) $3x - 2y + A = 0$ (b) $Ax + 2y + 1 = 0$ (c) $Ax + By = 0$
(d) $x^2 + y^2 = A$ (e) $y = Ax^{-1}$ (f) $y = A(x - 4)$

2 By differentiating and eliminating the constants A and B from the following equations, form differential equations:
(a) $y = A \cos(3t + B)$ (b) $y = A + B e^{3t}$ (c) $y = A e^{3x} + B e^{-3x}$
(d) $y = A e^{3x} + B e^{-2x}$ (first multiply each side by e^{2x})

(e) $y = e^{4x}(A + Bx)$ $\left(\text{first show that } \dfrac{dy}{dx} = 4y + B e^{4x}\right)$

3 Obtain the equation of the straight line of gradient $\frac{3}{10}$, which passes through $(5, -2)$, by finding a particular solution of the differential equation $\dfrac{dy}{dx} = \frac{3}{10}$.

4 A family of parabolas has the differential equation $\dfrac{dy}{dx} = 2x - 3$. Find the equation of that member of the family which passes through $(4, 5)$.

5 Find the general solution of the differential equation $6t\dfrac{dt}{ds} + 1 = 0$, and the particular solution given by the condition $s = 0$ when $t = -2$.

6 Find the particular solutions of the differential equation

$$\text{cosec } x \frac{dy}{dx} = e^x \text{ cosec } x + 3x$$

given by the conditions:
(a) $y = 0$ when $x = 0$ (b) $y = 3$ when $x = \pi/2$

7 Find the general solutions of the following differential equations:

(a) $\dfrac{dy}{dx} = y$ (b) $\dfrac{1}{x}\dfrac{dy}{dx} = \sqrt{(x-1)}$ (c) $(x+2)\dfrac{dy}{dx} = y$

(d) $\dfrac{dy}{dx} = \sec^2 y$ (e) $\dfrac{dv}{du} = v(v-1)$ (f) $\ln x \dfrac{dx}{dy} = 1$

(g) $\dfrac{dy}{dx} = \tan y$ (h) $\tan^{-1} y \dfrac{dy}{dx} = 1$ (i) $y\dfrac{dy}{dx} = x - 1$

(j) $(x^2 - 1)\dfrac{dy}{dx} = y$ (k) $\dfrac{d\theta}{dr} = \cos^2 \theta$ (l) $x^2 \dfrac{dy}{dx} = y + 3$

(m) $x\dfrac{dy}{dx} = y + xy$ (n) $\dfrac{d\phi}{d\theta} = \tan \phi \tan \theta$ (o) $\theta \dfrac{d\theta}{dr} = \cos^2 \theta$

(p) $\dfrac{y}{x}\dfrac{dy}{dx} = \ln x$

8 Find the particular solutions of the following differential equations which satisfy the given conditions:

(a) $(1 + \cos 2\theta)\dfrac{dy}{d\theta} = 2, \quad y = 1$ when $\theta = \pi/4$

(b) $\dfrac{dy}{dx} = x(y - 2), \quad y = 5$ when $x = 0$

(c) $(1 + x^2)\dfrac{dy}{dx} = 1 + y^2, \quad y = 3$ when $x = 2$

(d) $\dfrac{dy}{dx} = \sqrt{(1 - y^2)}, \quad y = 0$ when $x = \pi/6$

9 According to Newton's law of cooling, the rate at which the temperature of a body falls is proportional to the amount by which its temperature exceeds that of its surroundings. Suppose the temperature of an object falls from $200°$ to $100°$ in 40 minutes, in a surrounding temperature of $10°$. Prove that after t minutes, the temperature, T degrees, of the body is given by

$$T = 10 + 190e^{-kt} \qquad \text{where } k = \tfrac{1}{40} \ln \left(\tfrac{19}{9}\right)$$

Calculate the time it takes to reach $50°$.

10 A tank contains a solution of salt in water. Initially the tank contains 1000 litres of water with 10 kg of salt dissolved in it. The mixture is poured off at a rate of 20 litres per minute, and simultaneously pure water is added at a rate of 20 litres per minute. All the time the tank is stirred to keep the mixture uniform. Find the mass of salt in the tank after 5 minutes. The tank must be topped up by adding salt when the mass of salt in the tank falls to 5 kg; after how many minutes will it need topping up?

29.3 First order exact equations

The equation

$$2xy\dfrac{dy}{dx} + y^2 = e^{2x}$$

is not one in which the variables may be separated. However, the L.H.S. is $\dfrac{d}{dx}(xy^2)$ and the equation may be solved by integrating each side with respect to x; it is called an **exact equation** and the solution is

$$xy^2 = \tfrac{1}{2}e^{2x} + A$$

Qu. 9 Solve the following exact equations:

(a) $x^2\dfrac{dy}{dx} + 2xy = 1$ (b) $\dfrac{t^2\,dx}{x\,dt} + 2t\ln x = 3\cos t$

(c) $x^2\cos u\dfrac{du}{dx} + 2x\sin u = \dfrac{1}{x}$ (d) $e^y + x\,e^y\dfrac{dy}{dx} = 2$

29.4 Integrating factors

There are some differential equations which are not *exact* as they stand, but which may be made so by multiplying each side by an **integrating factor**.

Example 2

Solve $xy\dfrac{dy}{dx} + y^2 = 3x$.

[We cannot separate the variables. Can we find a function whose derivative is the L.H.S. as in Section 29.3? No. Then can we find a function whose derivative is $f(x) \times$ L.H.S.?

$$\dfrac{d}{dx}(xy^2) = y^2 + 2xy\dfrac{dy}{dx};\quad \text{this is no good.}$$

$$\dfrac{d}{dx}(x^2y^2) = 2xy^2 + 2x^2y \times \dfrac{dy}{dx} = 2x\left(y^2 + xy\dfrac{dy}{dx}\right) = 2x \times \text{L.H.S.}$$

The required integrating factor is $2x$.]

$$xy\dfrac{dy}{dx} + y^2 = 3x$$

Multiplying each side by $2x$,

$$2x^2y\dfrac{dy}{dx} + 2xy^2 = 6x^2$$

∴ $$x^2y^2 = 2x^3 + A$$

Qu. 10 Find the integrating factors required to make the following differential equations into exact equations, and solve them:

(a) $x\dfrac{dy}{dx} + 2y = e^{x^2}$ 　　　　(b) $x\,e^y\dfrac{dy}{dx} + 2e^y = x$

(c) $2x^2y\dfrac{dy}{dx} + xy^2 = 1$ 　　(d) $r\sec^2\theta + 2\tan\theta\dfrac{dr}{d\theta} = 2r^{-1}$

29.5 First order linear equations

A differential equation is *linear in y* if it is of the form

$$\frac{d^n y}{dx^n} + P_1\frac{d^{n-1}y}{dx^{n-1}} + P_2\frac{d^{n-2}y}{dx^{n-2}} + \ \dots\ + P_{n-1}\frac{dy}{dx} + P_n y = Q$$

where $P_1, P_2, \dots, P_n, Q$ are functions of x, or constants; it is of the nth order.

Thus a *first order linear equation* is of the form

$$\frac{dy}{dx} + Py = Q$$

where P, Q are functions of x or constants. This type of differential equation deserves special attention because an integrating factor, when required and if obtainable, is of a standard form.

Let us assume that the general first order linear equation given above can be made into an exact equation by using the integrating factor R, a function of x. If this is so,

$$R\frac{dy}{dx} + RPy = RQ \qquad\qquad \dots\ (1)$$

is an exact equation, and clearly from the first term the L.H.S. of (1) is

$\dfrac{d}{dx}(Ry) = R\dfrac{dy}{dx} + y\dfrac{dR}{dx}.$ Thus (1) may also be written

$$R\frac{dy}{dx} + y\frac{dR}{dx} = RQ \qquad\qquad \dots\ (2)$$

Equating the second terms on the L.H.S. of (1) and (2),

$$y\frac{dR}{dx} = RPy$$

$$\therefore\quad \frac{dR}{dx} = RP$$

Separating the variables,

$$\int \frac{1}{R}\, dR = \int P\, dx$$

$\therefore \qquad \ln R = \int P\, dx$
$\therefore \qquad R = e^{\int P\, dx}$

Thus

> the required integrating factor is $e^{\int P\, dx}$

The initial assumption that an integrating factor exists is therefore justified provided that it is possible to find $\int P\, dx$.

Example 3

Solve the differential equation $\dfrac{dy}{dx} + 3y = e^{2x}$, given that $y = \frac{6}{5}$ when $x = 0$.

The integrating factor is $e^{\int 3\, dx} = e^{3x}$. Multiplying each side of the given equation by e^{3x},

$$e^{3x}\frac{dy}{dx} + 3e^{3x}y = e^{5x}$$

The left-hand side of this is the derivative of $e^{3x}y$, so integrating both sides with respect to x gives

$$e^{3x}y = \tfrac{1}{5}e^{5x} + A$$

Therefore the general solution is

$$y = \tfrac{1}{5}e^{2x} + A\,e^{-3x}$$

But $y = \frac{6}{5}$ when $x = 0$, so $\frac{6}{5} = \frac{1}{5} + A$, $\therefore A = 1$.
Therefore the particular solution is

$$y = \tfrac{1}{5}e^{2x} + e^{-3x}$$

Example 4

Solve $\dfrac{dy}{dx} + y \cot x = \cos x$.

The integrating factor is

$$e^{\int \cot x\, dx} = e^{\ln \sin x} = \sin x \quad \text{(see Section 26.8)}$$

Multiplying each side of the given equation by $\sin x$,

$$\sin x \frac{dy}{dx} + y \cos x = \cos x \sin x$$

The left-hand side of this is the derivative of $y \sin x$, so integrating both sides gives:

$$y \sin x = \tfrac{1}{2} \sin^2 x + A$$

Therefore the general solution is

$$y = \tfrac{1}{2} \sin x + A \operatorname{cosec} x$$

Qu. 11 Find the general solution of $\dfrac{dy}{dx} + 2xy = x$. What is the particular solution given by $y = -\tfrac{1}{2}$ when $x = 0$?

Qu. 12 Show that the equation in Qu. 10 (a) is of the type under discussion, and find the required integrating factor as $e^{\int P \, dx}$.

Qu. 13 Solve: (a) $\dfrac{dy}{dx} - y \tan x = x$ (b) $\dfrac{dy}{dx} + y + 3 = x$

Exercise 29b

1 Solve the following exact differential equations:

(a) $y^2 + 2xy \dfrac{dy}{dx} = \dfrac{1}{x^2}$

(b) $xy^2 + x^2 y \dfrac{dy}{dx} = \sec^2 2x$

(c) $\ln y + \dfrac{x \, dy}{y \, dx} = \sec x \tan x$

(d) $(1 - 2x) e^y \dfrac{dy}{dx} - 2e^y = \sec^2 x$

2 Find, by inspection, the integrating factors required to make the following differential equations into exact equations, and solve them:

(a) $\sin y + \dfrac{1}{2} x \cos y \dfrac{dy}{dx} = 3$

(b) $\dfrac{dy}{dx} + \dfrac{y}{x} = \dfrac{e^x}{x}$

(c) $\dfrac{1}{x} \tan y + \sec^2 y \dfrac{dy}{dx} = 2e^{x^2}$

(d) $y e^x + y^2 e^x \dfrac{dx}{dy} = 1$

3 Solve the following first order linear equations:

(a) $\dfrac{dy}{dx} + 2y = e^{-2x} \cos x$

(b) $\dfrac{1}{t} \dfrac{ds}{dt} = 1 - 2s$

(c) $\dfrac{dy}{dx} + (2x + 1)y - e^{-x^2} = 0$

(d) $\dfrac{dr}{d\theta} + 2r \cot \theta = \operatorname{cosec}^2 \theta$

(e) $\dfrac{dr}{d\theta} + r \tan \theta = \cos \theta$

(f) $x \dfrac{dy}{dx} + 2y = \dfrac{\cos x}{x}$

4 Find the particular solutions of the following differential equations which satisfy the given conditions:

(a) $(x + 1) \dfrac{dy}{dx} - 3y = (x + 1)^4$ $y = 16$ when $x = 1$

(b) $\dfrac{du}{d\theta} + u \cot \theta = 2 \cos \theta$ $u = 3$ when $\theta = \dfrac{\pi}{2}$

5 Solve the following differential equations:

(a) $\dfrac{dz}{dt} + 3z = e^{2t}$ given that $z = 1$ when $t = 0$

(b) $x\dfrac{dV}{dx} + V = x^3$ given that $V = 1$ when $x = 1$

29.6 Simple harmonic motion

Simple harmonic motion (SHM) is a very common phenomenon in the physical world. It appears in many guises, but it always produces a second order differential equation of the form

$$\boxed{\dfrac{d^2 y}{dx^2} = -n^2 y}$$
   . . . (1)

This is called the SHM equation.

As we shall see, we can reduce it to two first order equations which can be solved by the methods already used in this chapter.

The first step is to write $\dfrac{dy}{dx}$ as p, which enables us to write

$$\dfrac{d^2 y}{dx^2} = \dfrac{dp}{dx}$$

and then, using the chain rule, we have

$$\dfrac{dp}{dx} = \dfrac{dp}{dy} \times \dfrac{dy}{dx} = p\dfrac{dp}{dy}$$

This enables us to write equation (1) as a first order differential equation:

$$p\dfrac{dp}{dy} = -n^2 y$$

which we can solve by separating the variables, as follows:

$$\int p \, dp = -n^2 \int y \, dy$$

hence

$$\tfrac{1}{2}p^2 = -\tfrac{1}{2}n^2 y^2 + c$$
   . . . (2)

where c is the constant of integration. However it is very convenient to express c in a different form. We choose a to represent the value of y for which p is zero, i.e.

$$0 = -\tfrac{1}{2}n^2 a^2 + c$$
$$\tfrac{1}{2}n^2 a^2 = c$$

Equation (2) now takes the form

$$p^2 = -n^2 y^2 + n^2 a^2$$
$$= n^2(a^2 - y^2)$$
$$\therefore \qquad p = n\sqrt{(a^2 - y^2)}$$

. . . (3)

Now $\quad p = \dfrac{dy}{dx}$, so

$$\frac{dy}{dx} = n\sqrt{(a^2 - y^2)}$$

. . . (4)

Once again we have a first order equation, and this too can be solved by separating the variables

$$\int \frac{dy}{\sqrt{(a^2 - y^2)}} = \int n\, dx$$

The integral on the left-hand side is a standard one which we met in Section 25.8, giving

$$\sin^{-1}(y/a) = nx + \alpha$$

where α is the (second) constant of integration. Rearranging this we have a general solution of the SHM equation, namely

$$y = a \sin(nx + \alpha)$$

. . . (5)

There is however an alternative form of this which is frequently more convenient. Using the 'addition' formula (see Section 18.2), we can write

$$y = a \sin nx \cos \alpha + a \cos nx \sin \alpha$$

and replacing $a \cos \alpha$ by A, and $a \sin \alpha$ by B, equation (5) can be expressed

$$\boxed{y = A \sin nx + B \cos nx}$$

For most purposes, the reader will find this is a very convenient form of the solution. It may be quoted whenever a general solution of the SHM equation is required. Example 5 shows how it is used.

Qu. 14 Verify, by differentiating twice, that $z = A \sin 4t + B \cos 4t$ is a solution of the equation

$$\frac{d^2 z}{dt^2} = -16z$$

for all values of A and B.

Qu. 15 Investigate the effect of taking the negative square root in equation (3) above.

Example 5

Find the general solution of the differential equation

$$25\frac{d^2r}{dt^2} + 4r = 0$$

and find the particular solution for which $r = 0$ and $\dfrac{dr}{dt} = 10$ when $t = 0$.

The given equation can be written

$$\frac{d^2r}{dt^2} = -\frac{4}{25}r$$

and apart from different symbols (r for y and t for x) this is a standard SHM equation with $n^2 = \frac{4}{25}$, i.e. $n = \frac{2}{5}$. Its general solution is:

$$r = A \sin \tfrac{2}{5}t + B \cos \tfrac{2}{5}t$$

When $t = 0$, $r = 0$

so $0 = B$

Hence $r = A \sin \tfrac{2}{5}t$

and differentiating this

$$\frac{dr}{dt} = \tfrac{2}{5}A \cos \tfrac{2}{5}t$$

But we are told that $\dfrac{dr}{dt} = 10$ when $t = 0$, so

$$10 = \tfrac{2}{5} \times A$$

$$\therefore \quad A = 25$$

Hence the solution which satisfies the given conditions is

$$r = 25 \sin \tfrac{2}{5}t$$

Exercise 29c

1 In this question identify the differential equations which represent SHM and, in these cases, write down the general solution:

(a) $\dfrac{d^2y}{dx^2} + 25y = 0$ (b) $36\dfrac{d^2y}{dx^2} + y = 0$ (c) $4\dfrac{d^2y}{dx^2} + 9y = 0$

(d) $\dfrac{d^2z}{dt^2} + z = 0$ (e) $\dfrac{d^2y}{dx^2} - 25y = 0$ (f) $\dfrac{d^2y}{dx^2} - 6x = 0$

(g) $\dfrac{d^2y}{dx^2} = -100y$ (h) $\dfrac{d^2r}{d\theta^2} + n^2r = 0$

2 Find the general solution of the equation

$$\frac{d^2v}{dt^2} + 25v = 0$$

and hence find the particular solution for which $v = 0$ and $\dfrac{dv}{dt} = 10$ when $t = 0$.

3 Find the general solution of the equation

$$\frac{d^2y}{dx^2} + 4y = 0$$

and hence find the particular solution for which $y = 1$ and $\dfrac{dy}{dx} = 6$ when $x = 0$.

4 Find the general solution of the equation

$$100\frac{d^2x}{dt^2} + x = 0$$

and hence find the particular solution for which $x = 20$ and $\dfrac{dx}{dt} = 0$ when $t = 0$.

5 Find the general solution of the equation

$$\frac{d^2y}{dx^2} + n^2 y = 0$$

and hence find the particular solution for which $y = 0$ and $\dfrac{dy}{dx} = a$ (where a is a constant) when $x = 0$.

6 Find the general solution of the equation

$$\frac{d^2x}{dt^2} + n^2 x = 0$$

and hence find the particular solution for which $x = a$ and $\dfrac{dx}{dt} = 0$ (where a is a constant) when $t = 0$.

7 Given that

$$4\frac{d^2x}{dt^2} + \pi^2 x = 0$$

and that $x = 10$ and $\dfrac{dx}{dt} = 2\pi$ when $t = 1$, find x in terms of t.

8 In the differential equation

$$\frac{d^2y}{dx^2} + 4y = 12$$

substitute $y = Y + 3$, and hence find a general solution of the differential equation.

Exercise 29d (Miscellaneous)

Solve the differential equations in nos. 1–6.

1 $\cos t \dfrac{dx}{dt} = x$ **2** $x\dfrac{dy}{dx} - y = x^2 \ln x$

3 $\cos \theta = \sin \theta \dfrac{d\theta}{dr}$ **4** $3\dfrac{d^2 y}{dx^2} + 4y = 0$

5 $(2x - 1)\dfrac{dy}{dx} + 8y = 4(2x - 1)^{-2}$

6 $9\dfrac{d^2 x}{dt^2} + 4x = 0$, given that $x = 2$ when $t = 0$, and $x = -4$ when $t = \pi$.

7 Solve the differential equation

$$x\dfrac{dy}{dx} + 2y = e^x \quad (x > 0)$$

given that $y = 1$ when $x = 1$. (C)

8 Find the solution of the differential equation

$$\dfrac{dy}{dx} = xy \ln x$$

which satisfies the initial conditions $x = 1$, $y = 1$. Give $\ln y$ in terms of x. (O & C)

9 Find the solution of the differential equation

$$ye^{2x}\dfrac{dy}{dx} = x$$

which satisfies the boundary condition $y = 2$ when $x = 0$. Give y in terms of x. (O & C)

10 Prove that if $y = f(x)$ satisfies the differential equation

$$\dfrac{dy}{dx} = -2xy$$

then so does $y = kf(x)$, where k is any real number.
Find the equation of the solution curve through the point $(0, 1)$ and sketch a graph showing several members of the family of solutions. (O & C: SMP)

11 Find the solution of the differential equation

$$\dfrac{dy}{dx} + y \cot x = \cos 3x$$

for which $y = 1$, when $x = \pi/6$. (JMB)

12 The temperature y degrees of a body, t minutes after being placed in a certain room, satisfies the differential equation

$$6\frac{d^2 y}{dt^2} + \frac{dy}{dt} = 0$$

By using the substitution $z = \frac{dy}{dt}$, find y in terms of t, given that $y = 63$ when

$t = 0$ and $y = 36$ when $t = 6 \ln 4$.

Find after how many minutes the rate of cooling of the body will have fallen below one degree per minute, giving your answer correct to the nearest minute. How cool does the body get?   (O & C)

13 In established forest fires, the proportion of the total area of the forest which has been destroyed is denoted by x, and the rate of change of x with respect to time, t hours, is called the destruction rate. Investigations show that the destruction rate is directly proportional to the product of x and $(1 - x)$. A particular fire is initially noticed when one half of the forest is destroyed, and it is found that the destruction rate at this time is such that, if it remained constant thereafter, the forest would be destroyed completely in a further 24 hours. Show that

$$12\frac{dx}{dt} = x(1 - x)$$

and deduce that approximately 73% of the forest is destroyed 12 hours after it is first noticed.   (L)

14 A chemical substance X decays, at a rate equal to twice the quantity of X present, so that $\frac{dx}{dt} = -2x$ where x is the quantity of X present at time t.

Given that initially $x = a$, find an expression for x in terms of a and t.
The quantity, y, of another substance Y changes so that its rate of increase is equal to $2ae^{-2t} - \frac{1}{2}y$. Given that initially $y = 0$, find an expression for y at time t.   (L)

15 At any instant, a spherical meteorite is gaining mass because of two effects: (a) mass is condensing onto it at a rate which is proportional to the surface area of the meteorite at that instant (b) the gravitational field of the meteorite attracts mass onto itself, the rate being proportional to the mass of the meteorite mass at that instant. Assuming that the two effects can be added together and that the meteorite remains spherical and of constant density, show that the radius r at time t satisfies the differential equation

$$\frac{dr}{dt} = A + Br \qquad \text{where } A \text{ and } B \text{ are constants}$$

If $r = r_0$ at $t = 0$, show that

$$r = r_0 e^{Bt} + \frac{A}{B}(e^{Bt} - 1)$$

                    (L)

Chapter 30

The trapezium rule and Simpson's rule

30.1 Introduction

In Chapter 24, we tackled the problem of finding an approximate solution to an equation and developed a method which could be used even when it was impossible to find an exact solution. In this chapter we shall be looking at two methods for estimating the area under a curve which can be used even when integration is out of the question. The first method depends on the formula for the area of a trapezium. For a trapezium like that in Figure 30.1, in which the lengths of the parallel sides are a and b, and where the distance between them is d, this formula for the area A is

$$A = \left(\frac{a+b}{2}\right)d$$

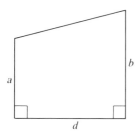

Figure 30.1

Consider the following problem. A cyclist travels along a straight road. She starts from rest and her speed in m s^{-1} measured at 2 second intervals is given by the table below.

time (s)	0	2	4	6	8	10
speed (m s^{-1})	0	1.0	2.8	4.9	6.4	7.4

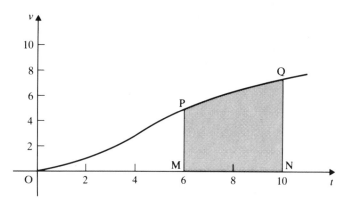

Figure 30.2

(This information is shown in the graph in Figure 30.2, which is not drawn to scale.) Find the distance travelled by the cyclist in the 4 seconds from $t = 6$ to $t = 10$.

When we did problems like this before (see Section 7.2), we used integration, but in this example, we do not know the function whose graph is shown in Figure 30.2. However, we can say that the distance we require is represented by the area bounded by the lines MN, MP, NQ and the curve PQ, and this area is almost the same as the area of the trapezium PQNM; in making this approximation, we have lost the area bounded by the curve PQ and the straight line PQ, but this is only a very small proportion of the total area. We can calculate the area of the trapezium, using the formula above, i.e.

$$A = \left(\frac{4.9 + 7.4}{2}\right) \times 4$$

$$= 24.6$$

So the distance required is approximately 24.6 m.

In the next section we shall see how this method can be applied more generally.

Qu. 1 Use the method above to estimate the distance travelled by the cyclist over the 2 second interval from $t = 4$ to $t = 6$.
Qu. 2 Estimate the distance travelled by the cyclist from $t = 6$ to $t = 10$, by dividing the area into two trapeziums, each two units wide. Would you expect this answer to be better than the one in the text? Justify your answer.

30.2 The trapezium rule

Suppose we wish to find the area under the curve shown in Figure 30.3. We draw lines parallel to the y-axis at (equal) intervals of d units, and we form an estimate of the area required by calculating the areas of the trapeziums shown. In this diagram there are four trapeziums, but any convenient number may be used; in general the more intervals there are, the better the approximation.

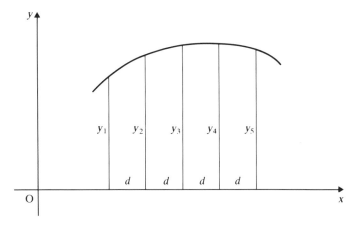

Figure 30.3

The area estimated by this method will be

$$\frac{y_1 + y_2}{2}d + \frac{y_2 + y_3}{2}d + \frac{y_3 + y_4}{2}d + \frac{y_4 + y_5}{2}d$$

i.e. $\boxed{\text{area} \approx \tfrac{1}{2}d(y_1 + 2y_2 + 2y_3 + 2y_4 + y_5)}$ . . . (1)

This is the trapezium rule for five ordinates.†

Qu. 3 Use the trapezium rule to estimate the area, from $x = 0.2$ to $x = 1$, under the curve given by

x	0.20	0.40	0.60	0.80	1.00
y	0.24	0.56	0.96	1.44	2.00

Given that the equation of the curve is $y = x^2 + x$, check your answer by integration.

Qu. 4 Find expressions similar to (1) for:
(a) eight ordinates   (b) nine ordinates
Now express the trapezium rule in words.
Qu. 5 Estimate the area under the curve given by the following table. Beware of the catch!

x	0	10	15	20	25
y	7	9	11	12	10

The following example has been chosen to illustrate the accuracy of the trapezium rule. We shall compare the answer with that obtained by another rule later.

† Ordinate means y-coordinate, see Section 2.1.

Example 1

Use the trapezium rule to estimate the area under the curve $y = 1/x$ from $x = 1$ to $x = 2$.

To begin with, let us take six ordinates. In this example, $d = 0.2$.

$$\text{Area} \approx \tfrac{1}{2} \times 0.2 \left\{ 1 + \frac{2}{1.2} + \frac{2}{1.4} + \frac{2}{1.6} + \frac{2}{1.8} + \frac{1}{2} \right\}$$

$$= 0.696 \qquad \text{correct to three significant figures}$$

Now by integration the area in Example 1 is

$$\int_1^2 \frac{1}{x}\, dx = \left[\ln x \right]_1^2$$

$$= \ln 2$$

$$= 0.693 \qquad \text{correct to three significant figures}$$

Qu. 6 Repeat the calculation of Example 1 but with eleven ordinates instead of six.

Qu. 7 Use the trapezium rule to find the distance travelled by the cyclist in Section 30.1 in the first ten seconds.

Readers who have access to a microcomputer should certainly write a program for evaluating definite integrals by the trapezium method. Since the computer will be doing the arithmetic, a large number of strips can be used and hence a high degree of accuracy can be achieved.

30.3 Simpson's rule

It will have been clear from Figure 30.3 that the trapezium rule with a small number of strips will not be very accurate for curves like the one illustrated. If, on the other hand, we were to try to join the tops of the ordinates by a smooth curve, we might expect to get a better estimate. The question then arises as to what curve to use – and there are a number of possibilities. But if we take three ordinates we can find a parabola in the form

$$y = ax^2 + bx + c$$

to pass through the three corresponding points.

Given a curve with three ordinates y_1, y_2, y_3 at *equal* intervals of d apart, take the y-axis along the middle ordinate and the x-axis through its foot as in Figure 30.4.

Let

$$y = ax^2 + bx + c$$

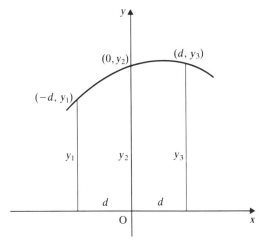

Figure 30.4

be the *parabola* through the points $(-d, y_1)$, $(0, y_2)$, (d, y_3); its equation is therefore satisfied by their coordinates.

$$\therefore \quad y_1 = ad^2 - bd + c$$
$$y_2 = \qquad\qquad c$$
$$y_3 = ad^2 + bd + c$$

The area under the parabola is

$$\int_{-d}^{d} (ax^2 + bx + c)\, dx = \left[\frac{ax^3}{3} + \frac{bx^2}{2} + cx \right]_{-d}^{d}$$

$$= \tfrac{2}{3}ad^3 + 2cd$$

[Note that we do not need to find the equation of the parabola because we can express this area in terms of the data y_1, y_2, y_3, d.]

Now

$$y_1 + y_3 - 2y_2 = 2ad^2$$
$$\therefore \qquad y_1 + 4y_2 + y_3 = 2ad^2 + 6c$$
$$\therefore \quad \tfrac{1}{3}d(y_1 + 4y_2 + y_3) = \tfrac{2}{3}ad^3 + 2cd$$

So an approximation for the area under the given curve is given by

$$\boxed{\text{area} \approx \tfrac{1}{3}d(y_1 + 4y_2 + y_3)}$$

This result is known as Simpson's rule and was published by Thomas Simpson in 1743.

Note It makes very little difference to the proof exactly what points we are given originally. If, for instance, we are told that the curve passes through (x_1, y_1), (x_2, y_2), (x_3, y_3), where $x_2 = \tfrac{1}{2}(x_1 + x_3)$, we can at once take new axes, parallel to the given ones, with the new origin at $(x_2, 0)$. Let $d = x_3 - x_2 = x_2 - x_1$; the rest of the proof is as above.

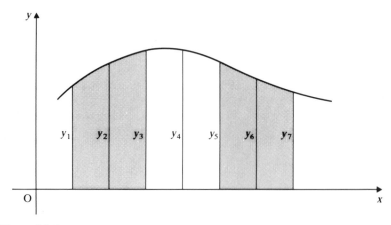

Figure 30.5

In practice we usually require the area under a curve with more than three ordinates and so, provided there is an *odd* number of ordinates, we may apply Simpson's rule a number of times. Thus with seven ordinates (see Figure 30.5) the area is

$$\tfrac{1}{3}d(y_1 + 4y_2 + y_3) + \tfrac{1}{3}d(y_3 + 4y_4 + y_5) + \tfrac{1}{3}d(y_5 + 4y_6 + y_7)$$

i.e. $\boxed{\text{area} = \tfrac{1}{3}d(y_1 + 4y_2 + 2y_3 + 4y_4 + 2y_5 + 4y_6 + y_7)}$

Qu. 8 Find similar expressions for the area with:
(a) five ordinates   (b) nine ordinates
Now express Simpson's rule for an odd number of ordinates in words.

The next example is the same as Example 1. This is so that the reader may compare the accuracy of Simpson's rule and the trapezium rule for this case.

Example 2

Use Simpson's rule to find an approximation for the area under the curve $y = 1/x$ between $x = 1$ and $x = 2$.

Five ordinates have been used, and $d = 0.25$.

$$\text{area} \approx \tfrac{1}{3} \times 0.25 \left\{ 1 + \frac{4}{1.25} + \frac{2}{1.5} + \frac{4}{1.75} + \frac{1}{2} \right\}$$

$$= 0.693 \qquad \text{correct to three significant figures}$$

This is a nearer value for ln 2 than the result obtained with the trapezium rule using eleven ordinates (see Qu. 6).

[When the arithmetic in Example 2 is done on a calculator, it will be seen that the result is 0.693 253 97, correct to eight decimal places, whereas the exact answer, ln 2, equals 0.693 147 18, correct to eight decimal places, so in this case the approximate method has yielded the first three significant figures correctly.

The reader should notice that the accuracy of the result depends on the method selected, the number of strips used and the shape of the graph, so there is no virtue in presenting an answer which includes all the figures shown by the calculator; indeed this could give a totally false impression.]

Qu. 9 Evaluate approximately $\int_1^2 \frac{1}{x} \, dx$ using Simpson's rule with eleven ordinates.

Qu. 10 Repeat Qu. 3, using Simpson's rule.

Exercise 30

1 Evaluate $\int_0^{\pi/4} \tan x \, dx$,

(a) by integration
(b) by using the trapezium rule with four strips
(c) by Simpson's rule with four strips
Comment on the accuracy of your answers.

2 Repeat no. 1, parts (b) and (c), for $\int_0^1 e^{x^2} \, dx$.

3 (x_1, y_1), (x_2, y_2), (x_3, y_3), where $x_2 = \frac{1}{2}(x_1 + x_3)$, are three points on the parabola $y = ax^2 + bx + c$. Prove that the area under the curve between the lines $x = x_1$ and $x = x_3$ is equal to $\frac{1}{3}(x_2 - x_1)(y_1 + 4y_2 + y_3)$.
Use this formula to find the area between the parabola $y = x(10 - x)$ and the x-axis. Check your answer by integration.

4 Evaluate $\int_0^1 e^{-x^2} \, dx$ by Simpson's rule taking ten intervals.

5 Estimate the area of a quadrant of a circle of radius 8 cm by dividing it into eight intervals and using:
(a) the trapezium rule   (b) Simpson's rule
Use the better of these results to find an approximate value of π.

6 The area in square centimetres of the cross-section of a model boat 28 cm long at intervals of 3.5 cm is as follows:

| 0 | 11.5 | 15.3 | 16.3 | 16.2 | 13.4 | 9.3 | 4.9 | 0 |

Find the volume of the boat.

7 A jug of circular cross-section is 16 cm high inside and its internal diameter is measured at equal intervals from the bottom:

height (cm)	0	4	8	12	16
diameter (cm)	10.2	13.8	15.3	9.3	9.9

What volume of liquid will the jug hold if filled to the brim?

8 The coordinates of three points on the curve $y = ax^3 + bx^2 + cx + d$ are $(x_1, y_1), (x_2, y_2), (x_3, y_3)$. Prove that, if $x_2 - x_1 = x_3 - x_2 = h$, the area under the curve between the lines $x = x_1$, $x = x_3$ is $\frac{1}{3}h(y_1 + 4y_2 + y_3)$.

Find the area between the curve, $y = x(x - 2)^2$ and the x-axis by means of Simpson's rule with three ordinates. Use integration to check that your answer is exact.

9 Use the binomial theorem to expand $(1 + x^3)^{10}$ in ascending powers of x, up to and including the term in x^9. Hence estimate I, where

$$I = \int_0^{0.2} (1 + x^3)^{10} \, dx$$

to three decimal places.

Make another estimate of I, again to three places, by using Simpson's rule with three ordinates, showing all your working.   (L)

10 Tabulate, to three decimal places, the values of the function

$$f(x) = \sqrt{(1 + x^2)}$$

for values of x from 0 to 0.8 at intervals of 0.1. Use these values to estimate

$$\int_0^{0.8} f(x) \, dx$$

(a) by the trapezium rule, using all the ordinates
(b) by Simpson's rule, using only the ordinates at intervals of 0.2   (L)

11 By considering suitable areas, or otherwise, show that, for any $n > 0$,

$$\tfrac{1}{2} \leqslant \int_0^1 (1 + x^n)^{-1} \, dx \leqslant 1$$

When $n = 4$, find a value (to three significant figures) for the integral, using Simpson's rule with five ordinates.   (O & C)

12 The integral $\int_0^{1/2} \sqrt{(1 - x^2)} \, dx$ is denoted by I. The value of I is estimated by using the trapezium rule, and T_1, T_2 denote the estimates obtained when one and two strips respectively are used. Calculate T_1 and T_2, giving your answers correct to three decimal places.

Assuming the error when using the trapezium rule is proportional to h^3, where h denotes the width of a strip, show that an improved estimate of I is given by $(8T_2 - T_1)/7$, and evaluate this expression correct to three decimal places.

Given that $y^2 = 1 - x^2$ is the equation of a circle whose centre is the origin and whose radius is 1 unit, show that $I = \dfrac{\pi}{12} + \dfrac{\sqrt{3}}{8}$. Hence calculate an estimate for the value of π.   (C)

Revision Exercise 6

1 (a) Find $\int \dfrac{e^x}{e^x + 1}\,dx$

(b) By using the substitution $x = \sin\theta$, or otherwise, show that

$$\int_0^{3/5} \dfrac{1}{(1-x^2)^{3/2}}\,dx = \tfrac{3}{4}$$ 　(C)

2 By expressing both logarithms to a common base, or otherwise, solve the equation

$$\log_3 x = \log_x 9$$

giving your answers correct to two places of decimals. 　(C)

3 A curve has parametric equations

$$x = 3e^{2t} - t \qquad y = e^{3t} - 2t$$

Find in terms of t:

(a) $\dfrac{dx}{dt}$ 　(b) $\dfrac{dy}{dt}$ 　(c) $\dfrac{dy}{dx}$

The gradient of the normal to the curve at the point P is $-\tfrac{1}{2}$.

(d) Find the value of t at P giving your answer in the form $t = \ln k$, where k is a constant. 　(L)

4 Given $f(x) = \dfrac{3x}{(x+2)(x-1)}$

express $f(x)$ in partial fractions. Hence evaluate

$$\int_{-1}^0 f(x)\,dx$$ 　(L)

5 By means of the substitution $u = e^x$, or otherwise, evaluate

$$\int_0^1 \dfrac{e^x}{1 + e^{2x}}\,dx$$

giving your answer correct to two decimal places. 　(JMB)

6 Express $\dfrac{1}{(3t+1)(t+3)}$ in partial fractions.

Use the substitution $t = \tan x$ to show that

$$\int_0^{\pi/4} \dfrac{1}{3 + 5\sin 2x}\,dx = \int_0^1 \dfrac{1}{(3t+1)(t+3)}\,dt$$

Hence show that $\displaystyle\int_0^{\pi/4} \dfrac{1}{3 + 5\sin 2x}\,dx = \tfrac{1}{8}\ln 3$ 　(L)

7 Evaluate

$$\int_1^e (2x + 1) \ln x \, dx$$

giving your answer in a simplified form in terms of e.   (JMB)

8 Evaluate each of the following integrals:

(a) $\displaystyle\int_0^1 \frac{1}{(2x + 1)^2} \, dx$

(b) $\displaystyle\int_{-1}^0 x^2 \sqrt{(1 + x)} \, dx$ (O & C)

9 Write down the series expansions of (i) e^{3x} (ii) $(1 + 2x)^{-1/2}$ in ascending powers of x up to and including the term in x^2.

Hence obtain the series expansion of

$$f(x) = \frac{e^{3x}}{\sqrt{(1 + 2x)}}$$

in ascending powers of x up to and including the term in x^2.

State the range of values of x for which the expansion of $f(x)$ is valid.   (O)

10 The number, N, of radioactive atoms present at time t seconds when a particular element decays is given by the equation $N = 10^{26} e^{-2t}$.

(a) State the number of radioactive atoms initially present.

(b) Sketch the graph of N against t.

(c) Calculate how long it takes for the number of radioactive atoms present to be reduced to half the number initially present.   (C)

11 Determine the range of values of x for which the sum to infinity of the geometrical progression

$$1 + \tfrac{1}{2}e^x + \tfrac{1}{4}e^{2x} + \tfrac{1}{8}e^{3x} + \dots$$

exists. Find the sum to infinity in this case.

Given that the sum of the first five terms is equal to half the sum to infinity, prove that $x = \tfrac{4}{5} \ln 2$.   (O)

12 Solve each of the equations, to find x in terms of a, where $a > 0$ and $a \neq e^2$:

(a) $a^x = e^{2x+1}$

(b) $2 \ln (2x) = 1 + \ln a$ (C)

13 (a) The finite region bounded by the x-axis, the curve $y = e^{-x}$, and the lines $x = \pm a$ is denoted by R. Find, in terms of a, the volume of the solid generated when R is rotated through one revolution about the x-axis.

(b) (i) By using a suitable substitution, or otherwise, evaluate

$$\int_0^1 x(1 - x)^9 \, dx$$

(ii) Find $\displaystyle\int 2x \tan^{-1} x \, dx$ (C)

14 The integral I is defined by

$$I = \int_0^{\pi/2} \cos^2 x \, dx \qquad \text{(i)}$$

Use the substitution $x = \pi/2 - y$ to show that

$$I = \int_0^{\pi/2} \sin^2 x \, dx \qquad \text{(ii)}$$

Hence by considering the sum of (i) and (ii), deduce the value of I.   (W)

15 Sketch, in separate diagrams, the graphs of:
(a) $y = x^2 - x^4$
(b) $y = x/(1 - 2x)$
(c) $y = 1 + \sin x$ (O & C)

16 Find the coordinates of the stationary points of the curve

$$y = \frac{(x - \alpha)^2}{(x - 1)(x - 2)}$$

Sketch the curve when:
(a) $\alpha > 2$ (b) $\frac{3}{2} < \alpha < 2$ (C)

17 Sketch the curve $y = (2x - 1)^2(x + 1)$, showing the coordinates of:
(a) the points where it meets the axes
(b) the turning points
(c) the point of inflexion
By using your sketch, or otherwise, sketch the graph of

$$y = \frac{1}{(2x - 1)^2(x + 1)}$$

Show clearly the coordinates of any turning points.   (L)

18 Find the set of values of k for which the equation

$$x^2 + 1 = k(x^2 + x + 1)$$

has real roots. Hence, or otherwise, find the coordinates of the turning points of the curve whose equation is

$$y = \frac{x^2 + 1}{x^2 + x + 1}$$

Sketch this curve, clearly labelling the turning points and any asymptotes.   (JMB)

19 Solve, for y in terms of $x > 0$, the differential equation

$$x\frac{dy}{dx} = 3(1 - y)$$

given that $y = \frac{1}{2}$ when $x = 2$.   (C)

20 By first substituting $y = ux$, where u is a function of x, or otherwise, solve the differential equation

$$x\frac{dy}{dx} - y = x$$

subject to the condition $y = 1$ when $x = 1$.   (O & C)

21 Express $\dfrac{1}{(1 + x)(3 + x)}$ in partial fractions.

Hence find the solution of the differential equation

$$\frac{dy}{dx} = \frac{y}{(1 + x)(3 + x)} \quad \text{where} \quad x > -1$$

given that $y = 2$ when $x = 1$. Express your answer in the form $y = f(x)$.

(L)

22 (a) Find $\displaystyle\int x\,e^{2x}\,dx$.

(b) Solve the differential equation

$$\frac{dy}{dx} = xy\,e^{2x} \quad \text{given that} \quad y = 1 \quad \text{when} \quad x = 0.$$ (O)

23 (a) Find, correct to two significant figures, all the real roots of the equation $10x = e^x$.

(b) Using the substitution $y = vx$, or otherwise, solve the differential equation

$$x\frac{dy}{dx} = y + x^2$$

where $y = 0$ when $x = -1$, expressing y in terms of x.   (C)

24 (a) Use integration by parts to find

$$\int x^{1/2} \ln x\,dx$$

(b) Find the solution of the differential equation

$$\frac{dy}{dx} = (xy)^{1/2} \ln x$$

for which $y = 1$ when $x = 1$.   (AEB)

25 Sketch the graph of the curve with equation $y = \ln(8 - x)$. By drawing a suitable straight line show that the equation $x = \ln(8 - x)$ has just one root α. Prove that α lies between 1 and 2.

Use an iterative method to find α, giving your answer correct to two decimal places.

Use Simpson's rule with 6 equal intervals to find an approximation to

$$\int_0^6 \{\ln(8-x)\}^2 \, dx$$

giving your answer correct to two decimal places. (O)

26 A curve has equation $y = x - 1 + \dfrac{1}{1+x}$

Calculate the coordinates of the turning points of the curve and determine their nature.

The finite region bounded by the curve, the x-axis from $x = 0$ to $x = 4$ and the line $x = 4$ is R. Express the area of R as an integral and show that its exact value is $4 + \ln 5$.

Use Simpson's rule with 4 intervals to find an estimate of the same integral, giving your answer to three decimal places. Hence find an approximation for $\ln 5$, giving your answer to two decimal places. (AEB)

27 Estimate the value of the integral

$$\int_{0.01}^{0.49} \frac{1}{1+2\sqrt{x}} \, dx$$

by using the trapezium rule with three ordinates, giving your answer to 2 decimal places.

Using the substitution $u^2 = x$, or otherwise, obtain the exact value of the integral. (L)

28 (a) The method known as Simpson's rule for evaluating the area under a curve uses the process of replacing the curve by a sequence of quadratic functions which can easily be integrated. It follows that $\displaystyle\int_{-h}^{+h} y \, dx$ is evaluated exactly using Simpson's rule if y is a quadratic function. Show that this is true if y is a cubic function.

(b) Write the first three terms of the expansion of $e^{-\frac{1}{2}x^2}$.

Find $\displaystyle\int_{-0.5}^{0.5} e^{-\frac{1}{2}x^2} \, dx$

(i) by direct integration of your expression
(ii) by using Simpson's rule on the function $e^{-\frac{1}{2}x^2}$
(iii) by using Simpson's rule on your expansion
(In both (ii) and (ii) take two strips of width 0.5).

(c) Find $\displaystyle\int_{-0.5}^{0.5} \frac{1}{1+\frac{1}{2}x^2} dx$

correct to 3 decimal places using an appropriate substitution. Using the binomial expansion say how this is related to (b) above. (O & C)

29 Use the trapezium rule, with ordinates $x = 1$, $x = 2$ and $x = 3$, to estimate the value of

$$\int_1^3 \sqrt{(40 - x^3)} \, dx \tag{C}$$

30 By means of the substitution $x = 6 \sin \theta$, or otherwise, prove that

$$\int_0^3 \sqrt{(36 - x^2)} \, dx = 3\pi + \tfrac{9}{2}\sqrt{3}$$

(a) Write down the expansion of $\sqrt{(36 - x^2)}$ in ascending powers of x up to and including the term in x^4. By integrating term by term obtain an approximation to the value of the integral

$$\int_0^3 \sqrt{(36 - x^2)} \, dx$$

giving your answer to three decimal places.
(b) Use Simpson's rule with six equal intervals to find an approximate value of the integral

$$\int_0^3 \sqrt{(36 - x^2)} \, dx$$

giving your answer to three decimal places.
(c) State which of the approximations in (a) and (b) is the more accurate and suggest a way in which each of the two methods could be modified to give more accurate approximations.   (O)

Answers

Chapter 1 (p1)

Exercise 1a (p1)

1 $3x + 17$ **2** $5x^2 - y^2$ **3** $x + 2x^2$
4 $5y - 2x - 25$ **5** $5y - 10$ **6** $4x - 43$
7 $6x - x^2$ **8** $2x^2 + 2h^2$ **9** $x^2 + 12$
10 $t^2 + 2 + 1/t^2$

Exercise 1b (p2)

1 $4x(3x + 2y)$ **2** $ab(b - a)$ **3** $2xy(x + 4y)$
4 $xy(z + u)$ **5** $\pi r(r + 2h)$ **6** $(p - q)(a + b)$
7 $(a + b)(x - y)$ **8** $(h - k)(p - q)$ **9** $(x + 2y)(x + 3y)$
10 $4ab(b^2 + a^2)$

Exercise 1c (p3)

1 $(p + 6)(p - 6)$ **2** $(10x + 7)(10x - 7)$
3 $(t + \frac{1}{2})(t - \frac{1}{2})$ **4** $2(x + 5)(x - 5)$
5 no factors **6** $3(5x + 4)(5x - 4)$
7 $(x + 15)(x - 1)$ **8** $(4 + 9y^2)(2 + 3y)(2 - 3y)$
9 $12x$ **10** $(a + 2b + c)(a - c)$

Exercise 1d (p4)

1 $(x - 2)(x - 7)$ **2** $(2y - 3)(y + 7)$ **3** $(2t + 1)(4t - 3)$
4 no factors **5** $(3 - s)^2$ **6** no factors
7 $(2x - 7)(x - 2)$ **8** $(4y + 3)^2$ **9** no factors
10 $(5 + 2c)^2$ **11** $2(2x + 3)(x + 1)$ **12** $(p - 8q)(p - q)$
13 $(2A + B)(A + 3B)$ **14** $3(7 - n)(1 - 2n)$ **15** $(2x^2 + 3)^2$
16 $(10a^3 - 3b^3)^2$

Exercise 1e (p4)

1 $(5x - 2)(7x + 3)$ **2** $2(x + 7)(x - 7)$ **3** $(2x + y)(x - y)$
4 $(x + a)(y + b)$ **5** $(x + 3)(y - 2)$ **6** $(x + 1)(x - 1)(2x + 3)$
7 $(x + 3)(2x^2 + 3x + 3)$ **8** $(x + 1)(12x + 5)$ **9** $20(x - 2)$
10 $2(x - 2)^2(3x - 1)$

Exercise 1f (p6)

1 $\frac{1}{4}$ **2** x/a **3** $1/(a - b)$ **4** -1 **5** $1/(x + 3)$
6 $xy/2$ **7** $c/(a + b)$ **8** x^2/y^2 **9** y/x **10** -5

Exercise 1g (p6)

1 $\dfrac{y - x}{xy}$ **2** $\dfrac{x^2 + y^2}{xy}$ **3** $\dfrac{1 + a}{a^2}$

4 $\dfrac{a + b}{a^2 b^2}$ **5** $\dfrac{2x}{(x - h)(x + h)}$ **6** $\dfrac{-h(2x + h)}{x^2(x + h)^2}$

7 $\dfrac{3x}{(1 - x)(2 + x)}$ **8** $\dfrac{-(x^2 - 2x + 4)}{(x^2 + 2)(2 + x)}$ **9** $\dfrac{n + 1}{n + 2}$

10 $\dfrac{x^2 + 3x + 3}{(x + 1)^2}$

Exercise 1h (p7)

1 $2/(T + t)$ **2** $\dfrac{x^2}{1 + x}$ **3** $-1/t$ **4** $-Tt$

5 $(2N + 1)(2N + 3)$ **6** $\sqrt{(a + b)}$
7 $(ad + bc)/(bd + ac)$ **8** $3x^2 + 3xh + h^2$

9 $\dfrac{1}{\sqrt{(1 + x^2)} \times (1 + x^2)} = \dfrac{1}{(1 + x^2)^{3/2}}$

10 $(1 - t)/(1 + t)$ [or $(t - 1)/(t + 1)$, whichever is positive]

Exercise 1i (p7)

1 6   **2** 10, 25   **3** 12   **4** 5, 25   **5** 7, 49
6 3, 4, 9   **7** 1, $\frac{1}{4}$ **8** 1, $\frac{1}{4}$, 1   **9** 10, 9   **10** $\frac{1}{2}$, $\frac{1}{9}$, $\frac{1}{4}$

Exercise 1j (p8)

1 $(x + 7)^2 + 1$ **2** $(x + 5)^2 + 15$ **3** $(t - 3)^2 + 4$
4 $(p - 2)^2 - 1$ **5** $(q + 10)^2 - 20$ **6** $4(x + 1\frac{1}{2})^2 + 1$
7 $(5z + 7)^2 + 11$ **8** $(3v - 1)^2 - 5$ **9** $2(x + 7)^2 - 100$
10 $5(w - 2)^2 - 8$

Exercise 1k (p9)

1 $m = (y - c)/x$ **2** $e = (a - b)/a$ **3** $x = y^2/(4a)$

4 $y = \dfrac{(K - k)(x - h)}{H - h} + k$ **5** $c = 4 + 3m$ **6** $x = (b - 1)/(a - 1)$

7 $l = T^2 g/(4\pi^2)$ **8** $g = 4\pi^2 l/T^2$ **9** $m = \dfrac{2x + 2y + 1}{2(2y - x)}$

10 $m = \dfrac{2x - 3y + 4}{3x - 2y + 2}$

Exercise 1l (p11)

1 3   **2** 2   **3** $\frac{1}{2}$ **4** 17
5 $7, 1\frac{1}{2}$ **6** $7, -2$ **7** $9, -11$ **8** $-5\frac{1}{2}, 7$
9 $0, -\frac{4}{5}$ **10** $+2\frac{1}{2}, -2\frac{1}{2}$ **11** $2, 3$ **12** $+2, -2$
13 $c(2T + 3t)/5$ **14** $t/5, 3t$ **15** $1/t, -T$

Exercise 1m (p14)

1 $2, -1$ **2** $2, -3$ **3** $-7/19, 8/19$
4 $-0.896, 2.18$, correct to 3 significant figures
5 $5, -2, \frac{1}{2}$ **6** $0, 0; 4, 4$ **7** $16, 4; -1, -64$
8 $0, 1; 2, 3$ **9** $10\frac{1}{2}, -12; 7, 2$ **10** $1, -1; 2, -6$
11 $10c, 7c$ **12** $tT, (t + T)$ **13** $t, 1/t; -1/t^3, -t^3$
14 $5a, 3a; 4a, 0$ **15** $2a, -a, 3a$

Exercise 1n (p15)

1 $0, +2, -2$ **2** $0, 0, 7$ **3** $0, -4, 5$ **4** $+4, -4, +1, -1$
5 $+2/3, -2/3$ **6** $0, 0, -k$ **7** $a, (a + b), (a - b)$ **8** 0
9 $+a, -a$ **10** $p + q$

Exercise 1o (p15)

1 (a) $(a + b)$ (or $-(a + b)$ if $a + b < 0$)   (b) $a^3 + b^3$
2 (a) $(K + 1)^2(K + 2)^2$ (b) $(N + 1)(N + 2)(2N + 9)$

3 (a) $\dfrac{4xh}{(x - h)^2(x + h)^2}$ (b) $\dfrac{-(2N + 5)}{(N + 2)(N + 3)}$

4 (a) $-\dfrac{1}{(n + 1)^2}$ (b) $2N(N^2 + 6N + 11)$

5 (a) $3, 9$ (b) $3\frac{1}{2}, \frac{3}{4}$

6 (a) $(u^2 - 3)/3$ (b) $\pm\sqrt{\{(u-1)/5\}}$
7 (a) $2a/3$ (b) $3a/7, -a$
8 (a) $2ct$ (b) $c(1-t^2)/t$
9 (a) $29a, 52a$ (b) $9a, 6a; a/9, -2a/3$
10 (a) 0   (b) $-k, 2k$

Chapter 2 (p17)

Qu. 1 $(-3, 2), (2, -3), (0, 0)$
Qu. 3   (a) 13   (b) $\sqrt{41}$ (c) $\sqrt{\{(r-p)^2 + (s-q)^2\}}$

Qu. 4   (a) $(5, 6)$ (b) $(-1, 4)$ (c) $(-\frac{3}{2}, -\frac{5}{2})$ (d) $\left(\dfrac{p+r}{2}, \dfrac{q+s}{2}\right)$

Qu. 5   (a) $\frac{9}{4}$ (b) $\frac{3}{2}$ (c) $-\frac{4}{5}$ (d) $-\frac{10}{11}$ (e) 0   (f) $(s-q)/(r-p)$
   (g) -1 (h) b/a
Qu. 6 $\frac{4}{3}, -\frac{3}{4}, -1$
Qu. 7 $\frac{12}{5}, -\frac{5}{12}, -1$
Qu. 8   (a) $-\frac{1}{3}$ (b) -4 (c) $\frac{1}{6}$ (d) $\frac{3}{2}$ (e) $-1/(2m)$ (f) a/b (g) $2/m$
Qu. 9   (a) parallel   (b) perpendicular   (c) neither
Qu. 10 $5, 20, -1$
Qu. 11 $2, 0, -\frac{5}{2}$
Qu. 12   (a) $(-\frac{1}{2}, 0), (1, 0)$ (b) $(0, -1)$
Qu. 13   (a) yes   (b) no   (c) no   (d) no   (e) yes   (f) yes
Qu. 14   (a) 0   (b) 2   (c) 3   (d) $\frac{1}{2}$ (e) -1
Qu. 15   (a) $y = \frac{1}{3}x$ (b) $y = -2x$ (c) $y = mx$
Qu. 16   (a) $\frac{1}{4}$ (b) $-\frac{5}{4}$ (c) $\frac{3}{2}$ (d) $\frac{7}{4}$ (e) q/p
Qu. 17   (a) $y = 3x + 2$ (b) $y = 3x + 4$ (c) $y = 3x - 1$
   (d) $y = \frac{1}{5}x + 2$ (e) $y = \frac{1}{5}x + 4$
Qu. 18   (a) $\frac{2}{3}, 2$ (b) $\frac{1}{4}, \frac{1}{2}$ (c) $-3, -6$ (d) $\frac{7}{3}, -\frac{5}{3}$ (e) $0, -4$
   (f) $-l/m, -n/m$
Qu. 19   (a) $y = 0$ (b) $x = 0$ (c) $x = 4$ (d) $y = -7$
Qu. 20   (a) $5x - 2y - 26 = 0$ (b) $5x + 2y - 1 = 0$
Qu. 21   (a) $3x - 2y - 19 = 0$ (b) $12x + 5y - 1 = 0$
Qu. 22   (a) $(4\frac{1}{2}, 1)$ (b) $(1, 5)$ (c) $(0, c)$ (d) $(-a, c - a)$
Qu. 23   no; they are parallel
Qu. 24 $(-\frac{3}{4}, 0), (\frac{2}{3}, 0)$

Exercise 2a (p20)

1 (a) 4   (b) 5   (c) 6   (d) 13   (e) $\sqrt{74}$ (f) 10
2 (a) $(3, 2)$ (b) $(5, \frac{5}{2})$ (c) $(1, 3)$ (d) $(0, \frac{7}{2})$
   (e) $(-\frac{1}{2}, -\frac{9}{2})$ (f) $(-6, -7)$
3 17   **4** $(-\frac{5}{2}, \frac{9}{2})$ **5** $(-\frac{3}{2}, -\frac{3}{2})$
6 P, R, S   **7** A, B, D; $\sqrt{50}$ **8** $13, 6\frac{1}{2}$

Exercise 2b (p31)

1 (a) $\frac{9}{5}$ (b) $-\frac{7}{3}$ (c) $-\frac{1}{14}$ (d) $\frac{1}{5}$
3 (a) 1 (b) -1 (c) $\sqrt{3}$ (d) $-1/\sqrt{3}$
4 (a) perpendicular (b) parallel (c) perpendicular (d) parallel
(e) perpendicular (f) neither
6 $\sqrt{50}$; $(3\frac{1}{2}, 4\frac{1}{2})$ **7** $\frac{1}{2}\sqrt{34}$; $(\frac{3}{4}, -1\frac{3}{4})$ **8** 10, 1, 2, 26; $\pm 2, \pm 4$
9 $-27, -1, 1, 27$; $-2, 0, 2$ **10** (a) yes (b) no (c) no (d) yes
11 $-\frac{10}{3}, +5$; $\frac{25}{3}$
12 (a) $(4, 0), (-3, 0), (0, -12)$ (b) $(\frac{2}{3}, 0), (\frac{1}{2}, 0), (0, 2)$
(c) $(0, 9)$, and touches x-axis at $(3, 0)$
(d) $(9, 0)$, and cuts y-axis, touches x-axis at $(0, 0)$
(e) $(-1, 0), (0, 25)$ and touches x-axis at $(5, 0)$
(f) $(1, 0), (-1, 0), (3, 0), (-3, 0), (0, 9)$
13 (a) $y = x$ (b) $y = -x$ (c) $y = \frac{1}{2}x$ (d) $y = \frac{1}{2}x - 4$ (e) $x = -5$
(f) $y = -\frac{2}{3}x + 5$
14 (a) $y = 11$ (b) $x = 4$ (c) $y = 6x - 10$
(d) $y = -8x + 2$ (e) $y = -\frac{2}{3}x - 1$
15 $y = \frac{1}{8}x$

Exercise 2c (p35)

1 (a) $4x - y - 1 = 0$ (b) $3x - y + 11 = 0$ (c) $x - 3y - 17 = 0$
(d) $3x + 4y - 41 = 0$ (e) $3x - 6y - 4 = 0$ (f) $20x + 12y + 31 = 0$
2 (a) $3x - 4y + 21 = 0$ (b) $5x + 4y - 23 = 0$ (c) $3x + 11y - 35 = 0$
(d) $x - 5y - 19 = 0$ (e) $2x + 3y - 7 = 0$ (f) $2x - y + 1 = 0$
3 (a) $(7, -7)$ (b) $(-\frac{3}{2}, -\frac{11}{2})$ (c) $(\frac{11}{7}, -\frac{13}{7})$ (d) $(4, -7)$
4 (a) $3x - 4y + 1 = 0$ (b) $5x - 2y + 16 = 0$ (c) $7x - y - 28 = 0$
(d) $3x - 4y - 6 = 0$
5 $2x - 5y + 19 = 0$ **6** $26x + 4y - 21 = 0$
7 $7x - 10y - 70 = 0$; $7x + 10y = 0$ **8** $2x - 7y - 3 = 0$ **9** $\frac{8}{21}$
10 $4x - 3y - 13 = 0$; 5

Exercise 2d (p35)

1 $5x + y - 33 = 0$
2 $2x + 7y - 14 = 0$; $2x - 7y - 14 = 0$
3 (a) $3x - 5y + 14 = 0$ (b) $3x + 5y - 14 = 0$ (c) $2x + 5y + 14 = 0$
4 $m_1 m_2 = -1$ (a) $5x + 2y - 11 = 0$ (b) $2x - 5y - 16 = 0$
5 $(0, 0), (2, \frac{3}{2}), (5, -\frac{3}{2})$; $y = 0, 9x + 2y - 21 = 0, (2\frac{1}{3}, 0)$
6 (a) $3x + 2y + 5 = 0$ (b) $2x + 7y - 19 = 0$ (c) $2x + 5y + 11 = 0$
7 (a) $2x - 3y - 14 = 0$ (b) $3x + 2y - 8 = 0, (\frac{32}{13}, \frac{4}{13})$
8 $\sqrt{85}, 6x + 7y - 85 = 0$
9 $(1, 8), 52$
11 (a) $AB = AC = 13$ (b) 12, 78 **12** $2x + y - 17 = 0, 72\frac{1}{4}$
13 $x - y = 0, 2x + 2y - 9 = 0, (\frac{3}{2}, 3), (3, \frac{3}{2}), \frac{3}{2}\sqrt{5}$
14 $x + 3y + 2 = 0, x - 3y - 4 = 0$ **15** $x + 4y - 9 = 0$

Chapter 3 (p37)

Qu. 1 (a) F (b) T (c) F (d) F
Qu. 2 (a) -2.5 (b) $-3, -5$ (c) $+5, -5$ (d) $+\sqrt{3}, -\sqrt{3}$
Qu. 3 (a) $\{x: x \in \mathbb{R}, x \neq 3\}, \mathbb{R}$ (b) $\{x: x \in \mathbb{R}, x \leqslant 10\}, \{y: y \in \mathbb{R}, 0 \leqslant y\}$
    (c) $\{x: x \in \mathbb{R}, |x| \leqslant 5\}, \{y: y \in \mathbb{R}, 0 \leqslant y \leqslant 5\}$
    (d) $\{x: x \in \mathbb{R}, x \neq \pm 5\}, \{y: y \in \mathbb{R}, y < 0 \text{ or } y > \frac{1}{25}\}$
    (e) $\mathbb{R}, \{y: y \in \mathbb{R}, 0 < y \leqslant \frac{1}{25}\}$
Qu. 4 (a) many-to-one (b) one-to-one (c) not a function
    (d) many-to-one
Qu. 7 Odd   **Qu. 8** 2   **Qu. 9** 9   **Qu. 10** 7.389
Qu. 11 1   **Qu. 12** 0.5

Exercise 3a (p43)

1 (a) $\{1, 4, 9, 16, 25\}$ (b) $\{1, \frac{1}{2}, \frac{1}{3}, \frac{1}{4}, \frac{1}{5}\}$ (c) $\{2, 4, 6, 8, 10\}$
    (d) $\{5, 9, 13, 17, 21\}$
2 (a) $\{0, 1, 4, 9\}$ (b) $\{-24, -6, 0, +6, +24\}$ (c) $\{0, 1, 16, 81\}$
    (d) $\{\frac{1}{2}, \frac{1}{3}, \frac{1}{4}, \frac{1}{5}, \frac{1}{6}, \frac{1}{7}, \frac{1}{8}\}$
3 (a) $\{1, 4, 9, 16, 25, 36, 49, 64, 81\}$ (b) $\{9, 16, 21, 24, 25\}$
    (c) $\{1, 2, 3, 4, 5, 6, 7, 8, 9\}$ (d) $\{\frac{1}{2}, 1, 1\frac{1}{2}, 2, 2\frac{1}{2}, 3, 3\frac{1}{2}, 4, 4\frac{1}{2}\}$
4 (a) F (b) T (c) T (d) T
5 $\{1, 2, 3\}$
6 (a) $\{5, 10, 15, \ldots 95\}, \{7, 14, 21, \ldots 98\}, \{35, 70\}, \{5, 7, 10, 14, \ldots 95, 98\}$
    (b) multiples of 35 (c) 19, 14, 2, 31
7 (a) $\{3, 6, 9, \ldots 18\}$ (b) $\{4, 8, 12, 16, 20\}$
    (c) $\{1, 2, 4, 5, 7, 8, 10, 11, 13, 14, 16, 17, 19, 20\}$
    (d) $\{1, 2, 3, 5, 6, 7, 9, 10, 11, 13, 14, 15, 17, 18, 19\}$
    (e) $\{1, 2, 5, 7, 10, 11, 13, 14, 17, 19\}$ (f) the same as (e)
8 (a) $0.\dot{3}$ (b) $0.\dot{2}8571\dot{4}$ (c) $0.\dot{2}\dot{7}$
9 $\frac{7}{9}$
10 (a) $\frac{4}{33}$ (b) $\frac{73}{111}$ (c) $\frac{3}{7}$

Exercise 3b (p47)

1 (a) 1 (b) 126 (c) $1\frac{27}{64}$ (d) -7 **2** $\{1, 6, 11, 16, 21, 26\}$
3 $\{y: y \in \mathbb{R}, y \geqslant 1\}$ **4** $\{y: y \in \mathbb{R}, 0 < y \leqslant 1\}$ **5** $\{x: x \in \mathbb{R}, x < 25\}$
6 fg: $x \mapsto 5x^2 + 1$, gf: $x \mapsto (5x + 1)^2$
7 (a) $(5 + h)^2 = 25 + 10h + h^2$ (b) $10 + h$ **8** $2a + h$
9 (a) 8 (b) -1000 (c) $\frac{1}{8}$ (d) $125a^3$ (e) $a^3/27$ (f) $a^3 + 3a^2h + 3ah^2 + h^3$
    (g) $6a^2h + 2h^3$ (h) $3a^2 + h^2$
10 (a) 56 (b) 91 (c) 2, F: $x \mapsto (x - 21)/7$

Exercise 3c (p52)

18 (a) translation a to the right (b) translation a vertically upwards
    (c) 'stretch', $\times k$, parallel to the y-axis (d) reflection in the x-axis
    (e) reflection in the y-axis

Exercise 3d (p62)

1 (a) $x = 7$ (b) $x = -3$ (c) $x = -0.2$ (d) $x = (a-1)/5$
2 (a) $t = 7$ (b) $t = 5.5$ (c) $t = 4$ (d) $t = 1/a + 5$
3 (a) $f^{-1}(x) = 24 - 2x$ (b) $f^{-1}(x) = 3 + 2x$ (c) $f^{-1}(x) = \frac{1}{2}(5x - 1)$
   (d) $f^{-1}(x) = (7 - 10x)/3$
4 (a) $f^{-1}(x) = 9x/5 + 32$ (b) $f^{-1}(x) = x/180 + 2$ (c) $f^{-1}(x) = x/(2\pi)$
   (d) $f^{-1}(x) = \frac{3}{5}(x + 9) - 7$
5 (a) $F^{-1}: t \mapsto \sqrt{(t-5)}, (t \geq 5)$ (b) $F^{-1}: t \mapsto t^2/25$ (c) $F^{-1}: t \mapsto \sqrt[3]{t} + 5$
   (d) $F^{-1}: t \mapsto t^3 - 1$
6 (a) $g^{-1}: x \mapsto 1/x + 3, (x \neq 0)$ (b) $g^{-1}: x \mapsto (1/x - 1)/2, (x \neq 0)$
   (c) $g^{-1}: x \mapsto 4 - 3/x, (x \neq 0)$ (d) $g^{-1}: x \mapsto x/(2 - x), (x \neq 2)$

Exercise 3e (p69)

1 (a) 2.5 (b) 0 (c) ∞ (d) 0
2 (a) 6 (b) 10 (c) 75 (d) ∞
3 (a) $f(0) = 1$ (b) not possible (c) not possible (d) 3
4 (a) continuous (b) discontinuous (c) discontinuous (d) continuous
5 $\pm 3, f(3) = 4, f(-3) = -2$

Exercise 3f (p69)

1 (a) $\{8, 23, 48, 83, 128\}$ (b) $\{\frac{1}{2}, \frac{2}{3}, \frac{3}{4}, \frac{4}{5}, \frac{5}{6}\}$
2 (a) 6 (b) 12 (c) 30 (d) -60
3 (a) 2 (b) -10 (c) -12 (d) $2(a-5)$
4 $\{2t: t \in \mathbb{Z}, t \geq 0\}$, non-negative integers
5 (a) $5(x+1)^2$ (b) $25x^2 + 1$
6 (a) $5x$ (b) $7 - x$ (c) $(7-x)/5$ (d) $7 - 5x$
7 $\{y: 0 < y \leq 1\}$
8 $gf(x) = x/(x^2 + 2x - 15), x \neq 0, 3, -5$
9 (a) one-to-one (b) one-to-one (c) many-to-one
   $fgh(x) = 10/(x^2 + 5) + 2$ $\{y: 2 < y \leq 4\}$
10 $a = 5, b = 2$
11 (a) 7 (b) 1
12 (a) $\{y: 0 \leq y \leq 2\}$
   (b) $\{x: x \geq 0\}, \{y: 0 < y \leq 4\}, \sqrt{(4/x - 1)}, \{x: 0 < x \leq 4\}, \{y: 0 \leq y < \infty\}$

Chapter 4 (p71)

Qu. 1 the circle
Qu. 2 $90°$
Qu. 3 $PQ \to 0, QO \to 0, PQ/QO = \frac{1}{3}$
Qu. 4 $3, 2\frac{1}{2}, 2.1, 2.01; 2$
Qu. 5 $Q \to P$; gradient of $PQ \to$ gradient of tangent at P; 2
Qu. 6 4
Qu. 7 $-3, -2, 1, 4$

Qu. 8 (a) $6x$ (b) $10x$ (c) x (d) $2cx$ (e) $2x$ (f) $2x$
Qu. 9 $4x^3$
Qu. 10 $6x^2$
Qu. 11 (a) $12x^2$ (b) $20x^3$ (c) $2ax$ (d) $4nx^{n-1}$ (e) $k(n+1)x^n$
Qu. 12 (a) $3x^2 + 4x + 3$ (b) $16x^3 - 6x$ (c) $2ax + b$
Qu. 13 (a) $12x^2 - 4x$ (b) $2x - 1$ (c) 5

Exercise 4a (p85)

1 $12x^{11}$ **2** $21x^6$ **3** 5 **4** 5 **5** 0 **6** $10x - 3$
7 $12x^3 - 6x^2 + 2x - 1$ **8** $8x^3 + x^2 - \frac{1}{2}x$ **9** $3ax^2 + 2bx + c$
10 $18x^2 - 8$ **11** $15x^2 + 3x$ **12** -1 **13** 0 **14** $12x^2 - 3$
15 $ax - 2b$ **16** $4x + 2$ **17** $6x - 3$ **18** $x^2 - 1$ **19** $2x - 1$
20 $6x$ **21** $x + \frac{7}{4}$ **22** $\frac{4}{3}x - \frac{1}{3}$ **23** x **24** $1; 2$ **25** $1; 1$
26 $3; -4$ **27** $-5; 4$ **28** $28; -36$ **29** $9; -24$ **30** $(4, 16)$
31 $(-2, -8), (2, 8)$ **32** $(0, 0)$ **33** $(\frac{3}{2}, -\frac{5}{4})$ **34** $(-1, 8), (1, 6)$
35 $(2, -12)$ **36** $(0, 1), (\frac{3}{2}, -\frac{11}{16})$ **37** $(-\frac{1}{3}, \frac{4}{27}), (1, 0)$
38 $(1, 4), (3, 0)$

Exercise 4b (p87)

1 (a) $4x - y - 4 = 0$ (b) $24x - y - 46 = 0$ (c) $x + y - 1 = 0$
  (d) $8x + y - 5 = 0$ (e) $18x + y + 54 = 0$
2 (a) $x + 4y - 18 = 0$ (b) $x + 24y - 1204 = 0$ (c) $x - y + 1 = 0$
  (d) $x - 8y - 25 = 0$ (e) $x - 18y + 3 = 0$
3 $9x - y - 27 = 0; x + 9y - 3 = 0$ **4** $16x - y = 0; x + 16y = 0$
5 $2x - y - 10 = 0$ **6** $4x + y - 3 = 0$ **7** $y + 4 = 0; y - 23 = 0$
8 $y - 10 = 0; y + 17 = 0$

Exercise 4c (p88)

1 $6, 6x - y + 2 = 0, (-\frac{2}{5}, -\frac{2}{5})$ **2** $10x - y - 16 = 0, (-4, -56)$
3 $5x - y - 1 = 0, (2, 4), (4, -8)$ **4** $4x - 2y + 5 = 0, (\frac{2}{3}, \frac{41}{27})$
5 $(0, 0), (1, 0), (2, 0), y = 2x, x + y - 1 = 0, y = 2x - 4$
6 $x - y + 3 = 0, x - 2y + 12 = 0, (6, 9)$
7 $y = -5x + 4, (2, -6), y = -4x + 2$
8 $(-2, 0), x - 2y + 2 = 0, x + 2y - 2 = 0, (0, 1)$
9 $y = 3x + 2, y = 3x + 6$ **10** $(-\sqrt{\frac{2}{3}}, -\frac{1}{3}\sqrt{\frac{2}{3}}), (0, 0), (\sqrt{\frac{2}{3}}, \frac{1}{3}\sqrt{\frac{2}{3}})$

Chapter 5 (p89)

Qu. 1 6.1 m, 12.2 m s^{-1}
Qu. 2 (a) 1.0 m, 10 m s^{-1} (b) $4.9 (2h + h^2)$ m, $4.9(2 + h)$ m s^{-1}
Qu. 3 9.8 m s^{-1}
Qu. 4 (a) 24.5 m, 24.5 m s^{-1} (b) 11 m, 22 m s^{-1} (c) 2.0 m, 20 m s^{-1}
  (d) $4.9 (4h + h^2)$ m, $4.9 (4 + h)$ m s^{-1}; 19.6 m s^{-1}

Qu. 5 (a) 6.9, 23.6, 50.1, 86.4 m below top   (b) 11.8, 21.6, 31.4, 41.2 m s^{-1}
(c) 26.5 m s^{-1}

Qu. 6 (a) 19.8, 29.6, 39.4, $10 + 9.8t$ m s^{-1}
(b) straight line through $(0, 10)$ of gradient 9.8

Exercise 5a (p94)

1 (a) 10.5 m, 10.5 m s^{-1} (b) 13, 15, $(15.4 - 4.9h)$ m s^{-1} (c) 15.4 m s^{-1}
2 $v = 24.5 - 9.8t$ (a) $t = 0$, 5 seconds   (b) 19.6, 29.4, 29.4, -29.4 m;
14.7, 4.9, -4.9, -34.3 m s^{-1}
(c) below ledge; falling   (d) $t = 2.5$; 30.6 m   (e) 2.4 m
3 $v = 3 + 2t$ (a) At O, 3 m s^{-1} (b) $t = 0$, or -3
(c) $t = -\frac{3}{2}, \frac{9}{4}$ m from O on the negative side   (d) -3 m s^{-1}
4 (a) 0, 8, 9, 8, 0, -7 m; on AO produced
(b) 6, 2, -2, -6 m s^{-1}; moving in direction $\overrightarrow{AO}$
(c) $t = 3$; 9 m from O, on OA

Exercise 5b (p96)

1 2.5 m s^{-2} **2** 3 m s^{-2} **3** (a) 18 km h^{-1} per s   (b) 64 800 km h^{-2}
4 (a) 3.6 km h^{-1} per s   (b) 1 m s^{-2} (c) 12 960 km h^{-2} **5** 6.25 s
6 -1.5 m s^{-2}; -1.5 **7** 130 km h^{-1}

Exercise 5c (p99)

1 (a) $+5.6$ m, $+0.7$ m s^{-1} (up), -9.8 m s^{-2} (decreasing speed)
(b) $+1.4$ m, -9.1 m s^{-1} (down), -9.8 m s^{-2} (increasing speed)
(c) -12.6 m, -18.9 m s^{-1} (down), -9.8 m s^{-2} (increasing speed)
2 24.9 m, 29.8 m s^{-1}; 9.8 m s^{-2}
3 (a) 31.5 m, -4.2 m s^{-1} (b) $t = 2\frac{4}{7}$ (c) 32.4 m   (d) 2.5 m
(e) -9.8 m s^{-2} (constant)
4 (a) 18, 54, 114 m s^{-2} (b) 58 m s^{-2}
5 (a) $t = 2$ (b) $t = \frac{2}{3}, \frac{32}{27}$ m from O on OA; $t = 2$, at O
(c) $\frac{32}{27}, \frac{64}{27}$ m   (d) 3 m s^{-1}
(e) 1 m from O, on OA; towards O (-1 m s^{-1}); increasing ($a = -2$ m s^{-2})
6 9 m from O on AO produced ($s = -9$); towards O ($+15$ m s^{-1});
decreasing ($a = -14$ m s^{-2})
7 (a) After 0, 1, 2 s   (b) 2, -1, 2 m s^{-1}; -6, 0, $+6$ m s^{-2} (c) 0 m s^{-1}
(d) 0 m s^{-2}

Exercise 5d (p100)

1 0.7   **2** 16 m s^{-1}, 14 m s^{-2}
3 0 cm s^{-1}, -4 cm s^{-2}, $1\frac{1}{2}$ s, 18 cm
4 (a) 1, 3 s, 4, 0 cm   (b) -6, $+6$ cm s^{-2} (c) -3 cm s^{-1}
5 0 cm s^{-1}, 16 cm, (-24 cm s^{-1})
6 $(24n - 5)$ cm, $(24n + 7)$ cm s^{-1}, 24 cm s^{-2}

Chapter 6 (p101)

Qu. 1 (a) $2x-4$ (b) $6x$ (c) $6x^2-10x$ (d) $2x-2$ (e) $3x^2-4x-3$

Qu. 2 (a) $(1,2)$ (b) $(-\frac{1}{3}, -5\frac{1}{3})$ (c) $(\frac{3}{4}, -\frac{1}{4})$

Qu. 3 (a) $\frac{5}{3}$, highest (b) $\frac{7}{6}$, lowest (c) $-\frac{3}{2}$, lowest (d) $-\frac{4}{5}$, highest

Qu. 4 (a) $-4x^{-5}$ (b) $-6x^{-3}$ (c) $-6x^{-4}$ (d) $-\frac{3}{2}x^{-4}$ (e) $-mx^{-m-1}$
(f) $4x-3-5x^{-2}$ (g) $1-3x^{-2}+8x^{-3}$

Qu. 5 A, E min, D, F max, B, C infl; G max, I min, H infl;
K max, J, L, infl

Qu. 6 (a) neg, pos, decreasing (b) pos, pos, increasing
(c) neg, zero, neither

Exercise 6a (p106)

1 (a) $6x-2$ (b) $10x+4$ (c) $2-4x$ (d) $6x+1$ (e) $48x+6$

2 (a) $(-2\frac{1}{2}, -8\frac{1}{4})$ (b) $(\frac{9}{14}, 7\frac{25}{28})$ (c) $(\frac{1}{3}, -\frac{1}{3})$ (d) $(-\frac{5}{8}, 7\frac{9}{16})$

3 (a) $2\frac{1}{2}$, lowest (b) -6, lowest (c) $\frac{4}{3}$, highest (d) -25, highest

4 (a) $-2\frac{1}{4}$, least (b) 4, greatest (c) 16, greatest (d) $-6\frac{1}{8}$, least

6 12.1 m, $1\frac{4}{7}$ s   **7** 50 m by 50 m   **8** 10 cm

9 250 m, 500 m, 125 000 m^2 **10** 50 m, 5 s   **11** 2 cm, 3 cm

Exercise 6b (p112)

1 (a) 0, infl (b) 0, y max (c) 2, y max; 3, y min (d) -3, y max; 5, y min
(e) -6, y max; -1, y min (f) 1, y min; 3, y max (g) -3, y min; 4, y max
(h) -6, y min; 1, y max (i) -5, y min; 3, y max
(j) $-\sqrt{\frac{27}{5}}$, y max; 0, infl; $\sqrt{\frac{27}{5}}$, y min (k) -2, y max; 2, y min

2 (a) $-\frac{16}{9}$, min; $\frac{16}{9}$, max (b) 0, max; -27, min (c) 0, max; $-\frac{256}{27}$, min
(d) -2, max; $+2$, min (e) $\frac{100}{27}$, max; -9 min

3 (a) $(-2, 16)$ max; $(2, -16)$ min (b) $(\frac{1}{3}, 2\frac{13}{27})$ max; $(3, -7)$ min
(c) $(0, 0)$ min; $(2, 4)$ max (d) $(\frac{1}{2}, 3)$ min
(e) $(3\frac{1}{3}, 181\frac{13}{27})$ max; $(12, -144)$ min

4 (a) 0, min (b) 3, infl (c) 0, infl; $\frac{27}{16}$, max (d) 19, infl; 3, min

5 18 cm^3; $x=1$ **6** $7\frac{11}{27}$ cm^3; $x=\frac{2}{3}$ **7** 2 cubic feet

8 $8/\pi$ cubic feet   **9** $\sqrt[3]{(5/\pi)}$ m; $2\sqrt[3]{(5/\pi)}$ m

Exercise 6c (p115)

1 $(0,0)$, $(3,0)$; $(0,0)$ min, $(2,4)$ max

2 $(0,0)$, $(6,0)$; $(0,0)$ max, $(4,-32)$ min

3 $(0,0)$, $(1,0)$; $(\frac{1}{3}, \frac{4}{27})$ max, $(1,0)$ min

4 $(-1,0)$, $(2,0)$,$(0,2)$; $(-1,0)$ min, $(1,4)$ max

5 $(0,0)$, $(2,0)$; $(0,0)$ min, $(1,1)$ max, $(2,0)$ min

6 $(0,0)$, $(8,0)$; $(0,0)$ infl, $(6,-432)$ min

7 $(\pm1,0)$, $(\pm3,0)$, $(0,9)$; $(0,9)$ max, $(\pm\sqrt{5}, -16)$ min

8 $(0,0)$, $(-\sqrt[3]{32},0)$; $(-2,-48)$ min

9 $(0,0)$, $(1\frac{1}{4},0)$; $(0,0)$ max, $(1,-1)$ min

10 $(0,0)$, $(\pm\sqrt{\frac{5}{3}},0)$; $(-1,2)$ max, $(0,0)$ infl, $(1,-2)$ min

Exercise 6d (p118)

2 $v = 6t^2 - 22t + 12$, $a = 12t - 22$
  (a) 4 m from O on BO produced ($s = -4$)
  (b) away   (c) 8 m s^{-1} ($v = -8$)   (d) decreasing   (e) 2 m s^{-2} ($a = +2$)
3 (a) 3 m from O on OB ($s = +3$)   (b) away   (c) 4 m s^{-1} ($v = -4$)
  (d) increasing   (e) 10 m s^{-2} ($a = -10$)
4 after $\frac{11}{6}$ s; $s = -\frac{143}{54}$
5 (a) 100 m from O on OA ($s = +100$); approaching A at 40 m s^{-1} ($v = +40$);
  retarding at 14 m s^{-2} ($a = -14$)   (b) $t = 3\frac{1}{3}$ to $t = 12$ (c) $t = 7\frac{2}{3}$

Exercise 6e (p119)

1 (a) $(1, 6)$ max, $(3, 2)$ min   (b) $(-1, 15)$ max, $(2, -12)$ min
  (c) $(-1, 2)$ max, $(1, -2)$ min   (d) $(1, -1)$ min, $(-\frac{1}{2}, 5\frac{3}{4})$ max
  (e) $(0, 0)$ max, $(-2, -16)$, $(2, -16)$ min   (f) $(-\frac{1}{3}, \frac{91}{27})$ max, $(1, 1)$ min
2 $(-2, 27)$ max, $(1, 0)$ min, $(-3\frac{1}{2}, 0)$
3 ± 1 **4** (a) max   (b) infl   **5** $y = 1$, $y = 1$, $y = 0$
6 $2\frac{4}{5}$, $x + 3y - 7 = 0$ **7** $a = 2$, $b = -4$, $c = -1$ **8** $x + t^2 y - 4t = 0$
9 $4x - y \pm 15 = 0$ **10** 256 cm^3 **11** 32 m
12 (a) $4\frac{1}{2} \text{ cm}^2$ (b) 4 cm^2 **13** $\frac{1}{144}(17x^2 - 16xl + 8l^2)$, min   **16** 48 m^2
17 $2\pi r(r + h)$ (a) $(12/r) - r$, $\pi r(12 - r^2)$ (b) $r = 2$
18 (a) 5 cm   (b) 6 cm   **19** $V = \pi r^2(5 - 2\pi r)$, $125/(27\pi) \approx 1.47 \text{ m}^3$
20 10 m by 10 m by 5 m

Chapter 7 (p121)

Qu. 1   (a) $2x + c$ (b) $mx + c$ (c) $x^3 + c$ (d) $\frac{3}{2}x^2 + c$ (e) $\frac{3}{5}x^5 + c$
    (f) $3x + x^2 + c$ (g) $\frac{1}{2}x^2 - \frac{1}{3}x^3 + c$ (h) $\frac{1}{2}ax^2 + bx + c$

Qu. 2   (a) $-\dfrac{1}{2}x^{-2} + c = \dfrac{-1}{2x^2} + c$ (b) $-\dfrac{1}{3}x^{-3} + c = \dfrac{-1}{3x^3} + c$

    (c) $-2x^{-1} + c$

Qu. 4 $y = 4x + 18$; a straight line of gradient 4 through $(-2, 10)$
Qu. 5 $v = 15 + 9.8t$, $s = 15t + 4.9t^2$
Qu. 6 $+9.8 \text{ m s}^{-1}$ (rising), -9.8, -29.4 m s^{-1} (falling); 14.7, 14.7 m (above start), -24.5 m (below)
Qu. 7   (a) 9   (b) 42   (c) -6 (d) 35
Qu. 8 $12\frac{2}{3}$ m
Qu. 9   (a) 13 m past O   (b) 5 m past O   (c) 7 m past O
    (d) 100 m short of O
Qu. 10   (a) 72   (b) 9   (c) 36   (d) 21
Qu. 11   (a) $3\frac{1}{4}$ (b) 9   (c) 2   (d) -8 (e) -38 (f) $9\frac{1}{4}$
Qu. 12   25
Qu. 13   (a) 9   (b) 81
Qu. 14 $2\frac{2}{3}$
Qu. 15 $\frac{1}{2}$

Exercise 7a (p123)

1 (a) $\frac{1}{2}x + c$, $\frac{1}{6}x^3 + c$, $\frac{1}{3}x^3 + \frac{3}{2}x^2 + c$, $\frac{4}{3}x^3 + 6x^2 + 9x + c$, $-\frac{1}{4}x^{-4} + c$, $\frac{2}{3}x^{-3} + c$

(b) $\frac{1}{2}at^2 + c$, $\frac{1}{12}t^4 + c$, $\frac{1}{3}t^3 - \frac{1}{2}t^2 - 2t + c$, $-\dfrac{1}{n}t^{-n} + c$, $-t^{-1} + 3t + t^2 + c$

(c) $ay^{-1} + c$, $-ky^{-1} + c$, $\frac{1}{3}y^3 - y + 6y^{-1} + c$

2 (a) $y = ax^3 + c$ (b) $s = \frac{3}{4}t^4 + c$ (c) $s = ut + \frac{1}{2}at^2 + c$ (d) $x = t + t^{-1} + c$
(e) $y = t + 3t^{-1} - 2t^{-2} + c$ (f) $A = -x^{-1} - x - \frac{2}{3}x^3 + c$

3 $x - 6y + 34 = 0$ **4** $y = x^2 + 5x - 25$ **5** $y = x^3 + 1/x - 8\frac{1}{2}$

6 $(1, 0), (3, 0)$ **7** $(4, 0)$; $y = 9\frac{13}{27} = \frac{256}{27}$ **8** $s = \frac{3}{2}t^2 + 8/t - 8$

9 $A = c - 3x^{-1} - \frac{1}{2}x^{-2} + x^{-3} + \frac{1}{4}x^{-4}$; $\frac{49}{64}$

Exercise 7b (p127)

1 $v = 20 + 9.81t$; $s = 20t + 4.90t^2$

2 $v = -12 + 9.8t$; $s = -12t + 4.9t^2$; -2.2 m s^{-1} (rising), $+7.6$, $+17.4$ m s^{-1}
(falling), -7.1, -4.4 m (above ground level), $+8.1$ m (below)

3 (a) $s = 3t + 3$ (b) $s = 2t^2 - t - 6$ (c) $s = t^3 + \frac{5}{2}t^2 - 2t - 13$
(d) $s = \frac{1}{3}t^3 + 5t + 2t^{-1} - 7$

4 (a) 32 (b) 328 (c) -21 (d) 16

5 (a) $s = 2t^2 + 3t + c$, 14 m (b) $s = \frac{1}{3}t^3 - 3t + c$, $3\frac{1}{3}$ m
(c) $s = \frac{1}{3}t^3 - \frac{3}{2}t^2 + 2t + c$, $3\frac{5}{6}$ m (d) $s = \frac{1}{2}t^2 + 3t + 1/t + c$, $179\frac{19}{20}$ m

6 $v = \frac{1}{2}At^2 + B$; $s = \frac{1}{6}At^3 + Bt + c$

7 (a) $v = \frac{3}{2}t^2 + 3$, $s = \frac{1}{2}t^3 + 3t$ (b) $v = 2t + \frac{1}{2}t^2$, $s = -3 + t^2 + \frac{1}{6}t^3$
(c) $v = -7\frac{1}{2} + 10t - \frac{1}{2}t^2$, $s = -7\frac{1}{2}t + 5t^2 - \frac{1}{6}t^3$
(d) $v = \frac{1}{4}t^2 + 5$, $s = \frac{1}{12}t^3 + 5t + c$ (e) $v = \frac{1}{3}t^3 + c$, $s = \frac{1}{12}t^4 + ct + 9\frac{11}{12} - c$

8 (a) $13\frac{1}{2}$ m past O (b) $2\frac{1}{2}$ m past O (c) 8 m past O (d) $7\frac{1}{2}$ m

9 (a) $s = -5 + 6t - t^2$, 5 m (b) 13 m

10 (a) $1\frac{2}{7}$ s (b) 8.1 m (c) 7.7, 2.9 m

Exercise 7c (p136)

1 (a) $3\frac{63}{64}$ (b) -2 (c) $10\frac{2}{3}$ (d) $36\frac{137}{144}$ **2** 50

3 (a) 26 (b) $58\frac{1}{3}$ (c) $22\frac{7}{60}$ (d) $2\frac{1}{2}$ **4** $5\frac{1}{3}$ **5** $-\frac{1}{6}$ **6** $-\frac{5}{12}, 2\frac{2}{3}$

7 (a) $-2\frac{1}{3}$ (b) 4 (c) $2\frac{9}{20}$ (d) $-\frac{1}{2}$ **8** $1\frac{1}{3}$ **9** $4\frac{1}{2}$

10 (a) $(0, 0), (4, 8), 5\frac{1}{3}$ (b) $(-2, 12), (1, 3), 13\frac{1}{2}$ (c) $(-1, 0), (3, 4), 10\frac{2}{3}$

Exercise 7d (p137)

1 $y = 3 - 3/x + 1/x^2$ **2** $f(x) = x^2 - 1 + 1/x$ **3** $20\frac{5}{6}$ **4** $-4\frac{1}{2}$

5 $6\frac{3}{4}$ **6** 36   **7** $\frac{1}{6}(4t^3 - 27t^2 + 60t)$, $4t - 9$, $7\frac{1}{3}$, $7\frac{7}{24}$

8 $4\frac{5}{6}$ m, 1 m s^{-2} **9** 14 m s^{-2}, 44 m   **10** $y = x^3 - 3x^2 + 4x + 8$, $10\frac{3}{4}$

11 $10\frac{2}{3}$ **14** (a) $(t^2 - 4t + 3)$ m s^{-1} (b) 1 (c) $\frac{4}{3}$ m   **15** 20 m s^{-1}, 467 m

Chapter 8 (p138)

Qu. 1 (a) $-4x^{-5}$ (b) $-6x^{-4}$ (c) $-\dfrac{2}{x^3}$ (d) $-\dfrac{4}{x^2}$ (e) $\dfrac{4}{x^3}$ (f) $-\dfrac{1}{x^4}$

(g) $\dfrac{4}{x^5}$ (h) $-\dfrac{3}{x^6}$ (i) $-\tfrac{1}{2}x^{-2}+c$ (j) $-2x^{-1}+c$ (k) $-\dfrac{1}{x}+c$

(l) $-\dfrac{1}{x^2}+c$ (m) $-\dfrac{1}{6x^2}+c$ (n) $-\dfrac{2}{15x^3}+c$

Qu. 2 (a) $\tfrac{1}{2}x^{-1/2}$ (b) $-\tfrac{2}{3}x^{-4/3}$ (c) $\tfrac{1}{2}x^{-1/2}$ (d) $\tfrac{1}{3}x^{-2/3}$ (e) $-\tfrac{1}{3}x^{-4/3}$
(f) $\tfrac{2}{3}x^{-4/3}$ (g) $3x^{1/2}$ (h) $-\tfrac{1}{3}x^{-3/2}$ (i) $\tfrac{4}{3}x^{3/4}+c$
(j) $\tfrac{4}{5}x^{5/2}+c$ (k) $\tfrac{2}{3}x^{3/2}+c$ (l) $\tfrac{3}{4}x^{4/3}+c$
(m) $2x^{1/2}+c$ (n) $-2x^{-1/2}+c$

Qu. 3 (a) $2(x+4)$ (b) $3(x+2)^2$ (c) $6(3x+1)$ (d) $-4(5-2x)$ (e) $3(x+4)^2$
(f) $6x^2(x^3+1)$ (g) $6x(5+x^2)^2$ (h) $-(2/x^2)(2+1/x)$
(i) $-6x^2(1-x^3)$ (j) $\tfrac{3}{2}(\tfrac{1}{2}x-7)^2$

Qu. 4 (a) $2x+3$ (b) $2x(2x^2+1)$ (c) $4(x-2)(x^2-x-1)$
(d) $2(x+1)(x+2)(2x+3)$

Qu. 6 (a) and (b) $\dfrac{2(3x-1)}{(x+3)^3}$

Qu. 7 (a) 1 (b) $\dfrac{dy}{dx}$ (c) $2x$ (d) $2y\dfrac{dy}{dx}$ (e) $y+x\dfrac{dy}{dx}$ (f) $2xy+x^2\dfrac{dy}{dx}$

(g) $y^2+2xy\dfrac{dy}{dx}$

Qu. 8 $\dfrac{2x-6y+3}{6x-2y+2}$

Qu. 9 $\dfrac{2x+y}{3y^2-x}$

Qu. 10 (a) $2x+\dfrac{2}{x^3},\ 2-\dfrac{6}{x^4}$ (b) $-\dfrac{1}{(x-1)^2},\ \dfrac{2}{(x-1)^3}$

Qu. 11 $\dfrac{1}{t},\ -\dfrac{1}{2t^3}$

Exercise 8a (p143)

1 (a) $4(2x+3)$ (b) $24(3x+4)^3$ (c) $-2(2x+5)^{-2}$ (d) $2(3x-1)^{-1/3}$
(e) $(3-2x)^{-3/2}$ (f) $12(3-4x)^{-4}$
2 (a) $\tfrac{1}{12}(3x+2)^4+c$ (b) $\tfrac{1}{6}(2x+3)^3+c$ (c) $-\tfrac{1}{3}(3x-4)^{-1}+c$
(d) $\tfrac{1}{3}(2x+3)^{3/2}+c$
3 (a) $\dfrac{-3}{(3x+2)^2}$ (b) $\dfrac{-4}{(2x+3)^3}$ (c) $\dfrac{-3}{2(3x+1)^{3/2}}$ (d) $\dfrac{-4}{3(2x-1)^{5/3}}$
4 (a) $-\tfrac{1}{2}(2x-3)^{-1}+c$ (b) $\tfrac{2}{3}\sqrt{(3x+2)}+c$ (c) $2(2x-1)^{1/4}+c$

5 (a) $18x(3x^2 + 5)^2$ (b) $(18x^2 + 10)(3x^3 + 5x)$ (c) $\dfrac{14x}{3}(7x^2 - 4)^{-2/3}$

(d) $-(36x^2 - 8)(6x^3 - 4x)^{-3}$ (e) $-\frac{2}{3}(6x - 5)(3x^2 - 5x)^{-5/3}$

6 (a) $\dfrac{-6x}{(3x^2 + 2)^2}$ (b) $\dfrac{-3x}{(2 + x^2)^{3/2}}$

7 (a) $3(3\sqrt{x} - 2x)^2 \left(\dfrac{3}{2\sqrt{x}} - 2 \right)$ (b) $\dfrac{1}{\sqrt{x}(2 - \sqrt{x})^2}$

8 (a) $\dfrac{-\frac{3}{2}\sqrt{x}}{(x^{3/2} - 1)^2}$ (b) $\dfrac{1}{2x^{3/2}\sqrt{(x - 1)}}$

9 (a) $\dfrac{-3(2x - 7)}{(x^2 - 7x)^4}$ (b) $\dfrac{1 - 4x^{3/2}}{\sqrt{x(x^2 - \sqrt{x})^3}}$

10 (a) $\dfrac{x^4 + 1}{x^2\sqrt{(x^4 - 1)}}$ (b) $\dfrac{-2(\sqrt{x} + 1)}{\sqrt{x}(x + 2\sqrt{x})^2}$

Exercise 8b (p146)

1 $1458 \text{ cm}^3 \text{ s}^{-1}$ **2** $16\pi \text{ cm}^2 \text{ s}^{-1}$ **3** $\frac{2}{27} \text{ cm s}^{-1}$ **4** $\frac{3}{2} \text{ cm s}^{-1}$
5 decreasing, $8\pi \text{ cm}^2 \text{ s}^{-1}$ **6** 24   **7** $1/(8\pi) \text{ cm s}^{-1}$ **8** $1/(2\pi) \text{ cm s}^{-1}$
9 $\frac{4}{45} \text{ cm s}^{-1}$ **10** (a) 6 cm   (b) $\frac{1}{6} \text{ cm min}^{-1}$ **11** 30   **12** $\frac{4}{15}$

Exercise 8c (p150)

1 $x(5x + 2)(1 + x)^2$
3 $2(x + 1)^2(2x - 1)$
5 $x^{-1/2}(x + 1)(5x + 1)$
7 $(2x^2 - 1)(x^2 - 1)^{-1/2}$
9 $-2x^{-3}(1 + 3x)$
11 $(1 + x)^{-2}$
13 $(1 - x^2)(x^2 + 1)^{-2}$
15 $26(5 - x)^{-2}$
17 $2(1 - x)(x + 2)^{-3}$
19 $x(3x + 4)(x + 1)^{-3/2}$

2 $(9x^2 + 1)(x^2 + 1)^3$
4 $x^2(5x + 1)(25x + 3)$
6 $x^2(14x + 3)(4x + 1)^{-1/2}$
8 $(15x^2 + 2x + 3)(6x + 1)^{-1/2}$
10 $2x(1 + x)^{-3}$
12 $-(x - 1)^{-2}$
14 $8(4 - x)^{-2}$
16 $(1 - 2x)(1 + 2x)^{-3}$
18 $3(1 - x)(x + 3)^{-5}$
20 $3x^{-1/2}(x + 3)^{-3/2}$

Exercise 8d (p153)

1 $\pm\frac{1}{3}$
3 $\frac{3}{7}$

2 $-1, \frac{11}{3}$
4 $-\frac{3}{2}$

5 $\dfrac{2(x - y - 1)}{2x - 2y - 3}$

6 $(9, 3), (-1, 3)$

7 (a) $\dfrac{-2y}{3x}$ (b) $\dfrac{y(2x - y)}{x(2y - x)}$

8 $\dfrac{4y - 3x}{3y - 4x}$

9 (a) $\dfrac{3t}{2}$ (b) $\dfrac{3\sqrt{x}}{2}$ **10** (a) $\dfrac{1}{t}$ (b) $\dfrac{t}{t+1}$

11 $2t - t^2$ **12** $\dfrac{9(t+2)^2}{4(t+3)^2}$

Exercise 8e (p155)

1 8π cm^2 **2** 9%   **3** $\frac{1}{2}x$
4 $\delta p/p = -\delta v/v$ **5** (a) $1\frac{1}{4}$ (b) $1\frac{1}{4}$ **6** 1.6π cm^3
7 4%   **8** 2%   **9** $1\frac{1}{3}\%$

Exercise 8f (p156)

1 (a) $-6x^{-7}$ (b) $\frac{3}{2}\sqrt{x}$ (c) $-\frac{1}{2}x^{-3/2}$ (d) $\frac{5}{2}x^{3/2}$
2 (a) $\frac{1}{7}x^7 + c$ (b) $-\frac{1}{5}x^{-5} + c$ (c) $-x^{-1} + c$ (d) $\frac{2}{3}x^{3/2} + c$
3 (a) $\frac{3}{2}x^{1/2}$ (b) $-\frac{3}{2}x^{-5/2}$ (c) $-\frac{1}{2}x^{-3/2}$ (d) $-x^{-3/2}$

4 (a) $-\frac{3}{2}x^{-5/2}$ (b) $-\dfrac{3\sqrt{2}}{2}x^{-5/2}$ (c) $\frac{3}{2}\sqrt{x}$ (d) $\frac{1}{2}x^{-1/2}$

5 (a) $8x(x^2+3)^3$ (b) $\dfrac{3x^2}{\sqrt{(2x^3-3)}}$

6 (a) $-\dfrac{2x}{(x^2-1)^2}$ (b) $-\dfrac{1}{\sqrt{x}(\sqrt{x}-1)^3}$

7 $x(5x-2)(x-1)^2$ **8** $\dfrac{2x^2-1}{\sqrt{(x^2-1)}}$

9 $\dfrac{x-2}{2(x-1)^{3/2}}$ **10** $\dfrac{4(x-1)}{(x+2)^3}$

11 $\dfrac{1}{2\sqrt{(x+1)}\sqrt{(x+2)^3}}$ **12** $-\dfrac{2x}{\sqrt{\{(x^2-1)^3(x^2+1)\}}}$

13 -1 **14** $\dfrac{3y-2x-4}{2y-3x-2}$ **15** $\dfrac{3x-2y}{2x}$

16 $-\dfrac{2t}{1-t^2}$ **17** $-\dfrac{1}{t}$ **18** -1 **19** 1%   **20** 3%   **21** 2%

22 $12x^2 - 12x - 9$, -24, 24 **23** $\dfrac{1}{t}$, $-\dfrac{1}{6t^3}$

24 $\frac{5}{3}$, $-\frac{3}{4}$ **25** $5x - 4y = 9$

Revision Exercise 1 (p159)

1 (a) $y = 4x + 4$ (b) $x = -2$
2 (a) A$(-3, 0)$ B$(0, 1.5)$ (b) $2y = x + 3$ (c) $(1.8, 2.4)$

3 (a) $\{y: y \in \mathbb{R}, 1 \leqslant y < 25\}$ (b) $f^{-1}x: \mapsto \frac{1}{3}(25/x + 2), 1 \leqslant x < 25$

(c) $fg: x \mapsto \dfrac{25}{3x^2 - 2}$ (d) $1\frac{1}{6}, 3$

5 (a) $x = 0, y = 1, (a, 0)$ (b) $x = 0, y = 1, (a, 0), (-a, 0)$
6 (a) $(1, 3)$ (b) $(-1, 1)$ (c) $(\frac{1}{2}, 1)$
7 (a) $V = \pi(27r - r^3)$ (b) $r = 3$
8 $x = 10/\sqrt{3}, C = 20\sqrt{3}$
9 20 m s^{-1}
10 $6t^2 - 30t + 24, 1 < t < 4$
11 (a) $A(2, 0)$ $B(-2, 32)$ (b) $C(-4, 0)$ (c) 108
12 $78\frac{2}{3}$
13 $y = 12x + 16, y = 12x - 16$
14 $\frac{1}{3}, \frac{16}{27}$
15 -1
16 (a) $0, 6$ (b) 162 m
18 (a) $f': x \mapsto 3, g': x \mapsto 2x$ (b) $3, 20$ (c) $(3x + 4)^2, 6(3x + 4)$
19 $f(x) = x^p, p \in \mathbb{Q}$

Chapter 9 (p163)

Qu. 1 $60 + 50/n; 60$
Qu. 2 (a) $\frac{3}{2}x^2 - 4x + c$ (b) $\frac{8}{3}x^3 + 3x^{-1} + c$ (c) $\frac{7}{8}x^{8/7} + c$
(d) $-t^2 + \frac{10}{3}t^{3/2} - 3t + c$
Qu. 3 (a) $17\frac{5}{6}$ (b) $\frac{7}{48}$ (c) $-5\frac{3}{5}$
Qu. 4 (a) (i) a cone, vertex C
(ii) two cones with common base, vertices A and C (b) sphere
(c) hemisphere (d) ring internal dia. 4, external dia. 8 (e) cylinder
Qu. 5 (a) $31\pi/5$ (b) $56\pi/15$
Qu. 6 (a) $(\frac{6}{5}, 0)$ (b) $(\frac{6}{5}, 3\sqrt{2}/8)$

Exercise 9a (p165)

4 (a) $\frac{3}{4}x^{4/3} + c$ (b) $\frac{4}{5}x^{5/4} + c$ (c) $\frac{5}{3}x^{6/5} + c$ (d) $\frac{3}{4}kx^{4/3} + c$ (e) $2x^{1/2} + c$
(f) $\frac{3}{2}x^{2/3} + c$ (g) $\frac{6}{5}x^{5/6} + c$ (h) $\frac{5}{2}x^{4/5} + c$ (i) $\frac{3}{5}x^{5/3} + c$ (j) $\frac{3}{10}x^{10/3} + c$
(k) $\frac{2}{5}x^{5/2} + c$ (l) $-3x^{-1/3} + c$
5 (a) $-\frac{1}{2}$ (b) 21 (c) $12\frac{2}{3}$

Exercise 9b (p175)

1 (a) $\frac{1}{3}x^3 - \frac{3}{2}x^2 + c$ (b) $-2x^{-1} + x^{-2} + c$ (c) $\frac{1}{3}t^3 + 4t - 3t^{-1} + c$
(d) $\frac{2}{3}t^{3/2} + 2t^{1/2} + c$
2 (a) $26\frac{2}{3}$ (b) $25\frac{2}{3}$ (c) $1\frac{11}{15}$ (d) $3\frac{19}{34}$ (e) $21\frac{1}{3}$ (f) $24\frac{2}{3}$
3 (a) 12 (b) $-31\frac{1}{4}$ (c) $1\frac{7}{24}$
4 (a) 9 (b) $11\frac{1}{4}$ (c) 12 (d) $2(\sqrt{3} - \sqrt{2})$
5 (a) $4\frac{1}{2}$, on the negative side of the y-axis (b) $4\frac{1}{2}$ (c) $1\frac{1}{3}$
6 $18\frac{2}{3}$ **7** -36 **8** $28\frac{4}{9}$

Exercise 9c (p180)

1 (a) 144π (b) $28\pi/15$ (c) 2π (d) $16\pi/15$
2 (a) 18π (b) $9\pi/2$ (c) $96\frac{3}{5}\pi$ (d) $34\frac{2}{15}\pi$
3 (a) $8\pi/3$ (b) $256\pi/15$ (c) $8\pi/3$ (d) $16\pi/15$
4 (a) 5π (b) $64\pi/15$ (c) $32\pi/3$ (d) $\frac{1}{2}\pi$
5 $\frac{1}{3}\pi r^2 h$ **6** $\frac{4}{3}\pi r^3$ **7** $661\frac{1}{3}\pi$ cm^3 **8** 1296π cm^3 **9** $27\frac{1}{2}\pi$ cm^3
10 $37\pi/10$

Exercise 9d (p185)

1 (a) $(\frac{12}{5},0)$ (b) $(0,\frac{3}{5})$ (c) $(\frac{8}{5},0)$ (d) $(0,\frac{7}{3})$
2 (a) $(\frac{2}{5},0)$ (b) $(0,\frac{83}{70})$
3 (a) $(8,\frac{4}{3})$ (b) $(\frac{3}{4},\frac{3}{5})$ (c) $(\frac{9}{4},\frac{27}{10})$ (d) $(\frac{8}{5},\frac{16}{7})$
4 (a) $(1\frac{1}{2},0)$ (b) $(\frac{8}{3},0)$ (c) $(0,\frac{10}{3})$ (d) $(\frac{5}{4},0)$
5 $\frac{1}{4}h$ above the base
6 $\frac{3}{8}r$
7 $9\frac{1}{7}$ cm
8 $(4r/(3\pi),\,4r/(3\pi))$

Exercise 9e (p186)

1 0, (a) $\frac{1}{4}$ (b) $-\frac{1}{4}$ **2** $\frac{2}{15}$ **3** A$(1,1\frac{1}{2})$, B$(4,3)$, $\frac{3}{2}\sqrt{5}$ **4** 134π
5 $\frac{128}{5}\pi$, 16π **6** $12\frac{2}{3}\pi$ **7** $\frac{1}{105}\pi$ **9** $y=2x-2$ **10** $10\frac{2}{3}$
12 $6\frac{3}{4}, 1\frac{4}{5}$ **13** $5\frac{3}{5}, 2\frac{4}{21}$ **14** $3\frac{1}{4}, \frac{73}{195}$

Chapter 10 (p188)

Qu. 1 (a) 2 (b) 6 (c) a (d) ab (e) 18 (f) 80 (g) $4a$ (h) 6 (i) 35
   (j) 16 (k) 36 (l) ab
Qu. 2 (a) 3 (b) 3 (c) 9 (d) 2 (e) 8 (f) 243 (g) 16 (h) 8
Qu. 3 '$0^0=1$' would have to be derived from '$0^n \div 0^n = 0^0$', but division by 0.
   or by 0^n, is meaningless
Qu. 4 bases: (a) 10 (b) 10 (c) 3 (d) 4 (e) 2 (f) $\frac{1}{2}$ (g) a
   logarithms: (a) 2 (b) 1.6021 (c) 2 (d) 3 (e) 0 (f) -3 (g) b
Qu. 6 $x=\log_c a$, $nx=\log_c a^n$
Qu. 7 (a) 10 (b) 100 (c) 0.1 (d) 1 (e) 0 (f) $\frac{1}{2}$
Qu. 8 (a) a (b) a^2 (c) $1/a$ (d) 1 (e) 0 (f) $\frac{1}{2}$

Exercise 10a (p189)

1 (a) 5 (b) $\frac{1}{2}$ (c) 48 (d) $\frac{1}{2}$ (e) a/b (f) 15 (g) 21 (h) p/q (i) $1/(4p)$
   (j) $9a/(2b)$
2 (a) $2\sqrt{2}$ (b) $2\sqrt{3}$ (c) $3\sqrt{3}$ (d) $5\sqrt{2}$ (e) $3\sqrt{5}$ (f) $11\sqrt{10}$
   (g) $5\sqrt{3}$ (h) $4\sqrt{2}$ (i) $6\sqrt{2}$ (j) $7\sqrt{2}$
3 (a) $\sqrt{18}$ (b) $\sqrt{12}$ (c) $\sqrt{80}$ (d) $\sqrt{24}$ (e) $\sqrt{72}$ (f) $\sqrt{216}$ (g) $\sqrt{128}$
   (h) $\sqrt{1000}$

4 (a) $\sqrt{5}/5$ (b) $\sqrt{7}/7$ (c) $-\sqrt{2}/2$ (d) $2\sqrt{3}/3$ (e) $\sqrt{6}/2$ (f) $\sqrt{2}/4$
  (g) $-\sqrt{3}/2$ (h) $3\sqrt{6}/8$ (i) $\sqrt{2}-1$ (j) $2+\sqrt{3}$
5 (a) $3\sqrt{2}$ (b) $6\sqrt{3}$ (c) $4\sqrt{7}$ (d) $5\sqrt{10}$ (e) $28\sqrt{2}$ (f) 0
6 (a) $\frac{6}{7}+\frac{2}{7}\sqrt{2}$ (b) $9+4\sqrt{5}$ (c) $-1+\sqrt{2}$ (d) $4-2\sqrt{3}$ (e) $-1-\sqrt{2}$
  (f) $\frac{1}{2}+\frac{3}{4}\sqrt{2}$
7 (a) $5+2\sqrt{6}$ (b) $\frac{1}{2}(5+\sqrt{3}+\sqrt{5}+\sqrt{15})$ (c) $-7+3\sqrt{6}$
  (d) $4+\sqrt{10}$ (e) $3+2\sqrt{2}$ (f) $\sqrt{2}$

Exercise 10b (p192)

1 (a) 5 (b) 3 (c) 2 (d) 7 (e) $\frac{1}{2}$ (f) 1 (g) -2 (h) -1 (i) 16 (j) 9
2 (a) 1 (b) $\frac{1}{3}$ (c) 1 (d) $\frac{1}{4}$ (e) $\frac{1}{8}$ (f) 2 (g) 9 (h) 1 (i) $\frac{1}{27}$ (j) $-\frac{1}{6}$
3 (a) $\frac{1}{2}$ (b) $\frac{1}{4}$ (c) $\frac{1}{2}$ (d) $\frac{1}{8}$ (e) $\frac{1}{9}$ (f) 2 (g) 2 (h) 9 (i) $1\frac{1}{2}$ (j) $1\frac{1}{2}$
4 (a) 16 (b) 36 (c) 4 (d) 6 (e) $1\frac{1}{2}$ (f) $1\frac{1}{3}$ (g) $\frac{1}{2}$ (h) $\frac{1}{8}$ (i) $\frac{1}{16}$ (j) $\frac{1}{27}$

Exercise 10c (p193)

1 (a) $\log_2 16 = 4$ (b) $\log_3 27 = 3$ (c) $\log_5 125 = 3$ (d) $\log_{10} 1\,000\,000 = 6$
  (e) $\log_{12} 1728 = 3$ (f) $\log_{16} 64 = \frac{3}{2}$ (g) $\log_{10} 10\,000 = 4$ (h) $\log_4 1 = 0$
  (i) $\log_{10} 0.01 = -2$ (j) $\log_2 \frac{1}{2} = -1$ (k) $\log_9 27 = \frac{3}{2}$ (l) $\log_8 \frac{1}{4} = -\frac{2}{3}$
  (m) $\log_{1/3} 81 = -4$ (n) $\log_e 1 = 0$ (o) $\log_{16} \frac{1}{2} = -\frac{1}{4}$ (p) $\log_{1/8} 1 = 0$
  (q) $\log_{81} 27 = \frac{3}{4}$ (r) $\log_{1/16} 4 = -\frac{1}{2}$ (s) $\log_a c = 5$ (t) $\log_a b = 3$
  (u) $\log_p r = q$ (v) $\log_b a = c$
2 (a) $2^5 = 32$ (b) $3^2 = 9$ (c) $5^2 = 25$ (d) $10^5 = 100\,000$ (e) $2^7 = 128$
  (f) $9^0 = 1$ (g) $3^{-2} = \frac{1}{9}$ (h) $4^{1/2} = 2$ (i) $e^0 = 1$ (j) $27^{1/3} = 3$
  (k) $a^2 = x$ (l) $3^b = a$ (m) $a^c = 8$ (n) $x^y = z$ (o) $q^p = r$
3 (a) 6 (b) 2 (c) 7 (d) 2 (e) $\frac{1}{3}$ (f) 0 (g) $\frac{1}{3}$ (h) 3 (i) 3 (j) -1

Exercise 10d (p196)

1 (a) $\log a + \log b$ (b) $\log a - \log c$ (c) $-\log b$ (d) $2\log a + \frac{3}{2}\log b$
  (e) $-4\log b$ (f) $\frac{1}{3}\log a + 4\log b - 3\log c$ (g) $\frac{1}{2}\log a$ (h) $\frac{1}{3}\log b$
  (i) $\frac{1}{2}\log a + \frac{1}{2}\log b$ (j) $1 + \lg a$ (k) $-2 - 2\lg b$
  (l) $\frac{1}{2}\log a - \frac{1}{2}\log b$
2 (a) $\log 6$ (b) $\log 2$ (c) $\log 6$ (d) $\log 2$ (e) $\log(ac)$ (f) $\log(xy/z)$
  (g) $\log(a^2/b)$ (h) $\log(a^2b^3/c)$ (i) $\log\sqrt{(x/y)}$ (j) $\log(p/\sqrt[3]{q})$
  (k) $\lg(100a^3)$ (l) $\lg(10a/\sqrt{b})$ (m) $\lg(a^2/2000c)$ (n) $\lg(10x^3/\sqrt{y})$
3 (a) 3 (b) 2 (c) 2 (d) 1 (e) $\log 2$ (f) $\log 7$ (g) $\log\frac{1}{2}$ (h) 0
  (i) 0 (j) 3 (k) 2 (l) $\frac{2}{3}$
4 (a) 2.322 (b) 0.6309 (c) 0.3155 (d) 1.161 (e) -2.585 (f) 6.838

Exercise 10e (p200)

1 (a) $-12, -12, -6, 0, 0, (x-2)$, or $(x+2)$ (b) $-1, 0, -2, 19, -21, (x-1)$
  (c) $0, 6, -2, 88, -24, x$ (d) $3, 0, 0, 3, 3, (x-1)$, or $(x+1)$
2 (a) 2 (b) 18 (c) -11 (d) -1 (e) 2 (f) $-2\frac{1}{2}$
3 (a) -3 (b) -10 (c) 2 (d) 4 (e) 4 (f) 2

4 $(x+3)(2x-1)$ **5** $(2x-1)(2x+3)(3x+1)$
6 (a) $(x-1)(x+2)(x-3)$ (b) $(x+1)(x-2)(x-3)$
(c) $(2x+1)(x-2)(x+2)$ (d) $(x+1)(x+2)(2x-1)$
(e) $(x+2)(x+3)(2x+1)$ (f) $(x^2+1)(2x-1)$
7 $a=3, b=2$ **8** $p=1, q=-3$ **9** $a=3, b=-1, c=-2$
10 $a=2, b=-1, c=-2$

Exercise 10f (p205)

1 (a) $5\sqrt{5}$ (b) $\sqrt{2}$ (c) $18\sqrt{3}$ **2** (a) $(11+6\sqrt{2})/7$ (b) $13+2\sqrt{2}$
3 (a) $\frac{1}{16}, \frac{8}{27}, \frac{1}{4}$ (b) $8, 27$ **4** $x-3x^{1/3}-2, 0$
5 (a) 8 (b) 2 **6** $2+2\lg a-3\lg b-\frac{1}{2}\lg c$
7 (a) $1\frac{1}{8}$ (b) 3.17
9 (a) $-2<x<5$ (b) either $x>5+\sqrt{3}$, or $x<5-\sqrt{3}$ (c) $2<x<3\frac{1}{2}$
10 (a) $x\geqslant 7\frac{1}{2}$, or $x\leqslant 5$ (b) $-7\leqslant x\leqslant 9$

Chapter 11 (p206)

Qu. 1 (a) 37, (i) (b) 0, (ii) (c) -8, (iii) (d) 17, (i)
Qu. 2 $f(t)\leqslant 30$
Qu. 4 (a) $\pm 8i$ (b) $\pm\sqrt{7}i$ (c) $\pm\frac{3}{2}i$ (d) $-3\pm 5i$
Qu. 5 $3\pm 5i$
Qu. 6 (a) $2\pm 3i$ (b) $\pm 5i/3$ (c) $(1\pm 5i)/2$ (d) $(3\pm 5i)/34$
Qu. 7 $\frac{5}{2}+\frac{1}{2}i$
Qu. 9 (a) $[a+c, 0]$ (b) $[ac, 0]$ (c) $[a-c, 0]$ (d) $[a/c, 0]$
Qu. 11 $-y+ix, -x-iy, y-ix$
Qu. 12 (a) 5 (b) 1 (c) 1 (d) 1 (e) 3 (f) $\sqrt{2}$
Qu. 13 (a) $45°$ (b) $0°$ (c) $-90°$ (d) $-45°$ (e) $60°$ (f) $120°$ (g) $-20°$
(h) $70°$
Qu. 14 (a) $\frac{2}{3}, -\frac{7}{3}$ (b) $-\frac{11}{5}, \frac{3}{5}$ (c) $-\frac{5}{2}, -\frac{1}{2}$ (d) $-\frac{1}{2}, -\frac{7}{2}$
Qu. 15 (a) $x^2-7x+12=0$ (b) $x^2-3x-2=0$ (c) $8x^2+4x-3=0$
(d) $3x^2-2x=0$
Qu. 16 $-3, \frac{7}{3}$

Exercise 11a (p212)

1 (a) $1\frac{1}{2}, 1$ (b) $3, -7$ (c) ± 2.5 (d) $0, -\frac{5}{7}$

2 (a) $\dfrac{3\pm\sqrt{11}}{2}$ (b) $\dfrac{-6\pm\sqrt{6}}{5}$ (c) $\dfrac{-7\pm\sqrt{61}}{2}$ (d) $\dfrac{3\pm\sqrt{89}}{4}$

3 (a) $\dfrac{7\pm\sqrt{61}}{6}$ (b) $\dfrac{-3\pm\sqrt{149}}{10}$ (c) $\dfrac{-13\pm\sqrt{153}}{2}$ (d) $\dfrac{7\pm\sqrt{73}}{6}$

4 (a) $\dfrac{15\pm\sqrt{165}}{4}$ (b) $0, \frac{48}{11}$ (c) no real solution (d) $5, \frac{3}{7}$

5 (a) $2\left(x - \dfrac{3+\sqrt{11}}{2}\right)\left(x - \dfrac{3-\sqrt{11}}{2}\right)$

(b) $5(x + 1.2 + \sqrt{0.24})(x + 1.2 - \sqrt{0.24})$

(c) $\left(x + \dfrac{7+\sqrt{61}}{2}\right)\left(x + \dfrac{7-\sqrt{61}}{2}\right)$

(d) $-2\left(x - \dfrac{3+\sqrt{89}}{4}\right)\left(x - \dfrac{3-\sqrt{89}}{4}\right)$

8 $|k| < 12$
10 (a) 3   (b) 5   (c) 10   (d) -17

Exercise 11b (p217)

1 (a) $-i$ (b) 1 (c) i (d) -1 (e) -1 (f) $-i$ (g) i
2 (a) $4 + 3i$ (b) 9 (c) $1 - 5i$ (d) $2i$
3 (a) $-7 + 22i$ (b) $8 + i$ (c) 2 (d) 25 (e) $u^2 + v^2$ (f) $2x^2 - 2y^2 + 5ixy$
  (g) $-3q + 2ip$ (h) $p^2 + 4q^2$

4 (a) $-i$ (b) $\dfrac{2+3i}{13}$ (c) $\dfrac{4+7i}{5}$ (d) $\dfrac{9+40i}{41}$ (e) $\dfrac{x-iy}{x^2+y^2}$ (f) $\dfrac{x+iy}{x^2+y^2}$

  (g) $4/13$
5 (a) $-5 + 12i$ (b) $-9 - 40i$ (c) $x^2 - y^2 + 2ixy$
6 (a) $-2 + 2i$ (b) $-2 - 2i$ (c) $-\frac{1}{4}(1 + i)$

7 (a) $2 \pm 5i$ (b) $\pm\frac{1}{2}\sqrt{7}i$ (c) $\dfrac{-3 \pm \sqrt{31}i}{4}$ (d) $\frac{1}{2}(-1 \pm 2i)$

10 $\frac{1}{2}, -1 \pm 2i$

Exercise 11c (p223)

1 (a) $\sqrt{2}, 45°$ (b) $\sqrt{13}, 146.3°$ (c) $\sqrt{13}, -146.3°$ (d) $5, -53.1°$
  (e) $5, 143.1°$ (f) $1, 60°$ (g) $1, 120°$ (h) $1, 180°$
2 (a) 1 (b) i (c) -1 (d) $-i$ (e) 1 (f) $\frac{1}{2}\sqrt{3} + \frac{1}{2}i$ (g) $\frac{1}{2}\sqrt{3} - \frac{1}{2}i$
  (h) $-\frac{1}{2} + \frac{1}{2}\sqrt{3}i$ (i) $-\frac{1}{2} - \frac{1}{2}\sqrt{3}i$ (j) $-\frac{1}{2}\sqrt{3} + \frac{1}{2}i$
3 (a) $5, 53.1°$ (b) $13, 22.6°$ (c) $\frac{1}{5}, -53.1°$ (d) $\frac{1}{13}, -22.6°$ (e) $65, 75.7°$
  (f) $5, -53.1°$ (g) $13, -22.6°$ (h) $65, -75.7°$ (i) $25, 106.3°$ (j) $169, 45°$
4 $2i, -2 + 2i, -4; 45°, 90°, 135°, 180°$
5 (a) $\frac{1}{2} + \frac{1}{2}\sqrt{3}i, i, -\frac{1}{2} + \frac{1}{2}\sqrt{3}i; 30°, 60°, 90°, 120°$
  (b) $2 + 2\sqrt{3}i, 8i, -8 + 8\sqrt{3}i; 30°, 60°, 90°, 120°$

6 $(a^2 - b^2) + 2abi, \dfrac{a - ib}{a^2 + b^2}$

8 $(ac - bd) + i(ad + bc)$ **9** $\pm(3 + 2i)$ **10** $\pm(2 - i)$

Exercise 11d (p226)

1 (a) $\frac{11}{2}, \frac{3}{2}$ (b) $-\frac{1}{2}, -\frac{1}{2}$ (c) $\frac{7}{3}, -2$ (d) $-1, -1$ (e) $1, -3$ (f)$1, -5$
(g) $4, 1$ (h) $3, -2$

2 (a) $x^2 - 3x + 4 = 0$ (b) $x^2 + 5x + 6 = 0$ (c) $2x^2 - 3x - 5 = 0$
(d) $3x^2 + 7x = 0$ (e) $x^2 - 7 = 0$ (f) $5x^2 - 6x + 4 = 0$
(g) $36x^2 + 12x + 1 = 0$ (h) $10x^2 + 25x - 16 = 0$

3 (a) $\frac{25}{4}$ (b) $\frac{3}{4}$ (c) $-\frac{5}{2}$ (d) $-\frac{25}{8}$

4 (a) $\frac{5}{9}$ (b) $\frac{16}{9}$ (c) $\frac{80}{27}$ (d) $\frac{80}{9}$

5 (a) 72 (b) 5 (c) $-\frac{9}{8}$ (d) -32

6 (a) $x^2 - 39x + 49 = 0$ (b) $x^2 - 7x - 1 = 0$ (c) $x^2 + 35x - 343 = 0$

7 (a) $2x^2 + 4x + 1 = 0$ (b) $x^2 - 4x + 2 = 0$ (c) $x^2 - 6x + 1 = 0$

8 $4x^2 - 49x + 36 = 0$

9 $\frac{35}{4}$

10 ± 6

12 (a) $-bc/a^2$ (b) $(b^2 - 2ac)/a^2$ (c) $b(3ac - b^2)/a^3$ (d) $-b/c$

13 (a) $ax^2 - bx + c = 0$ (b) $ax^2 + (b - 2a)x + a - b + c = 0$
(c) $a^2x^2 + (2ac - b^2)x + c^2 = 0$ (d) $cx^2 - bx + a = 0$

Exercise 11e (p227)

1 (a) $\varnothing$ (b) $\frac{2}{3}$ (c) $\frac{2}{3}$ (d) $\frac{2}{3}, +i, -i$

2 (i) (a) -4 (b) $-4, 7/5$ (c) $-4, 7/5$ (d) $-4, 7/5$
(ii) (a) $\varnothing$ (b) $\varnothing$ (c) $\pm\sqrt{(7/5)}$ (d) $\pm\sqrt{(7/5)}, \pm 2i$

3 (a) $10i, 10, 90°$ (b) $(3 - 4i)/5, 1, -53.1°$ (c) $16, 16, 0$

4 (a) $(3 + 2i)/13, \frac{1}{2}i$ (b) $\sqrt{5}, 63.4°, \sqrt{5}, -26.6°, 3 + i, 4 + 3i$

6 either $a = 1/\sqrt{2}, b = 1/\sqrt{2}$, or $a = -1/\sqrt{2}, b = -1/\sqrt{2}$
$z = -1 + 1/\sqrt{2} + i/\sqrt{2}$, or $-1 - 1/\sqrt{2} - i/\sqrt{2}$

7 (a) $3, -1, 1 + i$ (b) $(-1 \pm \sqrt{3}i)/2$

8 $\pm(3 + 2i)$

9 $\sqrt{2}/2, 45°; \frac{1}{2}, 90°; \sqrt{2}/4, 135°; \frac{1}{4}, 180°$

10 $1 + j, 2 - j; x^2 - 3(1 + j)x + (2 + 3j) = 0$

Chapter 12 (p229)

Qu. 1 $\begin{pmatrix} 17 & 23 & 29 \\ 14 & 20 & 34 \end{pmatrix}$

Qu. 2 (a) $\begin{pmatrix} 5 & 1 \\ 2 & 0 \\ 6 & 1 \end{pmatrix}$ (b) $\begin{pmatrix} 29 \\ 20 \end{pmatrix}$ (c) $(20 \quad 7)$ (d) $\begin{pmatrix} 6 & 5 \\ 8 & 5 \end{pmatrix}$

Qu. 5 (a) $\begin{pmatrix} 0 & 1 \\ -1 & 0 \end{pmatrix}$ (b) $\begin{pmatrix} 0 & -1 \\ -1 & 0 \end{pmatrix}$ (c) $\begin{pmatrix} 5 & 0 \\ 0 & 5 \end{pmatrix}$

Qu. 6 $\begin{pmatrix} 1 & 0 \\ 5 & 1 \end{pmatrix}$

Exercise 12a (p237)

1 (a) $\begin{pmatrix} 9 & 3 & 6 \\ 15 & 3 & 21 \end{pmatrix}$ (b) $\begin{pmatrix} 8 & -2 & 4 \\ 6 & 2 & 6 \end{pmatrix}$ (c) $\begin{pmatrix} 17 & 1 & 10 \\ 21 & 5 & 27 \end{pmatrix}$ (d) $\begin{pmatrix} 1 & 5 & 2 \\ 9 & 1 & 15 \end{pmatrix}$

2 $\mathbf{PS} = (6480 \quad 15\,000 \quad 21\,000 \quad 13\,200 \quad 19\,080 \quad 19\,800)$

3 (a) $(19 \quad 31)$ (b) $\begin{pmatrix} 14 & 19 & 24 \\ 17 & 22 & 27 \end{pmatrix}$ (c) not possible   (d) $\begin{pmatrix} 38 \\ 68 \end{pmatrix}$

4 $\begin{pmatrix} \frac{1}{2} & -2 \\ 7 & 10 \end{pmatrix}, \begin{pmatrix} 1\frac{1}{2} & -\frac{1}{2} \\ 11 & 9 \end{pmatrix}$ **5** $\begin{pmatrix} a & b \\ c & d \end{pmatrix}$ **6** $\begin{pmatrix} 2 & 0 \\ 0 & 2 \end{pmatrix}$ **7** $\begin{pmatrix} 6 \\ -8\frac{1}{2} \end{pmatrix}$

8 $\begin{pmatrix} 4 & 0 \\ 0 & 4 \end{pmatrix}$ **9** $\begin{pmatrix} 3 \\ -7 \end{pmatrix}$ **10** (a) $\begin{pmatrix} 11 & -1 & 29 \\ 29 & -1 & 62 \\ 1 & 1 & -7 \end{pmatrix}$ (b) $\begin{pmatrix} 19 & -2 \\ 9 & -4 \\ 24 & 0 \end{pmatrix}$

14 $\begin{pmatrix} ad-bc & 0 \\ 0 & ad-bc \end{pmatrix}$

Exercise 12b (p243)

1 (a) 1   (b) 14   (c) 30   (d) 1
2 (a) 0   (b) $\frac{2}{15}$ (c) a^2+b^2 (d) $ad-bc$
3 (b), (c), (d)
4 (a) 28   (b) ± 4 (c) 1, 4   (d) none

5 (a) $\begin{pmatrix} 7 & -4 \\ -5 & 3 \end{pmatrix}$ (b) $\begin{pmatrix} 5 & -3 \\ -3 & 2 \end{pmatrix}$ (c) $\begin{pmatrix} 7/20 & -11/20 \\ -2/20 & 6/20 \end{pmatrix}$

(d) $\dfrac{1}{x^2+1}\begin{pmatrix} x & 1 \\ -1 & x \end{pmatrix}$

Exercise 12c (p244)

1 (a) $\begin{pmatrix} 3 & -4 \\ -5 & 7 \end{pmatrix}$ (b) $\dfrac{1}{2}\begin{pmatrix} 3 & -2 \\ -11 & 8 \end{pmatrix}$ (c) $\dfrac{1}{2}\begin{pmatrix} 6 & -2 \\ -3 & 3 \end{pmatrix}$ (d) not possible

2 (a) $\dfrac{1}{2}\begin{pmatrix} \sqrt{2} & -\sqrt{2} \\ \sqrt{2} & \sqrt{2} \end{pmatrix}$ (b) $\dfrac{1}{2}\begin{pmatrix} 1 & -\sqrt{3} \\ \sqrt{3} & 1 \end{pmatrix}$ (c) $\dfrac{1}{5}\begin{pmatrix} 3 & 4 \\ -4 & 3 \end{pmatrix}$

(d) $\dfrac{1}{2}\begin{pmatrix} 1 & \sqrt{3} \\ \sqrt{3} & -1 \end{pmatrix}$

$3 \ \dfrac{1}{2}\begin{pmatrix} 4 & -2 \\ -5 & 3 \end{pmatrix}, \begin{pmatrix} -1 \\ 2 \end{pmatrix}$ $4 \ \dfrac{1}{20}\begin{pmatrix} 4 & -2 \\ -8 & 9 \end{pmatrix}, \dfrac{1}{20}\begin{pmatrix} -2 \\ 19 \end{pmatrix}$ $5 \ \begin{pmatrix} -5 \\ 4 \end{pmatrix}$

$6 \ \begin{pmatrix} -2 & -8 \\ 3 & 11 \end{pmatrix}$ $7 \ \dfrac{1}{25}\begin{pmatrix} 304 & 372 \\ 372 & 521 \end{pmatrix}$ $9 \ \begin{pmatrix} 17 \\ -7 \\ 19 \end{pmatrix}$ $10 \ \begin{pmatrix} 1 \\ 0 \\ 2 \end{pmatrix}$

$11 \ \dfrac{1}{14}\begin{pmatrix} 7 & -3 & -1 \\ 0 & 6 & 2 \\ 0 & 8 & -2 \end{pmatrix}$ $12 \ \dfrac{1}{14}\begin{pmatrix} 7 & -3 & -1 \\ 0 & 6 & 2 \\ 0 & 8 & -2 \end{pmatrix}$

Exercise 12d (p257)

1 (a) reflection in x-axis   (b) reflection in y-axis   (c) rotation through $90°$
(d) reflection in $x + y = 0$ (e) shear parallel to x-axis
2 $(6, 17), (22, 29), (9, 38); 6, 150$

3 $\begin{pmatrix} 0 & 1 \\ -1 & 0 \end{pmatrix}$; rotation, through $90°$ clockwise

4 $\pi a^2, \pi ab$

5 (a) $\begin{pmatrix} 4/5 & -3/5 \\ 3/5 & 4/5 \end{pmatrix}$ (b) $\begin{pmatrix} 0 & 5 \\ 5 & 0 \end{pmatrix}$

6 rotation and enlargement, $a^2 + b^2 = 1$
7 enlargement, with scale-factor $\sqrt{2}$ and reflection in the line
$y = (\tan 22\frac{1}{2}°)x; \ \lambda = \sqrt{2}, \ m = \tan 22\frac{1}{2}°$
8 reflection in $y = (\tan \alpha)x$, where $\cos 2\alpha = 3/5$
10 $\cos 2\theta = \cos^2 \theta - \sin^2 \theta, \ \sin 2\theta = 2 \sin \theta \cos \theta$

Exercise 12e (p259)

1 (a) $\begin{pmatrix} -13 \\ -31 \end{pmatrix}$ (b) $(22 \quad 15)$ (c) not possible   (d) $\begin{pmatrix} 0 & 3 & 1 & 2 \\ 0 & 7 & 3 & 4 \end{pmatrix}$

2 (a) $\begin{pmatrix} 5 & -7 \\ -2 & 3 \end{pmatrix}$ (b) $\dfrac{1}{2}\begin{pmatrix} 4 & -3 \\ -6 & 5 \end{pmatrix}$ (c) $\dfrac{1}{2}\begin{pmatrix} -5 & 3 \\ 4 & -2 \end{pmatrix}$ (d) not possible

3 (a) $\dfrac{1}{a^2 + b^2}\begin{pmatrix} a & -b \\ b & a \end{pmatrix}$ (b) $\begin{pmatrix} \cos \theta & -\sin \theta \\ \sin \theta & \cos \theta \end{pmatrix}$ (c) $\begin{pmatrix} 0 & a \\ 1/a & 0 \end{pmatrix}$

(d) not possible

4 (a) $\begin{pmatrix} -11 \\ 13 \end{pmatrix}$ (b) $\begin{pmatrix} 1 & 3 \\ -1 & -4 \end{pmatrix}$

5 $2x = 7y$

6 (19, 11), (39, 15), (31, 35); 216

7 $1, -\frac{1}{2}$

8 $(-19, -35), (21, -11)$

9 $\begin{pmatrix} -2 & 0 & 0 \\ 0 & -2 & 0 \\ 0 & 0 & -2 \end{pmatrix}, \frac{1}{2}\begin{pmatrix} -1 & 2 & 1 \\ 3 & -2 & -1 \\ -1 & 0 & 1 \end{pmatrix}$

10 (a) $\begin{pmatrix} 76.05 \\ 23.95 \end{pmatrix}$ (b) $\begin{pmatrix} 45.8 \\ 54.2 \end{pmatrix}$ (c) $\begin{pmatrix} 78.3 \\ 21.7 \end{pmatrix}$

12 $M = \begin{pmatrix} 0 & 1 \\ 1 & 0 \end{pmatrix}$, $R = \begin{pmatrix} \cos\theta & -\sin\theta \\ \sin\theta & \cos\theta \end{pmatrix}$; rotation about the origin, through an

angle $-\theta$; $\cos 2\theta = \cos^2\theta - \sin^2\theta$, $\sin 2\theta = 2\sin\theta\cos\theta$

13 $A^{-1} = \begin{pmatrix} \frac{1}{3} & 0 & 0 \\ 0 & \frac{1}{2} & \frac{1}{2} \\ 0 & \frac{3}{4} & \frac{1}{4} \end{pmatrix}$

14 $\begin{pmatrix} a^2 + bc & ab + bd \\ ac + cd & bc + d^2 \end{pmatrix}$

15 $M^2 = I$; -1; $2x = 3y$, $2v = -3u$; reflection in $2x = 3y$

16 $k = 2/\sqrt{5}$; rotation, 26.6°, clockwise

Revision Exercise 2 (p263)

1 $-\frac{3}{4}$, α and β are complex, $28x^2 - 85x + 98 = 0$

2 $-1\frac{1}{2} < x < -1$

3 (a) 2.32   (b) 5/3   (c) 0.693   (d) $a = 18$, $b = -2$

4 $A^{-1} = \begin{pmatrix} -1 & -3 & 2 \\ 0 & -2 & 1 \\ 1 & 2 & -1 \end{pmatrix}$ **5** (26, 9)   **6** 14/3

7 0.62   **8** $a = -1$, $b = -4$

9 $p = 6$, $q = 1$, $(x-1)(3x-4)(2x+1)$

10 1   **11** $0, -\frac{1}{2}$ **13** 68 months

14 (a) $2, -45°$ (b) $2, 60°$ (c) $2\sqrt{2}, 15°$ (d) $1/\sqrt{2}, -105°$

15 $\pm(3+2i)$ **16** $x^2 - 19x + 9 = 0$
18 (a) $-9/8$ (b) (i) $-\frac{1}{2} < x < 1$,   (ii) $x < 0$

19 $\dfrac{1}{4}\begin{pmatrix} 2 & -1 \\ 0 & 2 \end{pmatrix}$ **20** (a) $\mathbf{X} = \begin{pmatrix} -8 & 19 \\ 3 & -7 \end{pmatrix}$ (b) $\mathbf{Y} = \begin{pmatrix} -1 & -3 \\ 1 & 2\frac{1}{2} \end{pmatrix}$

Chapter 13 (p266)

Qu. 1   (a) 56   (b) 210

Qu. 2 $\dfrac{n!}{(n-r)!\,r!}$

Exercise 13a (p268)

1 720   **2** 360   **3** 243   **4** 72   **5** 24   **6** 27 000
7 900   **8** 120   **9** 719   **10** 48   **11** 5040   **12** 168
13 336, 144   **14** 3 628 800, 3 628 800   **15** 10 368 000

Exercise 13b (p270)

1 (a) 6   (b) 24   (c) 120   (d) 90   (e) 210   (f) 1320   (g) 330   (h) $\frac{1}{28}$
(i) 4   (j) 20   (k) 120   (l) 2520

2 (a) $\dfrac{6!}{3!}$ (b) $\dfrac{10!}{8!}$ (c) $\dfrac{12!}{8!}$ (d) $\dfrac{n!}{(n-3)!}$ (e) $\dfrac{(n+2)!}{(n-1)!}$ (f) $\dfrac{10!}{8!\,2!}$ (g) $\dfrac{7!}{4!\,3!}$

(h) $\dfrac{52!}{49!\,3!}$ (i) $\dfrac{n!}{(n-2)!\,2!}$ (j) $\dfrac{(n+1)!}{(n-2)!\,3!}$ (k) $\dfrac{(2n)!}{(2n-2)!\,2!}$ (l) $\dfrac{n!}{(n-r)!}$

3 (a) $20! \times 22$ (b) $25! \times 25$ (c) $13! \times 12$ (d) $14! \times 19$ (e) $n!(n+2)$
(f) $(n-2)!(n-2)$ (g) $(n-1)!(n+2)$ (h) $n!(n+2)^2$

4 (a) $\dfrac{16!}{12!\,4!}$ (b) $\dfrac{22!}{14!\,8!}$ (c) $\dfrac{18!}{7!\,11!}$ (d) $\dfrac{37!}{19!\,18!}$ (e) $\dfrac{(n+1)!}{r!(n-r+1)!}$

(f) $\dfrac{(n+2)!}{r!(n-r+2)!}$

Exercise 13c (p273)

1 282 240   **2** 362 880, 40 320   **3** 6720, 1680
4 $24 \times 17!$, $48 \times 16!$ **5** $\frac{1}{60} \times 13!$ **6** 768   **7** 16
8 144   **9** 30 240   **10** 528

Exercise 13d (p275)

1 (a) 45   (b) 15   (c) 35   (d) 126   (e) 70   (f) $\frac{1}{2}n(n-1)$
(g) $\frac{1}{6}n(n-1)(n-2)$ (h) $\frac{1}{2}n(n-1)$ (i) $\frac{1}{2}n(n+1)$ (j) $\frac{1}{2}n(n+1)$

2 78   **3** 70   **4** 252   **5** 126   **6** 30   **7** 252   **8** 286
9 792   **10** 200

Exercise 13e (p276)

1 1960   **3** 15 120   **4** 728   **5** $\frac{1}{2}n(n-3)$ **6** 48
7 120 960   **8** 240, 15 552   **9** 277 200   **10** 4200

Chapter 14 (p277)

Qu. 1 (a) 9, 11   (b) 14, 17   (c) 16, 32   (d) $\frac{1}{48}, \frac{1}{96}$ (e) $5^3, 6^3$ (f) $\frac{5}{6}, \frac{6}{7}$
(g) 25, 36   (h) 720, 5040   (i) $\frac{5}{81}, \frac{6}{243}$ (j) $-4, -6$ (k) 1, -1
(l) $\frac{1}{16}, -\frac{1}{32}$
Qu. 2 (i) (a) 6, 8   (b) 8, 16   (ii) (a) 0, -6 (b) 3, $1\frac{1}{2}$
Qu. 3 (a) 34   (b) 16
Qu. 4 8, $12\frac{1}{2}$, 10
Qu. 5 $2ac/(a+c)$
Qu. 6 (a) $n(2n+1)$ (b) $\frac{1}{6}(n+1)(n+2)(2n+3)$ (c) $\frac{1}{4}(n-1)^2 n^2$
(d) $n(2n-1)$ (e) $\frac{1}{3}n(2n+1)(4n+1)$ (f) $n^2(2n-1)^2$

Exercise 14a (p279)

1 (a) $1\frac{1}{2}$ (b) -3 (c) 0.1   (e) $\frac{1}{3}$ (g) n (i) $1\frac{1}{8}$ (j) -7 (l) -0.2
2 (a) 75, 147   (b) $-34, -82$ (c) $7\frac{1}{8}, \frac{1}{8}(5n-3)$ (d) $-148, 52-2n$
(e) $-13\frac{1}{2}, \frac{1}{2}(15-n)$ (f) 799, $3+4n$
3 (a) 23   (b) 13   (c) 31   (d) 21   (e) 91   (f) 13   (g) $2n$ (h) n
(i) n (j) $(l-a)/d+1$
4 (a) 2601   (b) 632   (c) 420   (d) 288   (e) 250.5   (f) $60\frac{1}{2}$ (g) $121x$
(h) $\frac{1}{2}n(2a+n-1)$ (i) $\frac{1}{2}n\{2a+(n-1)d\}$
5 (a) 444   (b) -80 (c) 20 100   (d) -520 (e) $n(2n+4)$ (f) $\frac{1}{8}n(11-n)$
6 2, 13, 220   **7** 33, -72 **8** 5   **9** 14, 4   **10** 7500
11 7650   **12** $3\frac{1}{2}, \frac{1}{10}, 148\frac{1}{2}$ **14** 60

Exercise 14b (p281)

1 (a) 3   (b) $\frac{1}{4}$ (c) -2 (d) -1 (f) a (g) 1.1   (j) 6
2 (a) $5 \times 2^{10}, 5 \times 2^{19}$ (b) $10(\frac{5}{2})^6, 10(\frac{5}{2})^{18}$ (c) $\frac{2}{3}(\frac{9}{8})^{11}, \frac{2}{3}(\frac{9}{8})^{n-1}$
(d) $3(-\frac{2}{3})^7, 3(-\frac{2}{3})^{n-1}$ (e) $\frac{2}{7}(-\frac{3}{2})^8, \frac{2}{7}(-\frac{3}{2})^{n-1}$ (f) $3(\frac{1}{2})^{18}, 3(\frac{1}{2})^{2n-1}$
3 (a) 9   (b) 8   (c) 7   (d) 8   (e) $n+1$ (f) n
4 (a) $2^{10}-2$ (b) $\frac{1}{2}(3^5 - \frac{1}{27})$ (c) $0.03(2^7-1)$ (d) $-\frac{16}{405}\{(\frac{3}{2})^8 - 1\}$

(e) $5(2^{n+1}-1)$ (f) $a\left(\dfrac{1-r^n}{1-r}\right)$

5 (a) $2(3^{12}-1)$ (b) $\frac{45}{2}\{1-(\frac{1}{3})^{20}\}$ (c) $-\frac{1}{3}(2^{50}-1)$ (d) $16\{1+(\frac{1}{2})^{17}\}$
(e) $11(1.1^{23}-1)$ (f) $1-(\frac{1}{2})^{13}$ (g) $3(2^n-1)$ (h) $\frac{3}{4}\{1-(-\frac{1}{3})^n\}$
6 2, $2\frac{1}{2}$, $157\frac{1}{2}$ **7** $\pm 3, \pm\frac{2}{3}$ **8** 6, $13\frac{1}{2}$ **9** £10 700 000
10 $6\frac{3}{4}$

Exercise 14c (p287)

1 2550   **2** 8   **3** 98   **4** $\frac{3}{4}, -\frac{3}{2}, 3$ **5** 16 400   **6** 432
7 $\frac{7}{2}, 2$ **8** 17, -2, 10th   **9** $1\frac{1}{2}, 2, 24$ **10** 3, 4; 3, 7, 11, 15, 19
11 $-2, 1, 4, 7, 10$ **12** $-3, -2$ **13** 18   **14** 18th, 655 360
15 14   **16** $-9, 5$ **17** 2, 4, 6, 8, 10   **18** 5808   **19** 6, 8, 10
20 $2\frac{1}{2}, 5, 7\frac{1}{2}, 10$

Exercise 14d (p289)

1 (a) $1\frac{1}{2}$ (b) 24 (c) $\frac{1}{3}$ (d) $\frac{13}{99}$ (e) $\frac{5}{9}$ (f) $\frac{6}{11}$ (g) $\frac{2}{3}$ (h) $40\frac{1}{2}$
2 (a) $\frac{8}{9}$ (b) $\frac{4}{33}$ (c) $3\frac{2}{9}$ (d) $2\frac{23}{33}$ (e) $1\frac{4}{999}$ (f) $2\frac{317}{330}$
3 $\frac{2}{3}$
4 $2, \frac{1}{2}, \frac{1}{4}$
5 $\frac{2}{5}, 60; \frac{3}{5}, 40$

Exercise 14f (p294)

1 (a) $1^3 + 2^3 + 3^3 + 4^3$ (b) $2^2 + 3^2 + \ldots + n^2$ (c) $2 + 6 + \ldots + (n^2 + n)$

(d) $\dfrac{1}{1 \times 2} + \dfrac{1}{2 \times 3} + \dfrac{1}{3 \times 4}$ (e) $2^2 + 2^3 + 2^4 + 2^5$ (f) $-1 + 4 - 9 + 16$

(g) $1 + 2^2 + \ldots + n^n$ (h) $-\frac{1}{3} + \frac{1}{4} - \frac{1}{5} + \frac{1}{6}$

(i) $n(n-1) + (n+1)n + (n+2)(n+1)$ (j) $\dfrac{n-2}{n-1} + \dfrac{n-1}{n} + \dfrac{n}{n+1}$

2 (a) $\displaystyle\sum_{1}^{n} m$ (b) $\displaystyle\sum_{1}^{n+1} m^4$ (c) $\displaystyle\sum_{1}^{5} \frac{1}{m}$ (d) $\displaystyle\sum_{2}^{5} 3^m$ (e) $\displaystyle\sum_{2}^{6} m(m+5)$ (f) $\displaystyle\sum_{1}^{5} \frac{m}{3^{m-1}}$

(g) $\displaystyle\sum_{1}^{5} \frac{m(2m+1)}{2(m+1)}$ (h) $\displaystyle\sum_{1}^{6} (-1)^m m$ (i) $\displaystyle\sum_{0}^{5} (-2)^m$ (j) $\displaystyle\sum_{1}^{5} (-1)^{m+1} m(2m+1)$

3 (a) $(n+1)(2n+1)$ (b) $\frac{1}{6}n(n-1)(2n-1)$ (c) $n^2(2n+1)^2$ (d) $n(n+2)$
   (e) $\frac{1}{2}n(3n+1)$ (f) $n(2n+3)$ (g) $\frac{1}{6}n(2n^2 + 3n + 7)$ (h) $\frac{1}{3}n(n+1)(n+2)$
   (i) $\frac{1}{6}n(n+1)(2n+7)$ (j) $\frac{2}{3}n(n+1)(2n+1)$ (k) $\frac{1}{3}n(2n-1)(2n+1)$
   (l) $\frac{1}{4}n(n+1)(n^2 + n + 2)$ (m) $\frac{1}{12}n(n+1)(n+2)(3n+1)$

Exercise 14g (p295)

1 1683   **2** 20   **5** 17   **6** 2   **7** $6n+7$ **8** $\frac{1}{3}n(n-1)(n+1)$
9 $27 + 29 + \ldots + 113$ **10** 4234   **11** $\frac{5}{2}(3^n - 1), 16$ **12** $3, 2, \frac{4}{3}, \frac{8}{9}$
14 $\frac{9}{4}, 3, \frac{15}{4}$ **15** 35   **16** $4, -12, 15\frac{7}{8}, 57\frac{7}{8}$ **18** $\frac{1}{6}n(2n^2 + 3n + 13)$
19 $(ar + b)/(r + 1), (br + a)/(r + 1)$ **20** $3, 12, 48, 3 \times 4^{n-1}$

Chapter 15 (p297)

Exercise 15a (p300)

1 (a) $a^5 + 5a^4b + 10a^3b^2 + 10a^2b^3 + 5ab^4 + b^5$
  (b) $x^3 + 3x^2y + 3xy^2 + y^3$
  (c) $x^4 + 8x^3y + 24x^2y^2 + 32xy^3 + 16y^4$
  (d) $1 - 4z + 6z^2 - 4z^3 + z^4$
  (e) $16x^4 + 96x^3y + 216x^2y^2 + 216xy^3 + 81y^4$
  (f) $64z^3 + 48z^2 + 12z + 1$
  (g) $a^6 - 6a^5b + 15a^4b^2 - 20a^3b^3 + 15a^2b^4 - 6ab^5 + b^6$
  (h) $a^3 - 6a^2b + 12ab^2 - 8b^3$
  (i) $81x^4 - 108x^3y + 54x^2y^2 - 12xy^3 + y^4$
  (j) $8x^3 + 4x^2 + \frac{2}{3}x + \frac{1}{27}$
  (k) $x^5 - 5x^3 + 10x - 10x^{-1} + 5x^{-3} - x^{-5}$
  (l) $\frac{1}{16}x^4 + x^2 + 6 + 16x^{-2} + 16x^{-4}$
  (m) $a^7 + 7a^6b + 21a^5b^2 + 35a^4b^3 + 35a^3b^4 + 21a^2b^5 + 7ab^6 + b^7$
  (n) $a^{10} - 5a^8b^2 + 10a^6b^4 - 10a^4b^6 + 5a^2b^8 - b^{10}$
  (o) $a^6 - 3a^4b^2 + 3a^2b^4 - b^6$
2 (a) 14 (b) 194 (c) $10\sqrt{2}$ (d) $160\sqrt{6}$ (e) 98 (f) $40\sqrt{2}$
3 $32 + 80x + 80x^2 + 40x^3 + 10x^4 + x^5$, 32.080 08
4 $1 + x + \frac{3}{8}x^2 + \frac{1}{16}x^3 + \frac{1}{256}x^4$, 1.104
5 $64 - 192x + 240x^2 - 160x^3 + 60x^4 - 12x^5 + x^6$, 63.616 96, 5

Exercise 15b (p303)

1 (a) $448x^5$ (b) $1080u^3$ (c) $-3168t^7$ (d) $1320x^3y^8$
2 (a) $84x^3$ (b) $-14\,080x^3$ (c) $945x^4$ (d) $190x^2$
3 (a) $\frac{105}{512}$ (b) 540 (c) 6048 (d) 1386
4 (a) 120 (b) -9120 (c) 4320 (d) 5670
5 (a) $15x^2$ (b) 20
6 (a) 70 (b) $3\frac{3}{4}$
7 (a) 6 (b) 14 (c) -16
8 $3/(5x)$
9 (a) $1 + 10x + 45x^2 + 120x^3$ (b) $1 + \frac{9}{2}x + 9x^2 + \frac{21}{2}x^3$
  (c) $1 - 11x + 55x^2 - 165x^3$ (d) $1 + 12x + 66x^2 + 220x^3$
  (e) $256 + 512x + 448x^2 + 224x^3$ (f) $128 - 224x + 168x^2 - 70x^3$
10 (a) 1.105 (b) 1029.13 (c) 0.965 (d) 253.96

Exercise 15c (p307)

1 (a) 10 (b) 5 (c) $-1/8$ (d) $-15/128$
2 (a) $1 - 2x + 3x^2 - 4x^3$, $-1 < x < 1$ (b) $1 + \frac{1}{3}x - \frac{1}{9}x^2 + \frac{5}{81}x^3$, $-1 < x < 1$
  (c) $1 + \frac{3}{2}x + \frac{3}{8}x^2 - \frac{1}{16}x^3$, $-1 < x < 1$ (d) $1 - x - \frac{1}{2}x^2 - \frac{1}{2}x^3$, $-\frac{1}{2} < x < \frac{1}{2}$
  (e) $1 - \frac{3}{2}x + \frac{3}{2}x^2 - \frac{5}{4}x^3$, $-2 < x < 2$ (f) $1 + \frac{3}{2}x + \frac{27}{8}x^2 + \frac{135}{16}x^3$, $-\frac{1}{3} < x < \frac{1}{3}$
  (g) $1 - 3x + 9x^2 - 27x^3$, $-\frac{1}{3} < x < \frac{1}{3}$ (h) $1 - \frac{1}{2}x^2$, $-1 < x < 1$
  (i) $1 - \frac{1}{3}x - \frac{1}{9}x^2 - \frac{5}{81}x^3$, $-1 < x < 1$ (j) $1 - x + \frac{3}{2}x^2 - \frac{5}{2}x^3$, $-\frac{1}{2} < x < \frac{1}{2}$

(k) $1 - x + \frac{3}{4}x^2 - \frac{1}{2}x^3$, $-2 < x < 2$ (l) $1 - 3x + \frac{3}{2}x^2 + \frac{1}{2}x^3$, $-\frac{1}{2} < x < \frac{1}{2}$

3 (a) 1.000 500   (b) 0.9612   (c) 0.998 999   (d) 1.0099   (e) 1.0102

4 (a) $1 + 2x + 2x^2 + 2x^3$ (b) $2 - 3x + 4x^2 - 5x^3$ (c) $1 - \frac{3}{2}x + \frac{7}{8}x^2 - \frac{11}{16}x^3$

5 $1 - 4x - 8x^2 - 32x^3$, 4.7958

Exercise 15d (p308)

1 $252(3x)^5(2y)^5$, 252

2 (a) $32x^5 + 40x^3 + 20x + \dfrac{5}{x} + \dfrac{5}{8x^3} + \dfrac{1}{32x^5}$ (b) $40\sqrt{6}$

3 $a^5 - 5a^4b + 10a^3b^2 - 10a^2b^3 + 5ab^4 - b^5$, 77 400

4 (a) $a^{11} + 11a^{10}b + 55a^9b^2 + 165a^8b^3$ (b) $8064x^5y^5$ (c) 5376

5 $x^5 + 10x^4 + 40x^3 + 80x^2 + 80x + 32$, $x^4 - 8x^3 + 24x^2 - 32x + 16$, 96

6 $4 - 28x + 85x^2 - 146x^3 + 155x^4$

7 (a) $1 - 5x + 20x^2 - 50x^3$ (b) $1 - 4x + 10x^2 - 20x^3$

8 (a) $1 - 3x + 6x^2 - 10x^3 + 15x^4$ (b) $1024 + 1280x + 720x^2 + 240x^3$, 1159

9 (a) $70(2x)^4 3^4$, $\frac{35}{8}$ (b) $1 + 4x + 12x^2 + 32x^3$

10 (a) 2520   (b) $1 + \frac{1}{3}x - \frac{1}{9}x^2$, 2.080

Chapter 16 (p310)

Qu. 1 (a) $\begin{pmatrix} 2 \\ 4 \end{pmatrix}$ (b) $\begin{pmatrix} 3 \\ -3 \end{pmatrix}$ (c) $\begin{pmatrix} -7 \\ -1 \end{pmatrix}$ (d) $\begin{pmatrix} 0 \\ 2 \end{pmatrix}$ (e) $\begin{pmatrix} 3 \\ 0 \end{pmatrix}$

Qu. 2 (a) $\sqrt{20}, 63.4°$ (b) $\sqrt{18}, -45°$ (c) $\sqrt{50}, -171.9°$ (d) $2, 90°$
(e) $3, 0°$

Qu. 3 (2, 4)

Qu. 4 (2, 3, 4)

Qu. 5 $\overrightarrow{AB} = \overrightarrow{DC} = \begin{pmatrix} 3 \\ 5 \\ 7 \end{pmatrix}$

Qu. 6 $\dfrac{1}{13}\begin{pmatrix} 3 \\ 4 \\ 12 \end{pmatrix}$

Qu. 8 $2x + 3y + z = 5$

Qu. 9 $x + 2y + z = 8$

Qu. 10 -75

Qu. 11 $x_1x_2 + y_1y_2 + z_1z_2 = 0$

Qu. 12 $101°$

Qu. 14 $76.7°, 72.1°, 22.6°$

Exercise 16a (p321)

1 (a) $\begin{pmatrix} 6 \\ 10 \end{pmatrix}$ (b) $\begin{pmatrix} 12 \\ -18 \end{pmatrix}$ (c) $\begin{pmatrix} -4 \\ 6 \end{pmatrix}$ (d) $\begin{pmatrix} 2 \\ -3 \end{pmatrix}$ (e) $\begin{pmatrix} 7 \\ -1 \end{pmatrix}$

(f) $\begin{pmatrix} 18 \\ -8 \end{pmatrix}$ (g) $\begin{pmatrix} -1 \\ 11 \end{pmatrix}$ (h) $\begin{pmatrix} 1 \\ 27 \end{pmatrix}$

2 (a) 5, 53.1° (b) 13, 112.6° (c) 10, $-90°$ (d) $\sqrt{2}$, $-45°$

3 $\begin{pmatrix} 8.66 \\ 5 \end{pmatrix}$

4 $-4.33\mathbf{i} + 2.5\mathbf{j}$
5 (a) $(12, 11\frac{1}{2})$ (b) $(21, 16)$ (c) $(-21, -5)$
6 (a) $\frac{1}{2}(\mathbf{c} - \mathbf{a})$ (b) $\mathbf{c} - \mathbf{a}$ (c) $\frac{1}{2}(\mathbf{c} - \mathbf{a})$
7 $\frac{1}{4}(\mathbf{a} + \mathbf{b} + \mathbf{c})$

Exercise 16b (p325)

1 (a) $\begin{pmatrix} 6 \\ 2 \end{pmatrix}$ (b) $\begin{pmatrix} 4\frac{2}{3} \\ 3 \end{pmatrix}$ (c) $\begin{pmatrix} 34 \\ -19 \end{pmatrix}$ (d) $\begin{pmatrix} 5.2 \\ 2.6 \end{pmatrix}$ (e) $\begin{pmatrix} 8.4 \\ 0.2 \end{pmatrix}$

(f) $\dfrac{1}{m+n}\begin{pmatrix} 2n + 10m \\ 5n - m \end{pmatrix}$

2 (a) $\begin{pmatrix} -4 \\ -6 \end{pmatrix}$ (b) $\begin{pmatrix} -5 \\ -3 \end{pmatrix}$ (c) $\begin{pmatrix} 17 \\ -69 \end{pmatrix}$ (d) $\begin{pmatrix} -4.6 \\ -4.2 \end{pmatrix}$ (e) $\begin{pmatrix} -2.2 \\ -11.4 \end{pmatrix}$

(f) $\dfrac{1}{m+n}\begin{pmatrix} -7n - m \\ 3n - 15m \end{pmatrix}$

3 $-2, 3$; $1.5, -0.5$
4 $3, -2$; $\frac{2}{3}, \frac{1}{3}$

5 $\begin{pmatrix} 5 \\ -5\sqrt{3} \end{pmatrix}$, $\begin{pmatrix} 20 + 5t \\ 15 - 5\sqrt{3}t \end{pmatrix}$, $\sqrt{3}$, $20 + 5\sqrt{3}$

6 $2, -1$
7 $2:3$
8 $-\frac{5}{12}\mathbf{b} + \frac{2}{3}\mathbf{c}$; $(\frac{3}{4} - \frac{5}{12}t)\mathbf{b} + \frac{2}{3}t\mathbf{c}$; ;$\overrightarrow{OM} = \frac{6}{5}\overrightarrow{OC}$; $-\frac{1}{6}$
9 $\frac{2}{3}\mathbf{b}$, $\frac{3}{5}\mathbf{a} + \frac{2}{5}\mathbf{b}$, $\frac{1}{3}$

Exercise 16c (p339)

1 (a) $\begin{pmatrix} 2 \\ 6 \\ 2 \end{pmatrix}$ (b) $\begin{pmatrix} -2 \\ 0 \\ 0 \end{pmatrix}$ (c) $\begin{pmatrix} 4 \\ 3 \\ 0 \end{pmatrix}$ (d) $\begin{pmatrix} -3 \\ 4 \\ -6 \end{pmatrix}$ (e) $\begin{pmatrix} 2k \\ 0 \\ -2k \end{pmatrix}$

2 (a) $\begin{pmatrix} 2 \\ 3 \\ 3 \end{pmatrix}$ (b) $\begin{pmatrix} 4 \\ 0 \\ 4 \end{pmatrix}$ (c) $\begin{pmatrix} 4 \\ 2.5 \\ 3 \end{pmatrix}$ (d) $\begin{pmatrix} 3.5 \\ 6 \\ 4 \end{pmatrix}$ (e) $\begin{pmatrix} 2k \\ 2k \\ 2k \end{pmatrix}$

3 (a) $\begin{pmatrix} 11 \\ 30 \\ 12 \end{pmatrix}$ (b) $\begin{pmatrix} -5 \\ 0 \\ 4 \end{pmatrix}$ (c) $\begin{pmatrix} 22 \\ 16 \\ 3 \end{pmatrix}$ (d) $\begin{pmatrix} -10 \\ 24 \\ -23 \end{pmatrix}$ (e) $\begin{pmatrix} 11k \\ 2k \\ -7k \end{pmatrix}$

4 $x + y + z = 3$
5 $3x - 3y + z = 1$
6 $(7, 4, 9)$
8 $(4, 5, 10)$
10 $3:1$

11 $\begin{pmatrix} x \\ y \\ z \end{pmatrix} = \begin{pmatrix} 0 \\ 2 \\ 4 \end{pmatrix} + t \begin{pmatrix} 2 \\ -3 \\ 1 \end{pmatrix}$

Exercise 16d (p348)

1 $2x - y + z = 6$
2 $x + y + z = 8$
4 $2x - 5y + z = 0$
 $2x - 5y + z = -7$
5 $3x + y - z = 4$

6 $\mathbf{r} = \begin{pmatrix} 2 \\ 1 \\ 1 \end{pmatrix} + t \begin{pmatrix} 4 \\ 1 \\ 1 \end{pmatrix}$

8 $37.2°$
9 $(1, -3, 1)$
11 $\mathbf{r} = (9 + 3t)\mathbf{i} + (9 + 4t)\mathbf{j} + (23 + 12t)\mathbf{k}$
 $B(3, 1, -1)$, $AB = 26$

12 $(1, 2, 1)$, $\cos^{-1}(12/13)$, $\mathbf{r.n} = 14$, where $\mathbf{n} = \begin{pmatrix} 12 \\ -9 \\ 20 \end{pmatrix}$

Exercise 16e (p350)

1 (a) $\mathbf{a} + \mathbf{c}$ (b) $\mathbf{c} - \mathbf{a}$ (c) $\frac{2}{3}\mathbf{a} + \frac{1}{2}\mathbf{c}$ (d) $\frac{1}{2}\mathbf{c} - \frac{2}{3}\mathbf{a}$ (e) $\frac{1}{2}\mathbf{c}$ (f) $\frac{1}{2}\mathbf{c} - \frac{1}{3}\mathbf{a}$
  (g) $\frac{1}{2}\mathbf{c} - \frac{2}{3}\mathbf{a}$ (h) $\frac{1}{3}\mathbf{a} + \mathbf{c}$ (i) $\mathbf{c} - \frac{2}{3}\mathbf{a}$ (j) $-\frac{1}{3}\mathbf{a} - \frac{1}{2}\mathbf{c}$
2 $30, -21$
3 (a) $\frac{1}{2}(\mathbf{a} + \mathbf{b})$ (b) $2\mathbf{b} - \mathbf{a}$ (c) $\frac{7}{10}\mathbf{a} + \frac{3}{10}\mathbf{b}$ (d) $\frac{5}{8}\mathbf{a} + \frac{3}{8}\mathbf{b}$ (e) $3\mathbf{a} - 2\mathbf{b}$
4 (a) 0 (b) $12, 15$ (c) $90°$
5 $44, 64.4°$
7 $\frac{3}{5}, \frac{6}{5}, 3:2$
8 $(5, 7, 18)$

9 $\begin{pmatrix} x \\ y \\ z \end{pmatrix} = \begin{pmatrix} 2 \\ 3 \\ 7 \end{pmatrix} + t \begin{pmatrix} -1 \\ 2 \\ 3 \end{pmatrix}$, $x - 2y - 3z = 0$

10 $2x + 2y + z = 5$
12 $(-3, -4, 0)$
13 3, 500 s, $1000\sqrt{10}$ m
14 $\mathbf{t} = \frac{1}{3}\mathbf{a} + \frac{2}{3}\mathbf{b}$, $\mathbf{m} = \frac{1}{2}\mathbf{a} + \mathbf{b}$, $OB:BK = 1:1$
15 (a) $(4, -1, -3)$, $(\frac{22}{9}, \frac{8}{9}, -\frac{17}{9})$ (c) $\frac{4}{9}$
17 $\frac{3}{2}\mathbf{b} - \frac{1}{2}\mathbf{c}$
18 $1:4$

19 (a) $\dfrac{1}{\sqrt{61}}(3\mathbf{i} - 4\mathbf{j} + 6\mathbf{k})$ (b) $8\mathbf{i} + (4 + \lambda)\mathbf{j} + 8\mathbf{k}$ (c) -9 (d) $4\mathbf{i} + \frac{1}{3}\mathbf{j}$

Chapter 17 (p354)

Qu. 1 (a) $\sin 10°$ (b) $-\tan 60°$ (c) $-\cos 20°$ (d) $-\sin 50°$
  (e) $\cos 20°$ (f) $-\sin 35°$ (g) $\tan 40°$ (h) $-\cos 16°$ (i) $-\mathrm{cosec}\, 50°$
  (j) $-\tan 37°$ (k) $-\cos 50°$ (l) $-\sin 70°$ (m) $-\tan 50°$
  (n) $\cot 20°$ (o) $\cos 67°$ (p) $\sin 50°$ (q) $-\sec 38°$ (r) $-\cot 24°$
  (s) $-\mathrm{cosec}\, 53°$ (t) $-\sec 8°$
Qu. 3 $360°, 180°$
Qu. 4 (a) $\frac{1}{2}$ (b) $\sqrt{3}/2$ (c) $1/\sqrt{2}$ (d) $1/\sqrt{3}$ (e) 2 (f) $2/\sqrt{3}$ (g) 1
  (h) $\sqrt{2}$
Qu. 5 (a) $\cot\theta$ (b) $\mathrm{cosec}\,\theta$ (c) $-\mathrm{cosec}\,\theta$ (d) $-\tan\theta$ (e) $\sec\theta$
  (f) $-\mathrm{cosec}\,\theta$ (g) $-\sin\theta$ (h) $\sin\theta$ (i) $-\tan\theta$ (j) $-\cos\theta$
  (k) $-\cos\theta$ (l) $\mathrm{cosec}\,\theta$

Exercise 17a (p360)

1 (a) 0　(b) 0　(c) −1　(d) −1　(e) $\frac{1}{2}$　(f) $-\sqrt{3}/2$　(g) $-\sqrt{3}$
　(h) $\sqrt{3}/2$　(i) $-\sqrt{3}/2$　(j) $1/\sqrt{2}$　(k) $-1/\sqrt{2}$　(l) $-1/\sqrt{2}$　(m) $-\sqrt{3}$
　(n) 1　(o) $1/\sqrt{3}$

3 360°

4 180°

5 (a) 180°　(b) 720°　(c) 240°　(d) 360°　(e) 360°

6 (a) 240°　(b) 225°　(c) none　(d) 230°, 310°　(e) 306.9°　(f) 300°
　(g) 240°, 360°　(h) 270°, 330°

7 (a) 30°, 150°, 210°, 330°　(b) 30°, 150°, 210°, 330°　(c) 15°, 75°, 195°, 255°
　(d) $67\frac{1}{2}$°, $157\frac{1}{2}$°, $247\frac{1}{2}$°, $337\frac{1}{2}$°　(e) 10°, 110°, 130°, 230°, 250°, 350°
　(f) 90°, 210°, 330°　(g) 45°, 135°, 225°, 315°
　(h) 35.3°, 144.7°, 215.3°, 324.7°　(i) 15°, 45°, 75°, ... 345°
　(j) 37.8°, 142.2°, 217.8°, 322.2°　(k) 11.6°, 48.4°, 191.6°, 228.4°
　(l) 23.9°, 83.9°, 143.9°, 203.9°, 263.9°, 323.9°

8 (a) −180°, −45°, 0°, 135°, 180°　(b) ±60°, ±90°
　(c) 0°, ±180°, −19.5°, −160.5°　(d) −150°, −30°, 90°
　(e) ±120°, ±180°　(f) ±60°, ±90°, ±120°　(g) 0°, ±180°
　(h) ±45°, ±135°　(i) ±90°, 11.5°, 168.5°　(j) ±40.9°, ±139.1°
　(k) ±90°, 41.8°, 138.2°　(l) −104.0°, −45°, 76.0°, 135°　(m) 23.6°, 156.4°
　(n) ±109.5°

9 (Maxima first)
　(a) 1, 90°; −1, 270°　(b) 3, 0°; −3, 180°　(c) 2, 0°; −2, 360°
　(d) $\frac{1}{2}$, 135°; $-\frac{1}{2}$, 45°　(e) 3, 270°; −1, 90°　(f) 5, 0°; 1, 60°
　(g) 1, 270°; $\frac{1}{3}$, 90°　(h) 1, 0°; $\frac{1}{7}$, 180°

10 (a), (c), (d), (e), (g)

12 (a) 180°　(b) 1080°　(c) 60°　(d) 360°　(e) 540°

Exercise 17b (p366)

1 (a) $\cos\theta$　(b) $\tan\theta$　(c) $\cos\theta\cot\theta$

2 (a) $\sin\theta$　(b) $\tan\theta$　(c) $\csc\theta\cot\theta$

3 (a) $\sec\theta$　(b) $\sec^2\theta\tan\theta$　(c) $\sin\theta$

4 (a) $\cot\theta$　(b) $\cos\theta$　(c) $\csc\theta\tan^2\theta$

5 (a) $a^2\cos^2\theta$　(b) $\dfrac{1}{a}\sec\theta$　(c) $a\cos\theta\cot\theta$

6 (a) $b^2\csc^2\theta$　(b) $b^2\cot\theta\csc\theta$　(c) $\dfrac{1}{b}\sin\theta\cos\theta$

7 (a) $a^2\tan^2\theta$　(b) $\dfrac{1}{a}\cot\theta$　(c) $\sin\theta$

8 0°, 60°, 300°, 360°　　9 270°　　10 45°, 63.4°, 225°, 243.4°
11 26.6°, 135°, 206.6°, 315°　　12 60°, 300°　　13 30°, 41.8°, 138.2°, 150°
14 (a) $\pm\frac{4}{5}$　(b) $\pm\frac{3}{4}$　　15 $\frac{15}{17}$, $-\frac{8}{15}$　　16 (a) $-\frac{25}{24}$, $-\frac{7}{25}$

22 $\dfrac{x^2}{a^2} + \dfrac{y^2}{b^2} = 1$ **23** $\dfrac{y^2}{b^2} - \dfrac{x^2}{a^2} = 1$ **24** $\dfrac{b^2}{y^2} - \dfrac{x^2}{a^2} = 1$

25 $(x-1)^2 + (y-1)^2 = 1$

Exercise 17c (p367)

1 (a) $-\cos 25°$ (b) $-\tan 27°$ (c) $\sec 51°$ (d) $\sin 35°$ (e) $\cot 46°$
   (f) $-\csc 36°$
2 (a) -1 (b) $-\frac{1}{2}\sqrt{3}$ (c) $\sqrt{3}$ (d) $\frac{1}{2}\sqrt{2}$ (e) $-\frac{2}{3}\sqrt{3}$ (f) $-\sqrt{2}$ (g) -1
   (h) $\frac{1}{2}$ (i) $\frac{1}{2}$
3 (a) $30°, 150°$ (b) $135°, 315°$ (c) $36.9°, 323.1°$
   (d) $22\frac{1}{2}, 112\frac{1}{2}°, 202\frac{1}{2}°, 292\frac{1}{2}°$ (e) $37.8°, 142.2°, 217.8°, 322.2°$
   (f) $60°, 300°$ (g) $80.5°, 299.5°$ (h) $14.4°, 105.6°$ (i) $96.0°$
4 (a) $0°, \pm 180°; -30°, -150°$ (b) $\pm 90°; -123.7°, 56.3°$ (c) $30°, 150°; 90°$
   (d) $\pm 131.8°$ (e) $30°, 150°$ (f) $\pm 66.4°, \pm 120°$
   (g) $45°, -135°; 63.4°, -116.6°$ (h) $\pm 60°; -23.6°, -156.4°$
5 (a) max $5, 90°$; min $1, 270°$ (b) max $4, 180°$; min $-2, 0°$
   (c) max $4, 60°$; min $-4, 180°$ (d) max $3, 180°$; min $0, 0°$
   (e) max $\frac{1}{4}, 180°$; min $\frac{1}{10}, 0°$ (f) max $1, 45°$; min $\frac{1}{5}, 135°$
6 (a) $\tan\theta$ (b) $\cos\theta$ (c) $\sin\theta$ (d) $-\cot\theta$ (e) $-\csc\theta$ (f) $-\sec\theta$
   (g) $-\sin\theta$ (h) $-\tan\theta$ (i) $\sin\theta$
7 (a) $\cot^2\theta$ (b) $\sin\theta$ (c) $-\csc\theta$ (d) 1 (e) 1 (f) $\sec\theta\csc\theta$
8 (a) $90°; 210°, 330°$ (b) $41.4°, 318.6°$ (c) $0°, 360°; 131.6°, 228.2°$
   (d) $23.6°, 156.4°; 16.6°, 163.4°$ (e) $60°, 300°$ (f) $56.3°, 236.3°$
   (g) $53.1°, 135°, 315°, 233.1°$
9 (a) $\frac{3}{5}, \frac{3}{4}$ (b) $-\frac{13}{12}, \frac{5}{13}$ (c) $\frac{8}{17}, \frac{8}{15}$ (d) $-\frac{21}{29}, -\frac{29}{20}$
14 $b^2 x^2 - a^2 y^2 = a^2 b^2$
15 $(x-1)^2 + (y-1)^2 = 1$
16 $a^2 b^2 - x^2 y^2 = a^2 y^2$
17 $x^2 y^2 - a^2 b^2 = a^2 y^2$
18 max $\sqrt{2}, 45°$; min $-\sqrt{2}, -135°$
19 $-36.9°, 90°$
20 (a) neither, $0 \leqslant y \leqslant 2$ (b) even, $-1 \leqslant y \leqslant 5$ (c) neither, $5 \leqslant y \leqslant 15$
   (d) even, $0 \leqslant y \leqslant 2$

Chapter 18 (p370)

Qu. 3 (a) $0°, 112.6°, 360°$ (b) $53.1°, 323.1°$ (c) $48.4°, 205.3°$
       (d) $119.6°, 346.7°$

Exercise 18a (p374)

1 (a) $\frac{1}{4}\sqrt{2}(\sqrt{3}+1)$ (b) $\frac{1}{4}\sqrt{2}(\sqrt{3}+1)$ (c) $\frac{1}{4}\sqrt{2}(\sqrt{3}+1)$ (d) $\frac{1}{4}\sqrt{2}(1-\sqrt{3})$
   (e) $-\frac{1}{4}\sqrt{2}(\sqrt{3}+1)$ (f) $\frac{1}{4}\sqrt{2}(\sqrt{3}-1)$ (g) $\frac{1}{4}\sqrt{2}(\sqrt{3}-1)$
   (h) $\frac{1}{4}\sqrt{2}(\sqrt{3}-1)$
2 (a) $\frac{56}{65}$ (b) $\frac{33}{65}$ (c) $\frac{33}{56}$

3 (a) $\frac{63}{65}$ (b) $-\frac{63}{16}$ (c) $-\frac{33}{56}$

4 (a) $\frac{56}{65}$ (b) $\frac{56}{33}$ (c) $-\frac{63}{65}$

5 $\frac{1}{3}$

6 -2

7 $45°$

8 $135°$

9 (a) $\cos(x+60°)=\sin(30°-x)$ (b) $\cos(45°-x)=\sin(45°+x)$
(c) $\tan(x+60°)$ (d) $\sin 26°$ (e) $\sec 39°$ (f) $\cos 15°=\sin 105°=\sin 75°$

10 (a) $\frac{1}{2}$ (b) $\frac{1}{2}$ (c) $\frac{1}{3}\sqrt{3}$ (d) 0 (e) $\frac{1}{2}$ (f) $\frac{1}{2}\sqrt{2}$ (g) $\frac{1}{3}\sqrt{3}$ (h) $\frac{1}{2}\sqrt{6}$

11 2

12 $\frac{12}{31}$

13 (a) $\frac{1}{3}$ (b) 1 (c) $-\frac{7}{4}$ (d) $2-\sqrt{3}$

16 (a) $9.9°, 189.9°$ (b) $157\frac{1}{2}°, 337\frac{1}{2}°$ (c) $49.1°, 229.1°$ (d) $56.5°, 236.5°$

Exercise 18b (p377)

1 $\sin 34°$　　**2** $\tan 60°$　　**3** $\cos 84°$　　**4** $\sin\theta$　　**5** $\cos 45°$

6 $\tan\theta$　　**7** $\cos 30°$　　**8** $\sin 4A$　　**9** $\cos\theta$　　**10** $\cos 6\theta$

11 $\frac{1}{2}\tan 4\theta$　　**12** $\frac{1}{2}\sin 2x$　　**13** $2\cot 40°$　　**14** $2\operatorname{cosec} 2\theta$

15 $\cos\theta$

Exercise 18c (p378)

1 (a) $\frac{1}{2}$ (b) 1 (c) $-\frac{1}{2}\sqrt{3}$ (d) $-\frac{1}{2}\sqrt{2}$ (e) $\frac{1}{2}\sqrt{2}$ (f) $2\sqrt{3}$ (g) 1 (h) $2\sqrt{2}$

2 (a) $\pm\frac{24}{25}, \frac{7}{25}$ (b) $\pm\frac{120}{169}, \frac{119}{169}$ (c) $\pm\frac{1}{2}\sqrt{3}, -\frac{1}{2}$

3 (a) $-\frac{24}{7}$ (b) $\frac{240}{161}$ (c) $\pm\frac{120}{119}$

4 (a) $\pm\frac{3}{4}, \pm\frac{1}{4}\sqrt{7}$ (b) $\pm\frac{4}{5}, \pm\frac{3}{5}$ (c) $\pm\frac{12}{13}, \pm\frac{5}{13}$

5 (a) $\frac{1}{3}, -3$ (b) $\frac{1}{2}, -2$ (c) $-\frac{2}{3}, \frac{3}{2}$

6 $\sqrt{2}-1$

7 $90°, 120°, 240°, 270°$

8 $0°, 180°, 360°; 60°, 300°$

9 $30°, 150°; 270°$

10 $56.4°, 123.6°; 270°$

11 $30°, 150°; 90°, 270°$

12 $0°, 180°, 360°; 85.2°, 274.8°$

13 $0°, 180°, 360°; 120°, 240°; 36.9°, 323.1°$

14 $0°, 180°, 360°; 30°, 150°, 210°, 330°$

15 $45°, 225°; 121.0°, 301.0°$

16 $18.4°, 161.6°, 198.4°, 341.6°$

17 (a) $y=2x^2-1$ (b) $2y=3(2-x^2)$ (c) $y(1-x^2)=2x$ (d) $x^2y=8-x^2$

Exercise 18d (p383)

1 $90°, 330°$

2 $94.9°, 219.9°$

3 $114.3°, 335.7°$

4 $204.6°, 351.7°$

5 72.6°, 319.3°
6 76.7°, 209.6°
7 28.1°, 208.1°; 159.5°, 339.5°
8 0°, 180°, 360°; 45°, 225°
10 max 2, 330°; min -2, 150°
11 max $\sqrt{13}$, 33.7°; min $-\sqrt{13}$, $-146.3°$
12 5, 53.1°
13 max $\sqrt{5}$, 63.4°; min $-\sqrt{5}$, $-116.6°$
14 $\sqrt{2}$, 45°; $-\sqrt{2}$, 225°
15 5, 126.9°; -5, 306.9°
16 2, 60°; -2, 240°
17 17, 298.1°; -17, 118.1°
18 $\sqrt{37}$, 170.5°; $-\sqrt{37}$, 350.5°
19 1, 240°; -1, 60°
20 5, 53.1°; -5, 233.1°

Exercise 18e (p385)

1 $\cos(x+y) - \cos(x-y)$ **2** $\cos(x+y) + \cos(x-y)$
3 $\cos 4\theta + \cos 2\theta$ **4** $\cos 2S - \cos 2T$ **5** $\cos 2x - \cos 8x$
6 $\cos 2x + \cos 2y$ **7** $\cos A + \cos B$ **8** $\cos B - \cos C$
9 $\cos 2x$ **10** $\cos 4x + \cos 60°$

Exercise 18f (p386)

1 $\sin(x+y) + \sin(x-y)$ **2** $\sin(x+y) - \sin(x-y)$
3 $\sin 4\theta + \sin 2\theta$ **4** $\sin 2S + \sin 2T$ **5** $\sin 8x - \sin 2x$
6 $\sin 2x - \sin 2y$ **7** $\sin 2x - \sin 6x$ **8** $\sin A + \sin B$
9 $\sin A - \sin B$ **10** $\sin R - \sin S$

Exercise 18g (p388)

1 $2\cos \frac{1}{2}(x+y) \cos \frac{1}{2}(x-y)$ **2** $2\sin 4x \cos x$
3 $2\cos(y+z) \sin(y-z)$ **4** $2\cos 6x \cos x$ **5** $-2\sin \frac{3}{2}A \sin \frac{1}{2}A$
6 $2\cos 3x \sin x$ **7** $2\sin 4A \sin A$ **8** $2\sin 6\theta \cos \theta$ **9** $\sqrt{3}\sin x$
10 $\sqrt{2}\cos(y-35°)$ **11** $-2\cos 4\theta \sin \theta$ **12** $-\sin x$
13 $-2\sin x \sin \frac{1}{2}x$ **14** $2\sin 2x \cos 80°$
15 $2\cos(45° - \frac{1}{2}x + \frac{1}{2}y) \cos(45° - \frac{1}{2}x - \frac{1}{2}y)$
16 $2\cos(45° - \frac{1}{2}A + \frac{1}{2}B) \cos(45° - \frac{1}{2}A - \frac{1}{2}B)$
17 $2\sin(\frac{3}{2}x + 45°) \cos(\frac{3}{2}x - 45°)$
18 $2\sin(x+45°) \cos(x-45°)$
19 $2\cos(45° - \frac{1}{2}A + \frac{1}{2}B) \sin(45° - \frac{1}{2}A - \frac{1}{2}B)$
20 $2\cos(30° + \theta) \cos(30° - \theta)$

Exercise 18h (p389)

14 30°, 90°, 150°, 210°, 270°, 330°; 45°, 135°, 225°, 315°
15 0°, 120°, 240°, 360°; 72°, 144°, 216°, 288°

16 0°, 180°, 360°; 45°, 135°, 225°, 315°
17 0°, 72°, 144°, 180°, 216°, 288°, 360°
18 175°, 355°
19 45°, 135°, 225°, 315°
20 25°, 205°

Exercise 18i (p390)

1 (a) $\frac{140}{221}$ (b) $-\frac{21}{221}$ (c) $\frac{171}{140}$
2 (a) $\frac{468}{493}$ (b) $-\frac{475}{493}$ (c) $\frac{475}{132}$
3 (a) $\frac{1}{2}$ (b) 1 (c) 1
4 (a) $\pm\frac{2}{3}$, $\pm\frac{1}{3}\sqrt{5}$ (b) $\pm\frac{4}{9}$, $\pm\frac{1}{9}\sqrt{65}$
5 (a) $\frac{5}{2}$, $-\frac{2}{5}$ (b) $\frac{2}{9}$, $-\frac{9}{2}$
6 (a) $\frac{840}{1369}$ (b) $-\frac{1081}{1369}$
7 60°, 300°
8 0°, 180°, 360°; 41.4°, 318.6°
9 0°, 180°, 360°; 60°, 120°, 240°, 300°
10 41.6°, 244.7°
11 79.8°, 347.6°
12 $9x = 4y^2 - 18$
13 $y(4 - x^2) = 4x$
14 $2(t + 2)^2/(1 + t^2)$
15 $(1 + t)/(1 - t)$
16 13, 292.6°; -13, 112.6°
17 37, 71.1°; -37, 251.1°
18 73, 311.1°; -73, 113.1°
21 60°, 120°; 30°, 90°, 150°
22 0°, 45°, 90°, 135°, 180°; 60°, 120°
23 0°, 90°, 180°
24 60°, 180°
25 45°, 135°; 30°, 150°

Chapter 19 (p392)

Qu. 1   54.1
Qu. 2   6.95
Qu. 3   (a) 6.49(5) (b) 72.4 (c) 32.2 (d) 43.8 (e) 76.3 (f) 123
(g) 32 600
Qu. 4   (a) $6°\,\text{s}^{-1}$ (b) 1 rev min^{-1}
Qu. 5   (a) $3000°\,\text{s}^{-1}$ (b) $2\frac{1}{7}°\,\text{h}^{-1}$
Qu. 6 $120° + 360n°$, or $240° + 360n°$
Qu. 7 $\frac{1}{4}\pi + n\pi$
Qu. 11 (a) 46.4° (b) 87.3°
Qu. 12 44.9°
Qu. 15 67.4°

Exercise 19a (p400)

1 (a) $A = 48°$, $b = 13.8$, $c = 15.4$ (b) $B = 56.1°$, $a = 6.53$, $c = 5.04$
  (c) $C = 45.1°$, $a = 231$, $b = 213$

2 (a) $B = 95°$, $a = 1.40$, $c = 1.80$ (b) $B = 19.7°$, $b = 4.63$, $c = 8.29$
  (c) $A = 32.7°$, $b = 244$, $c = 172$

3 (a) $B = 59.1°$, $A = 72.6°$, $a = 19.6$; or $B = 120.9°$, $A = 10.9°$, $a = 3.87$
  (b) $C = 26.7°$, $A = 24.3°$, $a = 4.18$
  (c) $B = 55.5°$, $C = 96.25°$, $c = 17.9$; or $B = 124.5°$, $C = 27.25°$, $c = 8.22$

4 (a) $A = 38.2°$, $B = 81.8°$, $C = 60°$ (b) $A = 54.6°$, $B = 78.1°$, $C = 47.2°$
  (c) $A = 64.2°$, $B = 43.5°$, $C = 72.4°$

5 (a) $a = 13$, $B = 32.2°$, $C = 87.8°$ (b) $b = 11.7$, $A = 72.3°$, $C = 54.7°$
  (c) $c = 7.60$, $A = 82.6°$, $B = 54.2°$

6 (a) $A = 29.5°$, $B = 38.0°$, $C = 112.4°$ (b) $A = 17.9°$, $B = 120°$, $C = 42.1°$
  (c) $A = 35.8°$, $B = 49.3°$, $C = 94.9°$

7 (a) $A = 11.6°$, $B = 73°$, $C = 48.4°$ (b) $a = 17.4$, $B = 33.8°$, $C = 41.9°$
  (c) $A = 31.2°$, $B = 44.6°$, $c = 58.0$

8 1.43 km

9 25.8 m

10 1.0°

11 347.3°, 3.64 nautical miles

12 200 m

Exercise 19b (p402)

1 (a) 90° (b) 45° (c) 60° (d) 120° (e) 30° (f) 270° (g) 450°
(h) 720° (i) 900° (j) 240° (k) 630° (l) 135°

2 (a) 2π (b) $\frac{1}{2}\pi$ (c) $\frac{1}{4}\pi$ (d) $\frac{1}{12}\pi$ (e) $\frac{1}{3}\pi$ (f) $\frac{2}{3}\pi$ (g) $\frac{5}{3}\pi$ (h) $\frac{3}{2}\pi$ (i) 3π
(j) $\frac{1}{6}\pi$ (k) $\frac{5}{6}\pi$ (l) $\frac{5}{2}\pi$

3 8 cm   **4** 9.6 cm   **5** 6 cm   **6** $\frac{4}{5}$ rad   **7** 3 cm²
8 4 rad   **9** 12 cm   **10** 4 cm²

Exercise 19c (p403)

1 (a) $\frac{1}{8}\pi$ (b) 6π (c) $\pi/900$ (d) $5\pi/24$

2 (a) 72° (b) 5° (c) 105° (d) 630°

3 2.705 cm   **4** $3/\pi$ **5** 1.2 rad, 68.8°   **6** 6.43 cm   **7** 4.03 cm²

8 (a) 151 cm² (b) 62.4 cm² (c) 88.4 cm²   **9** 24.1 cm²   **10** 22.4 cm²

11 $\frac{1}{2}r^2(2\pi - \theta + \sin\theta)$

Exercise 19d (p406)

1 (a) $\frac{1}{60}$ rev min⁻¹ (b) $\frac{1}{10}°$ s⁻¹ (c) $\pi/1800$ rad s⁻¹

2 (a) 1200° s⁻¹ (b) $20\pi/3$ rad s⁻¹

3 0.262 rad h⁻¹

4 (a) 40π rad s⁻¹ (b) 1.57 m s⁻¹

5 (a) 35.2 rad s⁻¹ (b) 336 rev min⁻¹

6 128 rad s^{-1}
7 1.99×10^{-7} rad s^{-1}, 30 km s^{-1}
8 4.8 km h^{-1}

Exercise 19e (p409)

1 $45° + n360°$, or $135° + n360°$
2 $n360°$
3 $60° + n180°$
4 $270° + n360°$
5 $120° + n360°$, or $240° + n360°$
6 $150° + n180°$
7 $\pi/3 + 2n\pi$, or $5\pi/3 + 2n\pi$
8 $3\pi/4 + n\pi$
9 $\pi/12 + n\pi$, or $5\pi/12 + n\pi$
10 $\pi/6 + 2n\pi$, or $11\pi/6 + 2n\pi$; $5\pi/6 + 2n\pi$, or $7\pi/6 + 2n\pi$
11 $\pi/3$ **12** $\pi/4$ **13** $\pi/4$ **14** $-\pi/6$ **15** $5\pi/6$
16 $-\pi/4$ **17** $-\pi/2$ **18** π **19** 0   **20** $\pi/2$

Exercise 19f (p414)

1 (a) $50.1°$ (b) $51.5°$ (c) $36.9°$ **2** (a) $67.4°$ (b) $71.6°$ (c) $28.1°$
3 (a) 22.0 cm (b) $65.2°$ **4** $29.4°$ **5** $97.9°$ **6** $54.7°$
7 (a) $1/\sqrt{3}$ (b) $1/\sqrt{5}$ **8** 6.53 cm, $54.7°$, $70.5°$ **9** $\tan^{-1}(1/\sqrt{2})$
10 $22.2°$ **11** $75.2°$ **12** $\sqrt{\frac{2}{3}}$ **13** $28.1°$ **14** $80.4°$

15 $\tan^{-1}\dfrac{c\sqrt{(a^2 + b^2)}}{ab}$

Exercise 19g (p415)

1 (a) $a = 13$, $B = 32.2°$, $C = 87.8°$ (b) $b = 11.7$, $A = 72.3°$, $C = 54.7°$
(c) $c = 7.59$, $A = 82.6°$, $B = 54.2°$
2 (a) $b = 73$, $A = 11.6°$, $C = 48.4°$ (b) $a = 17.4$, $B = 33.8°$, $C = 41.9°$
(c) $c = 57.9$, $A = 31.3°$, $B = 44.7°$
3 (a) $C = 99.4°$, $a = 9.54$, $b = 5.23$ (b) either, $B = 38.9°$, $C = 109.9°$, $c = 9.00$
or, $B = 141.1°$, $C = 7.7°$, $c = 1.28$ (c) $B = 146.8°$, $C = 13.2°$, $b = 24.0$
4 (a) 11.5 (b) 9.92 (c) not possible
5 (a) $72°$ (b) $150°$ (c) $67\frac{1}{2}°$ (d) $105°$

6 (a) $\dfrac{11\pi}{6}$ (b) $\dfrac{5\pi}{18}$ (c) $\dfrac{5\pi}{12}$ (d) $\dfrac{2\pi}{15}$

7 10.5 cm
8 π rad s^{-1}

9 (a) $\dfrac{1}{720}$ rev min^{-1} (b) $\dfrac{\pi}{21\,600}$ rad s^{-1}

10 -75 rad s^{-1}

11 4π

12 no solution

13 (a) no solution   (b) 2 solutions   (c) 1 solution

14 16

15 (a) 210   (b) 21

Revision Exercise 3 (p418)

1 10 080, 7560

2 $26^4 \times 999$, $(26 \times 25 \times 24 \times 23) \times 738$

3 $\frac{2}{3}$, 3

4 $a = 2$, $b = -3$, 1365

5 $n = 5$

6 $\dfrac{n!\,a^r}{r!(n-r)!}$, $a = -4$, $n = -6$

7 $a = 1\frac{1}{2}$, $b = -1\frac{1}{8}$, $|x| < \frac{1}{3}$

8 $n^2(2n^2 - 1)$

10 (a) 7   (b) 4

11 (b) $\mathbf{q} - 2\mathbf{p}$, $\mathbf{p} - 2\mathbf{q}$ (d) $(1 - \mu)\mathbf{p} + 2\mu\mathbf{q}$

12 (a) 1:4   (b) 5:2

13 $57.7°$

14 $\mathbf{d} = 2\mathbf{i} - \mathbf{j} + \mathbf{k}$, $29°$

15 $\mathbf{a} = \begin{pmatrix} 5 \\ 3 \\ 7 \end{pmatrix}$, C(6, 5, 9)

16 $\begin{pmatrix} 1 \\ -1 \\ 2 \end{pmatrix}$

18 (a) $\sec x$ (b) $\pi/3$, π, $5\pi/3$

19 (a) $82.0°$, $334.1°$ (b) (ii) $\frac{4}{5}$, $\dfrac{7\sqrt{2}}{10}$ (iii) 1

20 $R = \sqrt{8}$, $\alpha = \pi/6$; $\pi/12$, $7\pi/12$, $13\pi/12$, $19\pi/12$ $(+2n\pi)$

21 $\pm 2\pi/3 + 2n\pi$

22 $2\sin 2x \cos x$, $-\pi/2$, 0, $\pi/2$, π; $-\pi/3$, $\pi/3$; $n\pi/2$, $\pm\pi/3 + 2n\pi$

23 (a) $-169\sqrt{13}$ (b) $130.2°$, $342.4°$

24 $70.5°$, $131.8°$, $228.2°$, $289.5°$

25 (a) 7 cm   (b) $101.0°$ (c) 10.1 cm   (d) $115.1°$; $49.4°$, 2.76 cm

Chapter 20 (p422)

Qu. 1 (a) $1\frac{1}{2}$ (b) 2 (c) $\frac{1}{2}$ (d) $\frac{1}{2}$ (e) $\sin \alpha$ (f) $\cos \alpha$
(g) $\frac{2}{9}$ (h) 2 (i) $\sec^2 \alpha$

Qu. 3 $2 \cos \frac{1}{2}(A + B) \sin \frac{1}{2}(A - B)$

Qu. 6 (a) $-3 \sin 3x$ (b) $2 \sin x \cos x = \sin 2x$ (c) $4 \cos 2x$
(d) $-3 \cos^2 x \sin x$

Exercise 20a (p427)

1 (a) $-2 \sin 2x$ (b) $6 \cos 6x$ (c) $-3 \sin (3x - 1)$ (d) $2 \cos (2x - 3)$
(e) $15 \sin 5x$ (f) $8 \cos 4x$ (g) $-6 \cos \frac{3}{2}x$ (h) $\cos \frac{1}{2}(x + 1)$ (i) $2x \cos x^2$

2 (a) $-\frac{1}{3} \cos 3x + c$ (b) $\frac{1}{3} \sin 3x + c$ (c) $-\frac{1}{2} \cos 4x + c$ (d) $\sin 2x + c$
(e) $\frac{1}{12} \cos 6x + c$ (f) $\frac{3}{2} \sin 4x + c$ (g) $-\frac{1}{2} \cos (2x + 1) + c$
(h) $\frac{3}{2} \sin (2x - 1) + c$ (i) $-\frac{4}{3} \cos \frac{1}{2}x + c$

3 (a) $2 \sin x \cos x = \sin 2x$ (b) $-8 \cos x \sin x = -4 \sin 2x$
(c) $-3 \cos^2 x \sin x$ (d) $6 \sin^2 x \cos x$ (e) $-12 \cos^3 x \sin x$

(f) $\dfrac{\cos x}{2\sqrt{(\sin x)}}$ (g) $\dfrac{-\sin x}{2\sqrt{(\cos x)}}$ (h) $-6 \cos 3x \sin 3x = -3 \sin 6x$

(i) $4 \sin 2x \cos 2x = 2 \sin 4x$ (j) $-18 \sin^2 3x \cos 3x$

(k) $24 \sin^3 2x \cos 2x$ (l) $\dfrac{\cos 2x}{\sqrt{(\sin 2x)}}$

4 (a) $\cos x - x \sin x$ (b) $\sin 2x + 2x \cos 2x$ (c) $x(2 \sin x + x \cos x)$
(d) $\cos^2 x - \sin^2 x = \cos 2x$ (e) $(x \cos x - \sin x)/x^2$
(f) $-(2x \sin 2x + \cos 2x)/x^2$ (g) $(\sin x - x \cos x)/\sin^2 x$
(h) $x(2 \cos x + x \sin x)/\cos^2 x$ (i) $\sec^2 x$ (j) $-\text{cosec}^2 x$ (k) $\sec x \tan x$
(l) $-\text{cosec} \, x \cot x$

5 (a) 1 m (b) 2 m s^{-2} (c) 0.983 s

6 (a) $\frac{1}{3}\pi$ s (b) $-\frac{3}{2}\sqrt{3}$ cm s^{-1} (c) $-5, 3\frac{3}{4}, -3$ cm s^{-2}

7 (a) 5 (b) -20

8 (a) 0.841 (b) $\frac{5}{3}\sqrt{5}$ (c) $-\frac{17}{3}\sqrt{5}$

9 $\frac{2}{3}$

10 2π

11 $\frac{1}{3}\pi + \frac{1}{2}\sqrt{3}, \frac{1}{8}\pi^2 + 1$

12 $\sqrt{3} - \frac{1}{3}\pi, 2 - \frac{1}{8}\pi^2$

14 $\frac{1}{2}(1 + \cos 2x)$

16 $\frac{1}{4}(3 \sin x - \sin 3x)$

17 $\frac{1}{2}$

Exercise 20b (p430)

1 (a) $2 \sec^2 2x$ (b) $-3 \text{cosec}^2 3x$ (c) $6 \sec 2x \tan 2x$
(d) $-\text{cosec} \frac{1}{2}x \cot \frac{1}{2}x$ (e) $-2 \sec^2 (2x + 1)$
(f) $\sec (3x - 2) \tan (3x - 2)$ (g) $6 \text{cosec}^2 (3x + 2)$
(h) $-2x \, \text{cosec}^2 x^2$ (i) $(\sec^2 \sqrt{x})/(2\sqrt{x})$

2 (a) $2 \tan x \sec^2 x$ (b) $2 \sec^2 x \tan x$ (c) $-6 \cot^2 x \operatorname{cosec}^2 x$
(d) $-6 \operatorname{cosec}^2 x \cot x$ (e) $-4 \sec^2 2x \tan 2x$ (f) $-3 \operatorname{cosec}^2 3x \cot 3x$
(g) $\sec^3 2x \tan 2x$ (h) $8 \operatorname{cosec}^4 x \cot x$ (i) $(\sec^2 x)/(2\sqrt{\tan x})$
3 (a) $\tan x + x \sec^2 x$ (b) $\sec x (\sec^2 x + \tan^2 x)$ (c) $x(2 \cot x - x \operatorname{cosec}^2 x)$
(d) $3 \operatorname{cosec} x(1 - x \cot x)$ (e) $-\operatorname{cosec} x (\operatorname{cosec}^2 x + \cot^2 x)$
(f) $(x \sec^2 x - \tan x)/x^2$ (g) $\sec x (x \tan x - 2)/x^3$ (h) $x \sin x$
(i) $2x \sec^2 x \tan x$
4 (a) $\frac{1}{2} \tan 2x + c$ (b) $3 \sec x + c$ (c) $2 \cot \frac{1}{2}x + c$ (d) $-\frac{1}{9} \operatorname{cosec} 3x + c$
(e) $\sec^2 x + c$, or $\tan^2 x + c$ (f) $\tan x + c$ (g) $\sec x + c$
(h) $-\frac{1}{2} \cot 2x + c$ (i) $-\frac{1}{2} \operatorname{cosec} 2x + c$
5 $1 - \frac{1}{4}\pi$
6 2π
7 (a) $2\sqrt{3}$ (b) $5\sqrt{5}$ (c) $5\sqrt{3}$
9 $\cot^2 x = \operatorname{cosec}^2 x - 1$, $-\cot x - x + c$

Exercise 20c (p430)

1 (a) 1 (b) $\frac{2}{3}$ (e) $-\sin \alpha$
3 (a) $3 \cos 3x$ (b) $\frac{1}{2} \sec^2 \frac{1}{2}x$ (c) $-2x \sin x^2$
(d) $-\sin x/(2\sqrt{\cos x})$ (e) $-6 \operatorname{cosec}^3 x \cot x$
(f) $2 \sin x$ (g) $-18 \sec^3 2x \tan 2x$
(h) $(\cos 2x)/\sqrt{(\sin 2x)}$ (i) $12 \tan 2x \sec^2 2x$
4 (a) $\frac{1}{2} \sin 2x + c$ (b) $-\frac{1}{2} \cos (2x - 1) + c$ (c) $6 \sin \frac{1}{2}x + c$
(d) $2 \tan \frac{1}{2}x + c$ (e) $-\operatorname{cosec} x + c$ (f) $\frac{1}{2} \sec 2x + c$ (g) $-\operatorname{cosec} x + c$
(h) $\frac{1}{2} \tan 2x + c$ (i) $-\frac{1}{2} \cos x^2 + c$
5 (a) $\sin x + x \cos x$ (b) $\cos x \cos 2x - 2 \sin x \sin 2x$
(c) $2x \tan x (\tan x + x \sec^2 x)$ (d) $\sec x(x \tan x - 1)/x^2$
(e) $-(2 \sin 3x \sin 2x + 3 \cos 3x \cos 2x)/\sin^2 3x$
(f) $\cos x \tan 2x + 2 \sin x \sec^2 2x$ (g) $(x \cos x - 2 \sin x)/x^3$ (h) $x^2 \sin x$
6 (a) 1 (b) $\frac{4}{3}\sqrt{3}$ (c) $\frac{1}{2}\pi$ (d) $\frac{1}{4}$
7 (a) $\tan x - x + c$ (b) $\frac{1}{7} \sin 7x + \sin x + c$
(c) $6 \sin 2x - \sin 12x + c$ (d) $x - \frac{1}{2} \cos 2x + c$
9 (a) $1.8°$ (b) $36°$ (c) $300°$ (d) $1260°$
10 (a) $\pi/18$ (b) $\pi/12$ (c) $11\pi/6$ (d) $20\pi/9$
11 (a) 0.909 (b) 1.14 (c) 3.90 (d) -0.987
12 8 cm
13 $1\frac{3}{5}$ cm, $29.8°$
15 171 cm^2
16 1.93 rad
17 0.515 rad
18 $\frac{1}{3}\pi, \frac{2}{5}\pi, \frac{4}{5}\pi$ rad
20 $15°, 75°, 195°, 255°$

Chapter 21 (p433)

Qu. 2 $4x - 6y - 13 = 0$
Qu. 3 (a) $y = x \pm \sqrt{7}$ (b) $y = \sqrt{3}x \pm \sqrt{13}$

Qu. 4 (a) $(0,0)$ (b) $(0,0)$, $(3,6)$
Qu. 5 $g=-a$, $f=-b$, $c=(a^2+b^2-r^2)$
Qu. 6 (a) $3x-y=0$ (b) $x-4y+17=0$
(c) $4x+y-11=0$ (d) $3x+y-8=0$ (e) $4x+9y+5=0$

Exercise 21a (p436)

1 $x^2+y^2=25$ 2 $x^2+y^2-6x-2y+6=0$ 3 $4x-10y+29=0$
4 $5x-3y-4=0$ 5 $x+1$, $y^2=2x+1$ 6 $x^2=4y$
7 $2x^2+2y^2-x-1=0$ 8 $3x^2+3y^2+36x-38y+159=0$
9 $3x^2-y^2=48$ 10 $3x^2+4y^2=48$ 11 $x^2+y^2=9$
12 $y^2=4ax$ 13 $3x^2+4y^2=12$ 14 $y=0$ 15 $2x+3y-13=0$

Exercise 21b (p440)

1 (a) $4x-y-4=0$, $x+4y-18=0$ (b) $4x-y-2=0$, $x+4y-9=0$
(c) $y+2=0$, $x+1=0$ (d) $x+y+1=0$, $x-y-3=0$
(e) $6x+y+4=0$, $x-6y+50=0$ (f) $x+y-4=0$, $x-y=0$
(g) $2x-3y+1=0$, $3x+2y-5=0$
2 (a) $(\frac{1}{2},2)$ (b) $(2,-2)$ (c) $(6,\frac{2}{3})$ (d) $(-\frac{5}{2},-\frac{9}{4})$
3 $(1,0)$, $(3,0)$; $2x+y-2=0$, $x-2y-1=0$; $2x-y-6=0$, $x+2y-3=0$
4 $5x-y-11=0$, $3x+y+3=0$
5 $x+2y-1=0$, $x-2y+1=0$, $(0,\frac{1}{2})$
6 $x+4y-4c=0$
8 $3x-8y\pm10=0$
9 $x-y\pm4=0$
10 $n^2=a^2l^2+b^2m^2$

Exercise 21c (p443)

1 (a) $x^2+y^2-4x-6y+12=0$ (b) $x^2+y^2+6x-8y=0$
(c) $9x^2+9y^2-12x+6y+1=0$ (d) $x^2+y^2+10y=0$
(e) $x^2+y^2-6x+7=0$ (f) $144x^2+144y^2+72x-96y-47=0$
2 (a) $1,(-2,3)$ (b) $2,(1,2)$ (c) $\frac{3}{2},(\frac{3}{2},0)$ (d) $\frac{7}{2},(-\frac{3}{2},2)$ (e) $\frac{1}{4}\sqrt{2},(-\frac{1}{4},-\frac{1}{4})$
(f) $1,(\frac{1}{3},\frac{1}{2})$ (g) $\sqrt{(a^2+b^2)},(a,b)$ (h) $\sqrt{(g^2+f^2-c)},(-g,-f)$
3 (a), (d) if $a>0$, (f) if $b=0$, (g) if $c<0$
4 $x^2+y^2-4x-2y-15=0$
5 $(5,3)$, $\sqrt{10}$; $x^2+y^2-10x-6y+24=0$

Exercise 21d (p444)

1 $2x-16y+41=0$
2 $y^2=8(x-2)$
3 $3x^2+4y^2-24x+36=0$
4 $8x^2-y^2-18ax+9a^2=0$
5 $x^2+y^2+4x=0$
6 $3x^2+3y^2+8x=0$

7 $(x-a)(x-c)+(y-b)(y-d)=0$
8 (a) $x^2+y^2=144$ (b) $x^2+9y^2=324$
9 $x^2+y^2=36$
10 $xy=4$
11 $(1,2)$
12 $(-2,5)$
13 $y=2x$
14 $x^2+y^2-10x-8y+33=0$
15 $4x-3y-18=0,\ 13\frac{1}{2}$

Chapter 22 (p446)

Qu. 1 (a) 1 (b) $\frac{2}{13}$ (c) $\frac{1}{2}\sqrt{26}$ (d) $3\sqrt{2}$ (e) $\frac{16}{17}\sqrt{34}$ (f) $\frac{2}{13}\sqrt{13}$ (g) $\frac{3}{5}a$
(h) $\frac{4}{5}q$ (i) $\frac{1}{13}(12X-5Y+7)$ (j) $\frac{1}{17}(8x_1-15y_1)$

Exercise 22a (p450)

2 (a) $r=a$ (b) $\theta=\alpha$ (c) $r=a\sec\theta$ (d) $r=a\operatorname{cosec}\theta$ (e) $r=a\cos\theta$
(f) $r=2a\sin\theta$ (g) $a^2=r^2+c^2-2cr\cos\theta$ (h) $r=2a/(1+\cos\theta)$
5 (a) $r=a$ (b) $r^2=a^2\sec2\theta$ (c) $\theta=0$ (d) $r=2a/(1+\cos\theta)$
(e) $r=2\sin\theta$ (f) $r^2=2c^2\operatorname{cosec}2\theta$
6 (a) $x^2+y^2=4$ (b) $(x^2+y^2-ax)^2=a^2(x^2+y^2)$ (c) $x^2+y^2-ax=0$
(d) $4xy=c^2$ (e) $y^2=4ax$
7 (a) $1,60°$ (b) $2\sqrt{2},-45°$ (c) $2,\ \tan^{-1}\frac{4}{3}$ (d) $2,\ \tan^{-1}(-\frac{12}{5})$
(e) $\frac{1}{5}\sqrt{10},\ \tan^{-1}3$ (f) $c/\sqrt{(a^2+b^2)},\ \tan^{-1}(b/a)$

Exercise 22b (p458)

2 (a) $\frac{4}{3},\frac{4}{3}$ (b) $\pm\frac{3}{2},\pm3a$ (c) $-2,-\frac{1}{3}$ (d) $60°,(\sqrt{3}/2)b$
3 (a) $(y-2)^2=x-1$ (b) $x^3=y^2$ (c) $xy=1$ (d) $2x+y-5=0$
(e) $y^2=4ax$ (f) $y^2=x^2(x-1)$ (g) $x^2+4y^2=4$ (h) $y^2=(1-x^2)^3$

4 (a) $x=t^4,\ y=t^5$ (b) $x=t-2,\ y=t^2-2t$ (c) $x=\dfrac{2}{t^2-1},\ y=\dfrac{2t}{t^2-1}$

(d) $x=\dfrac{1}{1-t^3},\ y=\dfrac{t}{1-t^3}$ (e) $x=\dfrac{3t}{1+t^3},\ y=\dfrac{3t^2}{1+t^3}$

5 $3x-2y+1=0$
6 $-\frac{4}{13},\ -\frac{4}{3}$
7 $(\frac{1}{2}t^2,\frac{3}{2}t),\ 2y^2=9x$
8 $x=y(2x-1)^2$
9 $(1,1),(-1,-1),\sqrt{2}$
10 (a) $(p+q)y-2x=2pq$ (b) $pqy-x+(p+q)=0$
(c) $(p^2+pq+q^2)y-x=pq(p+q)$ (d) $(pq-1)y-2pqx+2(p+q)=0$

Exercise 22c (p460)

1 (a) $2y + 3x - 1 = 0$, $2x - 3y - 5 = 0$ (b) $y + 4x = 3$, $16y - 4x = 31$
  (c) $x + y + a = 0$, $x - y - 3a = 0$ (d) $y + x + 2c = 0$, $y - x = 0$
  (e) $2y + x + 9 = 0$, $2x - y + 3 = 0$
  (f) $3\sqrt{3}y + 2x - 12 = 0$, $6\sqrt{3}x - 4y - 5\sqrt{3} = 0$
2 (a) $ty - 2x - t^3 = 0$, $2y + tx = 6t^2 + t^4$
  (b) $ty - x - at^2 = 0$, $y + tx = 2at + at^3$
  (c) $y - tx + t^4 = 0$, $ty + x = 3t^5 + 4t^3$
  (d) $t^2 y + x - 2ct = 0$, $y - t^2 x = c/t - ct^3$
  (e) $bx \cos t + ay \sin t = ab$, $ax \sin t - by \cos t = \frac{1}{2}(a^2 - b^2) \sin 2t$
  (f) $bx \sec t - ay \tan t = ab$, $ax \sin t + by = (a^2 + b^2) \tan t$
3 (a) $(p + q)y - 2x = 2pq$, $py - x = p^2$
  (b) $y + pq(p + q)x = p^2 + pq + q^2$, $y + 2p^3 x = 3p^2$
  (c) $pqy + x = c(p + q)$, $p^2 y + x = 2cp$
  (d) $bx \cos \frac{1}{2}(p + q) + ay \sin \frac{1}{2}(p + q) = ab \cos \frac{1}{2}(p - q)$,
      $bx \cos p + ay \sin p = ab$
4 $2x + y - 12a = 0$, $(9a, -6a)$
5 $(-\frac{1}{8}c, -8c)$
6 $(-\frac{1}{2}, 4)$
7 $yt - x = at^2$; 2, 4; $2y - x = 4a$, $4y - x = 16a$
8 $y + x = 2c$, $9y + x = 6c$
9 $y + 2x = 12a$, $y - 4x + 72a = 0$
10 $(-c/t^3, -ct^3)$

Exercise 22d (p461)

4 $yt - x = at^2$, $y + tx = 2at + at^3$

Exercise 22e (p463)

4 $r = 2a/(1 - \cos \theta)$
5 $6\frac{1}{2}$
6 $r = a(1 - \cos \theta)$, $x^2 + 2ay = a^2$
7 $x - y + a = 0$, $x - 5y + 25a = 0$
8 $(\frac{121}{9}a, -\frac{22}{3}a)$

Chapter 23 (p464)

Note: Approximate answers have generally been rounded to 2 or 3 significant figures. The reader should not assume from the form of an answer that the result is exact.

Qu. 1 (a) s varies as the square of t (b) V varies as the cube of r
       (c) y varies inversely as the square of x
       (d) T varies as the square root of l (e) p varies inversely as v
       (f) the square of T varies as the cube of d
Qu. 2 M is increased by a factor of (a) 8   (b) 27

Qu. 3   (i) (a) $p = kq$ (b) $p = \dfrac{k}{v}$ (c) $v = kx^3$ (d) $U = k\sqrt{l}$ (e) $F = kc^2$

(f) $H = \dfrac{k}{d^2}$ (g) $T = \dfrac{k}{\sqrt{g}}$ (h) $A = ks^n$ (i) $A^3 = kv^2$

(ii) (a) $\dfrac{p_1}{p_2} = \dfrac{q_1}{q_2}$ (b) $\dfrac{p_1}{p_2} = \dfrac{v_2}{v_1}$ (c) $\dfrac{v_1}{v_2} = \dfrac{x_1^{\,3}}{x_2^{\,3}}$ (d) $\dfrac{U_1}{U_2} = \dfrac{\sqrt{l_1}}{\sqrt{l_2}}$

(e) $\dfrac{F_1}{F_2} = \dfrac{c_1^{\,2}}{c_2^{\,2}}$ (f) $\dfrac{H_1}{H_2} = \dfrac{d_2^{\,2}}{d_1^{\,2}}$ (g) $\dfrac{T_1}{T_2} = \dfrac{\sqrt{g_2}}{\sqrt{g_1}}$ (h) $\dfrac{A_1}{A_2} = \dfrac{s_1^{\,n}}{s_2^{\,n}}$

(i) $\dfrac{A_1^{\,3}}{A_2^{\,3}} = \dfrac{v_1^{\,2}}{v_2^{\,2}}$

Qu. 4 l is increased by a factor of (a) 4 (b) 9; T is increased by a factor of $\sqrt{2}$

Qu. 5   1.1 s

Qu. 6 $w = \dfrac{3.21 \times 10^{10}}{d^2}$

Qu. 7 w is multiplied by (a) $\frac{1}{4}$ (b) $\frac{1}{9}$

Qu. 8   (a) c varies as p (b) C varies as a^2 over a limited range
(c) w varies as r^3 (d) l varies inversely as b (e) S varies as l^2
(f) A varies as a^2 (g) a varies as $\sqrt{A}$ (h) V varies as a^3
(i) a varies as $\sqrt[3]{V}$

Qu. 9 $y = kxz^3$

Qu. 10 $W \propto \dfrac{hr^2}{t}$

Qu. 11   (a) $T = kmr^2$ (b) $T \propto mr^2$

Qu. 12 $F = k\dfrac{mv^2}{r}$

Qu. 13   (a) $\dfrac{z_1}{z_2} = \dfrac{x_1 y_1^{\,2}}{x_2 y_2^{\,2}}$ (b) $\dfrac{z_1}{z_2} = \dfrac{y_1 x_2^{\,2}}{y_2 x_1^{\,2}}$ (c) $\dfrac{z_1}{z_2} = \dfrac{x_1^{\,3} y_1^{\,2}}{x_2^{\,3} y_2^{\,2}}$ (d) $\dfrac{z_1}{z_2} = \dfrac{x_1 y_1}{x_2 y_2}$

(e) $\dfrac{z_1}{z_2} = \dfrac{x_1^{\,2} y_1^{\,2}}{x_2^{\,2} y_2^{\,2}}$ (f) $\dfrac{z_1}{z_2} = \dfrac{y_2 \sqrt{x_1}}{y_1 \sqrt{x_2}}$

Qu. 14   (a) $C = K + kx^3$, k, K constants   (b) £11.95

Qu. 15 $v = 4.2t$

Qu. 16   the cost in labour and materials before any copies are run off is £10.50

Qu. 17   (a) $y = -3x + 122$ (b) $y = 13.5x - 71.5$ (c) $y = -12x + 213$

Qu. 18 $y = 12x - 72$; 6 cm

Qu. 19 $R = 0.0005v^3$

Qu. 20 $k = 0.49$

Exercise 23a (p471)

1 5.70 cm²   2 29.9 km, $d \approx 3.57\sqrt{h}$ 3 155 cm, $l \approx 24.8(5)\ T^2$
4 25 m   5 0.242 kg, 11.0 cm, $m = \frac{1}{810}d^2$

6 (a) $C = 200\pi r$, yes   (b) $C = 5.08\pi r$, yes   **7** $2.8 \times 10^5 \text{ N m}^{-2}$ **8** 3584
9 15.6 cm^3, 11.2 cm
10 1 h 37 min, $T \approx 2.87 \times 10^{-6} d^{3/2}$

Exercise 23b (p476)

1 15.7 cm^2 **2** 454.5 rev min^{-1} **3** 48 litres s^{-1} **4** 675 kJ

5 185 cm^3, $V \approx 51.6 \dfrac{T}{p}$ **6** 0.70 kW, $0.001 \dfrac{V^2}{R}$

7 570 hertz, $f \approx 14.2 \dfrac{\sqrt{F}}{l}$ **8** 76 hertz   **9** 4.91 s

10 the former; ratio 16:15   **11** 88 m, $s = 10t + 3t^2$
12 54.4 m, $s = 0.2v + 0.006v^2$, 50 km h^{-1}

Exercise 23c (p485)

1 $A = 1.84D$; yes
2 $m = 1.02t$
3 $h_2 = 0.34h_1$
4 $\theta = 62 - \frac{1}{2}t$; no, cooler bodies lose heat more slowly
5 $P = 0.199s^{1.50}$

6 $p \propto \dfrac{1}{\sqrt{n}}$

7 $a = 2.0$, $b = 1.8$
8 $m = 1.3$, $c = 0.84$, $y = 6.9x^{1.3}$

Chapter 24 (p488)

Qu. 1   (a) 4.123   (b) 6.325   (c) 9.220   (d) 9.798

Exercise 24a (p494)

1 (a) 3.46   (b) 5.48   (c) 7.07   (d) 8.66
2 2.33, 2.29, 2.29; $x^3 - 12 = 0$
3 2.71
4 $x_{r+1} = (x_r^2 + 1)/5$; 0.208, 0.209, 0.209; $x_{r+1} = 5 - 1/x_r$; 0, $-\infty$, 5
5 0.1001
6 1.93
7 $x_{r+1} = 8 - 10/x_r$; -2, 13, 7.23; the sequence does not appear to converge, however it eventually converges to 6.45, the other root.
8 (a) 2.17, 2.15, 2.15   (b) 2.5, 1.6, 3.91; 2.15
9 2.19
10 6.54, 0.459

Exercise 24b (p500)

Nos 1, 2, 3, 5, 6, 8, 10 (i.e. not 4, 7, 9)

Exercise 24c (p504)

1 4.74	**2** 3.28	**3** 1.90	**4** 5.15	**5** 3.58
6 0.771	**7** 4.15	**8** 3.70	**9** 2.09	**10** 1.04

Exercise 24d (p505)

1 (a) 14.1 (b) 21.2 (c) 26.5 (d) 31.6
2 (a) 14.1 (b) 21.2 (c) 26.5 (d) 31.6
6 0.450   **7** 0.450   **8** 0.196   **9** 8.16   **10** 0.347
11 2.34, 4.68, 9.13 cm   **12** 0.653r **13** 4.1%   **14** 1.16r
15 $n = 1$, $x_2 = 1.260$, $x_3 = 1.312$ **16** 18.5   **17** 2.17   **18** 1.84
19 1.2   **20** 0.167

Revision Exercise 4 (p508)

2 $A = -1$, $B = 11$, $C = 3$
3 1.5, $\pi(39\pi + 176)/48$
4 $1 \leqslant f(x) \leqslant 4$, 21.8
5 times: $\pi/6$, $\pi/2$, $5\pi/6$, $3\pi/2$; displacements: $\frac{1}{2}$, 1, $\frac{1}{2}$, 5;
  accelerations: 3, -2, 3, -6; distance $= 10$
6 $a = -1.5$, 0
7 $BP^2 = x^2 + y^2 - 8x - 4y + 20$, centre (5, 10/3), radius 10/3
8 $y = 12x + 16$, $y = 12x - 16$
9 P($2/m^2$, $4/m$), $m = 2$, Q(-1, -1), R($-\frac{1}{2}$, 0)
10 (a) (i) $1/t$ (ii) $p = 1$, -4 (iii) $t = -1$, -3 (iv) $y^2 - 6y + 25 = 4x$
  (b) $y = 3 - \sin\theta$
11 (a) (i) ($19\frac{1}{4}$, 0) (ii) $4x = y^2 + 18y + 77$
  (b) (i) $(t^2 + 1)/(t^2 - 1)$, $\pm\sqrt{2}$, (ii) R(1.6, 0)
12 $3y + 4x = 34$, $x^2 + y^2 + 4x - 28y = 0$
13 $m > 0$, or $m < -4/9$; $9y + 4x = 12$
14 $xy^2 = a(x - a)^2$
16 $k = 8$, $n = 2$
17 $k = 2$, $n = 0.5$
18 (i) $\log T = b \log R + \log a$ (iii) $a = 0.2$, $b = 1.5$ (iv) 60 300 days
19 $a = 1.7$, $b = 1.3$
20 $a = 1.9$, $b = 2.5$
21 -0.2541
22 0.25, 0.32
23 (c) 0.88
24 2.605
25 $n = 2$, $x = 2.95$

Although either $\sin^{-1} x$, etc. or arcsin x, etc. can be used for the inverse trigonometrical functions, for convenience the former notation is used throughout the answers which follow.

Chapter 25 (p514)

Qu. 1 (a) $16x(2x^2+3)^3$ (b) $\dfrac{x-1}{\sqrt{(x^2-2x+1)}}$ (c) $-4(2x-1)^{-3}$

(d) $4\cos(4x-7)$

Qu. 2 (a) $\frac{1}{6}(x^2+1)^3+c$ (b) $\frac{1}{10}(2x+1)^5+c$

(c) $-\frac{1}{6}\cos 3x+c$ (d) $\frac{2}{9}(x^3+1)^{3/2}+c$

Qu. 3 (a) $\frac{1}{3}\cos^3 x-\cos x+c$ (b) $\sin x-\frac{2}{3}\sin^3 x+\frac{1}{5}\sin^5 x+c$

Qu. 4 $\frac{1}{3}\sec^3 x-\sec x+c$

Qu. 5 $\frac{1}{12}\sin^3 4x+c$

Qu. 6 $-\cos x+\frac{2}{3}\cos^3 x-\frac{1}{5}\cos^5 x+c$

Qu. 7 (a) $\frac{1}{15}(2x+1)^{3/2}(3x-1)+c$ (b) $\frac{1}{15}(2x+1)^{3/2}(3x-1)+c$

(c) $\frac{1}{504}(3x-2)^7(21x+2)+c$

Qu. 8 (a) $45°,\ \pi/4$ rad (b) $30°,\ \pi/6$ rad (c) $45°,\ \pi/4$ rad (d) $60°,\ \pi/3$ rad

(e) $30°,\ \pi/6$ rad (f) $0°,\ 0$ rad (g) $60°,\ \pi/3$ rad (h) $30°,\ \pi/6$ rad

(i) $30°,\ \pi/6$ rad (j) $60°,\ \pi/3$ rad (k) $90°,\ \pi/2$ rad

Qu. 9 (a) $\pi/9$ (b) $7\pi/18$ (c) $5\pi/6$ (d) $5\pi/3$ (e) $9\pi/4$

Qu. 10 (a) $57.3°$ (b) $1.7°$ (c) $71.6°$ (d) $41.0°$ (e) $36°$

Qu. 11 (a) 1.29 (b) 0.927 (c) 0.784

Qu. 12 (a) $3\cos u,\ \sin^{-1}\dfrac{x}{3}$ (b) $\cos u,\ \sin^{-1}5x$ (c) $2\cos u,\ \sin^{-1}\dfrac{3x}{2}$

(d) $\sqrt{7}\cos u,\ \sin^{-1}\dfrac{x}{\sqrt{7}}$

Qu. 13 (a) $\sin^{-1}\dfrac{x}{2}+c$ (b) $\dfrac{1}{\sqrt{3}}\sin^{-1}\sqrt{3}x+c$ (c) $\dfrac{1}{3}\sin^{-1}\dfrac{3x}{4}+c$

Qu. 15 $\tan^{-1}x+c$

Qu. 16 (a) $9\sec^2 u,\ \tan^{-1}\dfrac{x}{3}$ (b) $\sec^2 u,\ \tan^{-1}2x$ (c) $25\sec^2 u,\ \tan^{-1}\dfrac{3x}{5}$

(d) $3\sec^2 u,\ \tan^{-1}\dfrac{x}{\sqrt{3}}$

Qu. 17 (a) $\frac{1}{2}\tan^{-1}\dfrac{x}{2}+c$ (b) $\frac{1}{4}\tan^{-1}4x+c$

Exercise 25a (p516)

1 (a) $30x(5x^2-1)^2$ (b) $\dfrac{2-8x}{(2x^2-x+3)^3}$ (c) $\frac{2}{3}x(x^2+4)^{-2/3}$

(d) $-5\operatorname{cosec}^2 5x$ (e) $-5\sin(5x-1)$ (f) $\frac{1}{3}\sin\frac{2}{3}x$

(g) $\dfrac{1}{2\sqrt{x}}\sec^2\sqrt{x}$ (h) $4\sec^2 2x\tan 2x$

(i) $-\frac{1}{2}\cot x\sqrt{\operatorname{cosec} x}$

2 (a) $\frac{1}{12}(x^2-3)^6+c$ (b) $\frac{1}{18}(3x-1)^6+c$ (c) $\frac{1}{4}x^4+\frac{4}{3}x^3+2x^2+c$
(d) $-\frac{1}{2}(x^2+1)^{-1}+c$ (e) $-\frac{1}{4}(x^2+2x-5)^{-2}+c$ (f) $\frac{1}{3}(x^2-3x+7)^3+c$
(g) $-\frac{1}{4}(4x^2-7)^{-1}+c$ (h) $\frac{2}{9}(3x^2-5)^{3/2}+c$ (i) $\frac{1}{7}x^7+\frac{1}{2}x^4+x+c$
(j) $\frac{2}{3}\sqrt{(x^3-3x)}+c$ (k) $-\frac{1}{2}(2x^2-4x+1)^{-1/2}+c$
(l) $\frac{8}{7}x^7-\frac{12}{5}x^5+2x^3-x+c$

3 (a) $\sin 3x+c$ (b) $-\frac{1}{2}\cos(2x+3)+c$ (c) $\frac{1}{2}\sin^2 x+c$ (d) $\frac{1}{6}\sin 2x+c$
(e) $-\frac{1}{9}\cos^3 3x+c$ (f) $\frac{1}{3}\tan^3 x+c$ (g) $\frac{1}{5}\sec^5 x+c$ (h) $\frac{2}{3}\sin^{3/2}x+c$
(i) $-\frac{1}{2}\cot x^2+c$ (j) $2\sin\sqrt{x}+c$ (k) $-\frac{1}{3}\operatorname{cosec}^3 x+c$

4 (a) $\sin x-\frac{1}{3}\sin^3 x+c$ (b) $2\sin\frac{1}{2}x-\frac{4}{3}\sin^3\frac{1}{2}x+\frac{2}{5}\sin^5\frac{1}{2}x+c$
(c) $\frac{1}{6}\cos^3 2x-\frac{1}{2}\cos 2x+c$ (d) $\frac{1}{2}\sin(2x+1)-\frac{1}{6}\sin^3(2x+1)+c$
(e) $-\frac{1}{3}\cos^3 x+\frac{2}{5}\cos^5 x-\frac{1}{7}\cos^7 x+c$ (f) $\frac{1}{4}\sin^4 x-\frac{1}{6}\sin^6 x+c$
(g) $\tan x+\frac{1}{3}\tan^3 x+c$ (h) $\operatorname{cosec} x-\frac{1}{3}\operatorname{cosec}^3 x+c$
(i) $\sec x-\frac{2}{3}\sec^3 x+\frac{1}{5}\sec^5 x+c$

5 (a) $\frac{1}{2}(1-\cos x)$ (b) $\frac{1}{2}(1+\cos 6x)$

6 (a) $\frac{1}{2}x+\frac{1}{4}\sin 2x+c$ (b) $\frac{1}{2}x-\frac{1}{2}\sin x+c$ (c) $\frac{1}{2}x+\frac{1}{12}\sin 6x+c$

7 $\frac{1}{4}-\frac{1}{2}\cos 2x+\frac{1}{4}\cos^2 2x$, $\frac{1}{2}(1+\cos 4x)$

8 $\frac{3}{8}x+\frac{1}{4}\sin 2x+\frac{1}{32}\sin 4x+c$

9 (a) $\frac{1}{2}x-\frac{1}{4}\sin 2x+c$ (b) $\frac{1}{2}x+\frac{3}{4}\sin\frac{2}{3}x+c$
(c) $\frac{3}{8}x-\frac{1}{8}\sin 4x+\frac{1}{64}\sin 8x+c$ (d) $\frac{3}{8}x+\frac{1}{2}\sin x+\frac{1}{16}\sin 2x+c$

Exercise 25b (p520)

1 $\frac{1}{20}(4x-1)^{3/2}(6x+1)+c$ 2 $\frac{2}{375}(5x+2)^{3/2}(15x-4)+c$
3 $\frac{1}{224}(2x-1)^7(14x+1)+c$ 4 $\frac{2}{3}(x+4)\sqrt{(x-2)}+c$
5 $\frac{1}{30}(x-1)^5(5x+13)+c$ 6 $\frac{1}{168}(x-2)^6(21x^2+156x+304)+c$

7 $\dfrac{x^2-4x+8}{x-2}+c$ 8 $\frac{1}{3}(x-6)\sqrt{(2x+3)}+c$

9 $\frac{2}{135}(3x-4)^{3/2}(9x+8)+c$ 10 $\frac{1}{56}(x+5)^7(7x-5)+c$

Exercise 25c (p521)

1 $\frac{26}{15}$ 2 $\frac{1}{30}$ 3 $\sqrt{3}-\frac{2}{3}$ 4 $-\frac{7}{20}$ 5 $\frac{7}{36}$ 6 $\frac{8}{15}$
7 (a) $1-\frac{1}{2}\sqrt{3}$ (b) $\frac{256}{15}$ 8 (a) $-\frac{1}{10}$ (b) $\frac{4}{3}$
9 $2\sqrt{2}-\sqrt{3}$ 10 $\frac{9}{8}$

Exercise 25d (p525)

1 (a) $4\cos u,\ \sin^{-1}\dfrac{x}{4}$ (b) $\cos u,\ \sin^{-1}3x$ (c) $3\cos u,\ \sin^{-1}\frac{2}{3}x$

(d) $\sqrt{10}\cos u,\ \sin^{-1}\dfrac{x}{\sqrt{10}}$

2 (a) $\sin^{-1}\dfrac{x}{5}+c$ (b) $\frac{1}{2}\sin^{-1}2x+c$ (c) $\dfrac{1}{3}\sin^{-1}\dfrac{3x}{2}+c$ (d) $\sin^{-1}\dfrac{x}{\sqrt{3}}+c$

3 (a) $16\sec^2 u,\ \tan^{-1}\dfrac{x}{4}$ (b) $\sec^2 u,\ \tan^{-1}3x$ (c) $4\sec^2 u,\ \tan^{-1}\dfrac{\sqrt{3}}{2}x$

(d) $2\sec^2 u,\ \tan^{-1}\dfrac{x}{\sqrt{2}}$

4 (a) $\dfrac{1}{5}\tan^{-1}\dfrac{x}{5}+c$ (b) $\frac{1}{6}\tan^{-1}6x+c$ (c) $\dfrac{1}{4\sqrt{3}}\tan^{-1}\dfrac{\sqrt{3}}{4}x+c$

(d) $\dfrac{1}{\sqrt{5}}\tan^{-1}\dfrac{x}{\sqrt{5}}+c$

5 (a) $\dfrac{1}{3\sqrt{2}}\tan^{-1}\dfrac{\sqrt{2}}{3}x+c$ (b) $\dfrac{3}{\sqrt{5}}\sin^{-1}\dfrac{\sqrt{5}}{2}x+c$ (c) $\dfrac{1}{\sqrt{2}}\sin^{-1}\sqrt{\dfrac{2}{3}}x+c$

(d) $\dfrac{2}{\sqrt{15}}\tan^{-1}\sqrt{\dfrac{5}{3}}x+c$

6 (a) $\frac{1}{6}\pi$ (b) $\frac{1}{4}\pi$ (c) π (d) $\frac{1}{12}\pi$

7 (a) (i) $\sin^{-1}\dfrac{x}{3}+c$ (ii) $-\cos^{-1}\dfrac{x}{3}+c=-\cos^{-1}\dfrac{x}{3}+\dfrac{\pi}{2}+k=\sin^{-1}\dfrac{x}{3}+k$

(b) (i) $\frac{1}{3}\pi$ (ii) $\frac{1}{3}\pi$

8 (a) $\sin^{-1}\dfrac{x+1}{2}+c$ (b) $\frac{1}{3}\tan^{-1}\dfrac{x-3}{3}+c$

9 (a) $\dfrac{1}{5}\tan^{-1}\dfrac{x+3}{5}+c$ (b) $\sin^{-1}\dfrac{x-1}{2}+c$ (c) $\dfrac{1}{\sqrt{15}}\tan^{-1}\dfrac{(x-2)\sqrt{3}}{\sqrt{5}}+c$

(d) $\dfrac{1}{\sqrt{3}}\sin^{-1}\dfrac{x+1}{\sqrt{3}}+c$

10 (a) (i) $(x-3)^2+7$ (ii) $3(x-2)^2+2$ (iii) $2(x-1)^2+3$

(b) (i) $\dfrac{1}{2}\tan^{-1}\dfrac{x-1}{2}+c$ (ii) $\dfrac{1}{3\sqrt{2}}\tan^{-1}\dfrac{(x+1)\sqrt{2}}{3}+c$

(iii) $\dfrac{1}{3}\tan^{-1}\dfrac{x-2}{3}+c$ (iv) $\dfrac{1}{2\sqrt{3}}\tan^{-1}\dfrac{2(x-1)}{\sqrt{3}}+c$

Exercise 25e (p528)

1 $2\sin x-2x\cos x+c$
2 $\frac{1}{4}\sin 2x-\frac{1}{2}x\cos 2x+c$
3 $\frac{1}{2}x\sin (2x+1)-\frac{1}{4}\cos (2x+1)+c$
4 $\frac{1}{72}(x+1)^8(8x-1)+c$

5 $\frac{1}{27}(9x^2 - 2) \sin 3x + \frac{2}{9}x \cos 3x + c$
6 $\frac{1}{8}(1 - 2x^2) \cos 2x + \frac{1}{4}x \sin 2x + c$
7 $\frac{1}{6}x^3 + \frac{1}{8}(2x^2 - 1) \sin 2x + \frac{1}{4}x \cos 2x + c$
8 $\frac{1}{8} \sin 2x - \frac{1}{4}x \cos 2x + c$
9 $\frac{1}{2}(x^2 + 1) \tan^{-1} x - \frac{1}{2}x + c$
10 $-\frac{1}{14}(1 - x^2)^7 + c$
11 $\frac{1}{2} \sin^2 x + c$, or $-\frac{1}{4} \cos 2x + c$
12 $\frac{1}{8}(2t^2 - 2t \sin 2t - \cos 2t) + c$
14 $\frac{1}{2}\pi - 1$
15 $\frac{1}{4}\pi^2$

Exercise 25f (p528)

1 $\frac{2}{9}(x^3 - 1)^{3/2} + c$ **2** $-\frac{1}{4}(x^2 - 1)^{-2} + c$ **3** $-\frac{1}{6} \cos^3 2x + c$
4 $2\sqrt{\tan x} + c$ **5** $\frac{1}{4} \sin 4x - \frac{1}{12} \sin^3 4x + c$ **6** $\frac{1}{2}x - \frac{3}{4} \sin \frac{2}{3}x + c$

7 $\frac{3}{8}x + \frac{1}{8} \sin 4x + \frac{1}{64} \sin 8x + c$ **8** $-2\sqrt{2} \cos \dfrac{x}{2} + c$

9 $-3 \cos^4 \dfrac{x}{6} + c$ **10** $\frac{1}{10} \sin 5x + \frac{1}{2} \sin x + c$

11 $\frac{1}{270}(15x + 7)(3x - 7)^5 + c$ **12** $\frac{2}{3}(x - 10)\sqrt{(5 + x)} + c$

13 $\dfrac{1}{\sqrt{5}} \sin^{-1} \sqrt{\dfrac{5}{6}} x + c$ **14** $\dfrac{1}{\sqrt{8}} \tan^{-1} \sqrt{8x} + c$

15 $\sin^{-1} \dfrac{x + 2}{3} + c$ **16** $\dfrac{1}{\sqrt{6}} \tan^{-1} \sqrt{\dfrac{3}{2}}(x + 1) + c$

17 $\sin^{-1} \dfrac{x}{\sqrt{5}} - \sqrt{(5 - x^2)} + c$ **18** $\dfrac{1}{2}x\sqrt{(9 - x^2)} + \dfrac{9}{2} \sin^{-1} \dfrac{x}{3} + c$

19 $\dfrac{x}{4\sqrt{(4 - x^2)}} + c$ **20** $-\dfrac{\sqrt{(16 - x^2)}}{16x} + c$

21 (a) $-\sqrt{(1 - x^2)} + c$ (b) $2 \tan^{-1} x + c$ (c) $-\frac{1}{3}(1 - x^2)^{3/2} + c$
(d) $2 \sin^{-1} x + c$ (e) $2 \sin^{-1} x + \sqrt{(1 - x^2)} + c$

22 $\frac{2}{27}(3x + 20)\sqrt{(3x - 1)} + c$ **23** $\frac{1}{6}(x^2 + 2)^{3/2} + c$ **24** $-\dfrac{\sqrt{(1 - x^2)}}{x} + c$

25 $\dfrac{2}{5} \cos^5 \dfrac{x}{2} - \dfrac{2}{3} \cos^3 \dfrac{x}{2} + c$ **26** $-\frac{1}{3}\sqrt{(4 - x^2)} + c$ **27** $3 \sin^{-1} \dfrac{x}{6} + c$

28 $\frac{1}{168}(x + 3)^6(21x^2 - 66x + 61) + c$ **29** $2 \sin^{-1} \dfrac{x}{2} - \dfrac{1}{2}x\sqrt{(4 - x^2)} + c$

30 $2 \sin^{-1} \dfrac{x}{3} - \sqrt{(9 - x^2)} + c$ **31** $\dfrac{1}{2\sqrt{3}} \tan^{-1} \dfrac{\sqrt{3}}{2}(x - 2) + c$

32 $\frac{1}{2}x - \frac{5}{4} \sin \frac{2}{5}x + c$ **33** $\frac{2}{3}\sqrt{2} \sin \frac{3}{2}x + c$

34 $2 \sin^{-1} \frac{1}{2} x + \frac{1}{2} x \sqrt{(4 - x^2)} + c$ 35 $\frac{1}{5} \sec^5 x + c$ 36 $\frac{1}{9} \sin^{-1} \frac{3}{2} x^3 + c$

37 $-\frac{1}{2} \cos 2x + \frac{1}{3} \cos^3 2x - \frac{1}{10} \cos^5 2x + c$ 38 $\frac{1}{2} \tan^{-1} x + \dfrac{x}{2(1 + x^2)} + c$

39 $\frac{1}{2} \cos x - \frac{1}{8} \cos 4x + c$ 40 $\dfrac{1}{\sqrt{2}} \sec x + c$ 41 $\frac{1}{2} \tan^{-1} x^2 + c$

42 $\dfrac{1}{2} \sin x \sqrt{(1 - 2 \sin^2 x)} + \dfrac{1}{2\sqrt{2}} \sin^{-1} (\sqrt{2} \sin x) + c$

43 $\dfrac{1}{3} \sec^{-1} \dfrac{x}{3} + c$ 44 $\sqrt{\dfrac{(1 + x)}{(1 - x)}} + c$ 45 $\frac{3672}{125}$

46 $\frac{1}{2}$ 47 1   48 1   49 $-\frac{1}{4} \pi^2$

Chapter 26 (p530)

Qu. 1 the larger a, the larger the gradient; the reflection of $y = 2^x$ in the y-axis

Qu. 2 0.7, 1.1

Qu. 3 (a) 0.7×2^x, 1.1×3^x (b) 1.4, 1.9

Qu. 4 0.7×2^x

Qu. 6 (a) $4 e^{4x}$ (b) $2x e^{x^2}$ (c) $6x^2 e^{2x^3}$ (d) $-2x e^{-x^2}$

(e) $\sec^2 x \times e^{\tan x}$ (f) $\dfrac{1}{2\sqrt{x}} e^{\sqrt{x}}$

Qu. 7 (a) $\frac{1}{2} e^{x^2} + c$ (b) $-e^{\cos x} + c$ (c) $6 e^{x/3} + c$ (d) $\frac{3}{2} e^{2x} + c$
(e) $\frac{1}{12} e^{3x^2} + c$ (f) $-\frac{1}{2} e^{\cot 2x} + c$

Qu. 8 (a) $\log_{10} (100 a^2 b^{-1/3})$ (b) $\log_c \dfrac{B(1 + x)}{1 - x}$

Qu. 9 (a) $\log_c 2 + \log_c a$ (b) $2 \log_c a$ (c) $-\log_c a$ (d) $\log_c 2 - \log_c a$
(e) $\frac{1}{2} \log_c a$ (f) $\log_c a - \log_c 2$ (g) $-2 \log_c a$ (h) $-\log_c 2 - \log_c a$

Qu. 10 (a) $\ln (xy/e)$ (b) 2

Qu. 11 (a) x^2 (b) $1/x$ (c) $\sqrt{x}$ (d) $\sin x$ (e) $\frac{1}{2} x^2$ (f) $\frac{1}{2} x$

Qu. 12 (a) $2x e^{x^2}$ (b) $\dfrac{2x}{x^2 - 2}$ (c) $2 \cot x$ (d) $2x \cot (x^2)$

Qu. 13 $\dfrac{3x + 2}{2x(x + 1)}$

Qu. 14 (a) $\dfrac{1}{x}$ (b) $\dfrac{1}{x}$ (c) $\dfrac{3}{3x + 1}$ (d) $\dfrac{3}{x}$ (e) $\dfrac{3x^2}{x^3 - 2}$ (f) $\dfrac{3}{x - 1}$

Qu. 15 $4^x \ln 4$, $16 \ln 4$

Qu. 16 (a) 0.6931 (b) 1.0986

Qu. 17 (a) $10^x \ln 10$ (b) $2^{3x} \ln 64$

Qu. 18 $5^x \ln 5, \dfrac{5^x}{\ln 5} + c$

Qu. 19 $x \, 2^{x^2} \ln 4, \dfrac{2^{x^2}}{\ln 4} + c$

Qu. 20 (a) $\dfrac{3^{2x}}{\ln 9} + c$ (b) $\frac{1}{3} e^{x^3} + c$ (c) $\dfrac{2^{\tan x}}{\ln 2} + c$

Qu. 21 (a) $2 \ln x + c$ (b) $\frac{1}{3} \ln x + c$ (c) $\frac{1}{3} \ln (3x - 2) + c$ (d) $\frac{1}{3} \ln (x - 2) + c$

Qu. 22 (a) $\frac{1}{2} \ln (2x + 3) + c$ (b) $\ln \dfrac{1}{1 - x} + c$

Qu. 23 $\ln 8$

Qu. 24 (a) $\dfrac{1}{3(2 - x^3)} + c$ (b) $\frac{1}{3} \sin x^3 + c$ (c) $\frac{1}{3} e^{x^3} + c$ (d) $\ln \{k \sqrt[3]{(x^3 - 2)}\}$

(e) $\ln \{k \sqrt{(x^2 - 2x)}\}$ (f) $\ln \dfrac{k}{3 - x^2}$ (g) $\ln (k \sin x)$

Qu. 25 $x + \ln (x - 1) + c$
Qu. 26 (a) $\ln \frac{3}{4}$ (b) $-\ln 2$
Qu. 27 $-\ln 2$
Qu. 28 no

Qu. 29 $\dfrac{1}{x - 3}, \dfrac{1}{x - 3}$

Qu. 30 (a) $\ln \frac{3}{2}$ (b) $-\ln 5$
Qu. 31 $-\ln 3$

Exercise 26a (p535)

2 yes; (a) neither (b) even
3 even; $0 < y \leqslant 1$
4 0.9×2.5^x
5 (a) $4 e^x$ (b) $3 e^{3x}$ (c) $2 e^{2x+1}$ (d) $4x \, e^{2x^2}$
6 (a) $-e^{\cos x} \sin x$ (b) $e^{\sec x} \sec x \tan x$ (c) $e^{3 \tan x} 3 \sec^2 x$
(d) $2 e^{\sin 2x} \cos 2x$
7 (a) $e^x (x^2 + 2x)$ (b) $(x - 1) e^x / x^2$ (c) $\frac{1}{2} e^{\sin x} (1 + x \cos x)$
(d) $e^x \operatorname{cosec} x \, (2x - \cot x)$
8 (a) $6 e^{x/2} + c$ (b) $-e^{-x} + c$ (c) $3 e^{x/3} + c$ (d) $\frac{2}{3} e^{3x-1} + c$ (e) $\frac{1}{4} e^{x^2} + c$
(f) $-\frac{1}{3} e^{-x^3} + c$ (g) $-e^{\cos x} + c$ (h) $e^{\tan x} + c$ (i) $-e^{\cot x} + c$
(j) $-e^{1/x} + c$
9 $y = e^a (x - a + 1), \ y - e^2 x + e^2 = 0$
10 $\frac{1}{2} \pi (e^2 - 1)$

Exercise 26b (p538)

1 $\lg\left(\dfrac{a^3}{50}\right)$ **2** $\log_e \dfrac{x^2 e^3}{3}$ **3** $\log_e \dfrac{(x-3)^4}{(x-2)^3}$ **4** $\log_e \{k\sqrt{(1-y^2)}\}$

5 $\log_e a + \log_e 3$ **6** $3\log_e a$ **7** $\log_e a - \log_e 3$ **8** $-3\log_e a$
9 $\log_e 3 - \log_e a$ **10** $-\log_e 3 - \log_e a$ **11** $\tfrac{1}{3}\log_e a$
12 $\log_e \cos x - \log_e \sin x$ **13** $2\log_e \sin x - 2\log_e \cos x$
14 $\log_e (x-2) + \log_e (x+2)$ **15** $\tfrac{1}{2}\log_e (x+1) - \tfrac{1}{2}\log_e (x-1)$

Exercise 26c (p541)

1 (a) $\dfrac{1}{x}$ (b) $\dfrac{4}{x}$ (c) $\dfrac{2}{2x-3}$ (d) $\dfrac{1}{x-1}$ (e) $\dfrac{4}{x}$ (f) $\dfrac{2x}{x^2-1}$ (g) $\dfrac{2}{x}$ (h) $\dfrac{6}{x}$

(i) $\dfrac{2}{x+1}$ (j) $-\dfrac{1}{x}$ (k) $\dfrac{1}{x}$ (l) $\dfrac{1}{2x}$ (m) $-\dfrac{1}{x}$ (n) $-\dfrac{1}{x}$ (o) $-\dfrac{2}{x}$

(p) $\dfrac{1}{x\ln 10}$

2 (a) $-\tan x$ (b) $2\cot x$ (c) $6\operatorname{cosec} 6x$ (d) $-6\tan 2x$ (e) $-4\operatorname{cosec} 2x$
(f) $-4\tan 2x$ (g) $\operatorname{cosec} x$ (h) $\tan x$ (i) $\sec x$ (j) $-2x\cot x^2$
(k) $2\sec 2x$

3 (a) $\dfrac{1}{x^2-1}$ (b) $\dfrac{2x^2-1}{x(x^2-1)}$ (c) $\dfrac{3x-5}{2(x^2-1)}$ (d) $\dfrac{1}{\sqrt{(x^2-1)}}$

4 (a) $1+\ln x$ (b) $x+2x\ln x$ (c) $\dfrac{1}{x^2}(1-\ln x)$ (d) $\dfrac{1-2\ln x}{x^3}$

(e) $\dfrac{\ln x-1}{(\ln x)^2}$ (f) $\dfrac{2}{x}\ln x$ (g) $\dfrac{1}{x\ln x}$ (h) $\cos x$

5 (a) $5^x \ln 5$ (b) $x\, 2^{x^2}\ln 4$ (c) $\tfrac{2}{3}3^{2x}\ln 3$ (d) 1

6 (a) $3^x \ln 3,\ \dfrac{3^x}{\ln 3}+c$ (b) $x\, 2^{x^2}\ \ln 4, \dfrac{2^{x^2}}{\ln 4}+c$

7 (a) $\dfrac{1}{\ln 10}10^x+c$ (b) $\dfrac{2^{3x}}{\ln 8}+c$ (c) $\dfrac{3^{x^2}}{\ln 9}+c$ (d) $-\dfrac{2^{\cos x}}{\ln 2}+c$

8 $1+\ln x,\ x(\ln x-1)+c$

9 $2^x(1+x\ln 2),\ \dfrac{x\,2^x}{\ln 2}-\dfrac{2^x}{(\ln 2)^2}+c$

10 (a) $1/(x-2)$ (b) $1/(x-2)$
12 (a) $\{y:y>0\}$ (b) $\mathbb{R}$

Exercise 26d (p548)

1 (a) $\ln (kx^{1/4})$ (b) $\ln (kx^5)$ (c) $\ln \{k\sqrt{(2x-3)}\}$ (d) $\ln \{k\sqrt{(x+4)}\}$
(e) $\ln \{k(3-2x)^{-1/2}\}$ (f) $\ln \{k(1-x^2)^{-1/2}\}$ (g) $\ln \{k(x^2-1)^{3/2}\}$

(h) $\ln\{k(x^2+x-2)\}$ (i) $\ln\{k\sqrt[3]{(3x^2-9x+4)}\}$ (j) $x-\ln\{k(x+2)^2\}$
(k) $\frac{3}{2}x-\ln\{k(2x+3)^{9/4}\}$ (l) $-2x-\ln\{k(3-x)^6\}$
(m) $-x-\ln\{k(2-x)\}$ (n) $-2x-\ln\{k(x-4)^5\}$ (o) $\ln(k\sec x)$

(p) $\ln\left(k\sin^2\dfrac{x}{2}\right)$ (q) $\ln\{k\sqrt{\sin(2x+1)}\}$ (r) $\ln\left(k\cos^3\dfrac{x}{3}\right)$

2 (b) $\dfrac{2}{2x-1},\dfrac{2}{2x-1}$ (c) $\frac{1}{2}\ln 3,\ -\frac{1}{2}\ln 5$

3 (a) $\ln\frac{2}{3}$ (b) $\ln 2$

4 (a) $\dfrac{1}{3-x},\dfrac{1}{3-x}$ (b) $-\ln 1.5$ (c) $\ln 1.5$

5 (a) $\ln 2$ (b) $\frac{1}{3}\ln 2$ (c) $-\ln 2$ (d) $\frac{1}{2}\ln 5-\ln 3$ (e) $\frac{1}{2}\ln 3$ (f) $-\frac{1}{2}\ln 2$
 (g) $\ln 7$ (h) $2+\ln 4$ (i) $2+\ln 4$ (j) $-\frac{1}{2}-\ln\frac{3}{2}$ (k) $\frac{1}{2}\ln\frac{4}{3}$ (l) $\frac{1}{2}\ln 2$
 (m) $\frac{1}{2}\ln 3$

Exercise 26e (p550)

1 $\frac{1}{9}x^3(3\ln x-1)+c$
2 $-e^{-x}(x^2+2x+2)+c$
3 $e^x(x^3-3x^2+6x-6)+c$
4 $x\ln 2x-x+c$
5 $x\sin^{-1}(3x)+\frac{1}{3}\sqrt{(1-9x^2)}+c$
6 $-\frac{1}{2}(t^2+1)e^{-t^2}+c$
7 $1-2e^{-1}$
8 $1+e^2$
9 $\frac{1}{2}\pi-1$
10 $e-2$
11 $\frac{1}{4}(3e^4+1)$
12 $18\ln 9-104/9$
13 $\frac{1}{4}(e^2-1)$
14 $\frac{1}{9}(24\ln 2-7)$
15 $\frac{1}{9}(1-4e^{-3})$
16 $34e^5-4$
17 1
19 $-\frac{1}{2}e^{-x}(\sin x+\cos x)+c$
20 $\frac{1}{5}(e^\pi-2)$

Exercise 26f (p555)

1 (a) 1.1052   (b) 0.3679   (c) 1.6487
2 $1+x^3+\frac{1}{2}x^6+\frac{1}{6}x^9+\ ...\ +x^{3n}/n!+\ ...$
3 $1+\frac{1}{3}x+\frac{1}{18}x^2+\frac{1}{162}x^3+\ ...\ +x^n/(n!3^n)+\ ...$
4 $1-2x+2x^2-\frac{4}{3}x^3+\ ...\ +(-1)^n2^nx^n/n!+\ ...$
5 $e^2\{1+x+\frac{1}{2}x^2+\frac{1}{6}x^3+\ ...\ +x^n/n!+\ ...\}$

6 (a) $\ln 3 + \dfrac{1}{3}x - \dfrac{1}{18}x^2 + \dfrac{1}{81}x^3 - \ldots + (-1)^{n-1}\dfrac{x^n}{3^n \times n} + \ldots, \quad -3 < x \leqslant 3$

(b) $-\dfrac{1}{2}x - \dfrac{1}{8}x^2 - \dfrac{1}{24}x^3 - \dfrac{1}{64}x^4 - \ldots - \dfrac{x^n}{2^n \times n} \ldots, \quad -2 \leqslant x < 2$

(c) $\ln 2 - \dfrac{5}{2}x - \dfrac{25}{8}x^2 - \dfrac{125}{24}x^3 - \ldots - \dfrac{5^n x^n}{2^n \times n} - \ldots, \quad -\dfrac{2}{5} \leqslant x < \dfrac{2}{5}$

(d) $-x^2 - \dfrac{1}{2}x^4 - \dfrac{1}{3}x^6 - \dfrac{1}{4}x^8 - \ldots - \dfrac{x^{2n}}{n} - \ldots, \quad -1 < x < 1$

(e) $\dfrac{2}{3}x + \dfrac{2}{81}x^3 + \dfrac{2}{1215}x^5 + \ldots + \dfrac{2x^{2n-1}}{(2n-1)3^{2n-1}} + \ldots, \quad -3 < x < 3$

(f) $-\dfrac{3x}{2} - \dfrac{9}{32}x^3 - \dfrac{243}{2560}x^5 - \ldots - 2 \times \dfrac{3^{2n-1}x^{2n-1}}{(2n-1)4^{2n-1}} - \ldots, \quad -\dfrac{4}{3} < x < \dfrac{4}{3}$

7 $\ln\dfrac{2}{3} - \dfrac{1}{6}x - \dfrac{5}{72}x^2 - \ldots - \left(\dfrac{1}{2^n} - \dfrac{1}{3^n}\right)\dfrac{x^n}{n} - \ldots, \quad -2 \leqslant x < 2$

8 $-\ln 3 + \frac{4}{3}x + \frac{20}{9}x^2 + \ldots + 2^n\{1 + (-1)^n(\frac{1}{3})^n\}x^n/n + \ldots, \quad -\frac{1}{2} \leqslant x < \frac{1}{2}$

9 $-6x^2 + 28x^3 - 111x^4 + \ldots + (-1)^{n-1}(4^{n-1} - 3^{n-1})12x^n/n + \ldots,$
$-\frac{1}{4} < x \leqslant \frac{1}{4}$

10 $\frac{1}{2}\ln 2 + \frac{3}{4}x - \frac{5}{16}x^2 + \ldots + (-1)^{n-1}\{1 + (\frac{1}{2})^n\}x^n/(2n) + \ldots, \quad -1 < x \leqslant 1$

Exercise 26g (p555)

1 $x = 4$ or $x = \sqrt{2}$

2 -1.20

3 $(3, 9), (9, 3)$

4 (a) $\mathbb{R}, \{y : y \in \mathbb{R}, y \geqslant 1\}, \mathbb{R}^+$ (b) $g_1 g_2(x) = \ln(2 + 2x + x^2),$
neither; $g_2 g_1(x) = 1 + \ln(1 + x^2)$, even

5 $\{y : y \in \mathbb{R}, 0 < y < 1\}, \mathbb{R}^+, \{y : y \in \mathbb{R}, y > 1\}; \ f^{-1} : x \mapsto \ln(1/x), (0 < x < 1);$

$g^{-1} : x \mapsto 1 - 1/x, (x > 0); \ (gf)^{-1} : x \mapsto \ln\left(\dfrac{x}{x-1}\right), (x > 1)$

6 0.53

7 (a) 2π (b) even (d) no inverse (e) $D = \{x : 0 \leqslant x \leqslant \pi\}$

Chapter 27 (p557)

Qu. 1 (a) $\dfrac{3-x}{1-x^2}$ (b) $\dfrac{(x+2)(x-1)}{(x^2+1)(x+1)}$ (c) $\dfrac{3x^2 - x + 4}{(x-1)^2(x+1)}$

Qu. 2 (a) $\dfrac{1}{x-2} - \dfrac{1}{x+2}$ (b) $\dfrac{1}{2(1-x)} + \dfrac{1}{2(1+x)}$ (c) $\frac{1}{2} - \frac{1}{3}$ (d) $\dfrac{1}{n} - \dfrac{1}{n+1}$

Qu. 3 (a) $12A - 3B + 4C = 17, \ 6A - 4B + 3C = 5, \ 10A - 15B + 6C = -1$
(b) $A = 2, B = 1, C = -1$

Qu. 4 (a) $A = 1$, $B = -3$, $C = 4$ (b) $A = 2$, $B = 1$, $C = -3$
(c) $A = 5$, $B = -1$

Qu. 5 $A = 3$, $B = -2$, $C = -1$

Qu. 6 (a) $A = -\frac{2}{3}$, $B = \frac{2}{3}$, $C = 1$ (b) no

Qu. 7 (a) $\dfrac{1}{x-3} - \dfrac{1}{x+3}$ (b) $\dfrac{1}{2(2-x)} - \dfrac{1}{2(2+x)}$ (c) $\dfrac{1}{x-2} - \dfrac{2}{3x-5}$

(d) $\dfrac{1}{2(x+1)} - \dfrac{1}{x+2} + \dfrac{1}{2(x-3)}$ (e) $\dfrac{2}{1+2x} - \dfrac{1}{2-x}$

Qu. 8 (a) $\dfrac{1}{1-x} + \dfrac{2+x}{4+x^2}$ (b) $\dfrac{1}{x+1} - \dfrac{2x-1}{2x^2+x+3}$

(c) $\dfrac{1}{x+1} + \dfrac{1}{x-2} - \dfrac{2}{x+2}$ (d) $\dfrac{1}{2-x} + \dfrac{x}{3+x^2}$

Qu. 9 (a) $\dfrac{1}{x+3} - \dfrac{2}{(x+3)^2}$ (b) $\dfrac{5}{x-2} - \dfrac{3}{x-1} - \dfrac{4}{(x-1)^2}$

Qu. 10 $A = 3$, $B = -2$, $C = 1$, $D = 5$

Qu. 11 (a) $x + \dfrac{x+2}{(x-1)(x+3)}$ (b) $3 + \dfrac{x-1}{(x-2)(x+1)}$

Qu. 12 (a) $1 + \dfrac{2}{x+1} - \dfrac{1}{x-2}$ (b) $x - 1 - \dfrac{3}{4(x-2)} + \dfrac{3}{4(x+2)}$

Qu. 14 (a) $\frac{1}{6}\ln(x-3) - \frac{1}{6}\ln(x+3) + c$ (b) $\frac{1}{2}\ln(2x-3) - \frac{5}{2}(2x-3)^{-1} + c$

Qu. 15 $-\dfrac{1}{2}\ln(2-x) - \dfrac{1}{2}\ln(2+x) + c = \ln\dfrac{k}{\sqrt{(4-x^2)}}$

Qu. 16 no

Qu. 17 (a) $\ln\frac{25}{32}$ (b) $\ln 3$

Exercise 27a (p560)

1 (a) $\dfrac{x-12}{(x+3)(x-2)}$ (b) $\dfrac{7-3x-5x^2}{(x+2)^2(3x-1)}$ (c) $\dfrac{2-4x-3x^2}{(2+3x^2)(1-x)}$

(d) $\dfrac{-x^3+6x^2-7x+6}{(x^2+1)(x-1)^2}$

2 (a) $\dfrac{1}{3-x} - \dfrac{1}{3+x}$ (b) $\dfrac{1}{2(a-b)} + \dfrac{1}{2(a+b)}$ (c) $\frac{1}{5} - \frac{1}{6}$ (d) $\dfrac{1}{1-p} + \dfrac{1}{p}$

3 (a) $A = 3$, $B = 7$ (b) $A = 1$, $B = -1$, $C = 2$ (c) $A = 2$, $B = -1$, $C = -3$
(d) $A = 1$, $B = -2$, $C = 3$

4 (a) $A = 1$, $B = -1$ (b) $A = 2$, $B = 1$ (c) $A = 2$, $B = -1$, $C = 3$
(d) $A = 1$, $B = -2$, $C = 3$

5 (a) $A = 3$, $B = -\frac{1}{2}$, $C = -\frac{1}{2}$ (b) no (c) $A = 2$, $B = 3$, $C = 1$ (d) no

(e) $A = 1, B = 3, C = 2, D = -1$

6 $A = 1, B = 1, C = 1$ (a) $(x + 1)(x^2 - x + 1)$ (b) $(x - 2)(x^2 + 2x + 4)$
(c) $(x + 3)(x^2 - 3x + 9)$ (d) $(2x - 3)(4x^2 + 6x + 9)$
(e) $(3x + 5)(9x^2 - 15x + 25)$

Exercise 27b (p565)

1 (a) $\dfrac{2}{x + 3} - \dfrac{1}{x - 4}$ (b) $\dfrac{1}{2(5 - x)} - \dfrac{1}{2(5 + x)}$ (c) $\dfrac{4}{x + 1} + \dfrac{2}{x - 2} - \dfrac{3}{x - 3}$

(d) $\dfrac{3}{x - 1} - \dfrac{1}{x} + \dfrac{2}{x + 1}$

2 (a) $\dfrac{2}{x - 3} + \dfrac{3x - 1}{x^2 + 4}$ (b) $\dfrac{2}{x + 1} - \dfrac{1}{x^2 + 2}$ (c) $\dfrac{1}{x - 1} + \dfrac{2x}{x^2 + 5}$

(d) $\dfrac{3}{2x - 3} + \dfrac{1 - 3x}{2x^2 + 1}$

3 (a) $\dfrac{1}{x - 2} - \dfrac{3}{(x - 2)^2}$ (b) $\dfrac{1}{x - 1} - \dfrac{1}{x + 2} + \dfrac{2}{(x + 2)^2}$

(c) $\dfrac{23}{4(3x + 1)} - \dfrac{1}{4(x + 1)} - \dfrac{7}{2(x + 1)^2}$ (d) $x + \dfrac{1}{x + 2} + \dfrac{2}{x - 1} + \dfrac{1}{(x - 1)^2}$

4 (a) $\dfrac{1}{x - 2} + \dfrac{2}{x + 1} - \dfrac{3}{(x + 1)^2} + \dfrac{1}{(x + 1)^3}$

(b) $\dfrac{3}{x - 1} - \dfrac{1}{(x - 1)^2} - \dfrac{3}{x + 1} - \dfrac{2}{(x + 1)^2}$

5 (a) $x + 2 + \dfrac{1}{x - 3} - \dfrac{2}{x + 3}$ (b) $3 - \dfrac{2}{x - 1} - \dfrac{1}{x + 2}$

6 $\dfrac{1}{6(x + 2)} - \dfrac{7}{2x} + \dfrac{10}{3(x - 1)}$ **7** $\dfrac{3}{2x^2} - \dfrac{3}{4x} + \dfrac{3}{4(x + 2)}$

8 $\dfrac{5}{3 + x} + \dfrac{2}{4 - x} - \dfrac{3}{4 + x}$ **9** $\dfrac{1}{x - 1} - \dfrac{x}{x^2 + x + 1}$

10 $\dfrac{2}{(2x + 1)^2} - \dfrac{5}{2x + 1} + \dfrac{3}{x - 3}$

Exercise 27c (p569)

1 $\dfrac{1}{n} - \dfrac{1}{n + 2}$

2 $\dfrac{2}{n - 1} - \dfrac{3}{n} + \dfrac{1}{n + 1}$

3 (a) $\dfrac{n+4}{n(n+1)(n+2)}$ (b) $\dfrac{3}{2} - \dfrac{n+3}{(n+1)(n+2)}$ (c) $1\frac{1}{2}$

4 2

5 (a) $\dfrac{11}{18} - \dfrac{3n^2 + 12n + 11}{3(n+1)(n+2)(n+3)}$ (b) $\dfrac{n}{4(n+1)}$ (c) $\dfrac{n}{9(n+1)}$

(d) $\dfrac{3}{16} - \dfrac{2n+3}{8(n+1)(n+2)}$ (e) $\dfrac{11}{96} - \dfrac{1}{8(n+1)} - \dfrac{1}{8(n+2)} + \dfrac{1}{8(n+3)} + \dfrac{1}{8(n+4)}$

(f) $\dfrac{1}{6} - \dfrac{n+2}{(n+3)(n+4)}$

6 (a) $\dfrac{2n}{2n+1}$ (b) $\dfrac{1}{12} - \dfrac{1}{4(2n+1)(2n+3)}$ (c) $\dfrac{5}{24} - \dfrac{4n+5}{8(2n+1)(2n+3)}$

7 (a) $\dfrac{1}{2}\ln\dfrac{k(x-2)}{x}$ (b) $\dfrac{1}{17}\ln\dfrac{k(5x-2)}{x+3}$ (c) $\ln\dfrac{kx}{3x+1} - \dfrac{2}{x}$ (d) $\ln\dfrac{k}{\sqrt{(16-x^2)}}$

(e) $\dfrac{1}{6}\ln\dfrac{k(x-5)}{x+1}$ (f) $\ln\{k(x^2-4x-5)^{1/2}\}$ (g) $\ln\{k(x+2)\sqrt{(x^2+3)}\}$

(h) $\ln\dfrac{k(3+x)^2(2-x)}{(4-x)^3}$ (i) $2\ln\{k(2x+1)\} - \frac{1}{2}\ln\{(x-3)(x+3)^3\}$

(j) $\dfrac{1}{3}\ln\dfrac{k(x-2)}{x+1} - \dfrac{4}{x-2}$

Exercise 27d (p570)

1 $\tan^{-1}x + c$ **2** $\ln\{k(1+x^2)^{1/2}\}$ **3** $\tan^{-1}x + \ln\{k(1+x^2)^{1/2}\}$

4 $\ln\left(k\sqrt{\dfrac{1+x}{1-x}}\right)$ **5** $\ln\dfrac{k}{\sqrt{(1-x^2)}}$ **6** $c - \sqrt{(1-x^2)}$ **7** $\sin^{-1}x + c$

8 $\sin^{-1}x - \sqrt{(1-x^2)} + c$ **9** $-\ln\{k(1-x)\}$ **10** $-\ln\{k(x-1)\}$

11 $x - \ln(1+x) + c$ **12** $\dfrac{1}{1-x} + c$ **13** $\dfrac{1}{1-x} + \ln(1-x) + c$

14 $\ln\frac{4}{3} \approx 0.288$ **15** $\frac{1}{2}\ln 2 + \frac{1}{4}\pi \approx 1.13$ **16** $\ln\frac{45}{64} \approx -0.352$
17 $-3\ln 2 - \frac{1}{2}\ln 3 \approx -2.63$
18 $\pi/2,\ (2 + 2\ln 2, 0)$

Revision Exercise 5 (p572)

1 (a) $\frac{1}{3}\sqrt{(x^2+1)^3} + c$ (b) $\frac{2}{3}\sqrt{(x^3+3x-4)} + c$
(c) $\sin u - \frac{2}{3}\sin^3 u + \frac{1}{5}\sin^5 u + c$ (d) $\tan\theta + \frac{2}{3}\tan^3\theta + \frac{1}{5}\tan^5\theta + c$
(e) $\frac{1}{5}\sec^5 x - \frac{2}{3}\sec^3 x + \sec x + c$ (f) $-\frac{1}{2}\cos x^2 + c$ (g) $2\tan\sqrt{x} + c$

(h) $\frac{1}{4}\ln(2x^2+3)+c$ (i) $-\frac{1}{2}e^{-x^2}+c$ (j) $\ln\sec^2\frac{\theta}{2}+c$

2 (a) $\frac{1}{5}(x+1)\sqrt{(2x-3)^3}+c$ (b) $\frac{1}{324}(24x+1)(3x-1)^8+c$

(c) $y+16(y-4)^{-1}+c$ (d) $\frac{1}{\sqrt{5}}\sin^{-1}\frac{\sqrt{5}y}{2}+c$ (e) $\frac{1}{3\sqrt{3}}\tan^{-1}\sqrt{3u}+c$

(f) $\frac{1}{2\sqrt{2}}\tan^{-1}\frac{u-3}{2\sqrt{2}}+c$ (g) $\frac{1}{\sqrt{2}}\sin^{-1}\frac{(x-1)\sqrt{2}}{3}+c$

(h) $\frac{1}{2}y\sqrt{(4-y^2)}+2\sin^{-1}\frac{y}{2}+c$

3 (a) $\frac{1}{3}e^{3x}+c$ (b) $(\ln 10)^{-1}10^y+c$ (c) $-\frac{1}{3}e^{-x^3}+c$ (d) $\frac{1}{3}\ln x+c$
  (e) $\frac{1}{3}\ln(3x+4)+c$ (f) $-\frac{1}{2}\ln(2x-3)+c$ (g) $\frac{1}{3}\ln(x+3)+c$

(h) $\frac{1}{2}\ln\frac{1+x}{1-x}+c$ (i) $x(\ln x-1)+c$ (j) $2e^{\sqrt{x}}(\sqrt{x}-1)+c$

4 (a) $\frac{1}{3}\ln\frac{3+x}{3-x}+c$ (b) $\frac{1}{3}\ln\frac{y-3}{y}+c$ (c) $\frac{1}{x}+\ln\frac{x-1}{x}+c$

(d) $4(4-x)^{-1}+\ln(4-x)+c$ (e) $-\frac{4x+5}{2(x+1)^2}-\ln(x+1)+c$

(f) $\ln\frac{(x+1)^3}{x^2-x+1}+c$

5 (a) $2x\sin\frac{1}{2}x+4\cos\frac{1}{2}x+c$ (b) $\frac{1}{2}e^x(x-1)+c$
  (c) $\ln\sin y-y\cot y+c$ (d) $-\frac{1}{252}(21y+1)(1-3y)^7+c$
  (e) $(\ln 3)^{-2}3^x(x\ln 3-1)+c$ (f) $\frac{1}{4}x^2(2\ln 2x-1)+c$
  (g) $t(\ln t-1)+c$ (h) $x\tan^{-1}3x-\frac{1}{6}\ln(1+9x^2)+c$
  (i) $x(6-x^2)\cos x+3(x^2-2)\sin x+c$

6 (a) $\frac{1}{4}\ln(4x^2+3)-\frac{1}{2\sqrt{3}}\tan^{-1}\frac{2x}{\sqrt{3}}+c$

(b) $4\sqrt{(1+2y-y^2)}-3\sin^{-1}\frac{y-1}{\sqrt{2}}+c$

7 (a) $\pi/9$ (b) $\frac{1}{2\sqrt{2}}\tan^{-1}\frac{18-10\sqrt{2}}{31}$ (c) $\frac{1}{2}$ (d) $\frac{1}{2}\ln\frac{1}{5}$

8 (a) $-\frac{1}{5}\cos 5x+c$ (b) $3\sin\frac{1}{3}x+c$ (c) $\frac{1}{5}\ln\sec 5x+c$
  (d) $2\ln\sin\frac{1}{2}x+c$
9 (a) $3\tan\frac{1}{3}x+c$ (b) $-\frac{1}{4}\cot 4x+c$ (c) $\frac{1}{2}x-\frac{1}{4}\sin 2x+c$
  (d) $\frac{1}{2}x+\frac{1}{4}\sin 2x+c$ (e) $\tan x-x+c$ (f) $-\cot x-x+c$
10 (a) $\frac{1}{3}\cos^3 x-\cos x+c$ (b) $\sin x-\frac{1}{3}\sin^3 x+c$
  (c) $\frac{1}{2}\tan^2 x+\ln\cos x+c$ (d) $-\frac{1}{2}\cot^2 x-\ln\sin x+c$
11 (a) $\frac{1}{32}(12x-8\sin 2x+\sin 4x)+c$ (b) $\frac{1}{32}(12x+8\sin 2x+\sin 4x)+c$
  (c) $x-\tan x+\frac{1}{3}\tan^3 x+c$ (d) $-\frac{1}{3}\cot^3 x-\cot x+c$

(e) $\frac{1}{3}\tan^3 x + \tan x + c$ (f) $x + \cot x - \frac{1}{3}\cot^3 x + c$

12 (a) $x\sin^{-1}x + \sqrt{(1-x^2)} + c$ (b) $x\cos^{-1}x - \sqrt{(1-x^2)} + c$
  (c) $x\tan^{-1}x - \frac{1}{2}\ln(1+x^2) + c$ (d) $x\cot^{-1}x + \frac{1}{2}\ln(1+x^2) + c$

13 (a) $\frac{1}{2\sqrt{3}}\tan^{-1}\frac{2x}{\sqrt{3}} + c$ (b) $\frac{1}{8}\sqrt{(5+8x^2)} + c$ (c) $\frac{1}{6}\ln(2+3x^2) + c$

  (d) $\frac{1}{3}\sqrt{(3+x^2)^3} + c$ (e) $\frac{1}{4}\ln(3+2x^2) + \frac{1}{\sqrt{6}}\tan^{-1}\frac{x\sqrt{2}}{\sqrt{3}} + c$

  (f) $\frac{1}{2}\ln(x^2 - 4x + 7) + c$

14 (a) $\frac{1}{\sqrt{5}}\sin^{-1}\frac{\sqrt{5}x}{2} + c$ (b) $-\frac{2}{27}(3x+2)\sqrt{(1-3x)} + c$ (c) $\frac{1}{3}\ln\frac{3+x}{3-x} + c$

  (d) $3(16-x)^{-1} + c$ (e) $-\frac{1}{3}\sqrt{(6-x^2)^3} + c$ (f) $-\frac{3}{2}\ln(4-x^2) + c$

  (g) $\frac{1}{2}x\sqrt{(4-x^2)} + 2\sin^{-1}\frac{x}{2} + c$ (h) $-\frac{1}{2}\sqrt{(7-2x^2)} + c$

15 (a) $\frac{180}{\pi}\sin x° + c$ (b) $\frac{1}{32}\sin 4x - \frac{1}{8}x\cos 4x + c$ (c) $2\ln\tan\frac{1}{2}\theta + c$

  (d) $-\frac{1}{7}\cos^7 x + \frac{2}{9}\cos^9 x - \frac{1}{11}\cos^{11}x + c$ (e) $y\tan y + \ln\cos y + c$
  (f) $\sin x - x\cos x + c$ (g) $-\frac{1}{2}\cos x^2 + c$ (h) $(u^2-2)\sin u + 2u\cos u + c$
  (i) $\frac{1}{8}y - \frac{1}{32}\sin 4y + c$ (j) $-\frac{1}{42}(3\cos 7x + 7\cos 3x) + c$

Chapter 28 (p575)

Qu. 1 maximum at $(1, 1/e)$
Qu. 3 $(3, 8)$
Qu. 4 (a) i, ii, iii (b) ii (c) iii (d) iii (e) i, ii, iii (f) iii
  (g) i, ii, iii (h) iii

Qu. 5 (a) as $x \to 0, 2, 4, \frac{dy}{dx} \to \infty$

  (b) when $x = 0, \frac{dy}{dx} = \pm\sqrt{2}$; as $x \to -2, \frac{dy}{dx} \to \infty$

Exercise 28a (p581)

1 $(1, 4)$ max, $(3, 0)$ min
2 $(2, 3)$ min
3 $(2, -1)$ max, $(4, 3)$ min
4 $(1, 1)$ min
5 $(\pm 3, -405)$
6 none
8 $(\frac{1}{3}\pi, \frac{3}{4}\sqrt{3})$ max, $(\pi, 0)$ infl, $(\frac{5}{3}\pi, -\frac{3}{4}\sqrt{3})$ min
9 $(\frac{1}{2}\pi, \frac{1}{2})$ max
10 $(0, -1)$ max, $(2\pi, -1)$ max

11 $(0, \frac{2}{3})$ min, $(\frac{1}{4}\pi, \frac{2}{3}\sqrt{2})$ max, $(\frac{3}{4}\pi, -\frac{2}{3}\sqrt{2})$ min, $(\pi, -\frac{2}{3})$ max
$(\frac{5}{4}\pi, -\frac{2}{3}\sqrt{2})$ min, $(\frac{7}{4}\pi, \frac{2}{3}\sqrt{2})$ max, $(2\pi, \frac{2}{3})$ min
12 $(1, 1/e)$ max
13 $(2, 10 \tan^{-1} 2 - 2)$ max

15 $\left(2n\pi + \frac{1}{4}\pi, \frac{1}{\sqrt{2}} e^{2n\pi + \pi/4}\right)$ max, $\left(2n\pi + \frac{5}{4}\pi, -\frac{1}{\sqrt{2}} e^{2n\pi + 5\pi/4}\right)$ min

Exercise 28b (p587)

7 $-4 < y < 0$
8 $\frac{1}{6} < y < 1\frac{1}{2}$
9 $(2, 4)$ min
10 $(-11, -18)$ max, $(-3, -2)$ min

Exercise 28d (p594)

7 $x = 1$, $y = x + 1$, $(-1, -2)$, $(3, 6)$
8 $(0, 0)$, $(-2, -4)$
10 $(0, 0)$, $y = 1$, $x = 1$, $x = -1$

Chapter 29 (p595)

Qu. 1 $y = Ax + B$, $y = 3x - 5$
Qu. 2 $y = x^3 + A$
Qu. 3 $x^2 + y^2 = A$
Qu. 4 $s = \frac{1}{2}at^2 + At + B$; $s = ut + \frac{1}{2}at^2$

Qu. 5 (a) $\dfrac{d^2y}{dx^2} = 0$ (b) $\dfrac{dy}{dx} = \dfrac{y}{x}$ (c) $\dfrac{dr}{d\theta} + r \tan \theta = 0$ (d) $\dfrac{dy}{dx} = -\dfrac{y}{x}$

(e) $\dfrac{dy}{dx} = y$ (f) $x\dfrac{dy}{dx} = y \ln y$ (g) $y\dfrac{d^2y}{dx^2} = \left(\dfrac{dy}{dx}\right)^2$ (h) $x\dfrac{dy}{dx} \ln x = y$

(i) $(1 + x^2)\dfrac{dy}{dx} \tan^{-1} x = y$

Qu. 7 (a) $x^2 - y^2 + A = 0$ (b) $y = Ax$ (c) $x = Ae^{y^2/2}$ (d) $x = A \sin y$

(e) $\ln \sqrt{\dfrac{y-1}{y+1}} = e^x + A$ (f) $y^2 = 2\sqrt{(x^2 + 1)} + A$

Qu. 8 $v^2 = u^2 + 2as$
Qu. 9 (a) $x^2 y = x + A$ (b) $t^2 \ln x = 3 \sin t + A$ (c) $x^2 \sin u = \ln (kx)$
(d) $xe^y = 2x + A$

Qu. 10 (a) x, $x^2 y = \frac{1}{2}e^{x^2} + A$ (b) x, $x^2 e^y = \frac{1}{3}x^3 + A$ (c) $\dfrac{1}{x}$, $xy^2 = \ln (kx)$

(d) r, $r^2 \tan \theta = 2\theta + A$

Qu. 11 $y = \frac{1}{2} + Ae^{-x^2}$; $y = \frac{1}{2} - e^{-x^2}$

Qu. 12 x^2

Qu. 13 (a) $y = 1 + x \tan x + A \sec x$ (b) $y = x - 4 + Ae^{-x}$

Exercise 29a (p601)

1 (a) $\dfrac{dy}{dx} = \frac{3}{2}$ (b) $\dfrac{dy}{dx} = \dfrac{y + \frac{1}{2}}{x}$ (c) $\dfrac{dy}{dx} = \dfrac{y}{x}$ (d) $\dfrac{dy}{dx} = -\dfrac{x}{y}$ (e) $\dfrac{dy}{dx} = -\dfrac{y}{x}$

(f) $\dfrac{dy}{dx} = \dfrac{y}{x - 4}$

2 (a) $\dfrac{d^2 y}{dt^2} = -9y$ (b) $\dfrac{d^2 y}{dt^2} = 3\dfrac{dy}{dt}$ (c) $\dfrac{d^2 y}{dx^2} = 9y$ (d) $\dfrac{d^2 y}{dx^2} - \dfrac{dy}{dx} - 6y = 0$

(e) $\dfrac{d^2 y}{dx^2} - 8\dfrac{dy}{dx} + 16y = 0$

3 $3x - 10y - 35 = 0$

4 $y = x^2 - 3x + 1$

5 $s = A - 3t^2$, $s = 12 - 3t^2$

6 (a) $y = e^x - 3x \cos x + 3 \sin x - 1$ (b) $y = e^x - 3x \cos x + 3 \sin x - e^{\pi/2}$

7 (a) $y = Ae^x$ (b) $y = \frac{2}{15}(x - 1)(3x + 2)\sqrt{(x - 1)} + A$ (c) $y = A(x + 2)$
 (d) $x = \frac{1}{2}y + \frac{1}{4}\sin 2y + A$ (e) $v - 1 = Ave^u$ (f) $y = x \ln x - x + A$
 (g) $\sin y = Ae^x$ (h) $x = y \tan^{-1} y - \ln \sqrt{(1 + y^2)} + A$

(i) $y^2 = x^2 - 2x + A$ (j) $y = A\sqrt{\dfrac{x - 1}{x + 1}}$ (k) $r = \tan \theta + A$

(l) $y + 3 = Ae^{-1/x}$ (m) $y = Axe^x$ (n) $\cos \theta \sin \phi = A$
 (o) $r = \theta \tan \theta + \ln (A \cos \theta)$ (p) $2y^2 = x^2(\ln x^2 - 1) + A$

8 (a) $y = \tan \theta$ (b) $y = 2 + 3e^{x^2/2}$ (c) $y = \dfrac{7x + 1}{7 - x}$ (d) $y = \sin (x - \frac{1}{6}\pi)$

9 83.4 min

10 9.05 kg, 34.7 min

Exercise 29b (p606)

1 (a) $y^2 = \dfrac{A}{x} - \dfrac{1}{x^2}$ (b) $y^2 = \dfrac{1}{x^2}(\tan 2x + A)$ (c) $x \ln y = \sec x + A$

(d) $(1 - 2x)e^y = \tan x + A$

2 (a) $x^2 \sin y = 3x^2 + A$ (b) $xy = e^x + A$ (c) $x \tan y = e^{x^2} + A$
 (d) $ye^x = \ln (Ay)$

3 (a) $y = e^{-2x}(\sin x + A)$ (b) $s = \frac{1}{2} + Ae^{-t^2}$ (c) $y = e^{-x^2}(1 + Ae^{-x})$
 (d) $r = (\theta + A)\operatorname{cosec}^2 \theta$ (e) $r = (\theta + A) \cos \theta$ (f) $y = x^{-2}(\sin x + A)$

4 (a) $y = (x + 1)^4$ (b) $u = \sin \theta + 2 \operatorname{cosec} \theta$

5 (a) $z = \frac{1}{5}(e^{2t} + e^{-3t})$ (b) $V = \frac{1}{4}\left(x^3 + \dfrac{3}{x}\right)$

Exercise 29c (p609)

1 (a) $y = A \sin 5x + B \cos 5x$ (b) $y = A \sin (x/6) + B \cos (x/6)$
  (c) $y = A \sin (3x/2) + B \cos (3x/2)$ (d) $z = A \sin t + B \cos t$
  (e) not SHM   (f) not SHM, but $y = x^3 + Ax + B$
  (g) $y = A \sin 10x + B \cos 10x$ (h) $r = A \sin n\theta + B \cos n\theta$
2 $v = A \sin 5t + B \cos 5t$; $v = 2 \sin 5t$
3 $y = A \sin 2x + B \cos 2x$; $y = 3 \sin 2x + \cos 2x$
4 $x = A \sin t/10 + B \cos t/10$; $x = 20 \cos t/10$

5 $y = A \sin nx + B \cos nx$; $y = \dfrac{a}{n} \sin nx$

6 $x = A \sin nt + B \cos nt$; $y = a \cos nt$
7 $x = 10 \sin (\pi t/2) - 4 \cos (\pi t/2)$
8 $y = 3 + A \sin 2x + B \cos 2x$

Exercise 29d (p611)

1 $x = A(\sec t + \tan t)$
2 $y = x^2 \ln x - x^2 + Ax$
3 $r = \ln (A \sec \theta)$

4 $y = A \cos \left(\dfrac{2}{\sqrt{3}} x \right) + B \sin \left(\dfrac{2}{\sqrt{3}} x \right)$

5 $y = (2x - 1)^{-2} + A(2x - 1)^{-4}$
6 $x = 2 \cos \frac{2}{3}t - 2\sqrt{3} \sin \frac{2}{3}t$
7 $x^2 y = (x - 1)e^x + 1$
8 $\ln y = \frac{1}{2}x^2 \ln x - \frac{1}{4}x^2 + \frac{1}{4}$
9 $y^2 = 4\frac{1}{2} - e^{-2x}(x + \frac{1}{2})$
10 $y = e^{-x^2}$
11 $y \sin x = (-2 \cos 4x + 4 \cos 2x + 5)/16$
12 $y = 36 e^{-t/6} + 27$; 11 min; 27°
14 $x = a e^{-2t}$; $y = 4a(e^{-t/2} - e^{-2t})$

Chapter 30 (p613)

Qu. 1 7.7 m
Qu. 2 25.1 m
Qu. 3 0.816, $304/375 \approx 0.811$
Qu. 4 (a) $\frac{1}{2}d(y_1 + 2y_2 + 2y_3 + 2y_4 + 2y_5 + 2y_6 + 2y_7 + y_8)$
       (b) $\frac{1}{2}d(y_1 + 2y_2 + 2y_3 + 2y_4 + 2y_5 + 2y_6 + 2y_7 + 2y_8 + y_9)$
Qu. 5 240, to nearest 10 (first two ordinates are further apart than the others)
Qu. 6 0.694
Qu. 7 37.6 m
Qu. 8 (a) $\frac{1}{3}d(y_1 + 4y_2 + 2y_3 + 4y_4 + y_5)$
       (b) $\frac{1}{3}d(y_1 + 4y_2 + 2y_3 + 4y_4 + 2y_5 + 4y_6 + 2y_7 + 4y_8 + y_9)$
Qu. 9 0.6931
Qu. 10 $304/375$

Exercise 30 (p619)

1 (a) 0.347   (b) 0.350   (c) 0.347
2 (b) 1.49   (c) 1.46
3 $166\frac{2}{3}$
4 0.7468
5 (a) $49.4\ cm^2$ (b) $49.9\ cm^2$; 3.12
6 $310\ cm^3$
7 1.86 litres
8 $1\frac{1}{3}$
9 $1 + 10x^3 + 45x^6 + 120x^9$; 0.204; 0.204
10 (a) 0.879   (b) 0.879
11 0.867
12 0.467, 0.475; $\pi \approx 3.12$

Revision Exercise 6 (p621)

1 (a) $\ln A(e^x + 1)$
2 4.73, 0.21
3 (a) $6e^{2t} - 1$ (b) $3e^{3t} - 2$ (c) $(3e^{3t} - 2)/(6e^{2t} - 1)$ (d) $t = \ln 4$

4 $\dfrac{1}{x-1} + \dfrac{2}{x+2}$, $\ln 2$

5 0.43

6 $\dfrac{1}{8}\left(\dfrac{3}{3t+1} - \dfrac{1}{t+3}\right)$

7 $\frac{1}{2}(e^2 + 3)$
8 (a) $\frac{1}{3}$ (b) 16/105
9 $1 + 3x + \frac{9}{2}x^2$, $1 - x + \frac{3}{2}x^2$, $1 + 2x + 3x^2$; $|x| < \frac{1}{2}$
10 (a) 10^{26} (c) $\frac{1}{2}\ln 2$ s
11 $x < \ln 2$, $2/(2 - e^x)$
12 (a) $1/(\ln a - 2)$ (b) $(ae)^{1/2}/2$
13 (a) $\frac{1}{2}\pi(e^{2a} - e^{-2a})$ (b) (i) 1/110   (ii) $(x^2 + 1)\tan^{-1} x - x + c$
14 $\pi/4$

16 $(\alpha, 0), \left(\dfrac{3\alpha - 4}{2\alpha - 3}, -4(\alpha - 1)(\alpha - 2)\right)$

17 (a) $(-1, 0)$, $(\frac{1}{2}, 0)$; $(0, 1)$ (b) max $(-\frac{1}{2}, 2)$, min $(\frac{1}{2}, 0)$
   (c) $(0, 1)$;   min $(-\frac{1}{2}, \frac{1}{2})$
18 $\frac{2}{3} \leqslant k \leqslant 2$;   min $(1, \frac{2}{3})$, max $(-1, 2)$
19 $1 - 4/x^3$
20 $y = x \ln (ex)$

21 $\dfrac{1}{2(1 + x)} - \dfrac{1}{2(3 + x)}$, $y = \sqrt{\left(\dfrac{8(1 + x)}{3 + x}\right)}$

22 (a) $\frac{1}{4}e^{2x}(2x - 1) + c$ (b) $\ln y = \frac{1}{4}e^{2x}(2x - 1) + \frac{1}{4}$

23 (a) 0.11, 3.6   (b) $y = x^2 + x$

24 (a) $\frac{2}{9}x^{3/2}(3 \ln x - 2) + c$ (b) $\sqrt{y} = \frac{1}{9}x^{3/2}(3 \ln x - 2) + \frac{11}{9}$

25 1.82, 15.13

26 min $(0, 0)$, max $(-2, -4)$; 5.622, 1.62

27 0.27, $0.6 - \frac{1}{2} \ln 2$

28 (b) $e^{-\frac{1}{2}x^2} = 1 - \dfrac{x^2}{2} + \dfrac{x^4}{8} - \ldots;$ (i) 0.9599   (ii) 0.9608   (iii) 0.9609

     (c) 0.9612

29 10.6

30 (a) $6 - \dfrac{x^2}{12} - \dfrac{x^4}{1728}$, 17.222   (b) 17.219   (c) 17.219

Index

694